CW01085299

A Guide to Quantitative Finance

A Guide to Quantitative Finance

Tools and Techniques for Understanding and Implementing Financial Analytics

Marcello Minenna

Published by Risk Books, a Division of Incisive Financial Publishing Ltd

Haymarket House
28–29 Haymarket
London SW1Y 4RX
Tel: +44 (0)20 7484 9700
Fax: +44 (0)20 7484 9800
E-mail: books@riskwaters.com
Sites: www.riskbooks.com
      www.incisivemedia.com

Every effort has been made to secure the permission of individual copyright holders for inclusion.

© Incisive Media Investments Limited 2006

ISBN 1 904339 47 6

British Library Cataloguing in Publication Data
A catalogue record for this book is available from the British Library

Publisher: Laurie Donaldson
Assistant Editor: Hannah Berry

Typeset by Sunrise Setting Ltd, Torquay, UK

Printed and bound in Spain by Espacegrafic, Pamplona, Navarra

To
Antonella

Contents

Preface

In this book, an attempt has been made to organise the author's notes on quantitative finance laid down in response to actual know-how requirements arising during the preparation of mathematical finance lessons for different universities in Italy and abroad, and in further operational research carried out by the author at CONSOB.

Not only does this text present formulae, it also illustrates methods for solving quantitative problems. Topics and models were chosen with this in mind.

Paolo Verzella and Giovanna Maria Boi, two researchers at the University of Milan Bicocca, provided their contribution for the mathematical developments.

Marcello Minenna
Rome/Milan, 31st May 2006

About the author

Marcello Minenna is a senior enforcement officer at CONSOB (the Italian Securities and Exchange Commission) where he is in charge of analysing and developing quantitative models for surveillance.

Marcello has been teaching in the field of financial mathematics in several Italian and foreign universities.

He received his Phd in applied mathematics for social sciences from the State University of Brescia, his MA in mathematics in finance from Columbia University and his degree in economics from Bocconi University.

His research interests include quantitative models for surveillance and more general areas of finance.

Part I

Calculus

1

Set theory

1.1. BASICS

Definition 1.1. A *set* is a finite or infinite collection of objects whose order is irrelevant.

Definition 1.2. Given a set X, set Y is said to be a *subset of* X, written $Y \subset X$, if Y is a superset of X, ie, if

$$y \in Y \Rightarrow y \in X$$

$$\text{and}$$

$$\exists \text{ at least one } x' \in X : x' \notin Y$$

Definition 1.3. Given set X, the set made by all subsets of X is said to be the *part set proper of* X and is denoted by $\mathcal{P}(X)$.

1.2. CARDINALITY OF A SET

Definition 1.4. Sets E and F are said to have the same size (or *cardinality*) whenever a one-to-one correspondence can be made between their members, ie, whenever a relation exists so that any member of set E can be paired off to one member only of set F and *vice versa*.

Definition 1.5. Set E is said to be *finite* whenever a natural number N exists so that E has the same size as the set $\{1, 2, \ldots, N\}$.

Definition 1.6. A set is said to be *infinite* whenever it is not finite (ie, it does not fit the Definition 1.5).

Definition 1.7. Set E is said to be *countable* (it is usually said that since E is a countable set, it may be counted) if the sequence of the elements shows a one-to-one correspondence (See Definition 3.1).

Definition 1.8. If set E is finite or numerable, it is said to be *countably infinite*.

Theorem 1.1. *The set $\mathbb{R}$ of real numbers is infinite and uncountable.*

Definition 1.9. Set E is said to have the *power of the continuum*, that is set E is infinite and uncountable, if a one-to-one correspondence exists between its members and the members of $\mathbb{R}$.

Notation 1.1. Typically, the power of the continuum is denoted by **c**.

Definition 1.10. The *Dirichlet function* is any limit function of the sequence of functions $\{f_n(x)\}_{n\in\mathbb{N}}$ (see Definition 3.8) and is defined as

$$f_n(x) := \begin{cases} 1 & \text{if } x = q_1, q_2, \ldots, q_n \\ 0 & \text{otherwise} \end{cases} \tag{1.1}$$

Proposition 1.1. *The Dirichlet function can be written as*

$$f(x) := \lim_{n\to+\infty} f_n(x) = \begin{cases} 1 & \text{if } x \in \mathbb{Q} \\ 0 & \text{if } x \in \mathbb{R}\backslash\mathbb{Q} \end{cases}$$

$$= \mathbf{1}_{(\mathbb{Q})}(x) \tag{1.2}$$

where $\mathbf{1}_{(\mathbb{Q})}(x)$ is the index function (see Definition 6.3).

1.3.   SET OPERATIONS
Notation 1.2. Union is denoted by $\cup$.

Notation 1.3. Intersection is denoted by $\cap$.

Notation 1.4. The empty or null set (ie, a set with zero members) is denoted by $\varnothing$.

Definition 1.11. A_k is a *sequence*, ie, an ordered array of members.

Definition 1.12. If one defines $A = \bigcup_{k\in K} A_k$, set K is a *set indicator* for set A.

Proposition 1.2. *Given sets E, F, G, the following properties hold.*

- *Idempotency:*
  $E \cup E = E \cap E = E$
- *Commutation:*
  $E \cap F = F \cap E$
  $E \cup F = F \cup E$

- *Association:*
  $(E \cap F) \cap G = E \cap (F \cap G)$
  $(E \cup F) \cup G = E \cup (F \cup G)$
- *Distribution:*
  $(E \cap F) \cup G = (E \cup G) \cap (F \cup G)$
  $(E \cup F) \cap G = (E \cap G) \cup (F \cap G)$
- *Absorption:*
  $E \cup (E \cap F) = E$
  $E \cap (E \cup F) = E$

Set union and intersection can be applied to a countable infinity of sets (see Definition 1.7).

Definition 1.13. Given set X, subsets $X_1, X_2, \ldots, X_n$ are a *partition* of X if they satisfy the properties below:

- $X_i \cap X_j = \varnothing$ for any $i \neq j$;
- $X_i \neq \varnothing$ for all i;
- $\bigcup_i X_i = X$.

Definition 1.14. A *countable union of sets*, denoted by $\bigcup_{k=1}^{+\infty} A_k$, is the union of countably infinite sets (see Definition 1.7).

Definition 1.15. A *countable intersection of sets*, denoted by $\bigcap_{k=1}^{+\infty} A_k$, is the intersection of countably infinite sets (see Definition 1.7).

Proposition 1.3. *The distributive properties of set union and intersection may also be written as*

$$E \cup \left(\bigcap_{k=1}^{+\infty} A_k \right) = \bigcap_{k=1}^{+\infty} (A_k \cup E) \tag{1.3}$$

and

$$E \cap \left(\bigcup_{k=1}^{+\infty} A_k \right) = \bigcup_{k=1}^{+\infty} (A_k \cap E) \tag{1.4}$$

Notation 1.5. Often, Equations (1.3) and (1.4) are also denoted as

$$E \cup \left(\bigcap_{k \in K} A_k \right) = \bigcap_{k \in K} (A_k \cup E)$$

and

$$E \cap \left(\bigcup_{k \in K} A_k \right) = \bigcup_{k \in K} (A_k \cap E)$$

Definition 1.16. Sets E and F are said to be *disjoint* if their intersection is an empty set, ie,

$$E \cap F = \emptyset$$

Definition 1.17. The *difference* between sets E and F is the set $E \backslash F$ made up of the members of E which are not in F, that is

$$E \backslash F = E \cap F^c \qquad (1.5)$$

Proposition 1.4. *The union between two non-disjoint sets E and F may be written as the union of three disjoint non-empty sets:*

$$E \cup F = (E \backslash F) \cup (E \cap F) \cup (F \backslash E)$$

Definition 1.18. Set $E \backslash F$ is said to be *complementary* of F with respect to E.

Notation 1.6. The complementary of E is denoted by E^c or by $\overline{E}$.

Proposition 1.5 (De Morgan Laws). *We have the following:*

$$(E \cup F)^c = E^c \cap F^c \quad and \quad (E \cap F)^c = E^c \cup F^c \qquad (1.6)$$

Proposition 1.6. *Let E and F be two subsets of set X, then the equivalence below holds:*

$$[(E \cap F^c) \cup F] \cap [(E \cap F^c) \cup E^c] = [(E \cup F) \cap X] \cap [X \cap (E \cap F)^c]$$

Corollary 1.1. *Let E and F be two subsets of set X, then the equivalence below holds:*

$$[(E \cup F) \cap X] \cap [X \cap (E \cap F)^c] = (E \cup F) \cap (E \cap F)^c \qquad (1.7)$$

Proposition 1.7. *Let E and F be two sets, then the equivalence below holds:*

$$(E \cup F) \cap (E \cap F)^c = (E \cup F) \backslash (E \cap F)$$

Definition 1.19. The *symmetric difference*, denoted as $E \triangle F$, of subsets E and F of set X is defined as

$$E \triangle F := (E \backslash F) \cup (F \backslash E) \qquad (1.8)$$

Proposition 1.8. *The symmetric difference of subsets E and F of set X may also be written as*

$$E \triangle F = (E \cup F) \backslash (E \cap F) \qquad (1.9)$$

Definition 1.20. Let X be a countably infinite set of paired disjoint members, ie,

$$X := \{A_i\}_{i \in N}$$

where $A_i \cap A_j = \emptyset$ for all $i \neq j$; $i, j = 1, 2, \ldots, N$, then the *extension of set* X is defined to be any set X' which is also countably infinite, ie,

$$X' = \{E_k\}_{k \in N'}$$

where for all $E_k \in X'$, one has

$$E_k = \bigcup_{l \in \Lambda} A_l^{(k)}$$

where Λ is any subset N', and the superscript above set A_l denotes that this set of sets is referred to set E_k.

1.4. TOPOLOGY

Topology, from the Greek phrase "study of places" is the study of set properties.

Definition 1.21. Given a set X and a collection of subsets T of X, then T is defined to be the *topology* of X if:

(1) X and the null set $\emptyset$ are part of T;
(2) the union of any collection of members of T belongs to T;
(3) the intersection of any finite collection of members of T belongs to T.

Definition 1.22. The pair (X, T) is said to be the *topological space*.

Definition 1.23. Given a topology, a set is defined to be *open* if it is laid in T.

Definition 1.24. A set is *closed* if its complement is open.

Definition 1.25. Given two sets X and Y, their *cartesian product* (or *direct product*), denoted by $X \times Y$, is defined to be the set of all ordered pairs where the first element is taken from X and the second from Y.

Remark 1.1. Consequently, the definition of the cartesian product is extensible to n sets. Then, the cartesian product is the set of the n-tuple members where n members are taken from the n sets.

Definition 1.26. A *topological product* is the cartesian product of topological spaces.

1.4.1. Equivalence relationship between sets

Definition 1.27. A *relation* or *correspondence* between sets E and F is a subset G of the cartesian product $E \times F$.

Members $a \in E$ and $b \in F$ so that $(a, b) \in G$ are said to be *associated* or *correspondent members* of the relation. This is denoted by

$$a \overset{G}{\sim} b$$

which reads "a is in relation $\overset{G}{\sim}$ with b".

Definition 1.28. The *domain* of relation $\overset{G}{\sim}$ in $E \times F$ is defined to be the set of the first members in the pairs of G.

Definition 1.29. The *codomain* of relation $\overset{G}{\sim}$ in $E \times F$ is defined to be the set of the second members in the pairs of G.

Remark 1.2. The domain of G is a subset of E and the codomain of G is a subset of F.

Definition 1.30. The relation $\overset{G}{\sim}$ is *reflexive* if, for any $a \in E$, the pair $(a, a) \in G$.

Definition 1.31. The relation $\overset{G}{\sim}$ is *symmetric* if, for any pair (a, b) which belongs to G, the pair (b, a) also belongs to G.

Definition 1.32. The relation $\overset{G}{\sim}$ is *transitive* if, for all the pairs (a, b) and (b, c) belonging to G, the pair (a, c) also belongs to G.

Definition 1.33. A relation $\overset{G}{\sim}$ which is reflexive, symmetric and transitive is said to be an *equivalence relation* (see Figure 1.1).

Definition 1.34. An equivalence relation $\overset{G}{\sim}$ on set X subdivides the members of X into subsets $X_1, X_2, \ldots, X_n, \ldots$ defined as *equivalence classes*, whose members make up all of the members of X and are equivalent on the basis of relation $\overset{G}{\sim}$ (see Figure 1.2).

Remark 1.3. In other words, the mode to determine set G will determine the partition of X.

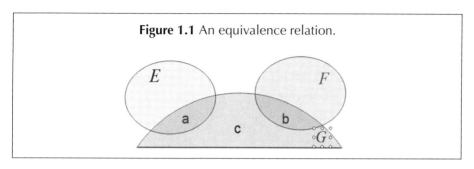

Figure 1.1 An equivalence relation.

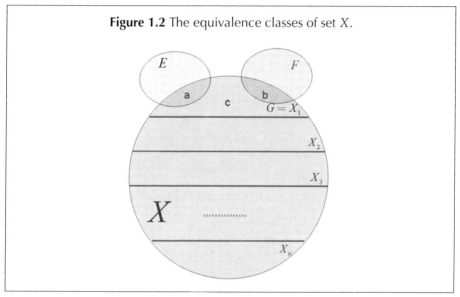

Figure 1.2 The equivalence classes of set X.

Remark 1.4. It may be demonstrated that equivalence classes of set X on the basis of the equivalence relation $\overset{G}{\sim}$ satisfy the properties which characterise a partition of X (see Definition 1.13):

(1) $X_i \cap X_j = \varnothing$ for any $i \neq j$;
(2) $X_i \neq \varnothing$ for all i;
(3) $\bigcup_i X_i = X$.

Definition 1.35. The equivalence classes of set X, in which the equivalence relation $\overset{G}{\sim}$ is defined, are the elements of the so-called *quotient set of X to* $\overset{G}{\sim}$. This set is denoted by

$$\frac{X}{\overset{G}{\sim}}$$

1.4.2. Real numerical space

Definition 1.36. Let n be a positive integer. The *n-dimensional real numerical space* is defined to be the set R^n, built as the cartesian product of n sets all equal to R, ie the pair of the nth ordinates as $(x_1, x_2, \ldots, x_n)$, with $x_1, x_2, \ldots, x_n$ being real numbers.

Definition 1.37. The members of R^n are defined to be the *points* of R^n and are usually denoted by a Block letter of the alphabet, eg, P:

$$P \in R^n \overset{\text{def}}{\Longleftrightarrow} P = (x_1, x_2, \ldots, x_n)$$

Definition 1.38. Real numbers $x_1, x_2, \ldots, x_n$ are the *coordinates* of P: x_1 is the first coordinate, x_n is the nth coordinate.

Definition 1.39. Point $\varnothing = (0, 0, \ldots, 0)$ is the *origin* of R^n.

Definition 1.40. Given two points of R^n:

$$A = (a_1, a_2, \ldots, a_n) \quad \text{and} \quad B = (b_1, b_2, \ldots, b_n)$$

where

$$a_1 \leq b_1, a_2 \leq b_2, \ldots, a_n \leq b_n$$

the set of points $P = (x_1, x_2, \ldots, x_n) \ni'$:

$$a_1 \leq x_1 \leq b_1, a_2 \leq x_2 \leq b_2, \ldots, a_n \leq x_n \leq b_n$$

is defined to be the *closed rectangle* and is denoted by $[A, B]$.

Remark 1.5. Consequently, the definition of an open, left or right semi-open rectangle (or interval) of boundaries of A and B will be derived from above.

Definition 1.41. Considering any of the four rectangles with boundaries A and B, point C of R^n with coordinates

$$c_1 = \frac{a_1 + b_1}{2}, \frac{a_2 + b_2}{2}, \ldots, \frac{a_n + b_n}{2}$$

is defined to be the *centre of the rectangle*.

Definition 1.42. Numbers

$$b_1 - a_1, b_2 - a_2, \ldots, b_n - a_n$$

are defined to be the *dimensions of the rectangle*.

Remark 1.6. Then, the definition of the *semi-dimensions of the rectangle* is derived, ie,

$$c_1 = \frac{b_1 - a_1}{2}, \frac{b_2 - a_2}{2}, \ldots, \frac{b_n - a_n}{2}$$

Definition 1.43. Given a point $C = (c_1, c_2, \ldots, c_n)$ of R^n and a real number $r \geq 0$, the set of points $P = (x_1, x_2, \ldots, x_n)$ such that the Euclidean distance between P and C is smaller than r, ie,

$$\overline{PC} \leq r$$

that is

$$\sqrt{(x_1 - c_1)^2 + (x_2 - c_2)^2 + \cdots + (x_n - c_n)^2}$$

is defined to be the *closed circle* of R^n with centre C and radius r.

Remark 1.7. Consequently, one may derive the definition of the open circle as the set of points $P = (x_1, x_2, \ldots, x_n) \ni' \overline{PC} < r$.

Definition 1.44. For $r > 0$, points P of $R^n \ni'$ where the Euclidean distance between P and C is larger than r, ie,

$$\overline{PC} > r$$

are said to be the *outer points* of the open or closed circle with centre C and radius r.

Definition 1.45. Given a point $P_0 \in R^n$, the *rectangular neighbourhood* is any open and non-null rectangle which has P_0 as its centre.

Definition 1.46. Given a point $P_0 \in R^n$ the *circular neighbourhood* is any open and non-null circle which has P_0 as its centre.

Definition 1.47. More generally, the *neighbourhood of P_0* is any subset of R^n which contains a rectangular or circular neighbourhood of P_0.

Definition 1.48. Any subset of R^n which contains the outer points of any circle whose centre is the origin and has a positive radius is defined to be the *neighbourhood of the point at infinity of R^n*.

Definition 1.49. A subset X of R^n is defined to be *limited* if there is a rectangle or a circle which contains it.

Definition 1.50. A point $P_0 \in R^n$ is defined to be an *inner point* of X when there is a neighbourhood of P_0 which is all contained inside X.

Notation 1.7. The inner points are also called *points at finite*.

Definition 1.51. The set of inner points of X is defined to be the *interior* of X and is denoted by the symbol $\mathring{X}$.

Definition 1.52. A point $P_0 \in R^n$ is defined to be in the *exterior* of X when there is a neighbourhood of P_0 which does not have any point also in X, ie, when a neighbourhood of P_0 and X are disjoint.

Notation 1.8. The outer points are also said to be *points at infinity*.

Definition 1.53. The set of the outer points of X is defined to be *the exterior* of X.

Definition 1.54. Any point $P_0 \in R^n$ is defined to be a *frontier point* for X when it is neither an inner nor an outer point of X, ie, points which both belong and do not belong to X will lie in any neighbourhood of P_0.

Definition 1.55. The set of the frontier points of X is defined to be *the frontier* of X.

Definition 1.56. A set $X \neq \varnothing$ of R^n is defined to be *open* (see Definition 1.81) if it coincides with its interior, ie, if it does not have any frontier point. Alternatively,

$$\forall P_0 \in X, \quad \exists I(P_0) \subseteq X$$

where $I(P_0)$ denotes the neighbourhood of P_0.

Remark 1.8. If $X \neq \varnothing$, set X is considered to be open by convention.

Definition 1.57. The set $E \subseteq \mathbb{R}^n$ is defined to be *convex* if for any two members of E, the segment between them is wholly contained in E, that is if for all $x.y \in E$ one has

$$tx + (1 - t)y \in E, \quad \forall t \in \mathbb{R}$$

1.4.2.1. Boundaries of a subset of $\mathbb{R}$

Definition 1.58. Given a set $A \subseteq \mathbb{R}$, the *minorant* of A is defined to be any real k so that

$$a \geq k, \quad \forall a \in A$$

Definition 1.59. Given a set $A \subseteq \mathbb{R}$, the *majorant* of A is defined to be any real number K so that

$$a \leq K, \quad \forall a \in A$$

Definition 1.60. Given a set $A \subseteq \mathbb{R}$, the real number s is defined to be the *infimum* of A and is denoted by

$$s = \inf A$$

if:

(1) s is a minorant of A, ie,

$$a \geq s, \quad \forall a \in A \tag{1.10}$$

(2) s is the maximum minorant of A, ie,

$$\forall \varepsilon > 0, \quad \exists a^* \in A : s \leq a^* \leq s + \varepsilon \tag{1.11}$$

Definition 1.61. Given a set $A \subseteq \mathbb{R}$, the real number S is defined to be the *supremum of A* and is denoted by

$$S = \sup A$$

if:

(1) S is a majorant of A, ie,

$$a \leq S, \quad \forall a \in A \tag{1.12}$$

(2) S is the minimum majorant of A, ie,

$$\forall \varepsilon > 0, \quad \exists a^* \in A : S - \varepsilon \leq a^* \leq S \tag{1.13}$$

Proposition 1.9. *Let s the infimum of set $A \subseteq \mathbb{R}$. Then, the sequence (see Definition 3.1) $\{a_n\}_{n \in \mathbb{N}}$ of the members of A exists so that it will converge to s for $n \to +\infty$, ie,*

$$\lim_{n \to +\infty} a_n = s \tag{1.14}$$

Remark 1.9. The same proposition holds for the supremum.

1.4.2.2. Intervals of $\mathbb{R}^n$

Definition 1.62. Any convex subset of $\mathbb{R}$ is defined to be an *interval I* of $\mathbb{R}$. The cartesian product of n intervals of $\mathbb{R}$ is defined to be the *interval **I*** of $\mathbb{R}^n$.

Notation 1.9. The class of all the intervals I of $\mathbb{R}$ is denoted by the symbol $\mathcal{I}$.

Notation 1.10. The class of all the intervals $\mathbf{I}$ of $\mathbb{R}^n$ is denoted by the symbol $\mathcal{I}^n$.

Remark 1.10. From Definition 1.62, the facts can be derived that a segment parallel to one of the axes is an interval of $\mathbb{R}^n$ for any $n > 1$.

Remark 1.11. Usually, an interval I of $\mathbb{R}$ is denoted by writing the boundaries, a and b, as $-\infty \leq a \leq b \leq +\infty$. By so doing, the *classification of intervals* of $\mathbb{R}$ can be established as follows:

- if a and b are both finite,

$$I = [a, b] \text{ is a closed bounded interval}$$
$$I = (a, b) \text{ is an open bounded interval}$$
$$I = [a, b) \text{ is a bounded, left closed, right open interval}$$
$$I = (a, b] \text{ is a bounded, left open, right closed interval}$$

- if a is finite and b is infinite,

$$I = [a, +\infty) \text{ is a left closed, right open, unbounded from above interval}$$
$$I = (a, +\infty) \text{ is an open, left closed, unbounded from above interval}$$

- if a is infinite and b is finite,

$$I = (-\infty, b] \text{ is a left open, right closed, unbounded from below interval}$$
$$I = (-\infty, b) \text{ is an open, right limited, unbounded from below interval}$$

- if $a = -\infty$ and $b = +\infty$,

$$I = (-\infty, +\infty) \text{ is an open and unbounded interval}$$

Definition 1.63. Let I be an interval of $\mathbb{R}$ with boundaries in a and b. The *length of I*, denoted by $l(I)$, is defined as

$$l(I) := \begin{cases} |b - a| & \text{if } I \text{ is bounded} \\ \infty & \text{if } I \text{ is unbounded} \end{cases}$$

Notation 1.11. The function $l(I)$ is also defined to be the length function of an interval I of $\mathbb{R}$.

Remark 1.12. However, any point $x \in \mathbb{R}$ may be considered as a "degenerate" interval of $\mathbb{R}$, because its length is equal to zero.

Definition 1.64. Let $\mathbf{I}$ be an interval of $\mathbb{R}^n$. The *length of* $\mathbf{I}$, denoted by $l(\mathbf{I})$, is defined as

$$
l(\mathbf{I}) := \begin{cases} 0 & \text{if there is at least one } i \in \{1, 2, \ldots, n\} \quad \text{so that } l(I_i) = 0 \\[2mm] \prod_{i=1}^{n} l(I_i) & \text{if } \forall i = 1, 2, \ldots, n \qquad\qquad\qquad\quad 0 < l(I_i) < \infty \\[2mm] \infty & \begin{aligned} &\text{if } \forall i = 1, 2, \ldots, n && l(I_i) < 0 \\ &\text{if there is at least one } i \in \{1, 2, \ldots, n\} && \text{so that } l(I_i) = \infty \end{aligned} \end{cases}
$$
$$(1.15)$$

Notation 1.12. The function $l(\mathbf{I})$ is also defined to be the length function of an interval $\mathbf{I}$ of $\mathbb{R}^n$.

Remark 1.13. If a set is broken down into a finite number of disjoint intervals, the length of this set is derived by adding the length of the many disjoint intervals which compose it.

Remark 1.14. However, one point $\mathbf{x} \in \mathbb{R}^n$ may be considered as a "degenerate" interval of $\mathbb{R}^n$, because its length is equal to zero.

Definition 1.65. Let $\{\mathbf{I}_i\}_{i\in N}$ be a sequence of disjoint-in-pairs countably infinite intervals of $\mathbb{R}^n$, $n \geq 1$, and let X' be a countably infinite set defined as

$$X' = \{\mathbf{E}_k\}_{k\in N'}$$

where for all $\mathbf{E}_k \in X'$, one has

$$\mathbf{E}_k = \bigcup_{l\in\Lambda} \mathbf{I}_l^{(k)}$$

where Λ is any subset of N' and the superscript on the interval $\mathbf{I}_l$ denotes that the set of intervals is referred to set $\mathbf{E}_k$. Then, *the extension of the length function* $l(\mathbf{I})$, defined on each of the members of $\{\mathbf{I}_i\}_{i\in N'}$, of any set $\mathbf{E}_k$ denoted by $l^*(\mathbf{E}_k)$ is defined as

$$l^*(\mathbf{E}_k) = \sum_{l\in\Lambda} l(\mathbf{I}_l^{(k)})$$

Theorem 1.2 ("Structure" of open sets in $\mathbb{R}$). *Let A an open non-null set of $\mathbb{R}$. Then, there is a sequence (unique, at least as far as the order of the members in the sequence, and possibly finite) of open intervals I_j disjoint in pairs, so that*

$$A = \bigcup_{j=1}^{+\infty} I_j$$

Definition 1.66. Let A be an open subset of $\mathbb{R}$. A *standard representation of A* is any representation of A as a union of intervals.

Definition 1.67. Let E be a set of $\mathbb{R}$ and $\{A_\alpha\}$ a family of open sets. Then $\{A_\alpha\}$ is defined to be a *coverage* of E if $E \subseteq \bigcup_\alpha A_\alpha$.

Remark 1.15. It is not always possible to break up a set into a finite number of disjoint intervals. In such cases, a countably infinite set of intervals is used in order to have a coverage of the set to be analysed.

Remark 1.16. The coverage of any interval, made up of a set of intervals, is a set whose length is greater than or equal to the length of the interval. Specifically, the length of the smallest coverage of the interval made up of a set of disjoint intervals is equal to the length of that interval (see Remarks 1.13 and 1.15).

Definition 1.68. Open sets $A_{\alpha_1}, A_{\alpha_2}, \ldots, A_{\alpha_N}$ are the *finite undercoverage* of a subset E of $\mathbb{R}$ if $E \subseteq \bigcup_{i=1}^{N} A_{\alpha_i}$.

Definition 1.69. A *set $E \subseteq \mathbb{R}$* is said to be *null* if its coverage can be made by a sequence of intervals whose total length is arbitrarily small, that is

$$\forall \varepsilon > 0 \quad \exists \{I_n\}_{n \geq 1} \ni'$$

$$-E \subseteq \bigcup_{n=1}^{+\infty} I_n$$

$$-\sum_{i=1}^{+\infty} l(I_n) = 0$$

Corollary 1.2. *Any countably infinite set E is a null set.*

Proposition 1.10. *The finite or countable union of a sequence of null sets is a null set.*

Remark 1.17. Sets which may be neither finite nor countable may be null (see Section 10.5.3.1).

1.4.2.3. Accumulation points

Definition 1.70. A point $P_0 \in R^n$ is defined to be an *accumulation point in* X if at least one point of X other than P_0 belongs to every neighbourhood of X.

Remark 1.18. An accumulation point may or may not belong to X.

Theorem 1.3. *If P_0 is an accumulation point of X, an infinite number of points of X will belong to every neighbourhood of X.*

Theorem 1.4. *Any infinite and bounded subset of R^n admits at least one point of R^n to be an accumulation point.*

Definition 1.71. Let X a subset of R^n. The *point* at infinity is said to be an *accumulation point* for X if at least one point of X belongs to every neighbourhood of X.

Definition 1.72. A *point P_0* at finite or infinite in R^n is defined to be an *accumulation point* for the set X when infinite points of X accumulate (then exist) in every neighbourhood of P_0.

Definition 1.73. A *derivative* of X denoted by one of the symbols DX, $D_r X$, $D(X)$, $D_r(X)$, is the set of the accumulation points at finite of X.

Definition 1.74. Let X be a set and U be a subset of X. A point $x \in X$ is defined to be an *adherence point of* U if any neighbourhood of x intersects U and:

- if $x \in U$; or
- if x is an accumulation point of U.

Lemma 1.1. *The derivative of X is an open set since, by definition, it is formed by the accumulation points at finite that is the inner points of X (See Definitions 1.50 and 1.56).*

Definition 1.75. The *closure* of X is the union of X with its derivative, ie, the set of the adherence points of X. The closure is denoted by the symbol $\bar{X}$, as in

$$\bar{X} = X \cup DX$$

Remark 1.19. In light of Definition 1.74, the closure of X coincides with the set of the points which either belong to X [1] or which are accumulation points at finite of X.

---

[1] For example, points at finite of X which are not accumulation points for X.

Theorem 1.5. *The necessary and sufficient condition for the set X to be closed is that set X coincides with its closure, ie, that it contains its derivative (See Definition 1.82).*

1.5. METRIC SPACES

Definition 1.76. Let X be a set. The *metrics on* X is defined to be a function $d : X \times X \mapsto [0, +\infty)$ on X so that:

(1) $d(x, y) \geq 0$ for all $x, y \in X$ (positiveness);
(2) $d(x, y) = 0 \Leftrightarrow x = y$ (non-degeneracy);
(3) $d(x, y) = d(y, x)$ for all $x, y \in X$ (symmetry);
(4) $d(x, z) \leq d(x, y) + d(y, z)$ for all $x, y, z \in X$ (the so-called triangular inequality).

Definition 1.77. The *metric space* is the pair (X, d).

Definition 1.78. Given a metric space (X, d), the *diameter of* X is defined as

$$\mathrm{diam} X := \sup_{x, y \in X} d(x, y)$$

Remark 1.20. The diameter of X is always non-negative and may be finite or equal to $+\infty$: in the first case, X is said to be *bounded*; in the second case case X is said to be *unbounded*.

Definition 1.79. Let (X, d) be a metric space and let $x \in X$. Then for any $\alpha \in \mathbb{R}^+$ the *open sphere of centre* x *and radius* α is the set $B(x, \alpha)$ denoted by

$$B(x, \alpha) := \{y \in X : d(x, y) < \alpha\} \tag{1.16}$$

Definition 1.80. Let (X, d) be a metric space and let $x \in X$. Then for any $\alpha \in \mathbb{R}^+$ the *closed sphere of centre* x *and radius* α is the set $\overline{B}(x, \alpha)$ denoted by

$$\overline{B}(x, \alpha) := \{y \in X : d(x, y) \leq \alpha\} \tag{1.17}$$

Definition 1.81. Given a metric space (X, d), a subset A of X is defined to be *open in* X if

$$\forall x \in A \quad \exists \alpha > 0 \ni' B(x, \alpha) \subset A \tag{1.18}$$

Definition 1.82. Given a metric space (X, d), a subset B of X is defined to be *open in* X if its complement, ie, $B^c \equiv X \backslash B$, is open in X (see Definition 1.81).

Definition 1.83. Given a metric space (X, d), the set of the open set of X defines a topology on X, called the *topology derived from metrics* (see Definition 1.23).

Definition 1.84. Given a metric space (X, d), *a sequence* $\{x_n\}_{n \in \mathbb{N}}$ *of values in* X *is convergent* (see Definition 3.3) *on* X *at value* x if for all $\varepsilon > 0$ there exists $N \in \mathbb{N}$ and for all $n \geq N$ the following holds:

$$d(x_n, x) < \varepsilon \quad \text{with } x \in X \tag{1.19}$$

Remark 1.21. The condition set by Equation (1.19) under Definition 1.84 may equally be formulated as

$$\lim_{n \to +\infty} d(x_n, x) = 0 \quad \text{with } x \in X \tag{1.20}$$

Definition 1.85. Given the metric space (X, d), a sequence $\{x_n\}_{n \in \mathbb{N}}$ of values in X is a defined to be a *Cauchy sequence* (see Definition 3.6) if for all $\varepsilon > 0$ there exists $N \in \mathbb{N}$ and for all $n, m \geq N$ the following holds:

$$d(x_n, x_m) < \varepsilon \tag{1.21}$$

Remark 1.22. The condition set by Equation (1.21) under Definition 1.85 may equally be formulated as

$$\lim_{n,m \to +\infty} d(x_n, x_m) = 0 \tag{1.22}$$

Proposition 1.11. *Any convergent sequence is a Cauchy sequence.*

Definition 1.86. A metric space (X, d) is defined to be *full* if any Cauchy sequence of values in X is convergent (see Definition 3.3) on X.

Definition 1.87. Let (X, d) be a metric space and let Y be a proper non-null subset of X. If set Y has the same metrics d as X, then the metric space (Y, d) is defined to be *the metric subspace of* (X, d).

Remark 1.23. Any proper non-null subset of a metric space is a metric space which has the same metrics. However, any new metric may still be defined on this subset.

Definition 1.88. Let (X, d) be a metric space and let (Y, d) be one metric subspace of (X, d). Then (Y, d) is said to be *dense* in (X, d) if

$$\forall \varepsilon > 0 \quad \text{and} \quad \forall x \in X \quad \exists y \in Y \ni' d(x, y) < \varepsilon$$

1.5.1. Euclidean space

Definition 1.89. Given two points of R^n:

$$A = (a_1, a_2, \ldots, a_n) \quad \text{and} \quad B = (b_1, b_2, \ldots, b_n)$$

the *Euclidean distance* or simply the distance between A and B, denoted by the symbol $\overline{AB}$, is the real non-negative number

$$\sqrt{(b_1 - a_1)^2 + (b_2 - a_2)^2 + \cdots + (b_n - a_n)^2}$$

Definition 1.90. The metric of a n-dimensional real numerical space is defined to be a *Euclidean metric* and is denoted by d_n; this metric is then the application which matches to any pair their distance, ie,

$$(A, B) \in R^n \times R^n \to \overline{AB} \in R_0^+$$

Definition 1.91. The *n-dimensional real Euclidean space* is the pair (R^n, d_n), ie, the n-dimensional real numerical space and its metric that is the Euclidean metric.

Definition 1.92. Given any topology on R, ie, the real line[2], the Cartesian product of the n pairs of R is a topological product called the *Euclidean ordinary topology on R^n*.

1.5.2. Metric spaces and accumulation points

Proposition 1.12. *Let (X, d) a metric space and let U and V two subsets of X. Then:*

(1) $\mathring{U} = (\overline{U^c})^c$;
(2) $\overline{U} = [(U^c)^\circ]^c$;
(3) $(U \cap V)^\circ = \mathring{U} \cap \mathring{V}$;
(4) $\overline{U \cup V} = \overline{U} \cup \overline{V}$;

Proposition 1.13. *Let (X, d) be a metric space and x a member of X. Also, let $\{x_n\}_{n \in \mathbb{N}}$ be a sequence of values in X convergent (see Definition 3.3) to x. Then x is an accumulation point for X.*

Corollary 1.3. *Let (X, d) be a metric space, $x \in X$ and let U be a subset of X. Then, if a sequence $\{x_n\}_{n \in \mathbb{N}}$ of elements of U exists which converges (see Definition 3.3) to x, this is the adherence point of U.*

---

[2]This line corresponds to a left and right unbound open interval; see Definition 1.62 and Remark 1.11.

Theorem 1.6. *Let (X, d) be a metric space and let U be a subset of X. Then U is a closed set in X if and only if any convergent sequence (see Definition 3.3) $\{x_n\}_{n \in \mathbb{N}}$ of members of U converges to a member x of U, ie,*

$$\lim_{n \to +\infty} d(x_n, x) = 0$$

$$x \in U \qquad\qquad (1.23)$$

$$\forall \{x_n\}_{n \in \mathbb{N}} \subseteq U$$

Proposition 1.14. *Let (X, d) be a full metric space and let U be a subset of X. Then the metric space (U, d), which is a metric subspace (see Definition 1.87) of (X, d), is full if and only if U is a closed set in X under the terms of Definition 1.82.*

Remark 1.24. Not all metric spaces may be full under the terms of Definition 1.86. For instance, if (X, d) is a full metric space and V is a non-closed subset of X, then the metric space (V, d) is not full.

Remark 1.25. Usually, a closed subset does not automatically constitute a full metric space as the example below demonstrates.

Example 1.1. If we consider $X \equiv \mathbb{Q}$ and $V \equiv [0, 1] \cap \mathbb{Q}$, it is clear that V (considered as a subset of $\mathbb{Q}$) is closed but not full.

Definition 1.93. The set X is defined to be *compact* if it is closed and bounded.

Proposition 1.15. *Let $E \subseteq \mathbb{R}$ be a compact subset of $\mathbb{R}$. Then the statements below are equivalent:*

(i) *E is closed and bounded;*
(ii) *a finite undercoverage may be derived from the coverage of E (see Definition 1.68).*

Definition 1.94. The set X contained in set Y is defined to be *dense in Y* if Y is a subset of DX, ie,

$$\begin{cases} X \subseteq Y \\ Y \subseteq \overline{X} \end{cases} \Rightarrow X \text{ dense in } Y \qquad\qquad (1.24)$$

Definition 1.95. The set X is said to be *discontinuous* if

$$\forall x, y \in X, \exists \text{ infinite members } w \notin X : x \leq w \leq y \qquad\qquad (1.25)$$

1.6. ALGEBRAS

Definition 1.96. Given a set X, *algebra* $(\mathcal{A})$ is a non-null collection of subsets of X with the following properties:

(1) null set $\emptyset \in \mathcal{A}$;
(2) $A \in \mathcal{A} A^c \in \mathcal{A}$;
(3) $A, B \in \mathcal{A} \Longrightarrow A \cup B \in \mathcal{A}$.

Notation 1.13. Property (2) means that algebra $\mathcal{A}$ is closed to complementation.

Notation 1.14. Property (3) means that algebra $\mathcal{A}$ is closed to the finite union of the sets which belong to $\mathcal{A}$.

Proposition 1.16. *Let X be a set. Then:*

- $\{\emptyset, X\}$ *is the smallest algebra of subsets of X;*
- $\mathcal{P}(X)$, *that is the set of the parts X (see Definition 1.3), is the largest algebra of all subsets of X.*

Proposition 1.17. *Let $\mathcal{A}$ an algebra defined on a set X. Then:*

- A, B *(or any finite number of sets)$\in \mathcal{A} \Longrightarrow A \cap B \in \mathcal{A}$;*
- $A, B \in \mathcal{A} \Longrightarrow A \backslash B \in \mathcal{A}$;
- $A, B \in \mathcal{A} \Longrightarrow A \triangle B \in \mathcal{A}$.

Proposition 1.18. *The set of all of the finite unions of the disjoint pairs of intervals of $\mathbb{R}$ is an algebra also defined as the algebra of the elementary sets of $\mathbb{R}$ and denoted by $\mathcal{E}_1$, and its members are defined as*

$$\mathcal{E}_1 := \left\{ E \subseteq \mathbb{R} \text{ where } E = \bigcup_{i=1}^{N} E_i \right\}$$

with:

- E_i *interval of $\mathbb{R}$;*
- $E_i \cap E_j = \emptyset$ *for all $i \neq j$;*
- $i, j = 1, 2, \ldots, N$;
- $N \in \mathbb{N}$.

Corollary 1.4. *The set of all the finite unions of disjoint pairs of intervals of $\mathbb{R}^n$ is an algebra also defined as the algebra of the elementary sets $\mathbb{R}^n$, denoted by $\mathcal{E}_n$, and its* *members are defined as*

$$\mathcal{E}_n := \left\{ E \subseteq \mathbb{R}^n \text{ where } E = \bigcup_{i=1}^{N} E_i \right\}$$

with:

- E_i *interval of* $\mathbb{R}^n$;
- $E_i \cap E_j = \varnothing$ *for all* $i \neq j$;
- $i, j = 1, 2, \ldots, N$;
- $N \in \mathbb{N}$.

1.7. σ-ALGEBRA

Definition 1.97. Given a set X, the σ-algebra $(\mathcal{M})$ is a non-null collection of subsets of X which has the following properties:

(1)   null set $\varnothing \in \mathcal{M}$;
(2)   if $E \in \mathcal{M}$, then $E^c \in \mathcal{M}$;
(3)   if $\{E_i\}_{i \in \mathbb{N}} \in \mathcal{M}$ and $A = \bigcup_{i=1}^{\infty} E_i$, then $A \in \mathcal{M}$.

Notation 1.15. Property (3) means that σ-algebra $\mathcal{M}$ is closed to the finite union of the sets which belong to $\mathcal{M}$.

Proposition 1.19. *Let X be a set. Then:*

- $\{\varnothing, X\}$ *is the smallest σ-algebra of the subsets of X;*
- $\mathcal{P}(X)$, *that is the set of the parts of X (see Definition 1.3), is the largest σ-algebra of all of the subsets of X.*

Corollary 1.5. *Let X be a set. Then all of the σ-algebras of the subsets of X hold the smallest σ-algebra of subsets X, ie, based on Proposition 1.19, $\{\varnothing, X\}$.*

Remark 1.26. The main difference between an algebra and a σ-algebra is in the closure to the finite union or the countable union of the sets contained in these algebras. As a matter of fact (based on Definition 1.96(3)), an algebra is a family of sets which is closed only to the finite union of the sets which belong to that algebra, while (based on Definition 1.97(3)) a σ-algebra is also closed to the union of a countable number of infinite sets which belong to that algebra.

Proposition 1.20. *Let $\mathcal{M}$ be a σ-algebra defined on a set X. Then:*

- $A_1, A_2, \ldots \in \mathcal{M} \Longrightarrow \bigcap_{i=1}^{+\infty} A_i \in \mathcal{M}$;
- $A, B \in \mathcal{M} \Longrightarrow A \backslash B \in \mathcal{M}$;
- $A, B \in \mathcal{M} \Longrightarrow A \triangle B \in \mathcal{M}$.

Proposition 1.21. *Let X be a set and let $\mathcal{G}_1$ and $\mathcal{G}_2$ be two families of subsets of X so that*

$$\mathcal{G}_1 \subseteq \mathcal{G}_2$$

Then

$$\sigma(\mathcal{G}_1) \subseteq \sigma(\mathcal{G}_2) \tag{1.26}$$

Proposition 1.22. *The algebra of the elementary sets of $\mathbb{R}$, $\mathcal{E}_1$, is not a σ-algebra.*

Corollary 1.6. *The algebra of the elementary sets of $\mathbb{R}^n$, $\mathcal{E}_n$, is not a σ-algebra.*

Definition 1.98. The *measurable space* is a set X and its σ-algebra. It is denoted by the pair $(X, \mathcal{M})$.

Definition 1.99. Subsets E of X which belong to $\mathcal{M}$ are called *$\mathcal{M}$-measurable*.

Definition 1.100. Let $(X, \mathcal{M})$ a measurable space and let $E, F \in \mathcal{M}$. A *restriction of $\mathcal{M}$ to the set E*, denoted by $\mathcal{M}_E$, is the family of subsets of E made up of the sets $E \cap F$ by varying F in $\mathcal{M}$, ie,

$$\mathcal{M}_E := \{E \cap F\} \tag{1.27}$$

Proposition 1.23. *Let $(X, \mathcal{M})$ be a measurable space and let $E, F \in \mathcal{M}$. Then $\mathcal{M}_E$ is a σ-algebra of set E.*

Corollary 1.7. *Let $(X, \mathcal{M})$ be a measurable space and let $(E, \mathcal{M}_E)$ be a measurable space derived from $(X, \mathcal{M})$ by the restriction of the σ-algebra $\mathcal{M}$ to set $E \in \mathcal{M}$. Then the following relation holds:*

$$\mathcal{M}_E \subseteq \mathcal{M} \tag{1.28}$$

Definition 1.101. Given a set X and one of its σ-algebra $(\mathcal{M})$, a *sub-σ-algebra* is a non-null collection $\mathcal{H}$ of subsets of X which has the same properties as the σ-algebra $(\mathcal{M})$ and is also totally contained in $\mathcal{M}$, ie, $\mathcal{H} \subseteq \mathcal{M}$.

Definition 1.102. A *filtration* on a measurable space $(X, \mathcal{M})$ is a countable or uncountable family of $\mathbb{F} = \{\mathcal{F}_t\}_{t \in T}$ of σ-algebras contained in $\mathcal{M}$ so that any σ-algebra of the family contains all of the sets contained in the preceding σ-algebra, ie,

$$t_1 < t_2 \Rightarrow \mathcal{F}_{t_1} \subset \mathcal{F}_{t_2}$$

Theorem 1.7. *The intersection of a family of σ-algebras defined over a set X is a σ-algebra over X.*

Definition 1.103. Let $\mathcal{G}$ a family of subspaces in a space X. The *σ-algebra generated by* $\mathcal{G}$, denoted by $\sigma(\mathcal{G})$, is the intersection of the σ-algebras of X which contain $\mathcal{G}$, ie,

$$\sigma(\mathcal{G}) = \bigcap_{\alpha \in \Lambda} \mathcal{M}_\alpha^{\mathcal{G}}$$

where for any $\alpha \in \Lambda$:

- $\mathcal{M}_\alpha^{\mathcal{G}}$ is a σ-algebra of X;
- $\mathcal{G} \subseteq \mathcal{M}_\alpha^{\mathcal{G}}$.

Proposition 1.24. *Let X be a non-null set and let E be a one-member subset of X so that $x \in X$, ie,*

$$E \equiv \{x\}$$

Then $\sigma(E)$, ie, the σ-algebra generated by E, may equally be denoted by $\sigma(\{x\})$ and write

$$\sigma(\{x\}) = \{\varnothing, X, \{x\}, X \backslash \{x\}\} \tag{1.29}$$

Remark 1.27. Based on Theorem 1.7, since $\sigma(\mathcal{G})$ is an intersection of σ-algebras, then it is a σ-algebra.

Remark 1.28. By construction, $\sigma(\mathcal{G})$ coincides with the smallest σ-algebra which contains $\mathcal{G}$, ie, it is contained in every σ-algebra which contains $\mathcal{G}$.

Remark 1.29. If $\mathcal{G}$ is a σ-algebra, then

$$\sigma(\mathcal{G}) = \mathcal{G}$$

Proposition 1.25. *The class of the σ-algebras which contain $\mathcal{G}$ is non-null.*

Proposition 1.26. *Let $\mathcal{A}$ and $\mathcal{A}'$ be two families of sets so that*

$$\mathcal{A} \subseteq \mathcal{A}' \subseteq \sigma(\mathcal{A}) \tag{1.30}$$

Then

$$\sigma(\mathcal{A}) \equiv \sigma(\mathcal{A}') \tag{1.31}$$

1.7.1. The Borel σ-algebra

Proposition 1.27. *The σ-algebra generated by $\mathcal{I}$, ie, the class of all the intervals I of $\mathbb{R}$, coincides with the σ-algebra generated by $\mathcal{E}_1$, ie, the algebra of the elementary sets of $\mathbb{R}$:*

$$\sigma(\mathcal{I}) \equiv \sigma(\mathcal{E}_1) \tag{1.32}$$

Definition 1.104. Having defined (X, T) as a topological space (see Definition 1.21), then $\sigma(T)$ is defined to be a *Borel σ-algebra* over X and is denoted by $\mathbb{B}(X)$.

Specifically, if $X \equiv \mathbb{R}$ and if τ is a topology over $\mathbb{R}$, the following definition holds.

Definition 1.105. If $(\mathbb{R}, \tau)$ is defined as a topological space (see Definition 1.21) then $\sigma(\tau)$ is defined to be a *Borel σ-algebra* over $\mathbb{R}$ and is denoted by $\mathbb{B}(\mathbb{R})$ or simply by $\mathbb{B}$.

Similarly, if $X \equiv \mathbb{R}^n$ and if τ^n is a topology over $\mathbb{R}^n$, the following definition holds.

Definition 1.106. If $(\mathbb{R}^n, \tau^n)$ is defined as a topological space (see Definition 1.21), then $\sigma(\tau^n)$ is defined to be a *Borel σ-algebra* over $\mathbb{R}^n$ and is denoted by $\mathbb{B}(\mathbb{R}^n)$ or simply by $\mathbb{B}_n$.

Remark 1.30. The comparison between the definition of the generated σ-algebra (see Definition 1.103) and the definition of the Borel σ-algebra over $\mathbb{R}$ may involve $\mathbb{B}$ being the smallest σ-algebra which contains a topology over $\mathbb{R}$, ie, all of the open intervals of $\mathbb{R}$.

Definition 1.107. Given the extended set of the real numbers $\overline{\mathbb{R}}$, the σ-algebra generated in $\overline{\mathbb{R}}$ by $\mathbb{B}$, $\{-\infty\}$, $\{+\infty\}$, denoted by $\overline{\mathbb{B}}(\overline{\mathbb{R}})$ or simply by $\overline{\mathbb{B}}$, is defined to be the *Borel σ-algebra* over $\overline{\mathbb{R}}$.

Definition 1.108. The *Borel set* is any set contained in $\mathbb{B}$.

Remark 1.31. Since $\mathbb{B}$ is a σ-algebra, it contains any countable union of open intervals of $\mathbb{R}$ (see Definition 1.97(3)). Specifically, one has the following.

- For all $a \in \mathbb{R}$, one has

$$(a, +\infty) = \bigcup_{n=1}^{+\infty} (a, a + n) \in \mathbb{B}$$

$$(-\infty, a) = \bigcup_{n=1}^{+\infty} (a - n, a) \in \mathbb{B}$$

ie, $\mathbb{B}$ *contains all of the open half-lines of* $\mathbb{R}$.
- For all $a, b \in \mathbb{R}$, one has

$$(-\infty, a) \cup (b, +\infty) \in \mathbb{B}$$

ie, $\mathbb{B}$ *contains all* $\mathbb{R}$.

Remark 1.32. Since $\mathbb{B}$ is a σ-algebra, it contains every complement of each countable union of $\mathbb{R}$ open intervals (see Definition 1.97(2)). Specifically, for all $a, b \in \mathbb{R}$, one will have

$$[(-\infty, a) \cup (b, +\infty)]^c = [a, b] \in \mathbb{B}$$

ie, $\mathbb{B}$ *contains all of the closed intervals.*

Remark 1.33. Combining the results of Remarks 1.31 and 1.32, one may derive that

$$[a, +\infty) = \bigcup_{n=1}^{+\infty} [a, a + n] \in \mathbb{B}$$

$$(-\infty, a] = \bigcup_{n=1}^{+\infty} [a - n, a] \in \mathbb{B}$$

ie, $\mathbb{B}$ *contains all of the closed half-lines of* $\mathbb{R}$.

Remark 1.34. Since $\mathbb{B}$ is a σ-algebra, it is closed to the countable intersection (see Proposition 1.20). Specifically, one has the following.

- For all $a, b \in \mathbb{R}$, one will have

$$(a, b] = (-\infty, b] \cap (a, \infty) \in \mathbb{B}$$
$$[a, b) = (-\infty, b) \cap [a, \infty) \in \mathbb{B}$$

ie, $\mathbb{B}$ *contains all of the semi-open intervals of* $\mathbb{R}$.

- For all $a, b \in \mathbb{R}$, one will have one of the following:

$$\{a\} = \bigcap_{n=1}^{+\infty} \left(a - \frac{1}{n}, a + \frac{1}{n} \right) \in \mathbb{B} \tag{1.33}$$

or

$$\{a\} = \bigcap_{n=1}^{+\infty} \left(a - \frac{1}{n}, a \right] \in \mathbb{B} \tag{1.34}$$

or

$$\{a\} = \bigcap_{n=1}^{+\infty} \left[a, a + \frac{1}{n} \right) \in \mathbb{B} \tag{1.35}$$

ie, *each and every real number belongs* to $\mathbb{B}$.

Remark 1.35. Under Equation (1.33), any real number belongs to $\mathbb{B}$ and any real number may be considered a generic set; moreover, $\mathbb{B}$ is a σ-algebra and benefits from Definition 1.97(3), ie, closure to the countable union. Hence, if A is a set which contains countable infinite numbers, ie, $A = \{a_1, a_2, \dots \}$, then

$$A = \bigcup_{n=1}^{+\infty} \{a_n\} \in \mathbb{B} \tag{1.36}$$

Remark 1.36. Since $\mathbb{B}$ is also an algebra (see Remark 1.26) it benefits from the properties of closure to the countable union (see Definition 1.96(3)). Hence, the remark above may also apply to sets which contain countably infinite real numbers, ie, given a set $B = \{b_1, b_2, \dots, b_N\}$, $N \in \mathbb{N}$, then

$$B = \bigcup_{n=1}^{N} \{b_n\} \in \mathbb{B}$$

Proposition 1.28. *A sufficient condition so that the set $A \subseteq \mathbb{R}$ belongs to $\mathbb{B}$ is that A contains countably infinite real numbers.*

Proposition 1.29. *The necessary condition so that the set $A \subseteq R$ does not belong to $\mathbb{B}$ is that A contains uncountably infinite real numbers[3].*

Remark 1.37. Since this condition stated in the theorem is necessary but not sufficient, it can be derived that some sets exist which have uncountably infinite members which belong to $\mathbb{B}$.

---

[3] An example of a set contained in $\mathbb{R}$ but which does not belong to $\mathbb{B}$ is a subset of the ternary Cantor set (see Section 10.5.3.1), built by using the *Cantor function*.

Theorem 1.8. *The Borel σ-algebra in $\mathbb{R}$ (ie, $\mathbb{B}(\mathbb{R})$ or $\sigma(\tau)$) coincides with the σ-algebra generated by class $\mathcal{I}$ of the intervals of $\mathbb{R}$, ie,*

$$\sigma(\tau) \equiv \sigma(\mathcal{I}) \tag{1.37}$$

where the symbol τ denotes a topology on $\mathbb{R}$.

Theorem 1.9. *The Borel σ-algebra in $\mathbb{R}$ (ie, $\mathbb{B}(\mathbb{R})$ or $\sigma(\tau)$) may also be generated with respect to the elements of algebra $\mathcal{E}_1$, ie,*

$$\sigma(\tau) \equiv \sigma(\mathcal{E}_1) \tag{1.38}$$

Proposition 1.30. *The Borel σ-algebra over $\mathbb{R}$ has the power of the continuum (see Definition 1.9).*

Linear algebra

2.1. BASIC DEFINITIONS

Definition 2.1. A *scalar* is any number a that belongs to the set $\mathbb{R}$ of real numbers.

Definition 2.2. The *row vector v* of order (or dimension) n is a set of n members entered on one row and n columns.

Definition 2.3. The *column vector u* of order (or dimension) n is a set of n members entered on n rows and one column.

Definition 2.4. A *matrix A* of order (m, n) or of size (m, n) is an array of $(m \cdot n)$ entries displayed on m rows and n columns.

Remark 2.1. Specifically, if all of the entries of A are real numbers[1], A is said to be defined over $\mathbb{R}^{m \times n}$; if one or several entries of A are complex numbers with a coefficient of the imaginary part other than zero, A is defined over $\mathbb{C}^{m \times n}$.

Remark 2.2. Usually, a matrix is denoted by a Block letter of the Latin alphabet. It looks like a table closed inside square brackets where a_{ij} is the entry of matrix A located at the ith row and at the jth column:

$$A = \begin{bmatrix} a_{11} & a_{12} & \cdots & a_{1n} \\ a_{21} & a_{22} & \cdots & a_{2n} \\ \vdots & \vdots & \vdots & \vdots \\ a_{m1} & a_{m2} & \cdots & a_{mn} \end{bmatrix} \tag{2.1}$$

or, in short,

$$A = [a_{ij}]$$

---

[1] Real numbers are the members of the subset of complex numbers whose coefficient of the imaginary is equal to zero.

Remark 2.3. A matrix of order $(1, 1)$ identifies a scalar; a matrix of order $(1, n)$ identifies a row vector of order n; a matrix of order $(m, 1)$ identifies a column vector of order m.

Definition 2.5. Given a matrix A of order (m, n), the *transpose of A*, denoted as A^T or as A', is the matrix of order (n, m) so that any entry is as follows:

$$a'_{ij} = a_{ji}$$

Remark 2.4. Then matrix A' is obtained by interchanging rows in A with the corresponding columns so that the ith line of A becomes the ith column of A' and, correspondingly, the jth column of A becomes the jth row of A'. This operation is called *transposition*.

Definition 2.6. A matrix A of order (mXn) is *symmetric* if it coincides with its transpose, ie,

$$A = A' \tag{2.2}$$

or if the following condition equivalent to Equation (2.2) holds:

$$a_{ij} = a_{ji}, \quad \forall i = 1, 2, \ldots, m; \; \forall j = 1, 2, \ldots, n$$

2.2. SQUARE MATRIX

Definition 2.7. A *square matrix* is a matrix which has the same number of rows and columns, ie, a matrix A of order (m, n) which satisfies the following condition:

$$m = n$$

Remark 2.5. If matrix A is a square matrix, then it may be simply stated that it is of order n (or, equally, of order m).

Definition 2.8. The *main diagonal* of a square matrix A of order n is the array of entries $\{a_{11}, a_{22}, \ldots, a_{nn}\}$ of matrix A.

Definition 2.9. A *diagonal matrix* of order n is a square matrix A of order n whose off-diagonal elements are zero entries. Therefore, a diagonal matrix may be represented as follows:

$$A = \begin{bmatrix} a_{11} & 0 & \cdots & 0 \\ 0 & a_{22} & \cdots & 0 \\ \vdots & \vdots & \vdots & \vdots \\ 0 & 0 & \cdots & a_{nn} \end{bmatrix} \tag{2.3}$$

Definition 2.10. A *scalar matrix* of order n is a diagonal matrix of order n whose elements entered in the main diagonal are all equal.

Definition 2.11. An *identity matrix* of order n, denoted as I_n, is a scalar matrix of order n with ones on the main diagonal.

Definition 2.12. An *upper* or *lower triangular matrix* of order n is a square matrix of order n whose entries under or (over) the main diagonal n are zero entries. An upper triangular matrix may be represented as

$$A = \begin{bmatrix} a_{11} & a_{12} & \cdots & a_{1n} \\ 0 & a_{22} & \cdots & a_{2n} \\ \vdots & \vdots & \vdots & \vdots \\ 0 & 0 & \cdots & a_{mn} \end{bmatrix} \tag{2.4}$$

Remark 2.6. The representation of a lower triangular matrix is absolutely specular to the upper triangular matrix represented at in Equation (2.4).

Definition 2.13. Let matrix A be of order (m, k) and matrix B be of order (k, n). Then matrices A and B are said to be *conformable for multiplication of order AB* because matrix A has the same number of columns as matrix B, and the matrix

$$C = AB \tag{2.5}$$

is defined to be the *product* of A times B.

In this situation, it is usually said that matrix A premultiplies matrix B and that matrix B postmultiplies A.

Remark 2.7. Any entry c_{ij} of matrix C, being the product of matrix A of order (m, k) times matrix B of order (k, n) (see Equation (2.5)) is the result of the scalar product between the ith row of matrix A and the jth row of matrix B, ie,

$$c_{ij} = \sum_{h=1}^{k} a_{ih} b_{hj}$$

Remark 2.8. The order of multiplication is important because generally, if A and B are conformable for multiplication also of order BA [2], the following holds:

$$AB \neq BA \tag{2.6}$$

---

[2] Apparently this happens when A and B are two matrices of the order (m, n) and (n, m), respectively.

Remark 2.9. In order to find the product between matrices A and B conformable of order AB equal to zero (ie, a matrix with all zero entries) it is not necessary that at least matrix A or matrix B has all zero entries. In other words, the following may hold:

$$AB = [0]$$

even if $A \neq [0]$ and $B \neq [0]$.

Remark 2.10. If Equation (2.6) is not verified, ie, matrix A and matrix B show

$$AB = BA$$

matrix A and matrix B are *commutative*.

2.2.1. Determinants

Definition 2.14. Given a square matrix A of order n, the *determinant* of A, denoted by $\det(A)$ or by $|A|$, is the scalar

$$\det(A) = \sum(\pm)a_{1j_1}a_{2j_2}\cdots a_{nj_n} \tag{2.7}$$

where the sum is applied to all of the possible $n!$ permutations $(j_1, j_2, \ldots, j_n)$ of $1, 2, \ldots, n$ and where $(\pm)$ stands for $+$ or $-$ based on the fact that it is an odd or even permutation $(j_1, j_2, \ldots, j_n)$ with respect to the fundamental permutation $(1, 2, \ldots, n)$.

Remark 2.11. Under the definition above, the determinant is the algebraic sum of all $n!$ products determined by multiplying the main diagonal entries $\{a_{11}, a_{22}, \ldots, a_{nn}\}$, where the first indexes are fixed and the second indexes are permuted. These products will be assigned the sign $+$ or $-$ based on the result of whether the second indexes' permutation is even or odd against the fundamental permutation.

Remark 2.12. Based on Definition 2.14 and of Remark 2.11, Equation (2.7) may also be written as

$$\det(A) = \sum(-1)^j a_{1j_1}a_{2j_2}\cdots a_{nj_n} \tag{2.8}$$

where exponent j is the number of inversions of permutation $(j_1, j_2, \ldots, j_n)$ against the fundamental permutation $(1, 2, \ldots, n)$ and where summation is applied to all $n!$ permutations.

Definition 2.15. Given a square matrix A of order n, the *minor complementary* to entry a_{ij} of matrix A, denoted as A_{ij}, is the determinant of the square submatrix derived from A by deleting the ith row and j^{th} column (ie, the row and the column that cross in a_{ij}).

Definition 2.16. Given a square matrix A or order n, the *algebraic complement* of entry a_{ij} of A, denoted by D_{ij} is

$$D_{ij} = (-1)^{i+j} A_{ij}$$

where A_{ij} is the minor complementary to entry a_{ij} of A.

Theorem 2.1 (First Laplace theorem). *The determinant of a square matrix A of order n is equal to the sum of the products of any line or column of A multiplied by their respective algebraic complement.*

2.2.1.1. *Properties of the determinants*

(1) The determinant of a matrix coincides with the determinant of its transpose.

(2) If two rows of matrix A are interchanged, the determinant of the new matrix is the opposite of the determinant of A.

(3) If a row of matrix A is moved up or down by p rows, the determinant of the new matrix is $(-1)^p |A|$.

(4) If two parallel rows of matrix A are equal or proportional, or if a row can be derived as a combination of other rows, then the determinant of A is zero.

(5) If the row of matrix A is multiplied by a scalar k, then the determinant of the new matrix is $k|A|$. In general, the following equivalence below holds $\det(kA) = k^n \det(A)$.

(6) If vector w is added to a row of matrix A, the determinant of the new matrix is equal to the summation of the determinant of A and of the determinant of a matrix which has vector w at the place of the correspondent row of A.

(7) The determinant of a matrix does not change if a linear combination of parallel rows is added to one (or several) rows.

(8) In general, it holds that $\det(A + B) \neq \det(A) + \det(B)$, where A and B are two square matrices.

(9) The determinant of a triangular or diagonal matrix is equal to the product of the entries of the main diagonal.

(10) If A is a square matrix and D is a scalar matrix of order k, then $\det(DA) = k^n \det(A)$.

(11) The equivalence $\det(AB) = \det(A)\det(B)$ holds, also known as the Binet–Cauchy theorem.

2.2.2. Inverse matrix

Definition 2.17. Given a square matrix A of order n, the *inverse matrix* of A, denoted as A^{-1} is the square matrix of order n which satisfies the following conditions:

$$AA^{-1} = A^{-1}A = I_n$$

Theorem 2.2. *The necessary and sufficient condition for a square matrix A of order n to admit an inverse matrix A^{-1} is*

$$\det(A) \neq 0$$

Definition 2.18. Given a square matrix A of order n, the *adjoint matrix* of A, denoted by A^+, is the transpose of the matrix whose entries are algebraic complements of the corresponding entries of A.

Remark 2.13. From the definition above it follows that

$$A^* = \begin{bmatrix} A_{11} & A_{12} & \cdots & A_{1n} \\ A_{21} & A_{22} & \cdots & A_{2n} \\ \vdots & \vdots & \vdots & \vdots \\ A_{n1} & A_{n2} & \cdots & A_{nn} \end{bmatrix}$$

the matrix of the algebraic complements of A, and the adjoint matrix of A is denoted as

$$A^+ = \begin{bmatrix} A_{11} & A_{21} & \cdots & A_{n1} \\ A_{12} & A_{22} & \cdots & A_{n2} \\ \vdots & \vdots & \vdots & \vdots \\ A_{1n} & A_{2n} & \cdots & A_{nn} \end{bmatrix} \tag{2.9}$$

Theorem 2.3. *If A is a square matrix of order n with $\det(A) \neq 0$, then its inverse, A^{-1}, is derived by dividing the adjoint matrix of A by the determinant A, ie,*

$$A^{-1} = \frac{A^+}{\det(A)} \tag{2.10}$$

$$= \frac{\begin{bmatrix} A_{11} & A_{21} & \cdots & A_{n1} \\ A_{12} & A_{22} & \cdots & A_{n2} \\ \vdots & \vdots & \vdots & \vdots \\ A_{1n} & A_{2n} & \cdots & A_{nn} \end{bmatrix}}{\det(A)}$$

2.2.2.1. Properties of the inverse matrix
(1) The transpose of the inverse coincides with the inverse of the transpose, ie, $(A^{-1})^T = (A^T)^{-1}$.
(2) The equivalence $(AB)^{-1} = B^{-1}A^{-1}$ holds.
(3) If A is invertible, then $AC = [0] \Leftrightarrow C = [0]$.

2.2.3. Quadratic forms

Definition 2.19. Let $\underline{x} = (x_1, x_2, \ldots, x_n)$ be any vector of $\mathbb{R}^n$ and let A be a square matrix of order $n > 1$. The *quadratic form* in vector $\underline{x}$, denoted by $Q(\underline{x})$, is the scalar quantity

$$Q(\underline{x}) = \underline{x}^T A \underline{x} \tag{2.11}$$

$$= \sum_{i=1}^{n} \sum_{j=1}^{n} a_{ij} x_i x_j$$

$$= a_{11} x_{11} + a_{12} x_1 x_2 + \cdots + a_{1n} x_1 x_n$$

$$+ a_{21} x_2 x_1 + a_{22} x_{22} + \cdots + a_{2n} x_2 x_n$$

$$\vdots$$

$$+ a_{n1} x_n x_1 + a_{n2} x_n x_2 + \cdots + a_{nn} x_{nn}$$

2.2.3.1. Classes of quadratic forms
(1) A quadratic form is *positive definite* if

$$Q(\underline{x}) > 0, \quad \forall \underline{x} \neq \mathbf{0}$$

(2) A quadratic form is *negative definite* if

$$Q(\underline{x}) < 0, \quad \forall \underline{x} \neq \mathbf{0}$$

(3) A quadratic form is *positive semi-definite* if

$$Q(\underline{x}) \geq 0, \quad \forall \underline{x} \in \mathbb{R}^n$$

and

$$Q(\underline{x}) = 0 \quad \text{for at least one } \underline{x} \neq \mathbf{0}$$

(4) A quadratic form is *negative semi-definite* if

$$Q(\underline{x}) \leq 0, \quad \forall \underline{x} \in \mathbb{R}^n$$

and

$$Q(\underline{x}) = 0 \quad \text{for at least one } \underline{x} \neq \mathbf{0}$$

(5) A quadratic form is *indefinite* if there is at least one pair of vectors $\underline{x}^1$ and $\underline{x}^2 \in \mathbb{R}^n$ where $Q(\underline{x})$ has the opposite sign.

Remark 2.14. The exclusive criterion to enter quadratic forms into one of the five types mentioned above is the structure of matrix A. Therefore, matrix A having a quadratic form $Q(\underline{x})$ is defined to be *positive definite, negative definite, positive semi-definite, negative semi-definite* or *indefinite* if $Q(\underline{x})$ is *positive definite, negative definite, positive semi-definite, negative semi-definite* or *indefinite*, respectively.

2.2.3.2. Cholesky factorisation

Theorem 2.4. *Let A a symmetric positive semi-definite square matrix of order n. Then the matrix*

$$(U^\mathsf{T})^{-1} A U^{-1} \tag{2.12}$$

where U is an upper triangular matrix so that $A = U^\mathsf{T} U$ (the so-called Cholesky factorisation), is equal to the Identity matrix of order n, ie,

$$(U^\mathsf{T})^{-1} A U^{-1} = I_n \tag{2.13}$$

Corollary 2.1. *If all entries of matrix A are multiplied by a constant c, constant c can be brought out from the Cholesky factorisation. In other words, for matrix A, as*

$$A = \begin{bmatrix} c \cdot a_{11} & c \cdot a_{12} \\ c \cdot a_{12} & c \cdot a_{22} \end{bmatrix}$$

then

$$A = c U^\mathsf{T} U \tag{2.14}$$

where matrix U has the form

$$U = \begin{bmatrix} \sqrt{a_{11}} & \frac{a_{12}}{\sqrt{a_{11}}} \\ 0 & \sqrt{a_{22} - \frac{a_{12}^3}{\sqrt{a_{11}}}} \end{bmatrix}$$

Corollary 2.2. *It should be noted that in this case, the matrix* $(U^T)^{-1}A(U)^{-1}$ *will be a diagonal matrix whose entries are equal to c, ie,*

$$(U^T)^{-1}A(U)^{-1} = cI_n \tag{2.15}$$

2.3. VECTOR SPACES

Definition 2.20. Let X be a set of vectors. It is said to be a *vector or linear space* if for two random vectors x and y of that space and a scalar k, one has

$$x + y \in X \quad \text{and} \quad kx \in X \tag{2.16}$$

Equally, the previous conditions may be summarised as

$$hx + ky \in X \tag{2.17}$$

where h is a scalar.

Notation 2.1. Conditions which denote a vector space X as described in Definition 2.20, ie, $x + y \in X$ and $kx \in X$, may be summarised in the statement below: "The vector space X is closed to addition and multiplication by a scalar".

Proposition 2.1. *The necessary condition so that a set of vectors X is a vector space is that it contains a zero vector.*

Definition 2.21. Let $x_1, x_2, \ldots, x_n$ be n vectors of a vector space X and let $k_1, k_2, \ldots, k_n$ be n scalars belonging to $\mathbb{R}$. The vector below is defined to be the *linear combination* of vectors $x_1, x_2, \ldots, x_n$ weighted by $k_1, k_2, \ldots, k_n$:

$$x = \sum_{i=1}^{n} k_i x_i \tag{2.18}$$

Remark 2.15. Scalars $k_1, k_2, \ldots, k_n$ in the right-hand side of Equation (2.18) are the *coefficients* of the linear combination.

Definition 2.22. N vectors $x_1, x_2, \ldots, x_n$ of a vector space X are *linearly dependent* if there are n not all zero scalars $k_1, k_2, \ldots, k_n$ belonging to $\mathbb{R}$ so that

$$x = \sum_{i=1}^{n} k_i x_i = 0$$

Definition 2.23. N vectors $x_1, x_2, \ldots, x_n$ of a vector space X are *linearly independent* if the zero vector can only be derived by using zero coefficients, ie,

$$x = \sum_{i=1}^{n} k_i x_i = 0 \Rightarrow k_1, k_2, \ldots, k_n = 0$$

Definition 2.24. Let X be a vector space and let U a subset of X. U is said to be a *vector subspace* of X, provided that U is vector space.

Definition 2.25. Let $x_1, x_2, \ldots, x_n$ be n vectors of a vector space X. These n vectors are said to form a *generators system for* X if any vector $x \in X$ can be derived from one of their linear combinations.

Definition 2.26. The *base of a vector space* X is a generator system of X which is linearly independent between them.

Theorem 2.5. *Given a vector space X and one of its bases, there is only one way to represent a generic vector x of X as a linear combination of the vectors of that basis.*

Remark 2.16. The base of $\mathbb{R}^3$ composed of the following three vectors

$$\begin{bmatrix} 1 \\ 0 \\ 0 \end{bmatrix} ; \begin{bmatrix} 0 \\ 1 \\ 0 \end{bmatrix} ; \begin{bmatrix} 0 \\ 0 \\ 1 \end{bmatrix}$$

is known as the *canonical base* of $\mathbb{R}^3$ and its vectors are called the *fundamental vectors* of $\mathbb{R}^3$. Broadly speaking, the definition below applies.

Definition 2.27. The *canonical base* of the vector space $\mathbb{R}^n$ is the set of the n fundamental vectors below of $\mathbb{R}^n$ (each one having n rows):

$$\begin{bmatrix} 1 \\ 0 \\ 0 \\ . \\ . \\ 0 \end{bmatrix} ; \begin{bmatrix} 0 \\ 1 \\ 0 \\ . \\ . \\ 0 \end{bmatrix} ; \ldots ; \begin{bmatrix} 0 \\ 0 \\ 0 \\ . \\ . \\ 1 \end{bmatrix}$$

Proposition 2.2. *Let X be a vector space which has a basis of n vectors. Then any other basis of X is also composed of n vectors.*

Definition 2.28. Let X be a vector space which has a basis of n vectors. Then X is defined to be a *n-dimensional* vector and can be written as

$$\dim(X) = n$$

Definition 2.29. Let X be a vector space and let U and V be two subspaces of X. The *intersection space* is a vector space of all of the vectors U and V equipped with addition and multiplication by a scalar and is denoted by

$$U \cap V$$

Definition 2.30. Two subspaces U and V of a vector space X are defined to be *disjoint* if their intersection space coincides with the zero vector, ie,

$$U \cap V \equiv 0$$

Definition 2.31. Let X be a vector space and let U and V be two subspaces of X. The set of vectors derived by adding two-by-two all vectors of U and of V is defined to be the *union* of subspaces U and V and is denoted by

$$U \cup V$$

Proposition 2.3. *The set of vectors derived from the union of two vector subspaces of the same vector space may not necessarily be a vector space.*

Definition 2.32. Let X be a vector space and let U and V be two subspaces of X. The *sum space* is a vector space of all vectors of U and of V (added two-by-two) equipped with addition and multiplication by a scalar and is denoted by

$$U + V$$

Theorem 2.6 (Sylvester). *Let X be a vector space and let U and V be two subspaces of X. Then one has*

$$\dim(U + V) = \dim(U) + \dim(V) - \dim(U \cap V)$$

Definition 2.33. Let X be a vector space and let U and V be two disjoint subspaces of X. The *direct sum* of U and V, denoted by

$$U \oplus V := \{x \in X \text{ where } \exists x_1 \in U, x_2 \in V \text{ s.t.} : x = x_1 + x_2\}$$

is the sum of all of the pairs of vectors so that the first vector belongs to U and the second vector belongs to V.

Remark 2.17. $U \oplus V$ is a vector subspace of X because it is closed to addition and multiplication by a scalar.

2.3.1. Vector space norms

Definition 2.34. Let X be a vector space over $\mathbb{R}$ (or over $\mathbb{C}$). The *norm over X* is a function $\|x\| : X \to \mathbb{R}$ (or $\mathbb{C}$) so that:

(1) $\|x\| \geq 0$ for all $x \in X$;
(2) $\|x\| = 0 \Leftrightarrow x = 0$;
(3) $\|\alpha x\| = |\alpha| \cdot \|x\|$ for all $x \in X$ and for all $\alpha \in \mathbb{R}$ (or $\mathbb{C}$);
(4) $\|x + y\| \leq \|x\| + \|y\|$ for all $x, y \in X$.

Definition 2.35. The *vector space norm* is the pair $(X, \|x\|)$.

Proposition 2.4. *Let $(X, \|x\|)$ be a vector space norm and let U be a vector subspace of X. Then $\|x\|$ is also a norm over U, that is $(U, \|x\|)$ is also a vector space norm[3], and is defined to be a* vector subspace norm *of the vector space norm $(X, \|x\|)$.*

2.3.1.1. Vector space norm and metric space

Proposition 2.5. *Given a vector space norm $(X, \|x\|)$, the function*

$$d(x, y) := \|x - y\| \tag{2.19}$$

is a metric over X, the so-called metrics derived from the norm.

Corollary 2.3. *Any vector space norm is also a metric space where the metric is derived from the norm.*

Based on the Corollary 2.3, vector space norms are also metric spaces. Consequently, it is possible to apply all of the concepts focused on in this section on metric spaces and summarised below (see Sections 1.5, 1.4.2.3 and 1.5.2) to vector space norms.

---

[3]$(U, \|x\|)$ is usually said to be a subspace of a vector space norm $(X, \|x\|)$ if U is considered as a vector space with a norm derived by restricting the norm over X to U.

Definition 2.36. Let $(X, \|x\|)$ be a vector space norm and let $x \in X$. Then the set $B(x, \alpha)$ is said to be the *open sphere of centre x and radius α* for any $\alpha \in \mathbb{R}^+$ and can be written as

$$B(x, \alpha) := \{y \in X : \|x - y\| < \alpha\}$$

Definition 2.37. Let $(X, \|x\|)$ be a vector space norm and let $x \in X$. Then, the set $\overline{B}(x, \alpha)$ is said to be the *closed sphere of centre x and radius α* and can be written as

$$\overline{B}(x, \alpha) := \{y \in X : \|x - y\| \leq \alpha\}$$

Definition 2.38. Given a vector space norm $(X, \|x\|)$, a subset A of X is defined to be *open in X* if

$$\forall x \in A \quad \exists \alpha > 0 \ni' B(x, \alpha) \subset A$$

Definition 2.39. Given a vector space norm $(X, \|x\|)$, a subset B of X is defined to be *closed in X* if the complement, ie, $B^c \equiv X \backslash B$, is open in X (see Definition 2.38).

Definition 2.40. Given a vector space norm $(X, \|x\|)$, *a sequence $\{x_n\}_{n \in \mathbb{N}}$ of values in X is said to be convergent over X to value x* if (see Definition 1.84) for all $\varepsilon > 0$ there exists $N \in \mathbb{N}$ and for all $n \geq N$ the following holds:

$$\|x_n - x\| < \varepsilon \quad \text{with } x \in X \tag{2.20}$$

Remark 2.18. Condition (2.20) in Definition 2.40 may also be written as

$$\lim_{n \to +\infty} \|x_n - x\| = 0 \quad \text{with } x \in X \tag{2.21}$$

Definition 2.41. Given a vector space norm $(X, \|x\|)$, a sequence $\{x_n\}_{n \in \mathbb{N}}$ of values in X is defined to be a *Cauchy sequence* (see Definition 3.6) if for all $\varepsilon > 0$ there exists $N \in \mathbb{N}$ and for all $n, m \geq N$ the following holds (see Definition 1.85 and Proposition 2.5)

$$\|x_n - x_m\| < \varepsilon \tag{2.22}$$

Remark 2.19. Condition (2.22) of Definition 2.41 may also be written as

$$\lim_{n, m \to +\infty} \|x_n - x_m\| = 0 \tag{2.23}$$

Proposition 2.6. *Any Cauchy sequence is convergent.*

Theorem 2.7. *Let $(X, \|x\|)$ be a vector space norm and let U be a subset of X. Then U is closed in X if and only if any convergent sequence (see Definition 3.3) $\{x_n\}_{n \in \mathbb{N}}$ of members of U is convergent to one member x of U, and can be written as*

$$\lim_{n \to +\infty} \|x_n - x\| = 0$$

$$x \in U \tag{2.24}$$

$$\forall \{x_n\}_{n \in \mathbb{N}} \subseteq U$$

Definition 2.42. Let $(X, \|x\|)$ be a vector space norm. A subset U of X is defined to be a *closed vector subspace of* X if:

(1) U is a vector subspace of X (see Definition 2.24);
(2) U is a closed set in X (see Definition 2.39) or, equally, any convergent sequence (see Definition 3.3) $\{x_n\}_{n \in \mathbb{N}}$ of members of U converges to a member x of U, and can be written as

$$\lim_{n \to +\infty} \|x_n - x\| = 0$$

$$x \in U \tag{2.24}$$

$$\forall \{x_n\}_{n \in \mathbb{N}} \subseteq U$$

2.3.1.1.1. Banach space

Definition 2.43. A vector space norm $(X, \|x\|)$ is defined to be *full* if any Cauchy sequence (see Definition 3.6) of values in X converges over X (see Definition 1.86).

Definition 2.44. A *Banach space* is a full vector space norm (see Definitions 2.35 and 2.43).

Definition 2.45. Let $(X, \|x\|)$ be a Banach space and let U be a non-null subset of X. Then the pair $(U, \|x\|)$ is defined to be a subspace of a Banach space or *Banach subspace* if U is a vector space norm whose norm coincides with the norm of X.

Proposition 2.7. *Let $(X, \|x\|)$ be a Banach space and $(U, \|x\|)$ be a subspace of $(X, \|x\|)$, then $(U, \|x\|)$ is full is and only if U is a closed set in X under Definition 2.39.*

Corollary 2.4. *Let $(X, \|x\|)$ be a Banach space and let $(U, \|x\|)$ a full subspace. Then $(U, \|x\|)$ is a closed vector space norm of $(X, \|x\|)$.*

2.3.2. Inner product space

Definition 2.46. Given a vector space X over $\mathbb{R}$ (or over $\mathbb{C}$) the *inner product* for all $x, y \in X$ is a function $\langle x, y \rangle : X \times X \to \mathbb{R}$ (or over $\mathbb{C}$) so that:

(1) $\langle x, x \rangle \geq 0$ for all $x \in X$;
(2) $\langle x, x \rangle = 0$ if and only if $x = \mathbf{0}$;
(3) $\langle x, y \rangle = \langle y, x \rangle$ for all $x, y \in X$;
(4) $\langle ax, y \rangle = a \langle x, y \rangle$ for all $a \in \mathbb{R}$;
(5) $\langle x + z, y \rangle = \langle x, y \rangle + \langle z, y \rangle$ for all $x, y, z \in X$.

Definition 2.47. The *inner product space* or *pre-Hilbert space* is the pair $(X, \langle x, y \rangle)$.

Proposition 2.8. *Addition, multiplication by a scalar and the inner product are defined to be continuous in a pre-Hilbert space* $(X, \langle x, y \rangle)$, *ie, if* $\{x_n^1\}_{n \in \mathbb{N}}$ *and* $\{x_n^2\}_{n \in \mathbb{N}}$ *are two sequences (see Definition 3.1) into* $(X, \langle x, y \rangle)$ *and convergent (see Definition 3.3) to* x^1 *and* x^2, *respectively, then*

$$\lim_{n \to +\infty} (x_n^1 + x_n^2) = x^1 + x^2 \tag{2.25}$$

$$\lim_{n \to +\infty} c \cdot x_n^1 = c \cdot x^1, \quad \forall c \in \mathbb{R} \tag{2.26}$$

$$\lim_{n \to +\infty} \langle x_n^1, x_n^2 \rangle = \left\langle \lim_{n \to +\infty} x_n^1, \lim_{n \to +\infty} x_n^2 \right\rangle = \left\langle x^1, x^2 \right\rangle \tag{2.27}$$

Definition 2.48. Given the pre-Hilbert space $(X, \langle x, y \rangle)$, two members x and y are defined to be *orthogonal* if

$$\langle x, y \rangle = 0 \tag{2.28}$$

and is denoted by $x \perp y$.

2.3.2.1. Inner product space, vector space norms and metric spaces

Proposition 2.9. *The inner product space* $(X, \langle x, y \rangle)$ *holds a norm (the so-called norm derived from the inner product) defined as*

$$\|x\| := \sqrt{\langle x, x \rangle} \tag{2.29}$$

Corollary 2.5. *The following equivalence holds:*

$$\|x\|^2 = \langle x, x \rangle \tag{2.30}$$

Definition 2.49. The *inner space product norm* or *pre-Hilbert space norm* is the pairing off between the inner product or pre-Hilbert space and the norm derived from the inner product:

$$(X, \langle x, y \rangle, \|x\|) := (X, \langle x, y \rangle, \sqrt{\langle x, x \rangle})$$

Proposition 2.10. *Any inner space vector norm (ie, pre-Hilbert space norm) is a vector space norm.*

Under Proposition 2.10, pre-Hilbert space norms are also space vector norms and then, under Corollary 2.3, they are also metric spaces. One may apply all of the concepts focused on in sections about metric spaces and space vector norms to them (see Sections 1.5, 1.4.2.3, 1.5.2 and 2.3.1.1).

Proposition 2.11. *Let $(X, \langle x, y \rangle, \|x\|)$ be an inner product space norm. Then the equivalences below hold.*

- *Equivalence of parallelogram:*

$$\|x + y\|^2 + \|x - y\|^2 = 2\|x\|^2 + 2\|y\|^2 \tag{2.31}$$

- *Equivalence of polarisation:*

$$4\langle x, y \rangle = \|x + y\|^2 - \|x - y\|^2 \tag{2.32}$$

Corollary 2.6. *A space vector norm is a pre-Hilbert space norm if it satisfies the equivalence of parallelogram.*

Definition 2.50. The pair $(U, \langle u, v \rangle)$ is defined to be a *subspace of a pre-Hilbert space* $(X, \langle x, y \rangle)$ if U is a vector subspace of X and $\langle u, v \rangle$ is the restriction of $\langle x, y \rangle$ to $U \times U$.

Definition 2.51. Given an inner space norm $(X, \langle x, y \rangle, \sqrt{\langle x, x \rangle})$, two members x and y, so that $x \perp y$, are said to be *orthonormal* if

$$\sqrt{\langle x, x \rangle} = \sqrt{\langle y, y \rangle} = 1$$

Proposition 2.12. *Let $(X, \langle x, y \rangle, \sqrt{\langle x, x \rangle})$ be an inner space product norm of size n and let x' be one non-zero vector of this space. Also, let U be the set of vectors of X orthogonal to x', ie,*

$$U = \{x \in X : x \perp x'\}$$

Then U is a vector subspace of X of size $(n-1)$ and is said to be a subspace *orthogonal to x'.*

Definition 2.52. Let $U_1, U_2, \dots$ be disjoint and closed subspaces of an inner space product norm $(X, \langle x, y \rangle, \sqrt{\langle x, x \rangle})$ so that:

- subspaces U_i are orthogonal two by two;
- any member x of X may only be represented as

$$x = u_1 + u_2 + \cdots \quad \text{where } u_i \in U_i$$

Then X is defined to be the *direct sum of subspaces* $U_1, U_2, \ldots$ (see Definition 2.33) and can be shown as

$$X = U_1 \oplus U_2 \oplus \cdots$$

Proposition 2.13. *If X is a vector space derived as a direct sum of disjoint and closed spaces $U_1, U_2, \ldots$, then the following equality holds:*

$$\dim X = \dim U_1 + \dim U_2 + \cdots$$

Proposition 2.14. *Let $(X, \langle x, y \rangle, \sqrt{\langle x, x \rangle})$ be an inner space product norm of size n and let U be a vector subspace of $(X, \langle x, y \rangle, \sqrt{\langle x, x \rangle})$. Also, let*

$$x' \in X : x' \neq 0 \quad \text{and} \quad x' \notin U$$

Then there is one vector $u' \in U$ only so that

$$(x' - u') \perp x'$$

or

$$\langle x' - u', x' \rangle = 0$$

This vector u' is defined to be the orthogonal projection *of x' over U.*

Definition 2.53. Let $(X, \langle x, y \rangle, \sqrt{\langle x, x \rangle})$ be an inner space product norm and let U be a non-null subset of X. The *orthogonal complement* of U (to X) denoted by $U^{\perp}$ is the set of all vectors of X orthogonal to vectors of U, ie,

$$U^{\perp} := \{x \in X : x \perp u, \ \forall u \in U\}$$

Proposition 2.15. *Let $(X, \langle x, y \rangle, \sqrt{\langle x, x \rangle})$ be an inner space product norm and let x' be one vector inside that space. Then*

$$(x')^{\perp} = \{x \in X : x \perp x'\} \tag{2.33}$$

is a closed vector subspace of X (see Definition 2.42).

2.3.2.1.1. Hilbert space

Definition 2.54. An inner product space norm $(X, \langle x, y \rangle, \sqrt{\langle x, x \rangle})$ is said to be *full* if any Cauchy sequence (see Definition 3.6) of values on X is convergent (see Definition 3.3) over X (see Definition 1.86).

Definition 2.55. *The Hilbert space* is a full inner product space norm (see Definitions 2.49 and 2.54).

Notation 2.2. Any hilbert space will generically be denoted as $\mathcal{H}$ which corresponds to the triple $(X, \langle x, y \rangle, \sqrt{\langle x, x \rangle})$ and identifies a full inner space product norm. Below, either

$$x \in X \Leftrightarrow x \in \mathcal{H}$$

is used, or

$$U \subset X \Leftrightarrow U \subset \mathcal{H}$$

Definition 2.56. Let $\mathcal{H}$ be a Hilbert space and let $U \subset \mathcal{H}$. Then the triple $(U, \langle x, y \rangle, \sqrt{\langle x, x \rangle})$ is defined as the subspace of a Hilbert space or *Hilbert subspace* if U is an inner product space norm whose inner product is equal to $\mathcal{H}$ and whose norm is the norm derived from the inner product norm.

Notation 2.3. Any Hilbert subspace will be generically denoted as $U^{\mathcal{H}}$ which corresponds to the triple $(U, \langle x, y \rangle, \sqrt{\langle x, x \rangle})$.

Proposition 2.16. *Let $\mathcal{H}$ a Hilbert space and $U^{\mathcal{H}}$ a subspace $\mathcal{H}$. Then $U^{\mathcal{H}}$ is full if and only if U is a closed set in X under Definition 2.39.*

Corollary 2.7. *Let $\mathcal{H}$ be a Hilbert space and let $U^{\mathcal{H}}$ be a full subspace of $\mathcal{H}$. Then $U^{\mathcal{H}}$ is a closed vector subspace norm of $\mathcal{H}$.*

Theorem 2.8. *Let $\mathcal{H}$ be a Hilbert space, let $U^{\mathcal{H}}$ be a closed subspace of $\mathcal{H}$ and let h be a member of $\mathcal{H}$. Then there is one $u^* \in U$ and one only which is closest to h, that is, by letting*

$$d := \inf_{u \in U} \|h - u\| \tag{2.34}$$

one has

$$d = \|h - u^*\| \tag{2.35}$$

Lemma 2.1. *Let* $U, U^{\mathcal{H}}, \mathcal{H}, h$ *and* u^* *be defined in the terms of the theorem above. Then the following orthogonal relation holds:*

$$\langle h - u^*, u \rangle = 0, \quad \forall u \in U \tag{2.36}$$

and $u^* \in U$ *is said to be the* orthogonal projection *of* h *over* U *(see Proposition 2.14).*

Theorem 2.9 (Orthogonal projections). *Let* $\mathcal{H}$ *a Hilbert space and* $U^{\mathcal{H}}$ *a closed subspace of* $\mathcal{H}$. *Then any vector* $h \in \mathcal{H}$ *can be only written as*

$$h = u + u^{\perp} \tag{2.37}$$

where $u \in U$ *and* $u^{\perp} \in U^{\perp}$.

Corollary 2.8. *If* $U^{\mathcal{H}}$ *(ie,* $(U, \langle x, y \rangle, \sqrt{\langle x, x \rangle})$*) is a closed subspace of a Hilbert space* $\mathcal{H}$ *(ie,* $(X, \langle x, y \rangle, \sqrt{\langle x, x \rangle})$*), then (see Definition 2.52)*

$$X = U \oplus U^{\perp}$$

Proposition 2.17. *Let* $h \in \mathcal{H}$, $u \in U$, $u^{\perp} \in U^{\perp}$ *and let* $U^{\mathcal{H}}$ *be a closed subspace* $\mathcal{H}$. *Then, given the only representation of any* h *of* $\mathcal{H}$ *as in Equation (2.37), the following pitagoric relation holds:*

$$\|h\|^2 = \|u\|^2 + \|u^{\perp}\|^2$$

Sequences and series

3.1. SEQUENCES

Definition 3.1. A *sequence*, denoted by $\{a_n\}_{n \subset \mathbb{N}}$, is a function that pairs off a natural to a real number, ie,

$$\{a_n\}_{n \in \mathbb{N}} := f : \mathbb{N} \to \mathbb{R} \tag{3.1}$$

Definition 3.2. *Property P* of the members of a sequence is defined to be *definitely valid for a sequence* a_n if and only if:

$$\exists \bar{n} \in \mathbb{N} : \forall n > \bar{n} \quad a_n \text{ holds property } P \tag{3.2}$$

3.1.1. Convergence/divergence

Definition 3.3. *A sequence* $\{a_n\}_{n \in \mathbb{N}}$ *is said to converge to real number l*, and is denoted by

$$\lim_{n \to +\infty} a_n = l \in \mathbb{R}$$

or

$$a_n \to l$$

if and only if for all $\varepsilon > 0$, there exists $N(\varepsilon)$ and for all $n \geq N(\varepsilon)$ one has

$$|a_n - l| < \varepsilon$$

ie, if and only if a_n definitely belongs to the interval $(l - \varepsilon, l + \varepsilon)$.

Definition 3.4. *A sequence* $\{a_n\}_{n \in \mathbb{N}}$ *is defined to diverge to* $+\infty$, and is denoted by

$$\lim_{n \to +\infty} a_n = +\infty$$

if and only if for all $k > 0$, there exists $N(k)$ and for all $n \geq N(k)$ one has

$$a_n > k$$

Definition 3.5. *A sequence* $\{a_n\}_{n\in\mathbb{N}}$ *is defined to diverge to* $-\infty$, *and is denoted by*

$$\lim_{n\to+\infty} a_n = -\infty$$

if and only if for all $k > 0$, *there exists* $N(k)$ *and for all* $n \geq N(k)$ *one has*

$$a_n < -k$$

Proposition 3.1. *If* $a_n \to l > 0(< 0)$, *then* $a_n > 0(< 0)$, *definitely. The converse is not true.*

Theorem 3.1. *If* $a_n \leq b_n \leq c$ *definitely and if* $a_n \to l$, $c_n \to l$, *then* $b_n \to l$.
If $a_n \leq b_n$ *definitely and if* $a_n \to +\infty$, *then* $b_n \to +\infty$. *Equally, if* $b_n \leq c_n$ *definitely and if* $c_n \to -\infty$, *then* $b_n \to -\infty$.

Theorem 3.2 (Boundaries of monotonic sequences). *A (definitely) growing sequence* $\{a_n\}_{n\in\mathbb{N}}$ *is always bounded. A boundary is finite if sequence* $\{a_n\}_{n\in\mathbb{N}}$ *is bounded above; it is* $+\infty$ *if sequence* $\{a_n\}_{n\in\mathbb{N}}$ *is not bounded above. The same goes for (definitely) decreasing sequences.*

Definition 3.6. *A sequence* $\{a_n\}_{n\in\mathbb{N}}$ *is said to be a Cauchy sequence if and only if*

$$\forall \varepsilon > 0 \quad \exists N(\varepsilon) \ni', \quad \forall n, m \geq N(\varepsilon)$$

holds for $|a_n - a_m| < \varepsilon$.

3.1.2. The Napier number
Theorem 3.3 (Napier). *Given a function*

$$f(x) = \left(1 + \frac{1}{x}\right)^x \tag{3.3}$$

one has

$$\lim_{x\to+\infty} f(x) = \lim_{x\to+\infty} \left(1 + \frac{1}{x}\right)^x = e \tag{3.4}$$

This is the so-called Napier number.

Corollary 3.1. *From Equation (3.4) it can be derived that*

$$\lim_{x\to+\infty} \left(1 + \frac{a}{x}\right)^x = e^a$$

Proposition 3.2. *The following equivalence holds:*

$$e^{\sum x} = \prod e^x$$

3.2. SERIES

Definition 3.7. Given any sequence of numbers $\{a_n\}_{n\in\mathbb{N}}$, a *series of numbers* (paired off to that sequence) is the summation of the members of sequence $\{a_n\}_{n\in\mathbb{N}}$.

Notation 3.1. The series of numbers paired to a sequence $\{a_n\}_{n\in\mathbb{N}}$ is denoted by

$$\sum_{n=0}^{+\infty} a_n$$

where the general a_n is said to be the *general series term*.

Proposition 3.3. *A geometric series or progression of power y is the following equivalence:*

$$\sum_{k=1}^{n} y^k = \frac{1 - y^n}{1 - y}$$

Corollary 3.2. *The following relation holds:*

$$\sum_{k=1}^{n-1} y^k = \frac{1 - y^n}{1 - y} - 1$$

3.3. SEQUENCE OF FUNCTIONS

Definition 3.8. A *sequence of functions* denoted by $\{f_n(x)\}_{n\in\mathbb{N}}$ is a function that pairs off a natural number to a function.

Definition 3.9. The *domain of the sequence of functions* $\{f_n(x)\}_{n\in\mathbb{N}}$ denoted by X is the set of values that the independent variable x may have inside any of the functions of this sequence.

3.3.1. Convergence/divergence

Definition 3.10. Let $\{f_n(x)\}_{n\in\mathbb{N}}$ be a sequence of functions and let X be its domain. Then $\{f_n(x)\}_{n\in\mathbb{N}}$ is defined to *converge punctually to function f over set $A \subseteq X$*, denoted by

$$\{f_n\}_{n\in\mathbb{N}} \to f$$

if for all $x \in A$ one has

$$\lim_{n \to +\infty} f_n(x) = f(x)$$

Definition 3.11. Let $\{f_n(x)\}_{n\in\mathbb{N}}$ be a sequence of functions and let X be its domain. It is said that $\{f_n(x)\}_{n\in\mathbb{N}}$ *converges punctually and monotonically from below to function f over set $A \subseteq X$ denoted by*

$$\{f_n\}_{n\in\mathbb{N}} \uparrow f$$

if for all $x \in A$ one has

$$f_1(x) \leq f_2(x) \leq \cdots \leq f_n(x) \leq \cdots$$

and

$$\lim_{n\to+\infty} f_n(x) = f(x)$$

Definition 3.12. Let $\{f_n(x)\}_{n\in\mathbb{N}}$ be a sequence of functions and let X be its domain. It is said that $\{f_n(x)\}_{n\in\mathbb{N}}$ is defined to *converge punctually and monotonically from above to f over set $A \subseteq X$, and is denoted by*

$$\{f_n\}_{n\in\mathbb{N}} \downarrow f$$

if for all $x \in A$ one has

$$f_1(x) \geq f_2(x) \geq \cdots \geq f_n(x) \geq \cdots$$

and

$$\lim_{n\to+\infty} f_n(x) = f(x)$$

Definition 3.13. Let $\{f_n(x)\}_{n\in\mathbb{N}}$ be a sequence of functions and let X be its domain. It is said that $\{f_n(x)\}_{n\in\mathbb{N}}$ is defined to *converge uniformly to function f over set $A \subseteq X$, and is denoted by*

$$\{f_n\}_{n\in\mathbb{N}} \overset{\text{uni}}{\to} f$$

if

$$\lim_{n\to+\infty} \sup_{x\in A} |f_n(x) - f(x)| = 0$$

Definition 3.14. Let $\{f_n(x)\}_{n\in\mathbb{N}}$ be a sequence of functions and let X be its domain. The *upper boundary of* $\{f_n(x)\}_{n\in\mathbb{N}}$, denoted by $\lim\sup_{n\to+\infty} f_n(x)$, is the equivalence defined as

$$\lim_{n\to+\infty} \sup f_n(x) := \inf_{n\in\mathbb{N}} \sup_{k\geq n} f_k(x) \tag{3.5}$$

Definition 3.15. Let $\{f_n(x)\}_{n\in\mathbb{N}}$ be a sequence of functions and let X be its domain. The *lower boundary of* $\{f_n(x)\}_{n\in\mathbb{N}}$, denoted by $\lim\sup_{n\to+\infty} f_n(x)$, is the equivalence defined as

$$\liminf_{n\to+\infty} f_n(x) := \sup_{n\in\mathbb{N}} \inf_{k\geq n} f_k(x) \tag{3.6}$$

Proposition 3.4. *Let* $\{f_n(x)\}_{n\in\mathbb{N}}$ *be a sequence of functions and let* X *be its domain. Then the following relations hold:*

$$\liminf_{n\to+\infty} f_n(x) \leq -\lim\sup_{n\to+\infty} f_n(x) \tag{3.7}$$

$$\liminf_{n\to+\infty}[-f_n(x)] = -\lim\sup_{n\to+\infty}[f_n(x)] \tag{3.8}$$

4

Differential calculus

4.1. DEFINITION OF DERIVATIVES

Definition 4.1. Given a function f defined over an open set A of $\mathbb{R}$, the *incremental ratio* of f at point x_0 referred to h is the infinitesimal change in the function f over the interval $[x_0, x_0 + h]$. This corresponds to the slope of the line between points $[x_0, f(x_0)]$ and $[(x_0 + h), f(x_0 + h)]$ and is defined as

$$\frac{f(x_0 + h) - f(x_0)}{h} \tag{4.1}$$

Definition 4.2. A function f defined over an open set A of $\mathbb{R}$ is said to be *differentiable* at point $x_0 \in A$ if the limit of the incremental ratio of the function exists, and is finite, for $x \to x_0$, that is for $h \to 0$.

The value of this limit is called the *derivative* of function f in x_0 and is denoted by $f'(x_0)$ or by $D[f(x)]_{x=x_0}$, ie,

$$D[f(x)]_{x=x_0} = f'(x_0) = \lim_{h \to 0} \frac{f(x_0 + h) - f(x_0)}{h} \tag{4.2}$$

The derivative of function f at point x_0 gives the slope of the tangent line to the graph of the function on the interval $[x_0, f(x_0)]$.

4.2. DIFFERENTIATION RULES

Proposition 4.1 (Product rule). *If f_1 and f_2 are two functions differentiable at x_0, their product is also differentiable as well, and can be written as*

$$D[f_1(x) \cdot f_2(x)]_{x=x_0} = D[f_1(x)]_{x=x_0} \cdot f_2(x_0) + D[f_2(x)]_{x=x_0} \cdot f_1(x_0)$$

Proposition 4.2 (Quotient rule). *If f_1 and f_2 are differentiable in x_0, then their quotient is also differentiable, and can be written as*

$$D\left[\frac{f_1(x)}{f_2(x)}\right]_{x=x_0} = \frac{D[f_1(x)]_{x=x_0} \cdot f_2(x_0) - D[f_2(x)]_{x=x_0} \cdot f_1(x_0)}{(f_2(x_0))^2}$$

Proposition 4.3 (Chain rule). *Let $y = F(t) = f[g(t)]$ be the composite function of $y = f(x)$ and of $x = g(t)$ [1].*

If g is differentiable in t_0 and f is differentiable in $x_0 = g(t_0)$, then $F(t)$ will be differentiable in t_0 and one has

$$D[F(t)]_{t=t_0} = F'(t_0) = f'(x_0) \cdot g'(t_0)$$

Proposition 4.4 (Leibniz rule). *Let:*

- *f be a two-variable function;*
- *a and b be two differentiable one-variable functions;*
- *$F(t) = \int_{a(t)}^{b(t)} f(t, x)\, dx;$*

then

$$\frac{d}{dt} F(t) = F'(t) = f(t, b(t))b'(t) - f(t, a(t))a'(t) + \int_{a(t)}^{b(t)} \frac{\partial}{\partial t} f(t, x)\, dx$$

Corollary 4.1. *Let:*

- *$F(t) = \int_{t}^{T} g(x)h(t, x)$, where $T > t$;*
- *$h(t, t) = 0$;*

then

$$\frac{d}{dt} F(t) = F'(t) = \int_{t}^{T} g(x) \frac{\partial}{\partial t} h(t, x)\, dx$$

Proposition 4.5 (De l'Hospital rule). *Let f and g be differentiable and $g'(x) \neq 0$ on an open interval I containing a. Now, if:*

- *$\lim_{x \to a} f(x) = 0$ and $\lim_{x \to a} g(x) = 0$;*
- *$\lim_{x \to a} f(x) = \pm\infty$ and $\lim_{x \to a} g(x) = \pm\infty$;*

then if one computes

$$\lim_{x \to a} \frac{f(x)}{g(x)}$$

the result will be the indeterminate form $\frac{0}{0}, \frac{\infty}{\infty}$, and the limit to be determined is

$$\lim_{x \to a} \frac{f(x)}{g(x)} = \lim_{x \to a} \frac{f'(x)}{g'(x)}$$

---

[1]For this compound function to exist, the codomain of function g must be contained in the domain of function f (or coincide with it).

4.3. MAIN THEOREMS

Theorem 4.1 (Lagrange theorem or the mean value theorem). *Let $f(x)$ be a continuous differentiable function on the closed interval $[a, b]$. Then, there will be at least one point $c \in [a, b]$ so that*

$$\frac{f(b) - f(a)}{b - a} = f'(c)$$

4.4. SERIES EXPANSIONS

Definition 4.3. The following expression is defined to be the MacLaurin series:

$$f(x) = \sum_{n=0}^{\infty} \frac{f^{(n)}(0)}{n!} x^n = f(0) + \frac{f'(0)}{1!} x + \frac{f''(0)}{2!} x^2 + \cdots \tag{4.3}$$

Example 4.1. The MacLaurin series for e^{tX} is

$$e^{tX} = 1 + tX + \frac{t^2}{2!} X^2 + \frac{t^3}{3!} X^3 + \frac{t^4}{4!} X^4 + o(t^5)$$

4.4.1. Remarkable series

Equation (4.3) is useful to provide a demonstration for the expressions below:

$$\sum_{j=0}^{\infty} \frac{(\lambda t)^j}{j!} = e^{\lambda t} \tag{4.4}$$

$$\sum_{x=0}^{\infty} y^x = \frac{1}{1 - y} \tag{4.5}$$

$$\sum_{n=0}^{\infty} \frac{(i\theta)^n}{n!} = \sum_{n=0}^{\infty} \frac{(-1)^n \theta^{2n}}{(2n)!} + i \sum_{n=1}^{\infty} \frac{(-1)^{n-1} \theta^{2n-1}}{(2n-1)!} \tag{4.6}$$

$$\sum_{n=0}^{\infty} \frac{(-1)^n x^{2n}}{(2n)!} = \cos x \tag{4.7}$$

$$\sum_{n=0}^{\infty} \frac{(-1)^{n-1} x^{2n-1}}{(2n-1)!} = \sin x \tag{4.8}$$

$$(a + b)^n = \sum_{k=0}^{n} \binom{n}{k} a^k b^{n-k} \tag{4.9}$$

$$\frac{z^n}{(1 - x)^n} = \sum_{k=0}^{\infty} \binom{k + n - 1}{k} x^k z^n \tag{4.10}$$

Integral calculus

5.1. BASICS

Definition 5.1. Let $f(t)$ be a real and continuous function in $[t_0, t_n]$, a compact interval in R. Then

$$\Pi = \{t_0, t_1, t_2, t_3, t_4, \ldots, t_n\}$$

is a *partition of* $[t_0, t_n]$ if:

$$t_0 \leq t_1 \leq t_2 \leq t_3 \leq t_4 \leq \cdots \leq t_n$$

Definition 5.2. Let the set of points Π, then the compact intervals

$$[t_0, t_1), [t_1, t_2), [t_2, t_3), [t_3, t_4), \ldots, [t_{n-1}, t_n)$$

are defined to be a *decomposition of* $[t_0, t_n]$.

Definition 5.3. Let $\Pi = \{t_0, t_1, t_2, t_3, t_4, \ldots, t_n\}$ be a partition of $[t_0, t_n]$. A subset χ of $[t_0, t_n]$ is defined to be the *choice relative to partition P*, when

$$\chi = \{s_1, s_2, \ldots, s_n\} \quad \text{with } t_{k-1} < s_k < t_k$$

Definition 5.4. The *width of decomposition* is the largest width of the intervals of a partition, ie,

$$\|\Pi\| = \max_{k=0,1,2,\ldots,n} (t_{k+1} - t_k)$$

Definition 5.5. Let $\Pi = \{t_0, t_1, t_2, t_3, t_4, \ldots, t_n\}$ be a partition of $[t_0, t_n]$, then the *variation of f* denoted by $V(f, \Pi)$ is

$$V(f, \Pi) = \sum_{k=0}^{n-1} |f(t_{k+1}) - f(t_k)|$$

or

$$V(f, \Pi) = \sum_{k=1}^{n} |f(t_k) - f(t_{k-1})|$$

Definition 5.6. Let $\Pi = \{t_0, t_1, t_2, t_3, t_4, \ldots, t_n\}$, a partition of $[t_0, t_n]$, be the *total variation* of f and be denoted by $V_{t_0}^{t_n}(f)$:

$$V_{t_0}^{t_n}(f) = \sup_{\Pi} V(f, \Pi)$$

Theorem 5.1. *Let* $\Pi = \{t_0, t_1, t_2, t_3, t_4, \ldots, t_n\}$ *be a partition of* $[t_0, t_n]$, *and let* $\Pi' = \{s_0, s_1, s_2, \ldots, s_m\}$ *where* $s_0 = t_2, s_1 = t_3, \ldots, s_m = t_n$, *a choice on partition* Π. *Then the following relation holds:*

$$V_{t_2}^{t_n}(f) = V_{t_0}^{t_n}(f) - V_{t_0}^{t_2}(f)$$

Definition 5.7. Let $\Pi = \{t_0, t_1, t_2, t_3, t_4, \ldots, t_n\}$ be a partition of $[t_0, t_n]$, then the following is a *first variation* of f and is denoted by $FV_{[0,T]}(f)$:

$$FV_{[t_0, t_n]}(f) = \lim_{\|\Pi\| \to 0} \sum_{k=0}^{n-1} |f(t_{k+1}) - f(t_k)|$$

Definition 5.8. Let $\Pi = \{t_0, t_1, t_2, t_3, t_4, \ldots, t_n\}$ be a partition of $[t_0, t_n]$, the following is the *quadratic variation* of f denoted by $\langle f \rangle (T)$:

$$\langle f \rangle (T) = \lim_{\|\Pi\| \to 0} \sum_{k=0}^{n-1} |f(t_{k+1}) - f(t_k)|^2$$

5.2. RIEMANN INTEGRAL

Definition 5.9 (Lower area; see Figure 5.1). If $f : [a, b] \to \Re$ is a limited function, the lower area of f for interval $[a, b]$ is the real number

$$s(f, [a, b]) = m(b - a) \tag{5.1}$$

where $m = \inf f([a, b])$.

Definition 5.10 (Upper area; see Figure 5.1). If $f : [a, b] \to \Re$ is a limited function, the area above f for interval $[a, b]$ is the real number

$$S(f, [a, b]) = M(b - a) \tag{5.2}$$

where $M = \sup f([a, b])$.

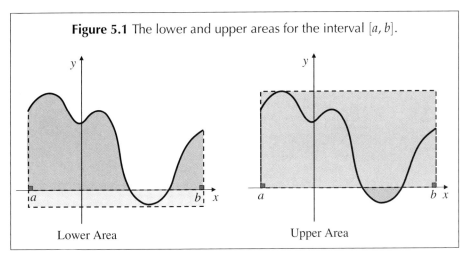

Figure 5.1 The lower and upper areas for the interval $[a, b]$.

Lower Area

Upper Area

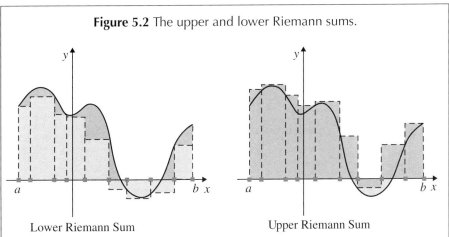

Figure 5.2 The upper and lower Riemann sums.

Lower Riemann Sum

Upper Riemann Sum

Definition 5.11 (Lower (Riemann) sum; see Figure 5.2). If $f : [a, b] \to \Re$ is a limited function and $P = \{x_0, x_1, \ldots, x_n\}$ is a partition of $[a, b]$, the lower sum of f for P is the real number

$$s(f, P) = \sum_{k=1}^{n} m_k (x_k - x_{k-1}) \tag{5.3}$$

where $m_k = \inf f([x_{k-1}, x_k])$.

Definition 5.12 (Upper (Riemann) sum; see Figure 5.2). If $f : [a, b] \to \Re$ is a limited function and $P = \{x_0, x_1, \ldots, x_n\}$ is a partition of $[a, b]$, the upper sum of f

Figure 5.3 The upper and lower sums of the function shown in Figure 5.1, but with reference to the denser partition.

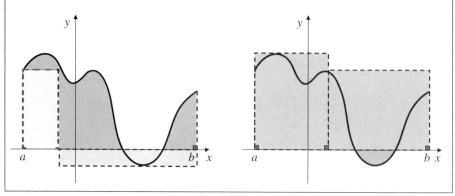

for P is the real number

$$S(f, P) = \sum_{k=1}^{n} M_k(x_k - x_{k-1}) \tag{5.4}$$

where $M_k = \sup f([x_{k-1}, x_k])$.

Definition 5.13. A partition $\Pi = \{t_0, t_1, t_2, t_3, t_4, \ldots, t_n\}$ tends to become denser if the decomposition tends to zero, ie, if the intervals $[t_0, t_1), [t_1, t_2), [t_2, t_3), [t_3, t_4), \ldots, [t_{n-1}, t_n)$ tend to zero, since the number of points inside the partition increases.

Lemma 5.1. *Given partitions P_1 and P_2 of the interval above (where P_2 is denser than P_1), for a function f limited on that interval one will have*

$$s(f, P_1) \leq s(f, P_2), \quad S(f, P_1) \geq S(f, P_2)$$

In order to better understand this lemma, it may be useful to compare Figure 5.1, which shows the areas below and above (actually referred to as a partition whose only points are the endpoints of the interval $[a, b]$), with Figure 5.3, which computes the upper and lower sums of the same function, but with reference to the denser partition, and then with Figure 5.2, where the partitions have seven more points.

Corollary 5.1. *For any function defined on a bounded interval, we have*

$$\inf_P S(f, P) \geq \sup_P s(f, P)$$

Notation 5.1. The expression in Corollary 5.1 may also be denoted as $\inf_P S(f, P) \doteq S$ and as $\sup_P s(f, P) \doteq s$.

Definition 5.14. Given P_n a partition of $[a, b]$ composed of n points, and given $f : [a, b] \to \Re$ a limited function, then $S_n = S(f, P_n)$ and $s_n = s(f, P_n)$ are defined to be the corresponding lower and upper Riemann sums.

Definition 5.15. Let $\{P_n\}$ be defined as the sequence of partitions of $[a, b]$ with a growing number n of points.

Definition 5.16. Given $\{P_n\}$ a succession of partitions of $[a, b]$ and given $f : [a, b] \to \Re$ a limited function, $\{S_n\}$ and $\{s_n\}$ are the corresponding sequences of the lower and upper Riemann sums, ie,

$$\{S_n\} = S(f, \{P_n\}), \quad \{s_n\} = s(f, \{P_n\})$$

Proposition 5.1. *The sequences $\{S_n\}$ and $\{s_n\}$ are monotonic, hence convergent (see Theorem 3.2): $\{s_n\}$ converges to the upper endpoint s, while $\{S_n\}$ converges to the lower endpoint S. Then,*

$$\lim_{n \to \infty} \{S_n\} = S, \quad \lim_{n \to \infty} \{s_n\} = s$$

Definition 5.17. The function f is said to be *integrable according to Riemann* if and only if there is a sequence $\{P_n\}$ of partitions of $[a, b]$ so that

$$\lim_{n \to \infty} \{S_n\} - \{s_n\} = 0$$

or

$$\lim_{n \to \infty} \{S_n\} = \lim_{n \to \infty} \{s_n\} \tag{5.5}$$

The quantity (5.5) is called a Riemann integral, ie,

$$\int_a^b f(x)\, dx = \lim_{n \to \infty} \{S_n\} = \lim_{n \to \infty} \{s_n\} \tag{5.6}$$

Definition 5.18. In expression (5.6), the function $f(x)$ is said to be the integrand and a and b are said to be boundaries of integration.

5.2.1. Classes of integrable functions

Theorem 5.2. *The necessary and sufficient conditions for a function to be integrable is to be bounded in* $[a, b]$.

Theorem 5.3. *A necessary condition for integrability of the function f(x) to be continuous in* $[a, b]$.

Theorem 5.4. *A sufficient condition for function f(x) to be integrable is to be monotonic and continuous in* $[a, b]$.

Proposition 5.2. *A limited function on a limited interval which has a finite or a countably infinite number of discontinuity points is integrable in that interval.*

5.2.2. Definite integral

Definition 5.19. The *definite integral* of $f(x)$ between a and b can be written as

$$\int_a^b f(x)\,dx$$

this is the number derived from

$$\int_a^b f(x)\,dx = \begin{cases} \int_a^b f(x)\,dx & \text{if } a < b \\ 0 & \text{if } a = b \\ -\int_b^a f(x)\,dx & \text{if } a > b \end{cases} \tag{5.7}$$

Definition 5.20. Let $P = \{x_0, x_1, \ldots, x_n\}$ be a partition of $[a, b]$, $\chi = \{z_1, z_2, \ldots, z_n\}$ a choice with respect to partition P. The real number

$$\sigma(f, P, \chi) = \sum_{k=1}^n f(z_k)(x_k - x_{k-1}) \tag{5.8}$$

is said to be the *Cauchy sum of f for P and χ*.

Proposition 5.3. *If we consider any continuous and monotonic f, for any partition P and for any choice χ with respect to P it shows*

$$s(f, P) \leq \sigma(f, P, \chi) \leq S(f, P)$$

Theorem 5.5. *If f is integrable according Riemann, ie,*

$$\int_a^b f(x)\,dx = \lim_{n\to\infty}\{S_n\} = \lim_{n\to\infty}\{s_n\} \tag{5.6}$$

and for any n, a choice χ_n with respect to P_n is made where $\{P_n\}$ is a sequence of partitions, for $n \to \infty$, then based on Theorem 3.1 it will also hold that

$$\int_a^b f(x)\,dx = \lim_{n\to\infty}\{\sigma_n\} \tag{5.9}$$

where $\{\sigma_n\} = \sigma(f, \{P_n\}, \{\chi_n\})$.

5.2.2.1. Definite integrals and variations

Theorem 5.6. *For the first variation, the following relation with the definite integral holds:*

$$FV_{[t_0,t_n]}(f) = \int_{t_0}^{t_n} |f'(t)|\,dt$$

Theorem 5.7. *The quadratic variation of differentiable functions is equal to zero.*

5.2.2.2. Propriety of the definite integral

Let f and g two integrable functions on $[a, b]$. Then the following properties hold.

(1) We have

$$\int_a^b f(x)\,dx = -\int_b^a f(x)\,dx$$

(2) If $f(x) \le g(x)$, for all $x \in [a, b]$, then

$$\int_a^b f(x)\,dx \le \int_a^b g(x)\,dx \tag{5.10}$$

(3) If $|f|$ is integrable on $[a, b]$, then

$$\left| \int_a^b f(x)\,dx \right| \le \int_a^b |f(x)|\,dx$$

(4) $f + g$ is integrable according to Riemann, ie,

$$\int_a^b [f(x) + g(x)]\,dx = \int_a^b f(x)\,dx + \int_a^b g(x)\,dx \tag{5.11}$$

(5) αf is integrable according to Riemann for any $\alpha \in R$ and one will have

$$\int_a^b \alpha f(x)\, dx = \alpha \int_a^b f(x)\, dx \tag{5.12}$$

(6) f is integrable according to Riemann. For any c inside interval $[a, b]$, the following relation holds:

$$\int_a^b f(x)\, dx = \int_a^c f(x)\, dx + \int_c^b f(x)\, dx \tag{5.13}$$

Theorem 5.8 (Lagrange theorem or mean value theorem).
Let $m = \inf_{x \in [a,b]} f(x)$ and $M = \sup_{x \in [a,b]} f(x)$ in $[a, b]$. Then, the following holds:

$$m \le \frac{1}{b-a} \int_a^b f(x)\, dx \le M$$

and, if $f(x)$ is continuous on $[a, b]$, then for any $\xi \in [a, b]$

$$f(\xi) = \frac{1}{b-a} \int_a^b f(x)\, dx$$

or

$$\int_a^b f(x)\, dx = (b-a)f(\xi)$$

5.2.3. Indefinite integrals

Definition 5.21. Let $f : [a, b] \to \mathbb{R}$; a function F is said to be the *antiderivative* of f in $[a, b]$ if:

- F is differentiable in $[a, b]$;
- $F'(x) = f(x)$ for all $x \in [a, b]$.

Theorem 5.9 (Fundamental theorem of integral calculus). *Let $f \in [a, b]$ be a continuous function, then the primitive function will be*

$$F'(x) = f(x), \quad \forall x \in [a, b]$$

Definition 5.22. Let $f(x)$ be integrable in the interval $[a, b]$; for any $x_0 \in [a, b]$, as x varies in $[a, b]$, the expression

$$F(x) = \int_{x_0}^x f(t)\, dt$$

is said to be the *integral function* of the integrand function f. For this function it can be shown that:

- $F(a) = 0$;
- $F(b) = \int_a^b f(x)\, dx$.

It can be derived that any integral function of a continuous function f is a primitive of f.

Definition 5.23. The set of the antiderivatives of a function f is called the *indefinite integral* and is denoted as

$$\int f(x)\, dx = \{F(x) + c \mid c \in R, F \text{ antiderivative of } f\}$$

It follows that

$$F'(x) = f(x) \Leftrightarrow \int f(x)\, dx = F(x) + c$$

and

$$\int F'(x)\, dx = F(x) + c$$

The following proposition can be derived from Definition 5.23.

Proposition 5.4. *Two antiderivatives of the same function differ by a constant number.*

Corollary 5.2. *The set of all the antiderivatives of a function f continuous in the closed interval $[a, b]$, given $x_0 \in [a, b]$, is given by the expression*

$$\int_{x_0}^x f(t)\, dt + c$$

where c is an arbitrary constant

Theorem 5.10 (Torricelli–Barrow theorem). *Let $f(x)$ continuous in $[a, b]$, then*

$$\int_a^b f(x)\, dx = V(b) - V(a)$$

where $V(x)$ is any antiderivative of $f(x)$ in $[a, b]$.

5.2.4. Improper integrals
Definition 5.24.

(a) Let $f(x) : (a; b] \to \Re$ be:
- unbounded for $x \to a^+$;
- integrable in any interval $[a + \varepsilon; b]$, for all $\varepsilon > 0$;

and let $I(\varepsilon) = \int_{a+\varepsilon}^{b} f(x)\,dx$.

If a finite $\lim_{\varepsilon \to 0^+} I(\varepsilon)$ exists, it is said that $f(x)$ is integrable in the improper or generalised sense on $[a, b]$. The improper (or generalised) integral is denoted as

$$\lim_{\varepsilon \to 0^+} I(\varepsilon) = \int_{a}^{b} f(x)\,dx \qquad (5.14)$$

(b) Let $f(x) : (a; b] \to \Re$ be:
- unbounded for $x \to b^-$;
- integrable in any interval $[a; b - \varepsilon]$, for all $\varepsilon > 0$;

and let $I(\varepsilon) = \int_{a}^{b-\varepsilon} f(x)\,dx$.

If a finite $\lim_{\varepsilon \to 0^+} I(\varepsilon)$ exists, it is said that $f(x)$ is integrable in the improper or generalised sense on $[a, b]$. The improper (or generalised) integral is denoted as

$$\lim_{\varepsilon \to 0^+} I(\varepsilon) = \int_{a}^{b} f(x)\,dx \qquad (5.14)$$

(c) Let $f(x) : [a; +\infty) \to \Re$ be integrable in any interval $[a, k)$, for all $k > a$, and let $I(k) = \int_{a}^{k} f(x)\,dx$.

If a finite $\lim_{k \to \infty} I(k)$ exists, $f(x)$ is integrable in the improper or generalised sense in $[a; +\infty)$ and the improper (or generalised) integral is denoted as

$$\lim_{k \to \infty} I(k) = \int_{a}^{+\infty} f(x)\,dx \qquad (5.14)$$

(d) Let $f(x) : (-\infty, b) \to \Re$ be integrable in any interval $(k, b]$, for all $k < b$ and let $I(k) = \int_{k}^{b} f(x)\,dx$.

If a finite $\lim_{k \to -\infty} I(k)$ exists, $f(x)$ is integrable in the improper or generalised sense on $(-\infty; k]$ and the improper (or generalised) integral is

$$\lim_{k \to -\infty} I(k) = \int_{-\infty}^{b} f(x)\,dx \qquad (5.14)$$

5.2.5. Criteria of integration

Criterion 5.1. *Integration by parts:*

$$\int_{a}^{b} u(t)v'(t)\,dt = u(t)v(t)\big|_{a}^{b} - \int_{a}^{b} u'(t)v(t)\,dt$$

Criterion 5.2. *The possibility of "horizontal" or "vertical" integration of a region defined by a function will determine the following equivalence:*

$$\int_{t=0}^{t=\infty} \int_{\tau=0}^{\tau=t} f(\tau)\,d\tau\,dt = \int_{\tau=0}^{\tau=\infty} \int_{t=\tau}^{t=\infty} f(\tau)\,dt\,d\tau$$

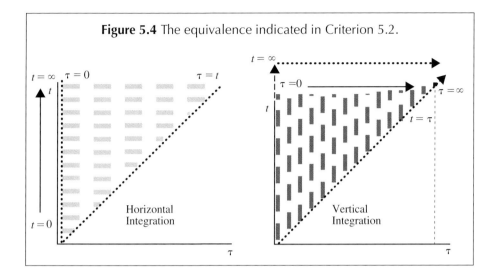

Figure 5.4 The equivalence indicated in Criterion 5.2.

Horizontal Integration

Vertical Integration

Figure 5.4 intuitively supports the equivalence indicated in Criterion 5.2.

Criterion 5.3. *Criterion 5.2 may be expressed as follows:*

$$\int_{t=0}^{t=\infty} f(t) \int_{\tau=0}^{\tau=t} g(\tau)\, d\tau\, dt = \int_{\tau=0}^{\tau=\infty} g(\tau) \int_{t=\tau}^{t=\infty} f(t)\, dt\, d\tau$$

Criterion 5.4. *Criterion 5.3 may be expressed as follows:*

$$\int_{t=-\infty}^{t=\infty} f(t) \int_{\tau=t}^{\tau=\infty} g(\tau)\, d\tau\, dt = \int_{\tau=-\infty}^{\tau=\infty} g(\tau) \int_{t=-\infty}^{t=\tau} f(t)\, dt\, d\tau$$

Figure 5.5 intuitively supports the equivalence indicated in Criterion 5.4.

Proposition 5.5. *Let function* $f : \mathbb{R} \to \mathbb{R}$, *then*

$$\int_{-T}^{0} f(-x)\, dx = \int_{0}^{T} f(x)\, dx \tag{5.15}$$

Proposition 5.6. *If function* $f : \mathbb{R} \to \mathbb{R}$ *is even, then*

$$\int_{-\infty}^{\infty} f(x)\, dx = 2 \int_{0}^{\infty} f(x)\, dx$$

$$\int_{-T}^{0} f(x) = \int_{0}^{T} f(x)$$

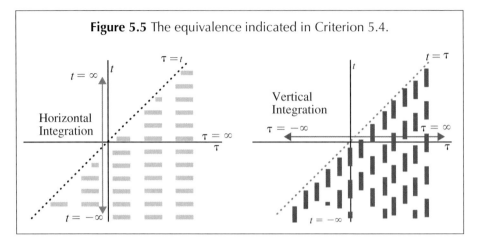

Figure 5.5 The equivalence indicated in Criterion 5.4.

Proposition 5.7. *If function* $f : \mathbb{R} \to \mathbb{R}$ *is odd, then*

$$\int_{-\infty}^{\infty} f(x)\, dx = 0 \qquad (5.16)$$

Criterion 5.5. *A function* $g(t)$ *derived from the translation to the right on the y-axis of a quantity T of a function* $f(t)$, *ie,*

$$g(t) = \begin{cases} 0 & 0 \le t \le T \\ f(t-T) & t \ge T \end{cases}$$

(See Figure 5.6) will determine the following equivalence in integral calculus:

$$\int_{0}^{x} g(t)\, dt = \int_{T}^{x+T} f(t-T)\, dt$$

Criterion 5.6. *A function* $f(t)$ *derived from the translation to the right on the y-axis of a quantity T of function* $g(t)$, *as defined in Criterion 5.5, will determine the following equivalence in integral calculus:*

$$\int_{0}^{x} f(t)\, dt = \int_{T}^{x+T} f(t-T)\, dt$$

Criterion 5.7. *The definition of function* $g(t)$ *vertically symmetric to function* $f(t)$, *ie,*

$$g(t) = f(-t)$$

(see Figure 5.7), will determine the following equivalence in integral calculus:

$$\int_{-\infty}^{0} f(t)\, dt = \int_{0}^{+\infty} g(t)\, dt$$

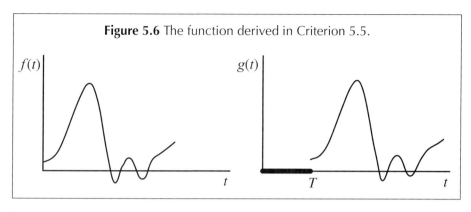

Figure 5.6 The function derived in Criterion 5.5.

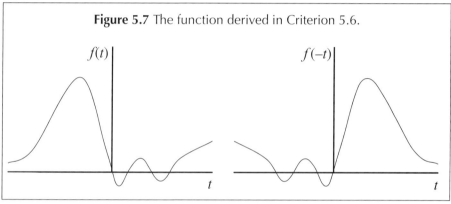

Figure 5.7 The function derived in Criterion 5.6.

Criterion 5.8. *The definition of $g(t)$, a vertically symmetric function of $f(t)$ translated to the right, ie,*

$$g(t) = f(\tau - t)$$

(see Figure 5.8) will determine the following equivalence in integral calculus:

$$\int_0^\infty f(t)\,dt = \int_{-\infty}^\tau g(t)\,dt$$

5.2.6. Remarkable integrals

5.2.6.1. Dirichlet integral

Definition 5.25. A Dirichlet integral is denoted as

$$\int_0^{+\infty} \frac{\sin\varepsilon}{\varepsilon}\,d\varepsilon = \frac{\pi}{2} \tag{5.17}$$

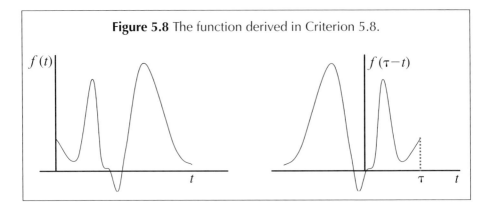

Figure 5.8 The function derived in Criterion 5.8.

Corollary 5.3. *The Dirichlet integral integrated over the whole domain of real numbers is equal to π, ie,*

$$\int_{-\infty}^{+\infty} \frac{\sin \varepsilon}{\varepsilon} \, d\varepsilon = \pi \tag{5.18}$$

Corollary 5.4. *The Dirichlet integral may be written as*

$$\int_{0}^{+\infty} \frac{\sin \varepsilon x}{\varepsilon} \, d\varepsilon = \mathrm{sgn}(x) \frac{\pi}{2} \tag{5.19}$$

where $\mathrm{sgn}(x)$ is the sign function (see Definition 6.1).

Corollary 5.5. *The Dirichlet integral may be written as*

$$\int_{-\infty}^{+\infty} \frac{\sin \varepsilon x}{\varepsilon} \, d\varepsilon = \mathrm{sgn}(x)\pi \tag{5.20}$$

where $\mathrm{sgn}(x)$ is the sign function (see Definition 6.1).

Corollary 5.6. *The Dirichlet integral may be written as*

$$\int_{0}^{+\infty} \frac{\sin \varepsilon|x|}{\varepsilon} \, d\varepsilon = \frac{\pi}{2} \tag{5.21}$$

Corollary 5.7. *The Dirichlet integral may be written as*

$$\int_{-\infty}^{+\infty} \frac{\sin \varepsilon|x|}{\varepsilon} \, d\varepsilon = \pi \tag{5.22}$$

5.2.7. Convolution

Definition 5.26. Convolution is the following integral calculus:

$$h(t) = \int_{-\infty}^{\infty} f(\tau)g(t-\tau)\,d\tau$$

or

$$h(t) = \int_{-\infty}^{\infty} f(t-\tau)g(\tau)\,d\tau$$

Notation 5.2. Convolution is usually denoted as

$$h(t) = f * g$$

Remark 5.1. Convolution is also often defined as

$$h(t) = \int_{-\infty}^{t} f(\tau)g(t-\tau)\,d\tau$$

or as

$$h(t) = \int_{0}^{\infty} f(t-\tau)g(\tau)\,d\tau$$

This equivalence derives from Criterion 5.8 of integration.

Proposition 5.8. *Convolution is commutative, ie,*

$$f * g = g * f$$

Proposition 5.9. *Convolution is distributive, ie,*

$$f * (g + h) = f * g + f * h$$

Proposition 5.10. *Convolution is associative, ie,*

$$f * (g * h) = (f * g) * h$$

Criterion 5.9. *Given $f(t)$ an integrable function in R and $u(t)$ such that*

$$u(t) = \begin{cases} 1 & \text{if } x \geq 0 \\ 0 & \text{if } x < 0 \end{cases}$$

(ie, $u(t)$ is the Heaviside function; see Definition 6.7), by translating u to the right of a quantity τ, the following holds:

$$\int_{-\infty}^{\tau} f(t)\,dt = \int_{-\infty}^{+\infty} f(t)u(\tau - t)\,dt$$

Figure 5.9 clearly shows this equivalence.

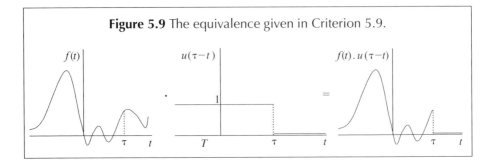

Figure 5.9 The equivalence given in Criterion 5.9.

5.2.8. Methods for numerical integral

5.2.8.1. The Newton–Cotes algorithm

The Newton–Cotes algorithm is used to compute definite integrals. It may provide an accuracy approximation to the 11th power functions with a $o(12)$ error.

Proposition 5.11. *The integral of a generic function $f : \mathbb{R} \to \mathbb{R}$ is approximated as*

$$\int_{\alpha}^{\beta} f(x)\, dx \approx \frac{d}{c} h \sum_{j=0}^{d} a_j \cdot f(x_j) \tag{5.23}$$

where:

- *d is the degree of the polynomial which approximates the integral;*
- *$n = d$ is the number of subintervals in interval $[x_0, x_d]$;*
- *$c = \sum_{j=0}^{d} a_j$;*
- *$h = (\beta - \alpha)/d$ is the width of the intervals;*
- *$x_j = \alpha + jh$ for $i = 0, 1, \ldots, d$;*
- *the values of a_j are reported in Figure 5.10.*

Corollary 5.8. *Given $f(x)$ of power D, the table below shows the values of d for which the Newton–Cotes algorithm polynomial gives the exact value of the definite integral, ie, $o(h)$ where $h > D$:*

					d					
	1	2	3	4	5	6	7	8	9	10
D	1	3	3	5	5	7	7	9	9	11
$o(h)$	2	4	4	6	6	8	8	10	10	12

Figure 5.10 The values of a_j from Proposition 5.11.

d	1	2	3	4	5	6	7	8	9	10
$c = \Sigma_i\, a_i$	2	6	8	90	288	840	17.280	28.350	89.080	598.752
a_0	1	1	1	7	19	41	751	989	2.587	16.067
a_1	1	4	3	32	75	216	3.577	5.888	15.741	106.300
a_2		1	3	12	50	27	1.323	-928	1.080	-48.525
a_3			1	32	50	272	2.989	10.496	19.344	272.400
a_4				7	75	27	2.989	-4.540	5.788	-260.550
a_5					19	216	1.323	10.496	5.788	427.368
a_6						41	3.577	-928	19.344	-260.550
a_7							751	5.888	1.080	272.400
a_8								989	15.741	-48.525
a_9									2.587	106.300
a_{10}										16.067

Remark 5.2. Polynomials with an even d are more accurate in approximating exactly functions with the same power D.

Remark 5.3. The Newton–Cotes algorithm for $d = 1$ is also known as the trapeze rule.

Remark 5.4. The Newton–Cotes algorithm for $d = 2$ is also known as the Simpson rule.

Remark 5.5. The Newton–Cotes algorithm for $d = 3$ is also known as the 3/8 Simpson rule.

Remark 5.6. The numerical computation of the integral coincides with the analytical computation. As indicated in Corollary 5.8, the Simpson algorithm, ie, $d = 2$, can exactly compute the integral of functions $f(x)$ whose power is 2, ie, $D = 2$.

Remark 5.7. The algorithm for $d = 7$ is more accurate than Simpson's, ie, $d = 2$.

The general notation of the Newton–Cotes algorithm is examined below where n, the number of subintervals of interval $[\alpha, \beta]$, is a multiple of d, the degree of the polynomial which approximates the integral.

Proposition 5.12. *The integral of any function* $f : \mathbb{R} \to \mathbb{R}$ *is approximated by*

$$\int_{\alpha}^{\beta} f(x)\,dx \approx \frac{n}{c} h \sum_{j=0}^{n} a_j^{(i)} \cdot f(x_j) \tag{5.24}$$

where:

- *d is the degree of the polynomial which approximates the integral;*
- $n = i \cdot d$, *where* $i = 1, 2, 3, \ldots, N$, *is the number of subintervals of interval* $[\alpha, \beta]$;
- $c = \sum_{j=0}^{n} a_j^{(i)}$;
- $h = (\beta - \alpha)/n$ *is the width of the interval;*
- $x_j = \alpha + jh$ *for* $i = 0, 1, \ldots, d$;
- *values of* $a_j^{(i)}$ *expressed with respect to* a_j *reported in Figure 5.10 are*

$$\begin{aligned}
a_j^{(i)} &= a_j & &\text{for } j < d \\
a_j^{(i)} &= 2a_0 & &\text{for } j = (i-k)d \quad 1 \le k < i, k \in \mathbb{N} \\
a_j^{(i)} &= a_{(2d-j)} & &\text{for } 2d > j > d \\
a_j^{(i)} &= a_{(3d-j)} & &\text{for } 3d > j > 2d \\
&\ \ \vdots & & \\
a_j^{(i)} &= a_{[(i-1)d-j]} & &(i-1)d > j > (i-2)d \\
a_j^{(i)} &= a_{(id-j)} & &\text{id} \ge j > (i-1)d
\end{aligned}$$

Corollary 5.9. *The values of* $a_j^{(2)}$ *are reported in Figure 5.11.*

Corollary 5.10. *The values of* $a_j^{(3)}$ *are reported in Figure 5.12.*

Remark 5.8. For $i = 1$, Equation (5.24) coincides with Equation (5.23).

5.3. RIEMANN–STIELTJES INTEGRAL

The Riemann–Stieltjes integral is a generalisation of the Riemann integral developed by the French mathematician Thomas Stieltjes (1856–1894). Observations made in Section 5.2, no other specifications are made below, are still valid also for the classes of the Riemann–Stieltjes integral.

Definition 5.27 (Riemann–Stieltjes lower sums). If $f : [a, b] \to \Re$ is a bounded function, $P = \{x_0, x_1, \ldots, x_n\}$ is a partition of $[a, b]$ and g is a monotonic

Figure 5.11 The values of $a_j^{(2)}$ from Corollary 5.9.

d	1	2	3	4	5	6	7	8	9	10
$c = \Sigma_i a_i$	4	12	16	180	576	1.680	33.809	55.711	178.160	1.197.504
a_0	1	1	1	7	19	41	751	989	2.587	16.067
a_1	2=2*1	4	3	32	75	216	3.577	5.888	15.741	106.300
a_2	1	2=2*1	3	12	50	27	1.323	−928	1.080	−48.525
a_3		4	2=2*1	32	50	272	2.989	10.496	19.344	272.400
a_4		1	3	14=2*7	75	27	2.989	−4.540	5.788	−260.550
a_5			3	32	38=19*2	216	1.323	10.496	5.788	472.368
a_6			1	12	75	82=41*2	3.577	−928	19.344	−260.550
a_7				32	50	216	1502=2*751	5.888	1.080	272.400
a_8				7	50	27	3.577	1978=989*2	15.741	−48.525
a_9					75	272	1.323	5.888	5174=2987*2	106.300
a_{10}					19	27	2.989	−928	15.741	32134=16067*2
a_{11}						216	2.989	10.496	1.080	106.300
a_{12}						41	1.323	−4.540	19.344	−48.525
a_{13}							3.577	10.496	5.788	272.400
a_{14}							751	−928	5.788	−260.550
a_{15}								5.888	19.344	472.368
a_{16}								989	1.080	−260.550
a_{17}									15.741	272.400
a_{18}									2.587	−48.525
a_{19}										106.300
a_{20}										16.067

function of $[a, b]$ in $\Re$, then the *Riemann–Stieltjes lower sum* of f with respect to P and to g is the real number

$$s_g(f, P) = \sum_{k=1}^{n} m_k(g(x_k) - g(x_{k-1})) \tag{5.25}$$

where $m_k = \inf f([x_{k-1}, x_k])$.

Definition 5.28 (Riemann–Stieltjes upper sum). If $f : [a, b] \to \Re$ is a bounded function, $P = \{x_0, x_1, \ldots, x_n\}$ is a partition of $[a, b]$ and g is a monotonic function of $[a, b]$ in $\Re$, then the *Riemann–Stieltjes upper sum* of f with respect to P and to g is the real number

$$S_g(f, P) = \sum_{k=1}^{n} M_k(g(x_k) - g(x_{k-1})) \tag{5.26}$$

where $M_k = \sup f([x_{k-1}, x_k])$.

Definition 5.29. Let $P = \{x_0, x_1, \ldots, x_n\}$ be a partition of $[a, b]$, let $\chi = \{z_1, z_2, \ldots, z_n\}$ be a choice with respect to P, let f be a function of $[a, b]$ in $\Re$

Figure 5.12 The values of $a_j^{(3)}$ from Corollary 5.10.

d	1	2	3	4	5	6	7	8	9	10
$c = \Sigma_i a_i$	6	18	24	270	864	2.520	50.338	83.072	267.240	1.796.256
a_0	1	1	1	7	19	41	751	989	2.587	16.067
a_1	2=2*1	4	3	32	75	216	3.557	5.888	15.741	106.300
a_2	2=2*1	2=2*1	3	12	50	27	1.323	-928	1.080	-48.525
a_3	1	4	2=2*1	32	50	272	2.989	10.496	19.344	272.400
a_4		2=2*1	3	14=2*7	75	27	2.989	-4.540	5.788	-260.550
a_5		4	3	32	38=19*2	216	1.323	10.496	5.788	427.368
a_6		1	2=2*1	12	75	38=19*2	3.557	-928	19.344	-260.550
a_7			3	32	50	216	1502=2*751	5.888	1.080	272.400
a_8			3	14=2*7	50	27	3.557	1978=989*2	15.741	-48.525
a_9			1	32	75	272	1.323	5.888	5174=2987*2	106.300
a_{10}				12	38=19*2	27	2.989	-928	15.741	32134=16067*2
a_{11}				32	75	216	2.989	10.496	1.080	106.300
a_{12}				7	50	82=41*2	1.323	-4.540	19.344	-48.525
a_{13}					50	216	3.557	10.496	5.788	272.400
a_{14}					75	27	1502=2*751	-928	5.788	-260.550
a_{15}					19	272	3.557	5.888	19.344	427.368
a_{16}						27	1.323	1978=989*2	1.080	-260.550
a_{17}						216	2.989	5.888	15.741	272.400
a_{18}						41	2.989	-928	5174=2987*2	-48.525
a_{19}							1.323	10.496	15.741	106.300
a_{20}							3.557	-4.540	1.080	32134=16067*2
a_{21}							751	10.496	19.344	106.300
a_{22}								-928	5.788	-48.525
a_{23}								5.888	5.788	272.400
a_{24}								989	19.344	-260.550
a_{25}									1.080	427.368
a_{26}									15.741	-260.550
a_{27}									2.587	272.400
a_{28}										-48.525
a_{29}										106.300
a_{30}										16.067

and let g be a monotonic function of $[a, b]$ in $\Re$. Then the real number

$$\sigma_g(f, P, \chi) = \sum_{k=1}^{n} f(z_k)(g(x_k) - g(x_{k-1})) \tag{5.27}$$

is defined as *the sum according to Cauchy–Stieltjes of f with respect to g, P and χ.*

Definition 5.30. Given $\{P_n\}$ a sequence of partitions of $[a, b]$, $f : [a, b] \to \Re$ a bounded function and g a monotonic function of $[a, b]$ in $\Re$, $\{S_n\}_g$, $\{s_n\}_g$ and $\{\sigma_n\}_g$ are defined to be the corresponding sequences of the lower and upper

Riemann–Stieltjes sums and of the Cauchy–Stieltjes sum, ie,

$$\{S_n\}_g = S_g(f, \{P_n\})$$
$$\{s_n\}_g = s_g(f, \{P_n\})$$
$$\{\sigma_n\}_g = \sigma_g(f, \{P_n\}, \{\chi_n\})$$

Definition 5.31. The function f is defined as *integrable according to Riemann–Stieltjes* if and only if a sequence $\{P_n\}$ of partitions of $[a, b]$ exists so that

$$\lim_{n \to \infty} \{S_n\} - \{s_n\} = 0$$

that is

$$\lim_{n \to \infty} \{S_n\} = \lim_{n \to \infty} \{s_n\} \tag{5.28}$$

The expression (5.28) is called the Riemann–Stieltjes integral, ie,

$$\int_a^b f(x)\, dx = \lim_{n \to \infty} \{S_n\} = \lim_{n \to \infty} \{s_n\} \tag{5.29}$$

Theorem 5.11. *If f is integrable according to Riemann–Stieltjes, ie,*

$$\int_a^b f(x)\, dg(x) = \lim_{n \to \infty} \{S_n\} = \lim_{n \to \infty} \{s_n\} \tag{5.29}$$

and for any n a choice of χ_n with respect to P_n is made, where $\{P_n\}$ is a sequence of partitions, for $n \to \infty$, then based on Theorem 3.1 the following also holds:

$$\int_a^b f(x)\, dg(x) = \lim_{n \to \infty} \{\sigma_n\} \tag{5.30}$$

5.3.1. Classes of integrable functions
Theorem 5.12. *If f is continuous on $[a, b]$ and g is monotonic on $[a, b]$, then the integral $\int_a^b f(x)\, dg(x)$ exists.*

Theorem 5.13. *If f is monotonic on $[a, b]$ and g (monotonic) and continuous on $[a, b]$, then the integral $\int_a^b f(x)\, dg(x)$ exists.*

5.3.2. Properties of the Riemann–Stieltjes integral
Let f and g be two integrable functions on $[a, b]$ according to the Riemann–Stieltjes rule. Then the following properties hold.

(1) Bilinearity

$$\int_a^b [\alpha f_1(x) + \beta f_2(x)] \, dg(x) = \alpha \int_a^b f_1(x) \, dg(x) + \beta \int_a^b f_2(x) \, dg(x)$$

$$\int_a^b f(x) \, d[\alpha g_1(x) + \beta g_2(x)] = \alpha \int_a^b f(x) \, dg_1(x) + \beta \int_a^b f(x) \, dg_2(x)$$

(2) Additivity

$$\int_a^b f(x) \, dg(x) = \int_a^c f(x) \, dg(x) + \int_c^b f(x) \, dg(x) \quad c \in [a, b]$$

5.3.3. Riemann integral and Riemann–Stieltjes integral

The Riemann–Stieltjes integral is a generalisation of the Riemann integral when the function g is not differentiable. It is also used in measure theory and in the more restricted field of probabilities; if a function g is identified with the cumulated probability function, it is known that function g is not differentiable in some cases: as in the discrete random variables (see Part II).

Proposition 5.13. *Let $f \in C^0[a, b]$ and $g \in C^1[a, b]$, with g monotonic. Then the following equivalence holds:*

$$\int_a^b f(x) \, dg(x) = \int_a^b f(x) g'(x) \, dx$$

Corollary 5.11. *Let $f \in C^0[a, b]$ and $g \in C^1[a, b]$, with g monotonic. Hereafter, the integration by parts rule applies for the Riemann–Stieltjes integrals:*

$$\int_a^b f(x) \, dg(x) = f(b)g(b) - f(a)g(a) - \int_a^b g(x) \, df(x)$$

Theorem 5.14. *Let $f \in C^0[a, b]$ and $g \in C^1[a, b]$ be two segment continuous functions, then*

$$\exists \int_a^b f(x) \, dg(x)$$

and

$$\int_a^b f(x) \, dg(x) = \int_a^b f(x) g'(x) \, dx + \sum_{i=0}^n f(P_i) \Delta_g(P_i)$$

where P_i are points of discontinuity of function g, and $\Delta_g(P_i)$ is the value of the jump of function g at the point of discontinuity P_i.

6

Remarkable functions

6.1. SIGN FUNCTION

Definition 6.1. A *sign function* is defined as

$$\text{sgn}(x) = \begin{cases} 1 & x > 0 \\ 0 & x = 0 \\ -1 & x < 0 \end{cases}$$

6.2. ABSOLUTE VALUE FUNCTION

Definition 6.2. An *absolute value* is defined as

$$|x| = x \cdot \text{sgn}(x)$$

where $\text{sgn}(x)$ is the sign function (see Definition 6.1).

Proposition 6.1. *Given functions $f(x)$ and $g(x)$, the following relation holds:*

$$|f(x) + g(x)| \leq |f(x)| + |g(x)|$$

Proposition 6.2. *Given functions $f(x)$ and $c \in \mathbb{R}$, the following relation holds:*

$$|cf(x)| = |c| \cdot |f(x)|$$

6.3. INDEX FUNCTION

Definition 6.3. An *index function* is defined as

$$1_{\{x \in (a,b)\}} \triangleq \begin{cases} 1 & \text{for } x \in (a, b) \\ 0 & \text{for } x \notin (a, b) \end{cases}$$

Notation 6.1. The expression $1_{\{x \in (a,b)\}}$ is often denoted as $1_{(a,b)}(x)$.

Proposition 6.3. *Given sets A and B, due to the index function, the following relation holds:*

$$1_{A \cup B} = 1_A + 1_B + 1_{A \cap B}$$

Proposition 6.4. *Based on the index function, the following relation holds:*

$$\int_a^b f(x)\, dx = \int_{-\infty}^{+\infty} 1_{\{x \in [a,b]\}} f(x)\, dx \tag{6.1}$$

Corollary 6.1. *Based on the index function, the following relation holds:*

$$\int_a^b dx = \int_{-\infty}^{+\infty} 1_{\{x \in [a,b]\}}\, dx$$

Proposition 6.5. *Based on the index function, the following relation holds:*

$$(a - b)^+ = a 1_{\{a > b\}} - b 1_{\{a > b\}} \tag{6.2}$$

6.4. DELTA FUNCTION

Definition 6.4. The *Kronecker delta*, ie, the discrete form of the delta function, is the following function:

$$\delta(t) \triangleq \begin{cases} 0 & \text{for } t \neq 0 \\ 1 & \text{for } t = 0 \end{cases}$$

Notation 6.2. The expression below is equivalent; it represents the delta function in its so-called non-centred version

$$\delta_{t_0}(t) \triangleq \delta(t - t_0) \triangleq \begin{cases} 0 & \text{for } t \neq t_0 \\ 1 & \text{for } t = t_0 \end{cases}$$

Theorem 6.1. *The following equivalence between the non-centred Kronecker delta and the index function holds:*

$$\delta_{t_0}(t) = 1_{\{t = t_0\}}$$

Definition 6.5. The *delta function*, also called the Dirac delta, is the continuous function defined as

$$\delta(t) \triangleq \begin{cases} 0 & \text{for } t \neq 0 \\ \infty & \text{for } t = 0 \end{cases}$$

where

$$\int_{-\infty}^{+\infty} \delta(t)\, dt = 1$$

Corollary 6.2. *For the definition of the delta function, the following expression also holds:*

$$\int_0^t \delta(t)\, dt = 1$$

Notation 6.3. The expression below is equivalent; it represents the delta function in the so-called non-centred version:

$$\delta_{t_0}(t) \triangleq \delta(t - t_0) \triangleq \begin{cases} 0 & \text{for } t \neq t_0 \\ \infty & \text{for } t = t_0 \end{cases}$$

Definition 6.6. The Lorenzed distribution is the function defined for $\varepsilon > 0$, ie,

$$\delta_\varepsilon(t) = \frac{1}{\pi} \frac{\varepsilon}{\varepsilon^2 + t^2}$$

where

$$\delta_\varepsilon(t) = \int_{-\infty}^{+\infty} \frac{1}{\pi} \frac{\varepsilon}{\varepsilon^2 + t^2} \, dt = 1$$

Theorem 6.2. *The integral of the product of any continuous function by the delta function is always equal to the value at point zero of this function, ie,*

$$\int_{-\infty}^{+\infty} f(t)\delta(t) \, dt = f(0)$$

Corollary 6.3. *Theorem 6.2 also holds for any interval of integration which includes the value at which the delta function blows up (see also Corollary 6.2).*

Theorem 6.3. *The integral of the product of any continuous function by the delta function evaluated at point $(t - t_0)$ is always equal to the value in t_0 of this function, ie,*

$$\int_{-\infty}^{+\infty} f(t)\delta(t - t_0) \, dt = f(t_0)$$

Corollary 6.4. *Theorem 6.3 also holds for any interval of integration which includes the value at which the function blows up (see also Corollary 6.2).*

Theorem 6.4. *The fundamental equation which defines the kth derivative of $\delta(t)$, denoted by $(d/dt)\delta(t) \doteq \delta^{(k)}(t)$, is*

$$\int_{-\infty}^{+\infty} f(t)\delta^{(k)}(t) \, dt = -\int_{-\infty}^{+\infty} \frac{df}{dt}\delta^{(k-1)}(t) \, dt$$

Corollary 6.5. *Based on Theorem 6.4, the following relation between $\delta^{(k)}(t)$ and $\delta(t)$ is derived:*

$$\int_{-\infty}^{+\infty} f(t)\delta^{(k)}(t) \, dt = -(1)^k \left[\frac{d^k}{dt^k} f(t) \Big|_{t=0} \right]$$

Proposition 6.6. *Let $f(\tau) = \delta(\tau)$, convolution is (see Section 5.2.7)*

$$h(t) = \int_0^t \delta(\tau)g(t - \tau)\,d\tau = g(t)$$

Corollary 6.6. *Convolution between a function $f(t)$ and the non-centred delta function (see Notation 6.3) is defined by the following expression:*

$$h(t) = \int_{-\infty}^{+\infty} f(\tau)\delta(t - t_0 - \tau)\,d\tau = f(t - t_0)$$

6.5. HEAVISIDE FUNCTION

Definition 6.7. A *Heaviside function* is denoted as

$$\begin{cases} \theta(x) = 1 & \text{if } x \geq 0 \\ \theta(x) = 0 & \text{if } x < 0 \end{cases} \tag{6.3}$$

or as

$$\begin{cases} \theta(x) = 1 & \text{if } x > 0 \\ \theta(x) = \frac{1}{2} & \text{if } x = 0 \\ \theta(x) = 0 & \text{if } x < 0 \end{cases} \tag{6.4}$$

Notation 6.4. A so-called non-centred Heaviside function is denoted as

$$\theta_{x_0}(x) \triangleq \theta(x - x_0) \triangleq \begin{cases} 1 & \text{for } x \geq x_0 \\ 0 & \text{for } x < x_0 \end{cases}$$

or as

$$\theta_{x_0}(x) \triangleq \theta(x - x_0) \triangleq \begin{cases} \theta(x) = 1 & \text{if } x > x_0 \\ \theta(x) = \frac{1}{2} & \text{if } x = x_0 \\ \theta(x) = 0 & \text{if } x < x_0 \end{cases}$$

Theorem 6.5. *If the Heaviside function is expressed as in Equation (6.3), it may also be expressed by the index function, ie,*

$$\theta_{x_0}(x) \triangleq \theta(x - x_0) \triangleq 1_{\{x \geq x_0\}} \tag{6.5}$$

Remark 6.1. If the Heaviside function is expressed as in Equation (6.4), it may also be expressed by the sign function, ie,

$$\theta(x) \triangleq \frac{1}{2} + \frac{1}{2}\operatorname{sgn}(x) \tag{6.6}$$

6.5.1. Heaviside function and Dirac delta

Proposition 6.7. *The following equivalence below holds between $\theta(x)$ and $\delta(x)$:*

$$\frac{d}{dx}\theta(x) = \delta(x) \tag{6.7}$$

where $\delta(x)$ is the Kroneker delta (see Definition 6.4).

Corollary 6.7. *The following equivalence holds between $\theta_{x_0}(x)$ and $\delta_{x_0}(x)$:*

$$\frac{d}{dx}\theta_{x_0}(x) = \delta_{x_0}(x) \tag{6.8}$$

where $\delta_{x_0}(x)$ is the non-centred Kroneker (see Definition 6.2).

Proposition 6.8. *The following equivalence holds between $\theta(x)$ and $\delta(x)$:*

$$\theta(x) = \int_{-\infty}^{x} \delta(t)\, dt \tag{6.9}$$

where $\delta(x)$ is the delta function (see Definition 6.5).

Corollary 6.8. *The following equivalence holds between $\theta_{x_0}(x)$ and $\delta_{x_0}(x)$:*

$$\theta_{x_0}(x) = \int_{-\infty}^{x-x_0} \delta(t)\, dt = \int_{-\infty}^{x} \delta(t - x_0)\, dt \tag{6.10}$$

where $\delta_{x_0}(x)$ is the delta function (see Definition 6.3).

6.6. GAMMA FUNCTION

The Gamma function was derived by Euler to compute the factorial of a number in the set of real numbers.

Definition 6.8. The *Gamma function*, denoted by $\Gamma(n)$, is defined, for any $n > 0$, as

$$\Gamma(n) = \int_{0}^{\infty} t^{n-1} e^{-t}\, dt \tag{6.11}$$

Theorem 6.6. *The Gamma function has a recursive representation as follows:*

$$\Gamma(n) = (n-1)\Gamma(n-1)$$

Proposition 6.9. *For a value of $1/2$, the Gamma function is equal to π, ie,*

$$\Gamma\left(\frac{1}{2}\right) = \pi \tag{6.12}$$

Theorem 6.7. *Given a function $\Gamma(n)$, for any $n \in \mathbb{N}$,*

$$\Gamma(n) = (n-1)!$$

6.7. ERF FUNCTION

Definition 6.9. The Erf function, denoted by erf z, is defined as

$$\text{erf } z \doteq \frac{2}{\sqrt{\pi}} \int_0^z e^{-x^2} \, dx \tag{6.13}$$

Some useful equivalences can be derived from this function:

$$\frac{\sqrt{\pi}}{2} = \int_0^{+\infty} e^{-x^2} \, dx \tag{6.14}$$

$$\sqrt{\pi} = \int_{-\infty}^{+\infty} e^{-x^2} \, dx \tag{6.15}$$

Complex numbers

7.1. BASICS

Definition 7.1. Complex numbers are represented as pairs of real numbers, ie, $z = (a, b)$.

Definition 7.2. The notation $z = x + iy$ is said to be the cartesian or algebraic form of complex numbers; x is said to be the real part of z and is denoted by $\text{Re}(z)$ (or also by $\Re z$) and y is said to be the imaginary part and is denoted by $\text{Im}(z)$ (or also by $\Im z$).

Notation 7.1. $\Re z$ can also be denoted as $\Re[z]$.

Notation 7.2. $\Im z$ can also be denoted as $\Im[z]$.

Proposition 7.1. *For any complex number $z = a + ib$, a corresponding conjugate complex number exists so that $\bar{z} = a - ib$.*

7.2. OPERATIONS

Proposition 7.2. *Equally, the usual four operations $+, -, *, /$, are defined for complex numbers. The same rules for real numbers apply as a logic extension:*

$$(x + iy) + (h + id) = (x + h) + i(y + d)$$
$$(x + iy) - (h + id) = (x - h) + i(y - d)$$
$$(x + iy) * (h + id) = (xh - yd) + i(ad + yh)$$
$$(x + iy)/(h + id) = (x + iy) * (h - id)/(h * h + d * d) = \cdots$$

Corollary 7.1. *The sum of two complex numbers a and b is made by using the rule of the parallelogram; it is represented in a Gauss plan as in Figure 7.1.*

Corollary 7.2. *The difference of two complex numbers a and b is represented in a Gauss plan in Figure 7.2. It is derived from the other diagonal of the parallelogram (oriented towards the vertex of the first member and reported by the parallel transposed starting from origin O).*

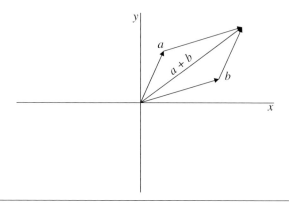

Figure 7.1 A Gauss plan of the rule of a parallelogram.

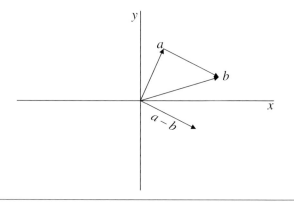

Figure 7.2 The difference of two complex numbers represented in a Gauss plan.

Proposition 7.3. *The module or the absolute value $|z|$ of a complex number $z = x + iy$ is defined so that*

$$|z| = |x + iy| = \sqrt{x^2 + y^2}$$

that is

$$|z|^2 = |x + iy|^2 = x^2 + y^2$$

Corollary 7.3. *The modules of a complex number z and of its conjugate $\bar{z}$ are identical:*

$$|z| = |x + iy| = |x - iy| = |\bar{z}| = \sqrt{x^2 + y^2}$$

that is

$$|z|^2 = |x + iy|^2 = |x - iy|^2 = |\bar{z}|^2 = x^2 + y^2$$

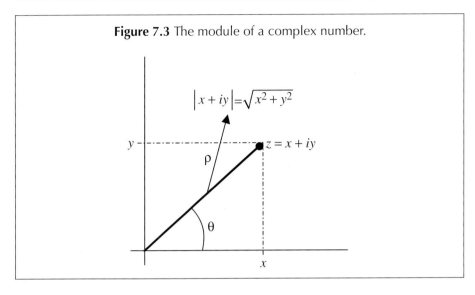

Figure 7.3 The module of a complex number.

Definition 7.3. The module of z (indicated by ρ in Figure 7.3) is the length of the vector (positive or zero). The angle between the vector and the positive x-axis (anticlockwise) is said to be the argument of the complex number (or $\text{Arg}(z)$; indicated by θ in Figure 7.3).

7.2.1. Representation of a complex number

Proposition 7.4. *A complex number may be represented as a function of the module and of the argument as follows:*

$$z = x + iy = \rho(\cos\theta + i\sin\theta) \tag{7.1}$$

ie, the polar algebraic (or trigonometric) form of a complex number.

Corollary 7.4. *Given a complex number z of Proposition 7.4, the corresponding conjugate complex number is*

$$\bar{z} = x - iy = \rho(\cos\theta - i\sin\theta)$$

Corollary 7.5. *Given a complex number $z = \rho(\cos\theta + i\sin\theta)$, for the trigonometric relation applied to the right triangle, $\theta = \text{arctg}(y/x)$ (see Figure 7.3).*

Proposition 7.5. *A complex number may be written as an exponential, ie,*

$$z = x + iy = \rho e^{i\theta} \tag{7.2}$$

Corollary 7.6. *For complex numbers the following equivalence holds (Euler's formula):*

$$z = \rho e^{i\theta} = \rho(\cos\theta + i\sin\theta) \tag{7.3}$$

Corollary 7.7. *For complex numbers the following equivalence holds:*

$$z = \rho e^{-i\theta} = \rho(\cos\theta - i\sin\theta) \tag{7.4}$$

Corollary 7.8. *The product of two complex numbers a and b is represented in a Gauss plan as in Figure 7.4. Specifically, the product of two complex numbers is a complex number whose module is the product of the modules and whose argument is the sum of the arguments (clockwise, graphically), ie,*

$$z = a \cdot b$$
$$= (a_1 + ia_2) \cdot (b_1 + ib_2)$$

and using Equation (7.2),

$$z = \rho_1 e^{i\theta_1} \cdot \rho_2 e^{i\theta_2}$$
$$= \rho_1 \rho_2 e^{i(\theta_1 + \theta_2)}$$

Proposition 7.6. *For the module of a complex number $z = x + iy$, the following relation also holds:*

$$|z| = |x + iy| = \sqrt{x^2 + y^2} = \sqrt{(x + iy) \cdot (x - iy)} = \sqrt{z \cdot \bar{z}} \tag{7.5}$$

or

$$|z|^2 = |x + iy|^2 = x^2 + y^2 = (x + iy) \cdot (x - iy) = z \cdot \bar{z}$$

Theorem 7.1. *The square of the module of the difference of two complex numbers is*

$$|z_1 - z_2|^2 = \rho_1^2 + \rho_1^2 - 2\rho_1\rho_2 \cos(\theta_1 - \theta_2) \tag{7.6}$$

This equivalence is known as the Carnot theorem.

Corollary 7.9. *The division of two complex numbers a and b is represented in a Gauss plan as in Figure 7.5. Specifically, the division of two complex numbers is a complex number whose module is the division of the modules and whose argument is*

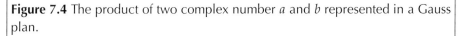

Figure 7.4 The product of two complex number a and b represented in a Gauss plan.

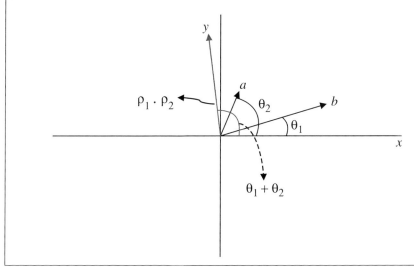

the difference of the arguments (anticlockwise, graphically), ie,

$$z = a/b$$
$$= (a_1 + ia_2)/(b_1 + ib_2)$$

and using Equation (7.2),

$$z = \rho_1 e^{i\theta_1}/\rho_2 e^{i\theta_2}$$
$$= \frac{\rho_1}{\rho_2} e^{i(\theta_1 - \theta_2)}$$

Proposition 7.7. *The argument of a complex number can be summed or subtracted by integer multiples of 2π (ie, the round angle) without any change in the resulting complex number, ie,*

$$\rho \cdot e^{i\theta} = \rho \cdot e^{i(\theta + 2k\pi)} \tag{7.7}$$

Proposition 7.8. *Complex numbers may be elevated to an integer n power to be denoted by*

$$z^n = \rho^n \cdot e^{in\theta} = \rho^n[\cos(n\theta) + i\sin(n\theta)] \tag{7.8}$$
$$z^{-n} = \rho^{-n} \cdot e^{-in\theta} = \rho^{-n}[\cos(n\theta) - i\sin(n\theta)] \tag{7.9}$$

93

Figure 7.5 The division of two complex numbers a and b represented in a Gauss plan.

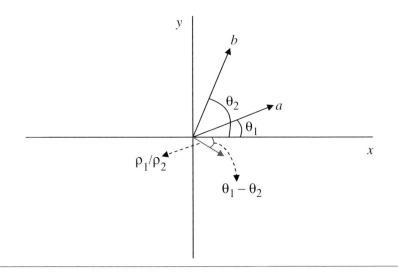

Corollary 7.10. *Cosine may be expressed by complex numbers as*

$$\cos(n\theta) = \tfrac{1}{2}(e^{in\theta} + e^{-in\theta}) \tag{7.10}$$

Corollary 7.11. *Sine may be expressed by complex numbers as*

$$\sin(n\theta) = \frac{1}{2i}(e^{in\theta} - e^{-in\theta})$$

Proposition 7.9. *Complex numbers raised to the power of a fraction are computed as*

$$z^{1/n} = \rho^{1/n} \cdot e^{i(\theta n^{-1}+2kn^{-1}\pi)} = \rho^{1/n}\cos\left(\theta\frac{1}{n} + 2k\frac{1}{n}\pi\right) + i\sin\left(\theta\frac{1}{n} + 2k\frac{1}{n}\pi\right)$$

Proposition 7.10. *The reciprocal of a complex number is*

$$\frac{1}{z} = \frac{\bar{z}}{z\bar{z}} = \frac{x - iy}{x^2 + y^2} \tag{7.11}$$

Corollary 7.12. *Proposition 7.10 applied to complex number $v = i$ implies that $1/i = -i$.*

Theorem 7.2. *For any complex number $z = a + ib$, the following equivalence holds:*

$$\frac{(z - \bar{z})}{2i} = b = \text{Im}(z) \tag{7.12}$$

Theorem 7.3. *For any complex number $z = a + ib$, the following equivalence holds:*

$$\mathrm{Re}\left(\frac{z}{i}\right) = b = \mathrm{Im}(z) \tag{7.13}$$

Theorem 7.4. *For $\theta = \pi$, the following equivalence holds based on Equation (7.3):*

$$e^{i\pi} = -1 \tag{7.14}$$

Theorem 7.5. *Defining $z = e^{it}$ and $\bar{z} = e^{-it}$, the following equivalences hold:*

$$\left.\begin{array}{l} \lim\limits_{t\to\infty} z = \lim\limits_{t\to\infty} e^{it} \\ \lim\limits_{t\to-\infty} z = \lim\limits_{t\to-\infty} e^{it} \\ \lim\limits_{t\to\infty} \bar{z} = \lim\limits_{t\to\infty} e^{-it} \\ \lim\limits_{t\to\infty} \bar{z} = \lim\limits_{t\to-\infty} e^{-it} \end{array}\right\} = (1+i)[-1;1]$$

7.3. COMPLEX FUNCTION

Definition 7.4. Based on Definition 7.2, the generic complex function $f(z)$: $\mathbb{C} \to \mathbb{C}$ may be denoted as

$$f(z) = \Re[f(z)] + i\Im[f(z)] \tag{7.15}$$

Definition 7.5. Based on the definition of the generic complex function $f(z)$: $\mathbb{C} \to \mathbb{C}$, $\overline{f(z)}$ is defined to be the complex conjugate of the function $f(z)$.

Theorem 7.6. *Based on the definition of the generic complex function $f(z) : \mathbb{C} \to \mathbb{C}$, if*

$$\overline{f(z)} = f(-z)$$

then

$$\Re[f(z)] \text{ is an even function,} \quad ie, \Re[f(z)] = \Re[f(-z)]$$
$$\Im[f(z)] \text{ is an odd function,} \quad ie, -\Im[f(z)] = \Im[f(-z)]$$

Differential equations

8.1. ORDINARY DIFFERENTIAL EQUATION

8.1.1. First-order ODE

8.1.1.1. Linear equations

Theorem 8.1. *Given a linear homogeneous ordinary differential equation (ODE)*

$$y'(x) + a(x)y(x) = 0 \tag{8.1}$$

the solution is

$$y(x) = -e^{-\int a(x)\,dx} \tag{8.2}$$

Theorem 8.2. *Given a linear ODE*

$$a(x)y'(x) + a'(x)y(x) + c(x) = 0 \tag{8.3}$$

where $a'(x) = (d/dx)a(x)$, the solution is

$$y(x) = -\frac{K}{a(x)} - \frac{1}{a(x)} \int c(x)\,dx \tag{8.4}$$

Theorem 8.3. *Given a linear ODE*

$$y'(x) + a(x)y(x) + c(x) = 0 \tag{8.5}$$

the solution is

$$y(x) = -\frac{K}{e^{\int a(x)\,dx}} - e^{-\int a(x)\,dx} \int c(x) \cdot e^{\int a(x)\,dx}\,dx$$

8.1.1.2. Riccati's equation

Theorem 8.4. *Given the following ODE*

$$y'(x) = ay^2(x) + b(x)y(x) + c(x) \tag{8.6}$$

by substituting

$$y(x) = -\frac{E'(x)}{aE(x)} \tag{8.7}$$

Equation (8.6) may be simplified into a second-order linear ODE:

$$E''(x) - b(x)E'(x) + ac(x)E(x) \tag{8.8}$$

8.1.2. Second-order ODE

Theorem 8.5. *Let a constant coefficient second-order linear ODE*

$$y''(x) - by'(x) + acy(x) = 0 \tag{8.9}$$

The solution to Equation (8.9) is

$$y(x) = A_1 e^{(b + \sqrt{b^2 - 4ac})/2x} + A_2 e^{(b - \sqrt{b^2 - 4ac})/2x} \tag{8.10}$$

Example 8.1. Let this Cauchy problem

$$\begin{aligned} y''(x) - by'(x) + acy(x) &= 0 \\ y(0) &= 0 \\ y'(0) &= 1 \end{aligned} \tag{8.11}$$

by applying Theorem 8.5 and by using the following expression

$$d = \sqrt{b^2 - 4ac} \tag{8.12}$$

one will have

$$y(x) = A_1 e^{((b+d)/2)x} + A_2 e^{((b-d)/2)x} \tag{8.13}$$

defining

$$\alpha_1 = \frac{b + d}{2}, \quad \alpha_2 = \frac{b - d}{2} \tag{8.14}$$

To facilitate notation, Equation (8.13) is re-arranged as follows:

$$y(x) = A_1 e^{\alpha_1 x} + A_2 e^{\alpha_2 x} \tag{8.15}$$

In order to specify boundary conditions, the first-order derivative (8.15) of the general solution is computed as

$$y'(x) = A_1 e^{\alpha_1 x} \alpha_1 + A_2 e^{\alpha_2 x} \alpha_2 \tag{8.16}$$

By using Equations (8.15) and (8.16) the boundary conditions will become

$$y(0) = A_1 + A_2 = 0 \tag{8.17}$$
$$y'(0) = A_1 \alpha_1 + A_2 \alpha_2 = 1 \tag{8.18}$$

The values of A_1 and A_2 are explicitly derived under Equations (8.17) and (8.18), ie,

$$\begin{cases} A_1 = \dfrac{1}{\alpha_1 - \alpha_2} \\[2mm] A_2 = \dfrac{1}{\alpha_2 - \alpha_1} \end{cases} \tag{8.19}$$

the expressions of Equation (8.19) are then substituted into the general solution (8.15) and recalling Equation (8.14) one gets

$$y(x) = \frac{e^{((b+d)/2)x} - e^{((b-d)/2)x}}{d}$$

9

Transforms

Definition 9.1. Given $f(x)$, a continuous function for $x \geq 0$, a function $\mathcal{F}$ is defined to be the *integral transform* of f, and can be written as

$$\mathcal{F}[f(x)](t) = \int_\alpha^\beta K(t, x)f(x)\, dx \tag{9.1}$$

The domain is the set of $t \in \mathbf{C}$, then the integral converges. Function $K(t, x)$ is defined to be the *kernel* of the transformation.

9.1. LAPLACE TRANSFORM

9.1.1. Definition and examples

Definition 9.2. Given $f(x)$, a continuous function for $x \geq 0$, a *unilateral Laplace transform* of f is the function $\mathcal{L}$ defined by

$$\mathcal{L}[f(x)](t) = \int_0^{+\infty} f(x)e^{-tx}\, dx$$

whose domain is the set of $t \in \mathbf{C}$ so that the integral converges.

Definition 9.3. Given $f(x)$, a continuous function, a *bilateral Laplace transform* of f is a function $\mathcal{L}$ defined by

$$\mathcal{L}[f(x)](t) = \int_{-\infty}^{+\infty} f(x)e^{tx}\, dx$$

or by

$$L[f(x)](t) = \int_{-\infty}^{+\infty} f(x)e^{-tx}\, dx$$

whose domain is the set of $t \in \mathbf{C}$ such that the integral converges[1].

Criterion 9.1. *Since the set of t, such that the integral converges, belongs to complex numbers, the search for "the region of convergence of the integral" (ie, convergence radius) must be made with reference to t to be intended as a complex number, ie, $t = \sigma + i\omega$ where σ is the real part of t (or $\Re t$) and ω the imaginary part of t (or $\Im t$). Specifically, to determine the convergence radius, it is necessary to make the following steps:*

(1) *identify the quantity which gives the solution of the integral;*
(2) *use the module of this quantity to measure the convergence radius;*
(3) *t is broken down into the real (ie, $\Re t$) and the imaginary (ie, $\Im t$) parts;*
(4) *then, identify the constraints in $\Re t$ and $\Im t$ to determine the convergence of the integral, ie, the convergence radius of the integral.*

Notation 9.1. Below, both $L[f(x)](t)$ and $L[f(t)](s)$ will be used equally.

Example 9.1. Let $f(x) = 1$ and $x \geq 0$, then the value of $L[f(x)](t) = 1/t$ with $t > 0$. As a matter of fact:

$$L[f(x)](t) = \int_0^{+\infty} 1e^{-tx}\, dx$$

$$= \lim_{A \to \infty} -\frac{1}{t}e^{-tA} + \frac{1}{t} = \frac{1}{t}$$

To determine the convergence radius, the steps indicated in Criterion 9.1 will be followed:

(1) the integral converges since $e^{-tx} \to 0$ for $x \to \infty$;
(2) the module of this quantity, $|e^{-tx}|$, is necessary to measure the convergence radius;

---

[1]Here we have used

$$\int_{-\infty}^{+\infty} f(x)e^{tx}\, dx = \int_{-\infty}^{0} f(x)e^{tx}\, dx + \int_{0}^{+\infty} f(x)e^{tx}\, dx$$

$$= \int_{0}^{+\infty} f(x)e^{-tx}\, dx + \int_{-\infty}^{0} f(x)e^{-tx}\, dx$$

$$= \int_{-\infty}^{+\infty} f(x)e^{-tx}\, dx$$

(3) t is broken down into the real (ie, $\Re t$) and into the imaginary (ie, $\Im t$), $|e^{-x(a+ib)}|$, parts where $a = \Re t$ and $b = \Im t$;

(4) the convergence radius is determined as

$$|e^{-x(a+ib)}| = |e^{-xa}||e^{-ixb}|$$

for Corollary 7.6 and for Proposition 7.3 one will have

$$= |e^{-xa}|(\cos^2 bx + \sin^2 bx)$$
$$= e^{-x\Re t}$$

the convergence radius is the value of $\Re t$ so that the quantity $e^{-x\Re t} \to 0$ for $x \to \infty$, ie, being $x \geq 0$ when $\Re t > 0$.

Example 9.2. Let $f(t) = t$, then the value of $\mathcal{L}[f(t)](s) = 1/s^2$ with $s > 0$.

Example 9.3. Let $f(x) = e^x$ with $x \geq 0$, then the value of $\mathcal{L}[f(x)](t) = 1/(t-1)$ with $t > 1$.

Example 9.4. Let $f(x) = e^{-x}$ with $x \geq 0$, then the value of $\mathcal{L}[f(x)](t) = 1/(t+1)$ with $t > -1$.

Example 9.5. Let $f(x) = e^{ax}$ with $a > 0$ and $x \geq 0$, then the value of $\mathcal{L}[f(x)](t) = 1/(t-a)$ with $t > a$.

Example 9.6. Let $f(x) = \cos wx$, then the value of $\mathcal{L}[f(x)](t) = t/(t^2 + w^2)$ with $t > 0$.

Example 9.7. Let $f(x) = x^n$, for $n \geq 1$, then the value of $\mathcal{L}[f(x)](t) = n!/(t^{n+1})$ with $t \neq 0$.

Example 9.8. Let $f(x) = e^{-x^2}$, then the value of $\mathcal{L}[f(x)](t) = e^{t^2/4}\sqrt{\pi}$.

9.1.2. Laplace transform and Dirac delta

Proposition 9.1. *Let $f(x) = \delta(x)$, then the value of $\mathcal{L}[f(x)](t) = 1$.*

Corollary 9.1. *The computational result of Proposition 9.1 is also valid for the bilateral Laplace transform, under the characteristics of the definition of $\delta(x)$.*

Proposition 9.2. *Let $f(x) = (d^k/dx^k)\delta(x) \doteq \delta^{(k)}(x)$, then the value of $\mathcal{L}[f(x)](t) = t^k$.*

Corollary 9.2. *The computational result of Proposition 9.2 is also valid for the unilateral Laplace transform, under the characteristics of the definition of $\delta(x)$.*

9.1.3. Properties and examples

A list of Laplace transform properties and some examples are given in the following.

Notation 9.2. A capital letter denotes the Laplace transform of a function.

9.1.3.1. Linearity

A Laplace transform is linear; defining a as a scalar, one will have the following relation:

$$\mathcal{L}(aF) = aF$$
$$\mathcal{L}(f + g) = F + G$$

Example 9.9. Recalling Proposition 9.1 and the results of Example 9.3, one will have

$$\mathcal{L}[3\delta(t) - 2e^t] = \frac{3s - 5}{s - 1}$$

9.1.3.2. One-to-one relation

If $\mathcal{L}(f) = \mathcal{L}(g)$, then $f = g$.

Example 9.10. Reconsidering Example 9.9:

$$\mathcal{L}[3\delta(t) - 2e^t] = \frac{3s - 5}{s - 1}$$
$$\mathcal{L}^{-1}\left(\frac{3s - 5}{s - 1}\right) = 3\delta(t) - 2e^t$$

9.1.3.3. Time scaling

If $g(t) = f(at)$ with $a > 0$, then $G(s) = a^{-1}F(s/a)$.

9.1.3.4. Exponential scaling

If $g(t) = e^{at}f(t)$ with $a > 0$, then $G(s) = F(s - a)$.

Example 9.11. The value of $\mathcal{L}(e^{-t}\cos t)$ is derived by applying the property above. To this end, the results of Example 9.6 are recalled and for the exponential scaling property it derives:

$$\mathcal{L}(e^{-t}\cos t) = \frac{s + 1}{s^2 + 2 + 2s}$$

9.1.3.5. Time delay

Let $f(t)$ and $g(t)$ be defined as in Figure 5.6, and be denoted as

$$g(t) = \begin{cases} 0 & 0 \le t \le T \\ f(t - T) & t \ge T \end{cases}$$

then

$$G(s) = e^{-sT} F(s)$$

9.1.3.6. Multiplication by t

Given the relation

$$g(t) = tf(t)$$

hence

$$G(s) = -\frac{d}{ds} F(s)$$

Example 9.12. Given $f(t) = e^{-t}$, $g(t) = te^{-t}$, $L(g(t))$ is computed by using the property above:

$$L[te^{-t}] = -\frac{d}{ds} L[e^{-t}]$$

By using results of Example 9.4, one will have

$$= \frac{1}{(s+1)^2}$$

9.1.4. Laplace transform and differential calculus

Proposition 9.3. *Given a function $f(t)$ to be differentiable, the following holds:*

$$L[f'(t)](s) = sF(s) - f(0)$$

Proposition 9.4. *Given a function $f(t)$ to be differentiable k times, the following holds:*

$$L[f^{(k)}(t)](s) = s^k L[f(t)] - s^{k-1} f(0) - s^{k-2} f'(0) - s^{k-3} f''(0) - \cdots$$
$$- s^3 f^{(k-4)}(0) - s^2 f^{(k-3)}(0) - s f^{(k-2)}(0) - f^{(k-1)}(0)$$

Example 9.13. Given $f(t) = e^t$, $f\prime(t) = e^t$, then

$$L[f(t)] = L[f'(t)] = \frac{1}{s-1}$$

by using Proposition 9.3 and recalling the result of Example 9.3, the same result is determined:

$$\mathcal{L}[e^t] = s\mathcal{L}[e^t] - e^0$$

$$= \frac{1}{s-1}$$

9.1.5. Laplace transform and ODEs

Laplace transforms are used to transform an ODE into an algebraic equation.

Example 9.14. Given the ODE

$$\begin{cases} y'(t) + y(t) = 1 \\ y(0) = 0 \end{cases}$$

the Laplace transform is applied:

$$\mathcal{L}[y'(t)] + \mathcal{L}[y(t)] = \mathcal{L}[1]$$

By using Proposition 9.3 and the results of Example 9.1, one will have

$$sY(s) - y(0) + Y(s) = \frac{1}{s}$$

By solving for $Y(s)$,

$$Y(s) = \frac{1}{s} - \frac{1}{(s+1)}$$

To finalise the solution of the Cauchy system above, one has to invert the Laplace transform and to find $y(t)$, ie,

$$y(t) = \mathcal{L}^{-1}\left[\frac{1}{s} - \frac{1}{(s+1)}\right]$$

$$y(t) = 1 - e^{-t}$$

which is, in fact, the solution of the Cauchy problem.

9.1.6. Laplace transforms and integral calculus

Laplace transforms are used to transform the computation of an integral into an algebraic operation.

Proposition 9.5. *Given a function $f(t)$ to be integrable and $g(t) = \int_0^t f(\tau)\, d\tau$, the following holds:*

$$G(s) = \frac{1}{s}F(s)$$

Example 9.15. Given $f(t) = \delta(t)$, $g(t) = \int_{-\infty}^{\infty} \delta(\tau) \, d\tau = 1$ (see Definition 6.5), then $G(s) = \mathcal{L}[1] = 1/s$ (see Example 9.1). One verifies that by applying Proposition 9.5, one has the same result:

$$G(s) = \frac{1}{s}\mathcal{L}[\delta(t)]$$

Actually, recalling the results of Proposition 9.1 the same result is determined:

$$G(s) = \frac{1}{s}$$

9.1.6.1. Laplace transforms and convolution
Laplace transforms are used to transform convolution into a multiplication.

Proposition 9.6. *Given a convolution (see Definition 5.26 and Notation 5.1), ie,*

$$h(t) = \int_0^{\infty} f(\tau)g(t - \tau) \, d\tau$$

the Laplace transform of $h(t)$ is given by the equivalence

$$H(t) = \mathcal{L}[h(t)] = \mathcal{L}(f * g) = F(s)G(s)$$

Example 9.16. Given $f(\tau) = \delta(\tau)$ and g any integrable function, the proposition above is used to find

$$\mathcal{L}[f * g] = F(\delta(\tau))G(s)$$

Based on the results of Proposition 9.1, one will have

$$H(s) = G(s)$$

This result is the same as that derived by using convolution where one of the functions is the Dirac delta (see Proposition 6.6), where $h(t) = g(t)$.

9.2. FOURIER TRANSFORM
9.2.1. Definitions and examples
Definition 9.4. Given $f(x)$ a continuous function for all x, the *Fourier transform* of f, is a function $\mathcal{F}$ defined as

$$\mathcal{F}[f(x)](t) = \int_{-\infty}^{+\infty} f(x)e^{-itx} \, dx$$

or as (for this equivalence, see also Corollary 7.7)

$$\mathcal{F}[f(x)](t) = \int_{-\infty}^{+\infty} f(x)\cos(tx)\,dx - i\int_{-\infty}^{+\infty} f(x)\sin(tx)\,dx \qquad (9.2)$$

or as

$$\mathcal{F}[f(x)](t) = \int_{-\infty}^{+\infty} f(x)e^{itx}\,dx$$

or as (for this equivalence, see also Corollary 7.6)

$$\mathcal{F}[f(x)](t) = \int_{-\infty}^{+\infty} f(x)\cos(tx)\,dx + i\int_{-\infty}^{+\infty} f(x)\sin(tx)\,dx \qquad (9.3)$$

and whose domain is the set $t \in \mathbf{C}$ so that the integral converges.

Remark 9.1. If one compares Equations (9.2) and (9.3) to the definition of the complex number (see Definition 7.2), one may derive that

$$\int_{-\infty}^{\infty} f(x)\cos(tx)\,dx = \Re[\mathcal{F}[f(x)](t)]$$

$$\int_{-\infty}^{\infty} f(x)\sin(tx)\,dx = \Im[\mathcal{F}[f(x)](t)]$$

Example 9.17. Let $f(x) = e^{-a|x|}$ with $a > 0$. The value of $\mathcal{F}[f(x)](t) = 2a/(a^2 + t^2)$:

$$\mathcal{F}[f(x)](t) = \int_{-\infty}^{+\infty} e^{-a|x|}e^{-itx}\,dx$$

$$= \lim_{A\to-\infty} \frac{1}{a-it}e^{ax-itx}\Big|_A^0 + \lim_{B\to\infty} \frac{1}{-a-it}e^{-ax-itx}\Big|_0^\infty$$

$$= \frac{2a}{a^2 + t^2}$$

Example 9.18. Let $f(x) = 1$ for all x. The following is a demonstration that this Fourier transform is equal to $2\pi\delta(t)$; to this purpose, $f(x) = 1$ is studied for $x \geq 0$ and then $f(x) = 1$ for $x < 0$.
For $x \geq 0$, one can interpret $f(x) = 1$ as $\lim_{\alpha\to 0} e^{-\alpha x}$ for $x \geq 0$, ie,

$$\mathcal{F}[f(x)](t) = \lim_{\alpha\to 0} \int_0^{+\infty} e^{-\alpha x - itx}\,dx$$

$$= \lim_{\alpha\to 0} \lim_{A\to\infty} \frac{1}{-\alpha - it}e^{-\alpha x - itx}\Big|_0^A$$

The Fourier transform of $f(x) = 1$ for $x \geq 0$ is

$$\int_0^{+\infty} e^{-itx}\, dx = \frac{1}{it} + \pi\delta(t) \tag{9.4}$$

For $x < 0$, one can interpret $f(x) = 1$ as $e^{-\alpha x}$ for $x < 0$, ie,

$$\mathcal{F}[f(x)](t) = \lim_{\alpha \to 0} \int_0^{+\infty} e^{-\alpha x + itx}\, dx$$

$$= \lim_{\alpha \to 0} \lim_{A \to \infty} \frac{1}{-\alpha + it} e^{-\alpha x + itx}\Big|_0^A$$

It follows that the Fourier transform of $f(x) = 1$ for $x < 0$ is

$$\int_{-\infty}^0 e^{-itx}\, dx = \pi\delta(t) - \frac{1}{it} \tag{9.5}$$

Combining Equation (9.5) with (9.4), the resulting Fourier transform for $f(x) = 1$ is

$$\mathcal{F}[f(x)](t) = \int_{-\infty}^{+\infty} e^{-itx}\, dx = \frac{1}{it} + \pi\delta(t) - \frac{1}{it} + \pi\delta(t) = 2\pi\delta(t) \tag{9.6}$$

Example 9.19. Let

$$f(x) = \operatorname{sgn}(x) = \begin{cases} 1 & x > 0 \\ 0 & x = 0 \\ -1 & x < 0 \end{cases}$$

ie, the sign function as defined in Definition 6.1. The value of $\mathcal{F}[f(x)](t) = 2/it$

Example 9.20. Let

$$f(t) = \begin{cases} 1 & -T \leq t \leq T \\ 0 & |t| > T \end{cases}$$

One computes the Fourier transform:

$$F(w) = \int_{-\infty}^{+\infty} e^{-itw}\, dt$$

For Corollary 7.11 one will have

$$= \frac{2\sin wT}{w}$$

Example 9.21. Let $f(t) = \cos(w_0 t)$. One computes the Fourier transform as follows.

For Corollary 7.10 one will have

$$= \frac{1}{2}\mathcal{F}[1](w - w_0) + \frac{1}{2}\mathcal{F}[1](w + w_0)$$

Using result (9.6) one will have

$$= \pi\delta(w - w_0) + \pi\delta(w + w_0)$$

Example 9.22. Let $f(t) = \sin(w_0 t)$. One computes the Fourier transform as follows.

For Corollary 7.11, one will have

$$= \frac{1}{2i}\mathcal{F}[1](w - w_0) - \frac{1}{2i}\mathcal{F}[1](w + w_0)$$

Using result (9.6), one will have

$$= \frac{1}{i}\pi\delta(w - w_0) - \frac{1}{i}\pi\delta(w + w_0)$$

Using Corollary 7.12, one will have

$$= -i\pi\delta(w - w_0) + i\pi\delta(w + w_0)$$

Example 9.23. Let

$$f(t) = \sum_{k=-\infty}^{\infty} a_k e^{ikw_0 t}$$

One computes the Fourier transform:

$$F(w) = \int_{-\infty}^{+\infty} \sum_{k=-\infty}^{\infty} a_k e^{ikw_0 t} e^{-itw}\, dt$$

By using result (9.6) one will have

$$2\pi \sum_{k=-\infty}^{\infty} a_k \delta(w - kw_0)$$

Theorem 9.1. *Given* $f(x) : \mathbb{C} \to \mathbb{R}$, *then*

$$\mathcal{F}[f(x)](-t) = \overline{\mathcal{F}[f(x)](t)}$$

where $\overline{\mathcal{F}[f(x)](t)}$ *denotes the conjugate complex (see Definition 7.5) of the Fourier transform* $\mathcal{F}[f(x)](t)$.

Theorem 9.2. *The inverse of the general Fourier transform*

$$\mathcal{F}(t) = \int_{-\infty}^{+\infty} f(x)e^{-itx}\,dx$$

is given by

$$f(x) = \frac{1}{2\pi}\int_{-\infty}^{+\infty} e^{itx}\mathcal{F}(t)\,dt \tag{9.7}$$

Proof. We have

$$f(x) = \frac{1}{2\pi}\int_{\omega=-\infty}^{+\infty} e^{itx}\mathcal{F}(t)\,dt$$

(by using the definition of $\mathcal{F}(t)$ and one property of the integrals)

$$= \int_{\tau=-\infty}^{+\infty} f(\tau)\left(\frac{1}{2\pi}\int_{\omega=-\infty}^{+\infty} e^{-it(\tau-x)}\,dt\right)d\tau$$

and using (9.6), the property of the delta function, as in Theorem 6.3 we have proved the equality. □

Corollary 9.3. *The inverse of the generic Fourier transform*

$$\mathcal{F}(t) = \int_{-\infty}^{+\infty} f(x)e^{itx}\,dx$$

is given by

$$f(x) = \frac{1}{2\pi}\int_{-\infty}^{+\infty} e^{-itx}\mathcal{F}(t)\,dt \tag{9.8}$$

9.2.2. Fourier transforms and Laplace transforms
Proposition 9.7. *If $f(x) = 0$ for $x < 0$ and if the imaginary axis lies in the convergence radius of $\mathcal{L}(it)$, then*

$$\mathcal{F}[f(x)](t) = \mathcal{L}[f(x)](it)$$

It can be derived that if the imaginary axis does not lie in the convergence radius of $\mathcal{L}(it)$, then $\mathcal{F}(t)$ does not exist.

Remark 9.2. Given the definition of the Laplace transform (see Definition 9.3), where $s \in R$, ie,

$$\mathcal{L}[f(x)](t) = \int_{0}^{+\infty} e^{-st}f(t)\,dt$$

$s \in C$, ie, $s = \sigma + i\omega$, where $\Re s = \sigma$, $\Im s = \omega$, letting $\sigma = 0$, one will have

$$\mathcal{L}[f(x)](it) = \int_0^{+\infty} e^{-i\omega t} f(t)\, dt = \mathcal{F}[f(x)](t)$$

obtaining the equivalence stated in Proposition 9.7 as a result.

Proposition 9.8. *If $f(x) \neq 0$ for $x < 0$, the values of the Fourier and Laplace transforms may show extremely different results.*

Theorem 9.3. *The inverse of the generic bilateral Laplace transform*

$$\mathcal{L}(t) = \int_{-\infty}^{+\infty} f(x) e^{-tx}\, dx$$

is given by

$$f(x) = \frac{1}{2\pi i} \int_{\sigma-i\infty}^{\sigma+i\infty} e^{tx} \mathcal{L}(t)\, dt$$

with a convergence radius $\Re t \geq \sigma$.

9.2.3. Fourier transforms and Dirac delta

Proposition 9.9. *Let $f(x) = \delta(x)$, then the value of $\mathcal{F}[f(x)](t) = 1$*

Proposition 9.10. *If one defines*

$$\delta_K(x) = \frac{\sin Kx}{\pi x}$$

then the following holds:

$$\delta_K(x) = \frac{\sin Kx}{\pi x} = \frac{1}{2\pi} \int_{-K}^{K} e^{itx}\, dt, \quad \forall K \in \mathbb{R} \tag{9.9}$$

Proposition 9.11. *If one defines*

$$\delta_K(x) = \frac{\sin Kx}{\pi x}$$

then the following holds:

$$\lim_{x \to \pm\infty} \delta_K(x) = 0 \tag{9.10}$$

Proposition 9.12. *If one defines*

$$\delta_K(x) = \frac{\sin Kx}{\pi x}$$

then the following holds:

$$\int_{-\infty}^{+\infty} \delta_K(x)\, dx = \lim_{K \to \infty} \int_{-K}^{K} \delta_K(x)\, dx = 1 \qquad (9.11)$$

Proposition 9.13. *If one defines*

$$\delta_K(x) = \frac{\sin Kx}{\pi x}$$

then the following holds:

$$\lim_{x \to 0} \delta_K(x)\, dx = \frac{K}{\pi} \qquad (9.12)$$

Proposition 9.14. *The function*

$$\delta_K(x) = \frac{\sin Kx}{\pi x}$$

has a period of

$$\frac{\pi}{K} \qquad (9.13)$$

Proposition 9.15. *The function*

$$\delta_K(x) = \frac{\sin Kx}{\pi x}$$

for $K \uparrow \infty$ assumes the following expression:

$$\lim_{K \to \infty} \delta_K(x) = \begin{cases} \infty & x = 0 \\ 0 & x \neq 0 \end{cases} \qquad (9.14)$$

Theorem 9.4. *The Dirac delta function may also be defined as*

$$\delta(x) = \frac{1}{2\pi} \int_{-\infty}^{+\infty} e^{itx}\, dt$$

which coincides with the definition of the Fourier transform as in Example 9.18, ie, for $\mathcal{F}(t) = 1$.

Corollary 9.4. *The non-centred Dirac delta function may also be defined as*

$$\delta(x - x_0) = \frac{1}{2\pi} \int_{-\infty}^{+\infty} e^{it(x-x_0)}\, dt$$

or as

$$\delta(x - x_0) = \frac{1}{2\pi} \int_{-\infty}^{+\infty} e^{-it(x-x_0)}\, dt$$

9.2.4. Properties and examples

A list of the properties of Fourier transforms and some examples are given below.

Notation 9.3. The Fourier transform of a function is denoted by a capital script letter.

9.2.4.1. Linearity

The Fourier transform is linear; defining a as a scalar, the relation below holds:

$$\mathcal{F}(aF) = aF$$
$$\mathcal{F}(f + g) = F + G$$

9.2.4.2. One-to-one relation

If $\mathcal{F}(f) = \mathcal{F}(g)$, then $f = g$.

9.2.4.3. Time scaling

If $g(t) = f(at)$, with $a > 0$, then $G(w) = a^{-1}F(w/a)$.

Corollary 9.5. *If $a \in R$, the expression becomes*

$$G(w) = \frac{1}{|a|}F\left(\frac{w}{a}\right)$$

9.2.4.4. Time delay

Let $f(t)$ and $g(t)$ defined as in Figure 5.6, and denoted as

$$g(t) = \begin{cases} 0 & 0 \leq t \leq T \\ f(t - T) & t > T \end{cases}$$

Then

$$G(w) = e^{-iwT}F(w)$$

9.2.4.5. Multiplying by t

Given the equivalence

$$g(t) = tf(t)$$

then

$$G(w) = i\frac{d}{dw}F(w)$$

9.2.4.5.1. Multiplying by t^k Given the equivalence

$$g(t) = t^k f(t)$$

then

$$G(w) = i^k \frac{d^k}{dw^k} F(w)$$

9.2.4.6. Product of functions
Given the equivalence

$$h(t) = f(t)g(t)$$

then

$$H(w) = \frac{1}{2\pi} \int_{-\infty}^{+\infty} F(\tilde{w})G(w - \tilde{w}) \, d\tilde{w}$$

9.2.5. Fourier transform and differential calculus

Proposition 9.16. *Given a function $f(t)$ to be differentiable, the following holds:*

$$\mathcal{F}[f'(t)](w) = iwF(w)$$

Proposition 9.17. *Given a function $f(t)$ to be differentiable k times, the following holds:*

$$\mathcal{F}[f^{(k)}(t)](w) = (iw)^k \mathcal{F}[f(t)](w)$$

9.2.6. Fourier transform and partial differential equations

Fourier transforms are used to transform a partial differential equation (PDE) into an ODE.

Example 9.24. Let a PDE, also called a wave equation, be

$$\begin{cases} \dfrac{\partial^2 u(x,t)}{\partial t^2} = \dfrac{\partial^2 u(x,t)}{\partial x^2} \\[2mm] u(x,0) = f(x) \\[2mm] \dfrac{\partial u(x,0)}{\partial t} = 0 \end{cases} \tag{9.15}$$

whose famous solution (determined by d'Alembert) is

$$u(x,t) = \tfrac{1}{2}[f(x+t) + f(x-t)] \tag{9.16}$$

One determines this result by applying the Fourier transforms. Specifically, this transformation is applied on both of the members of the equation with reference to the variable x. The left member is

$$\frac{\partial^2}{\partial t^2} \int_{-\infty}^{+\infty} u(x, t) e^{-isx} \, dx$$

To determine the right member of the "wave equation" one recalls Proposition 9.17; by simplifying, one gets

$$\frac{\partial^2}{\partial t^2} \mathcal{F}[u(x, t)](s) + s^2 \mathcal{F}[u(x, t)](s) = 0$$

This equation is an ODE whose solution is in the form

$$\mathcal{F}[u(x, t)](s) = A e^{ist} + B e^{-ist} \tag{9.17}$$

then, by recalling the initial conditions of the Cauchy problem (9.15) rearranged by applying the Fourier transform with respect to x and to solution (9.17), we have the following.

(1) $u(x, 0) = f(x)$, becomes, by using the Fourier transform with respect to x,

$$\mathcal{F}[u(x, 0)](s) = \mathcal{F}[f(x)](s)$$

and by specifying this result with respect to solution (9.17), one has

$$A e^{is0} + B e^{-is0} = \mathcal{F}[f(x)](s)$$
$$\mathcal{F}[f(x)](s) = A + B \tag{9.18}$$

(2) By using the Fourier transform with reference to the variable x, $\partial u(x, 0)/\partial t = 0$ becomes

$$\mathcal{F}\left[\frac{\partial u(x, 0)}{\partial t}\right](s) = 0$$

and specifying this result on solution (9.17), one has

$$\mathcal{F}\left[\frac{\partial u(x, 0)}{\partial t}\right](s) = is A e^{is0} - is B e^{-is0} = 0$$
$$A = B \tag{9.19}$$

Solving the system of Equations (9.18) and (9.19), one has

$$\begin{cases} A = \dfrac{\mathcal{F}[f(x)](s)}{2} \\[2mm] B = \dfrac{\mathcal{F}[f(x)](s)}{2} \end{cases} \tag{9.20}$$

Substituting (9.20) inside (9.17), one has

$$\mathcal{F}[u(x,t)](s) = \frac{\mathcal{F}[f(x)](s)}{2}e^{ist} + \frac{\mathcal{F}[f(x)](s)}{2}e^{-ist} \tag{9.21}$$

Then to find the solution $u(x,t)$ of PDE (9.15), Equation (9.21) is inverted by using Theorem 9.2, ie,

$$\frac{1}{2\pi}\int_{-\infty}^{+\infty} e^{ixs}\mathcal{F}[u(x,t)](s)\, ds$$

$$= \frac{1}{2\pi}\int_{-\infty}^{\infty}\left[e^{ixs}\left(\frac{\mathcal{F}[f(x)](s)}{2}e^{ist} + \frac{\mathcal{F}[f(x)](s)}{2}e^{-ist}\right)\right] ds$$

$$u(x,t) = \frac{1}{2}[f(x+t) + f(x-t)]$$

9.2.7. Fourier transforms and integral calculus

Fourier transforms are used to transform the calculus of an integral into an algebraic operation.

Proposition 9.18. *Given a function $f(t)$ to be integrable and $g(t) = \int_{-\infty}^{t} f(\tau)\, d\tau$, the following holds:*

$$G(w) = \frac{1}{is}F(w) + \pi F(0)\delta(w)$$

9.2.7.1. Transforms and convolution

Fourier transforms are used to transform convolution into a multiplication.

Proposition 9.19. *Given a convolution (see Definition 5.26), ie,*

$$h(t) = \int_{-\infty}^{\infty} f(\tau)g(t-\tau)\, d\tau$$

the Fourier transform of $h(t)$ is given by the following equivalence:

$$H(t) = \mathcal{F}[h(t)] = \mathcal{F}(f*g) = F(s)G(s)$$

Part II

Probability

Measure theory

10.1. BASICS

10.1.1. Outer measure

Definition 10.1. Given a measurable space $(X, \mathcal{P}(X))$ and given an algebra $\mathcal{A} \subseteq \mathcal{P}(X)$, a *finitely additive measure* is a function $\mu : \mathcal{A} \to [0, +\infty]$ which satisfies the following conditions:

(i) $\mu(\varnothing) = 0$;
(ii) if $A, B \in \mathcal{A}$ and $A \cap B = \varnothing$, then $\mu(A \cup B) = \mu(A) + \mu(B)$.

Definition 10.2. An *outer measure* of the measurable space $(X, \mathcal{P}(X))$ is a function $\mu^* : \mathcal{P}(X) \to [0, +\infty]$ which satisfies the following conditions:

(i) $\mu^*(\varnothing) = 0$;
(ii) if $E, F \in X$, $E \subseteq F$, then $\mu^*(E) \leq \mu^*(F)$ (ie, *monotony*);
(iii) if $\{A_i\}_{i \in \mathbb{N}} \subseteq \mathcal{P}(X)$, then $\mu^*(\bigcup_{i=1}^{\infty} A_i) \leq \sum_{i=1}^{\infty} \mu^*(A_i)$ (ie, *countable sub-additivity*).

Proposition 10.1. *Given a measurable space $(X, \mathcal{P}(X))$, let $\mathcal{J} \subseteq \mathcal{P}(X)$ and $\rho : \mathcal{J} \to [0, +\infty]$ so that:*

(i) $\varnothing \in \mathcal{J}$;
(ii) $X \in \mathcal{J}$;
(iii) $\rho(\varnothing) = 0$.

For any $E \subseteq X$,

$$\mu^*(E) := \inf_{\{E_i\}_{i \in \mathbb{N}}} \left\{ \sum_{i=1}^{\infty} \rho(E_i) \right\} \tag{10.1}$$

where:

- $E_i \in \mathcal{J}$;
- $E \subseteq \bigcup_{i=1}^{\infty} E_i$;

then μ^* is an outer measure.

Corollary 10.1. *In the measurable space* $(\mathbb{R}, \mathcal{P}(\mathbb{R}))$, *the* outer measure *of any set* $A \subseteq \mathbb{R}$, *denoted by* $\mu^*(A)$, *is the real non-negative number given by*

$$\mu^*(A) := \inf_{\{I_i\}_{i\in\mathbb{N}}} \left\{ \sum_{i=1}^{\infty} l(I_i) \right\} \tag{10.2}$$

where:

- $\{I_i\}_{i\in\mathbb{N}}$ *is a sequence of intervals of* $\mathbb{R}$;
- $A \subseteq \bigcup_{i=1}^{\infty} I_i$.

Theorem 10.1. *A set* $A \subseteq \mathbb{R}$ *is empty if and only if the outer measure is equal to zero.*

Theorem 10.2. *The outer measure of an interval of* $\mathbb{R}$ *coincides with its length.*

Theorem 10.3. *The outer measure of a set* $A \subseteq \mathbb{R}$ *is* translation invariant, *ie,*

$$\mu^*(A) = \mu^*(A + x) \tag{10.3}$$

for all $A \subseteq \mathbb{R}$ *and for all* $x \in \mathbb{R}$, *x scalar.*

10.1.2. Measure

Definition 10.3. A *measure* on a measurable space $(X, \mathcal{M})$ is the non-negative function $\mu : \mathcal{M} \to [0, +\infty]$ so that:

(1) $\mu(\varnothing) = 0$;
(2) if $\{E_i\}_{i\in\mathbb{N}} \in \mathcal{M}$ is a sequence of disjoint sets of pairs, ie, $E_i \cap E_j = \varnothing$ for all $i \neq j, i, j = 1, 2, \ldots$, then

$$\mu\left(\bigcup_{i=1}^{\infty} E_i \right) = \sum_{i=1}^{\infty} \mu(E_i) \tag{10.4}$$

or μ is a *countably additive* function on the σ-algebra $\mathcal{M}$.10.3.

Definition 10.4. The *measure space* is a measurable space held by a measure.

Definition 10.5. A *measure space* $(X, \mathcal{M}, \mu)$ is said to be σ-*finite* (see Propositions 10.4 and 10.12) if a sequence of sets $\{X_i\}_{i\in\mathbb{N}} \in \mathcal{M}$ exists so that:

(1) $X = \bigcup_{i=1}^{+\infty} X_i$;
(2) $\mu(X_i) < +\infty$, for all $i \in \mathbb{N}$.

Definition 10.6. Let $(X, \mathcal{M}, \mu)$ be a measure space and let E be an element of $\mathcal{M}$. The *restrictions of μ on set E*, denoted by μ_E, is the non-negative function defined over $\mathcal{M}_E$ as follows:

$$\mu_E(F) := \mu(E \cap F), \quad \forall F \in \mathcal{M} \tag{10.5}$$

Proposition 10.2. *The function $\mu_E : \mathcal{M}_E \to [0, +\infty]$ is one measure on a measurable space $(E, \mathcal{M}_E)$.*

Remark 10.1. From Definition 1.100, from Definition 10.6 and Proposition 10.2 it can be derived that starting from a measure space $(X, \mathcal{M}, \mu)$ of set X it is always possible to shift to a measure space $(E, \mathcal{M}_E, \mu_E)$ of set E through the restriction of the σ-algebra $\mathcal{M}$ to set E and of measure μ to measure μ_E defined on the σ-algebra $\mathcal{M}_E$.

Definition 10.7. Given a measure space $(X, \mathcal{M}, \mu)$ and a σ-algebra $\mathcal{N} \subseteq \mathcal{M}$, the *restriction of measure μ from σ-algebra $\mathcal{M}$ to σ-algebra $\mathcal{N}$*, denoted by $\mu_{\mathcal{N}}$ is the measure defined over $\mathcal{N}$ as follows:

$$\mu_{\mathcal{N}}(E) := \mu(E), \quad \forall E \in \mathcal{N}$$

Definition 10.8. Given the measure space $(X, \mathcal{M}, \mu)$, sets $E, F \in \mathcal{M}$ are said to be *independent* of measure μ if

$$\mu(E \cap F) = \mu(E)\mu(F)$$

Definition 10.9. Let $\mathcal{F}_1$ and $\mathcal{F}_2$ be two sub-σ-algebras of a σ-algebra $\mathcal{M}$ which belongs to the measure space $(X, \mathcal{M}, \mu)$. $\mathcal{F}_1$ and $\mathcal{F}_2$ are said to be *independent* with respect to measure μ if any set in $\mathcal{F}_1$ is independent of any set of $\mathcal{F}_2$, ie,

$$\mu(E \cap F) = \mu(E)\mu(F), \quad \forall E \in \mathcal{F}_1, \forall F \in \mathcal{F}_2$$

Definition 10.10. Given a set X and an algebra $\mathcal{A}$ of that set, a *measure on algebra* $\mathcal{A}$ is a function $\mu : \mathcal{A} \to [0, +\infty]$ so that:

(1) $\mu(\varnothing) = 0$;
(2) if $\{E_i\}_{i \in \mathbb{N}} \in \mathcal{A}$ is a sequence of disjoint sets of pairs, ie, $E_i \cap E_j = \varnothing$ for all $i \neq j, i, j = 1, 2, \ldots$;

(3) if $\bigcup_{i=1}^{\infty} E_i \in \mathcal{A}$, then

$$\mu\left(\bigcup_{i=1}^{\infty} E_i\right) = \sum_{i=1}^{\infty} \mu(E_i)$$

ie, μ is a *countably additive function* on algebra $\mathcal{A}$.

Definition 10.11. Given a measure space $(X, \mathcal{M}, \mu)$ and an algebra $\mathcal{A}$ of set X, the *restriction of measure μ to algebra $\mathcal{A}$* , denoted by $\mu_{\mathcal{A}}$, is the measure defined over $\mathcal{A}$ as

$$\mu_{\mathcal{A}}(E) := \mu(E), \quad \forall E \in \mathcal{A}$$

Definition 10.12. Let $(X, \mathcal{M}, \mu)$ be a measure space and let $\mathcal{G}$ be a family of subsets of X which is neither an algebra nor a σ-algebra on X. The *restriction of measure μ to σ-algebra $\mathcal{M}$ to the family of sets $\mathcal{G}$*, denoted by $\mu_{\mathcal{G}}$, is the non-negative function on $\mathcal{G}$ denoted as follows:

$$\mu_{\mathcal{G}}(E) := \mu(E), \quad \forall E \in \mathcal{G}$$

Remark 10.2. As function $\mu_{\mathcal{G}}$, as above, is defined neither on an algebra nor on a σ-algebra, this function is not a measure.

Definition 10.13. A measure μ on the measurable space $(X, \mathcal{M})$ is said to be *finite* if

$$\mu(X) < +\infty \tag{10.6}$$

Definition 10.14. A measure μ on the measurable space $(X, \mathcal{M})$ is said to be *σ-finite* if a sequence of sets exists $\{X_i\}_{i \in \mathbb{N}} \subseteq \mathcal{M}$ so that

$$\mu(X_i) < +\infty, \quad \forall i \in \mathbb{N} \tag{10.7}$$

10.1.3. Absolutely continuous measures and equivalent measures

Definition 10.15. Let ν and μ be two measures defined on the measurable space $(X, \mathcal{M})$. A measure ν is said to be *absolutely continuous* with respect to μ if for any $E \in \mathcal{M}$ so that $\mu(E) = 0$ one has

$$\nu(E) = 0T$$

Notation 10.1. If ν is an *absolutely continuous measure* with respect to μ, ν is said to be *dominated by* μ. This relation is denoted by writing

$$\nu \ll \mu$$

Definition 10.16. Let ν and μ two measures defined on the measurable space $(X, \mathcal{M})$. If for all $E \in \mathcal{M}$ one has

$$\nu \ll \mu \quad \text{and} \quad \mu \ll \nu$$

or if

$$\nu(E) = 0 \Leftrightarrow \mu(E) = 0$$

then ν and μ are said to be *equivalent measures*.

Notation 10.2. The equivalence relation between two measures ν and μ is denoted by

$$\nu \equiv \mu$$

10.1.4. Property of measures

Proposition 10.3. *Let $(X, \mathcal{M}, \mu)$ be a measure space. The following properties hold.*

(1) Finite Additivity: *if $E_1, E_2, \ldots, E_n$ are elements of $\mathcal{M}$ being disjoint in pairs (ie, $E_i \cap E_j = \varnothing$ for all $i \neq j, i, j = 1, 2, \ldots, n$), one has*

$$\mu\left(\bigcup_{i=1}^{n} E_i\right) = \sum_{i=1}^{n} \mu(E_i) \tag{10.8}$$

(2) Monotony: *if $E, F \in \mathcal{M}$ and $E \subseteq F$, one has*

$$\mu(E) \leq \mu(F) \tag{10.9}$$

(3) Continuity from below: *if $\{E_i\}_{i \in \mathbb{N}} \in \mathcal{M}$, $E_1 \subseteq E_2 \subseteq E_3 \subseteq \cdots$, and $E = \bigcup_{i=1}^{\infty} E_i$, one has*

$$\mu(E) = \mu\left(\bigcup_{i=1}^{\infty} E_i\right) = \lim_{i \to +\infty} \mu(E_i) \tag{10.10}$$

(4) Continuity conditioned from above: *if $\{E_i\}_{i \in \mathbb{N}} \in \mathcal{M}$, $E_1 \supseteq E_2 \supseteq E_3 \supseteq \cdots$, and $\mu(E_1) < +\infty$, one has*

$$\lim_{i \to +\infty} \mu(E_i) = \mu\left(\bigcap_{i=1}^{\infty} E_i\right) \tag{10.11}$$

10.2. REMARKABLE MEASURES

Definition 10.17. Given the measurable space $(X, \mathcal{P}(X))$, the *counting measure* is defined as the function $\mu : \mathcal{P}(X) \to [0, +\infty]$ so that for all $E \in \mathcal{P}(X)$ one has

$$\mu(E) := \#E \tag{10.12}$$

where $\#E$ reads as the "number of elements contained in set E".

Notation 10.3. The counting measure of the measurable space is usually denoted by $\mu_\#$.

Proposition 10.4. *The measure space* $(\mathbb{R}, \mathcal{P}(\mathbb{R}), \mu_\#)$, *where* $\mu_\#$ *is the counting measure, is not σ-finite (see Definition 10.5).*

Definition 10.18. Given the measurable space $(X, \mathcal{P}(X))$ and $x_0 \in X$, the *Dirac measure centred at point* x_0 is the function $\delta_{x_0} : \mathcal{P}(X) \to [0, +\infty]$ so that for all $E \in \mathcal{P}(X)$ one has

$$\delta_{x_0}(E) := \begin{cases} 1 & \text{if } x_0 \in E \\ 0 & \text{elsewhere} \end{cases} \tag{10.13}$$

Definition 10.19. Given the measurable space $(\mathbb{R}, \mathcal{P}(\mathbb{R}))$, the *Dirac measure concentrated in the origin* is the function $\delta_0 : \mathcal{P}(\mathbb{R}) \to [0, +\infty]$ so that for all $E \in \mathcal{P}(\mathbb{R})$ one has

$$\delta_0(E) := \begin{cases} 1 & \text{if } 0 \in E \\ 0 & \text{elsewhere} \end{cases} \tag{10.14}$$

Definition 10.20. Given the measurable space $(X, \mathcal{P}(X))$, the sequence of points $\{x_n\}_{n \in \mathbb{N}} \in X$ and the corresponding sequence of non-negative members $\{w_n\}_{n \in \mathbb{N}}$, the *weight counting* measure is the function $\mu : \mathcal{P}(X) \to [0, +\infty]$ so that for all $E \in \mathcal{P}(X)$ one has

$$\mu(E) := \sum_{x_n \in E} w_n \tag{10.15}$$

Proposition 10.5. *The weight counting measure identified by Equation (10.15) is a measure.*

10.2.1. Probability measures

Definition 10.21. Given the measurable space $(X, \mathcal{M})$, the *probability measure* is a measure $P : \mathcal{M} \to \mathbb{R}$ so that

$$P(X) = 1 \tag{10.16}$$

Proposition 10.6. *If in the measure space $(X, \mathcal{P}(X), \mu)$, where μ is the weight counting measure as in Definition 10.20, one has*

$$\mu(X) = \sum_{n \in \mathbb{N}} \omega_n = 1$$

then μ is a probability measure.

Definition 10.22. Given the measurable space $(X, \mathcal{P}(X))$, let $X = \{x_n\}_{n=1}^N$ and $\{\omega_n\}_{n=1}^N$ a finite sequence of non-negative members whose general term is $\omega_n = 1/N$, then the *equiprobability measure* on X is the function $= \mu : \mathcal{P}(X) \to [0, +\infty]$ so that for all $E \in \mathcal{P}(X)$ one has

$$\mu(E) := \sum_{x_n \in E} \omega_n$$

10.3. EXTENSION OF A MEASURE

Definition 10.23. Let $(X, \mathcal{M}, \mu)$ be a measure space and let $\mathcal{N}$ be a σ-algebra on X so that $\mathcal{M} \subseteq \mathcal{N}$. Then the *measure extension* μ from σ-algebra $\mathcal{M}$ to σ-algebra $\mathcal{N}$ is a measure $\mu' : \mathcal{N} \to [0, +\infty]$ so that for all $E \in \mathcal{M}$ one has

$$\mu'(E) = \mu(E)$$

Definition 10.24. Let X be a non-null set, let $\mathcal{A}$ be an algebra on X, and let $\sigma(\mathcal{A})$ be the correspondent generated σ-algebra, then $\mathcal{A} \subseteq \sigma(\mathcal{A})$. Also, let $\mu_\mathcal{A} : \mathcal{A} \to [0, +\infty]$ be one measure of the algebra $\mathcal{A}$. Then, the *extension of measure $\mu_\mathcal{A}$ from algebra $\mathcal{A}$ to the σ-algebra generated by $\mathcal{A}$*, denoted by $\sigma(\mathcal{A})$, is defined to be one measure $\mu_{\sigma(\mathcal{A})} : \sigma(\mathcal{A}) \to [0, +\infty]$ so that for all $E \in \mathcal{A}$ one has

$$\mu_\mathcal{A}(E) = \mu_{\sigma(\mathcal{A})}(E)$$

Theorem 10.4 (Caratheodory extension). *Let $(X, \mathcal{P}(X))$ be a measurable space and μ_0 one measure on one algebra $\mathcal{A} \subseteq \mathcal{P}(X)$. Also, let $E \in \mathcal{P}(X)$ and $\mu^* : \mathcal{P}(X) \to [0, +\infty]$ be a function defined as follows:*

$$\mu^*(E) := \inf_{\{E_i\}_{i \in \mathbb{N}}} \left\{ \sum_{i=1}^{\infty} \mu_0(E_i) \right\}$$

where:

- $E_i \in \mathcal{A}$;
- $E \subseteq \bigcup_{i=1}^{\infty} E_i$.

Then, the following statements hold.

(1) μ^* *is one outer measure of the measurable space* $(X, \mathcal{P}(X))$.

(2) *A function* μ^* *restricted (see Definition 10.11) to algebra* $\mathcal{A}$ *is one measure on that algebra. It is equal to* μ_0, *ie,*

$$\mu_{\mathcal{A}}^* = \mu_0$$

(3) *A function* μ^* *restricted to* $\sigma(\mathcal{A})$, *ie, to the* σ-*algebra generated by* $\mathcal{A}$, *is one measure, ie,*

$$\mu_{\sigma(\mathcal{A})}^* \text{ is one measure on the measurable space } (X, \sigma(\mathcal{A}))$$

(4) Uniqueness of extension: *if* μ_1 *is one measure on* $\sigma(\mathcal{A})$ *so that its restriction to algebra* $\mathcal{A}$ *coincides with* μ_0, *then*

$$\mu_1 = \mu_{\sigma(\mathcal{A})}^*$$

10.4. COMPLETE MEASURE SPACES

Definition 10.25. Given the measure space $(X, \mathcal{M}, \mu)$, it is said that the set $D \in \mathcal{M}$ has a *measure zero*, or that D is a *negligible set*, if D is measurable and the measure is zero, that is, if

$$\mu(D) = 0$$

Definition 10.26. Given the measure space $(X, \mathcal{M}, \mu)$ it is said that the σ-*algebra* $\mathcal{M}$ is *complete with respect to measure* μ if $\mathcal{M}$ holds all of the subsets of the negligible sets, ie, if for any $D \in \mathcal{M}$ so that $\mu(D) = 0$ and for any $F \subseteq D$ one has

$$F \in \mathcal{M}$$

and

$$\mu(F) = 0$$

Definition 10.27. The *measure space* $(X, \mathcal{M}, \mu)$ is said to be *complete* if its σ-algebra $\mathcal{M}$ is full with respect to the measure μ.

Proposition 10.7. *Any measure space whose* σ-*algebra coincides with the part set is complete.*

Definition 10.28. Given a measure space $(X, \mathcal{M}, \mu)$ the *class of the negligible sets of* $\mathcal{M}$ denoted by the letter $\mathcal{D}$ is the family of all of the subsets of $\mathcal{M}$ whose measure is zero, ie,

$$\mathcal{D} := \{D \in \mathcal{M} \ni' \mu(D) = 0\} \qquad (10.17)$$

Notation 10.4. The generic class of sets $A \in \mathcal{M}$ is denoted by $\{A\}$, ie, $\mathcal{M} = \{A\}$.

Theorem 10.5. *Let* $(X, \mathcal{M}, \mu)$ *be an incomplete measure space and let* $\mathcal{D}$ *be the class of negligible sets of* $\mathcal{M}$*. Then the class* $\widetilde{\mathcal{M}}$ *of the subsets of* X *defined as*

$$\widetilde{\mathcal{M}} = \{E \cup F\} \qquad (10.18)$$

where:

- $E \in \mathcal{M}$;
- $F \subseteq D$ *for any* $D \in \mathcal{D}$ *is a* σ-*algebra on* X; *it is complete with respect to the measure* $\widetilde{\mu}$ *defined with respect to the measure* μ *as follows*

$$\widetilde{\mu}(E \cup F) := \mu(E) \qquad (10.19)$$

Notation 10.5. The σ-algebra $\widetilde{\mathcal{M}}$ is said to be the *completion of* $\mathcal{M}$ with respect to measure μ.

Notation 10.6. Measure $\widetilde{\mu}$ is said to be the *completion of measure* μ.

Corollary 10.2. *The measure space* $(X, \widetilde{\mathcal{M}}, \widetilde{\mu})$ *is complete.*

Corollary 10.3. *Let* $(X, \mathcal{M}, \mu)$ *be an incomplete measure space and let* $(X, \widetilde{\mathcal{M}}, \widetilde{\mu})$ *be the corresponding measure space which makes the completion. Then one has*

$$\mathcal{M} \subseteq \widetilde{\mathcal{M}} \qquad (10.20)$$

Corollary 10.4. *Let* $(X, \mathcal{M}, \mu)$ *be a measure space and let* $(X, \widetilde{\mathcal{M}}, \widetilde{\mu})$ *be its complete measure space. If for any* $D \in \mathcal{D}$ *any subset* F *of* D *corresponds to the empty set,* $\varnothing$, *then the two measure spaces coincide, ie,*

$$(X, \mathcal{M}, \mu) = (X, \widetilde{\mathcal{M}}, \widetilde{\mu})$$

then the measure space $(X, \mathcal{M}, \mu)$ *is also complete.*

Corollary 10.5. *The measure* $\widetilde{\mu}$ *defined on the measurable space* $(X, \widetilde{\mathcal{M}})$ *is the extension of the measure* μ *defined on the measurable space* $(X, \mathcal{M})$ *from* σ-*algebra* $\mathcal{M}$ *to* σ-*algebra* $\widetilde{\mathcal{M}}$ *(see Definition 10.23), ie, for all* $E \in \mathcal{M}$ *one has*

$$\widetilde{\mu}(E) = \mu(E) \tag{10.21}$$

Corollary 10.6. *Measure* $\widetilde{\mu}$ *as in Corollary 10.5 is unique.*

10.5. LEBESGUE MEASURE IN $\mathbb{R}$

10.5.1. Construction of Lebesgue measure in $\mathbb{R}$

The procedure to construct the Lebesgue measure in $\mathbb{R}$ is based on three consecutive steps:

(1) extension of the length function defined on class $\mathcal{I}$ of the intervals of $\mathbb{R}$ to the measure m_0 defined on algebra $\mathcal{E}_1$;
(2) shift from measure m_0 on algebra $\mathcal{E}_1$ to measure m_1 on σ-algebra $\mathbb{B}$;
(3) extension, by completion, of measure m_1 on the σ-algebra $\mathbb{B}$ to measure $\widetilde{m}_1$ on the σ-algebra $\widetilde{\mathbb{B}}$.

Definition 10.29. Let $\mathcal{E}_1$ be the algebra of the elementary sets of $\mathbb{R}$ and set $E \in \mathcal{E}_1$, ie,

$$E = \bigcup_{i=1}^{N} I_i$$

where $\{I_i\}_{i=1,2,\dots,N}$ is a sequence of N intervals of disjoint pairs whose length is $l(I_i), i = 1, 2, \dots, N$ (see Definition 1.63). Then a function $m_0 : \mathcal{E}_1 \to [0, +\infty]$ is defined as

$$m_0(E) := \sum_{i=1}^{N} l(I_i) \tag{10.22}$$

Proposition 10.8. *A function* m_0 *is a measure on algebra* $\mathcal{E}_1$, *ie,*

(1) $m_0(\varnothing) = 0$;
(2) *if* $\{E_i\}_{i \in \mathbb{N}} \in \mathcal{E}_1$ *is a sequence of disjoint sets of pairs (ie,* $E_i \cap E_j = \varnothing$ *for all* $i \neq j$, $i, j = 1, 2, \dots$ *) and* $\bigcup_{i=1}^{\infty} E_i \in \mathcal{E}_1$, *then*

$$m_0 \left(\bigcup_{i=1}^{\infty} E_i \right) = \sum_{i=1}^{\infty} m_0(E_i)$$

Remark 10.3. A measure m_0 is the extension of the length function defined on class $\mathcal{I}$ of the intervals of $\mathbb{R}$ to the elements of algebra $\mathcal{E}_1$ (see also Definition 1.65, this extension is unique, Theorem 10.4(4)).

Proposition 10.9. *Let m_0^* be the outer measure on $(\mathbb{R}, \mathcal{P}(\mathbb{R}))$ defined as*

$$m_0^*(E) := \inf_{\{E_i\}_{i \in \mathbb{N}}} \left\{ \sum_{i=1}^{\infty} m_0(E_i) \right\} \tag{10.23}$$

where:

- $E_i \in \mathcal{E}_1$;
- $E \subseteq \bigcup_{i=1}^{\infty} E_i$;
- $E \in \mathcal{P}(\mathbb{R})$;

and let m_1 be its restriction to $\mathbb{B}$, ie, for all $E \in \mathbb{B}$,

$$m_1(E) = (m_0^*)_{\mathbb{B}}(E) \tag{10.24}$$

then, under Theorem 10.4(3), m_1 is one measure on the measurable space $(\mathbb{R}, \mathbb{B})$ and the triple $(\mathbb{R}, \mathbb{B}, m_1)$ identifies a measure space.

Proposition 10.10. *The measure space $(\mathbb{R}, \mathbb{B}, m_1)$ is incomplete.*

Proposition 10.11. *The incomplete measure space $(\mathbb{R}, \mathbb{B}, m_1)$ is associated to the complete measure space $(\mathbb{R}, \widetilde{\mathbb{B}}, \widetilde{m}_1)$ where:*

- $\widetilde{\mathbb{B}}$ *is the σ-algebra derived from $\mathbb{B}$ applying Equation (10.18) in this case, ie,*

$$\widetilde{\mathbb{B}} = \{E \cup F\}$$

   where:

   - $E \in \mathbb{B}$;
   - $F \subseteq D$ *for any $D \in \mathcal{D}^{\mathcal{L}}$;*
   - $\mathcal{D}^{\mathcal{L}}$ *is the class of the negligibles of $\mathbb{B}$;*
- $\widetilde{m}_1$ *is the completion of measure m_1 derived by applying Equation (10.19) in this case, ie,*

$$\widetilde{m}_1(E \cup F) = m_1(E)$$

Corollary 10.7. *The Lebesgue σ-algebra $\widetilde{\mathbb{B}}$ contains the Borel σ-algebra $\mathbb{B}$ (see Equation (10.20)), ie,*

$$\mathbb{B} \subset \widetilde{\mathbb{B}} \tag{10.25}$$

Proposition 10.12. *The Lebesgue measure space, $(\mathbb{R}, \widetilde{\mathbb{B}}, \widetilde{m}_1)$, is σ-finite (see Definition 10.5).*

Definition 10.30. The elements of $\widetilde{\mathbb{B}}$ are said to be *Lebesgue measurable sets* of $\mathbb{R}$ and $\widetilde{\mathbb{B}}$ is said to be the *Lebesgue σ-algebra* in $\mathbb{R}$. A measure $\tilde{m}_1$ is said to be a *Lebesgue measure* in $\mathbb{R}$.

Corollary 10.8. *A measure $\tilde{m}_1$ defined on the measurable space $(\mathbb{R}, \widetilde{\mathbb{B}})$ is the extension of measure m_1 defined on the measurable space $(\mathbb{R}, \mathbb{B})$ from σ-algebra $\mathbb{B}$ to σ-algebra $\widetilde{\mathbb{B}}$ (see Definition 10.23 and Corollary 10.5), ie, for all $E \in \mathbb{B}$ one has*

$$\tilde{m}_1(E) = m_1(E) \tag{10.26}$$

Corollary 10.9. *A measure $\tilde{m}_1$ as in Corollary 10.8 is unique (see Theorem 10.4(4)).*

10.5.2. Properties of Lebesgue measure in $\mathbb{R}$

Proposition 10.13. *Given the measure space $(\mathbb{R}, \widetilde{\mathbb{B}}, \tilde{m}_1)$, the following properties hold.*

(1) Extension of length. *The Lebesgue measure of an interval $I \subseteq \mathbb{R}$ coincides with the length of that interval, ie,*

$$\tilde{m}_1(I) = l(I) \tag{10.27}$$

(2) Countable additivity. *For any sequence $\{E_i\}_{i \in \mathbb{N}}$ of sets belonging to $\widetilde{\mathbb{B}}$ which are disjoint in pairs (ie, $E_i \cap E_j = \varnothing$ for all $i \neq j; i, j = 1, 2, \ldots$), one has*

$$\tilde{m}_1\left(\bigcup_{i=1}^{+\infty} E_i\right) = \sum_{i=1}^{+\infty} \tilde{m}_1(E_i) \tag{10.28}$$

(3) Finite additivity. *For any finite sequence $\{E_i\}_{i=1,2,\ldots,n}$ of sets belonging to $\widetilde{\mathbb{B}}$ which are disjoint in pairs (ie, $E_i \cap E_j = \varnothing$ for all $i \neq j; i, j = 1, 2, \ldots, n$), one has*

$$\tilde{m}_1\left(\bigcup_{i=1}^{n} E_i\right) = \sum_{i=1}^{n} \tilde{m}_1(E_i) \tag{10.29}$$

(4) Monotony. *If $E \subseteq F$, then*

$$\tilde{m}_1(E) \leq \tilde{m}_1(F) \tag{10.30}$$

(5) *If $E \subseteq F$ and $\tilde{m}_1(E) \leq +\infty$, then*

$$\tilde{m}_1(F) - \tilde{m}_1(E) = \tilde{m}_1(F \backslash E) \tag{10.31}$$

(6) Continuity from below. *If $\{E_i\}_{i\in\mathbb{N}} \in \tilde{\mathbb{B}}$ is a sequence of sets so that $E_1 \subseteq E_2 \subseteq \cdots$, and $E = \bigcup_{i=1}^{\infty} E_i$, one has*

$$\tilde{m}_1(E) = \tilde{m}_1\left(\bigcup_{i=1}^{\infty} E_i\right) = \lim_{i\to+\infty} \tilde{m}_1(E_i) \tag{10.32}$$

(7) Continuity conditioned from above. *If $\{E_i\}_{i\in\mathbb{N}} \in \tilde{\mathbb{B}}$ is a sequence of sets so that $E_1 \supseteq E_2 \supseteq \cdots$, and $\tilde{m}_1(E_1) < +\infty$, one has*

$$\lim_{i\to+\infty} \tilde{m}_1(E_i) = \tilde{m}_1\left(\bigcap_{i=1}^{\infty} E_i\right) \tag{10.33}$$

(8) Invariance by translation. *The Lebesgue measure of interval $I \subseteq \mathbb{R}$ is not modified if this interval is translated by x, for all $x \in \mathbb{R}$, x scalar, ie,*

$$\tilde{m}_1(I) = \tilde{m}_1(I + x), \quad \forall x \in \mathbb{R} \tag{10.34}$$

Corollary 10.10. *The Lebesgue measure of a point $a \in \mathbb{R}$, is zero, ie,*

$$\tilde{m}_1(\{a\}) = 0$$

Proposition 10.14. *If μ is an invariant measure by translation on $\mathbb{B}$ with the property that $\mu(K) < +\infty$ for any compact set $K \subseteq \mathbb{B}$, then a non-negative constant γ exists so that*

$$\mu(E) = \gamma\tilde{m}(E), \quad \forall E \in \tilde{\mathbb{B}}$$

10.5.3. Subsets of $\mathbb{R}$ and Lebesgue measure

Based on the finite and countable additivity property of measure and based on Corollary 10.10, the Lebesgue measure of a finite number or a countable infinity of disjoint points which belong to the set $\mathbb{R}$ of real numbers is zero.

More generally, the following theorem holds.

Theorem 10.6. *All of the countable subsets of $\mathbb{R}$ have a Lebesgue measure zero.*

Theorem 10.7. *The necessary and sufficient condition so that a set $E \in \tilde{\mathbb{B}}$ is that two sets $F, G \in \mathbb{B}$ exist so that:*

- $F \subseteq E \subseteq G$;
- $\tilde{m}_1(G\backslash F) = 0$

10.5.3.1.   Uncountable sets with a Lebesgue measure zero: the Cantor ternary set

Theorem 10.6 states that any countable set of $\mathbb{R}$ belongs to $\tilde{\mathbb{B}}$ and has a Lebesgue measure zero.

However, one must observe that there are also uncountable sets belonging to $\tilde{\mathbb{B}}$ which have a null Lebesgue measure. A typical example is the Cantor ternary set. Given an interval $I = [0, 1] \subseteq \mathbb{R}$, this is broken down into three parts and the *middle third*, ie, the interval $(\frac{1}{3}, \frac{2}{3})$, is removed to get the set $C_1 \subseteq \tilde{\mathbb{B}}$ defined as

$$C_1 = [0, \tfrac{1}{3}] \cup [\tfrac{2}{3}, 1]$$

The set C_1 is formed by the union of two closed and disjoint intervals, ie, $[0, \frac{1}{3}]$ and $[\frac{2}{3}, 1]$, each of them having a Lebesgue measure equal to $\frac{1}{3}$ which coincides with its length (see property Proposition 10.13(1)). Then the middle third is taken away from each of the two intervals that make up C_1 to obtain the set $C_2 \subseteq \tilde{\mathbb{B}}$ defined as

$$C_2 = [0, \tfrac{1}{9}] \cup [\tfrac{2}{9}, \tfrac{1}{3}] \cup [\tfrac{2}{3}, \tfrac{7}{9}] \cup [\tfrac{8}{9}, 1]$$

The set C_2 is formed by the union of four closed disjoint pairs, ie, $[0, \frac{1}{9}], [\frac{2}{9}, \frac{1}{3}], [\frac{2}{3}, \frac{7}{9}]$ and $[\frac{8}{9}, 1]$, each of them having a Lebesgue measure equal to $\frac{1}{9}$, which coincides with its length.

By repeating this procedure, at the nth repetition one will get a set $C_n \subseteq \tilde{\mathbb{B}}$ defined as the union of 2^n closed disjoint intervals, each one of them having a length of $1/3^n$. Therefore, the total length of set C_n (and then its Lebesgue measure) is

$$\tilde{m}_1(C_n) = (\tfrac{2}{3})^n \tag{10.35}$$

Definition 10.31. The *Cantor ternary set*, denoted by C, is the closed set defined as

$$C = \bigcap_{n=1}^{+\infty} C_n \tag{10.36}$$

Proposition 10.15. *The Cantor set is uncountable, ie, it has the power of the continuum.*

Proposition 10.16. *Although uncountable, the Cantor set has a Lebesgue measure zero, ie,*

$$\tilde{m}_1(C) = 0 \tag{10.37}$$

10.5.3.2. Uncountable sets according to Lebesgue

The σ-algebra $\widetilde{\mathbb{B}}$ of the complete measure space $(\mathbb{R}, \widetilde{\mathbb{B}}, \widetilde{m}_1)$ does not coincide with the part set of $\mathbb{R}$, $\mathcal{P}(\mathbb{R})$, ie, with the largest σ-algebra containing $\mathbb{R}$ (see Proposition 1.19).

There are some sets contained in $\mathcal{P}(\mathbb{R})$ which do not belong to $\widetilde{\mathbb{B}}$ and then they are not measurable according to $\widetilde{m}_1$.

Given a set Q_1 defined as

$$Q_1 := \mathbb{Q} \cap [-1, 1] \tag{10.38}$$

and the closed interval $[0, 1]$, the equivalence relation (see Definition 1.33) is considered among the elements of this interval and defined as

$$x \overset{G}{\sim} y \Leftrightarrow x - y \in Q_1 \tag{10.39}$$

where $x, y \in [0, 1]$.

Proposition 10.17. *The equivalence relation in Equation (10.39) allows one to partition (see Definition 1.13 and Remark 1.4) interval $[0, 1]$ of the union of the disjoint equivalence classes (see Definition 1.34) E_{α_i} where α_i is the representative of the generic equivalence class E_{α_i}, ie,*

$$[0, 1] = \bigcup_{\alpha_i} E_{\alpha_i} \tag{10.40}$$

and

$$E_{\alpha_i} \cap E_{\alpha_j} = \varnothing, \quad \forall i \neq j \tag{10.41}$$

Proposition 10.18. *Any equivalence class E_{α_i} contains a countable infinity of elements and the number of equivalence classes is infinitely uncountable, ie, the set of the equivalence classes has the power of the continuum (see Definition 1.9).*

Theorem 10.8. *If V is the quotient set (see Definition 1.35) of the closed interval $[0, 1]$ with respect to the equivalence relation 10.39, ie, if*

$$V := \frac{[0, 1]}{\overset{G}{\sim}} \tag{10.42}$$

then V is not a Lebesgue-measurable set, ie,

$$V \notin \widetilde{\mathbb{B}} \tag{10.43}$$

10.5.4. Lebesgue measure in $\mathbb{R}^n$

10.5.4.1. Construction of the Lebesgue measure in $\mathbb{R}^n$

The procedure to construct the Lebesgue measure in $\mathbb{R}^n$ is based on three consecutive steps:

(1) extension of the length function defined on class $\mathcal{I}^n$ of intervals of $\mathbb{R}^n$ to measure m_0 defined on the algebra $\mathcal{E}_n$;
(2) shift from measure m_0 on algebra $\mathcal{E}_n$ to measure m_n on the σ-algebra $\mathbb{B}_n$;
(3) extension, by completion, of measure m_n on the σ-algebra $\mathbb{B}_n$ to measure $\widetilde{m}_n$ on the σ-algebra $\widetilde{\mathbb{B}}_n$.

Definition 10.32. Let $\mathcal{E}_n$ be the algebra of the elementary sets of $\mathbb{R}^n$ and let $E \in \mathcal{E}_n$, ie,

$$E = \bigcup_{i=1}^{N} \mathbf{I}_i$$

where $\{\mathbf{I}_i\}_{i=1,2,\dots,N}$ is a sequence of N intervals of disjoint pairs whose length $l(\mathbf{I}_i)$ (see Definition 1.64). Then function $m_0 : \mathcal{E}_n \to [0, +\infty]$ is defined as

$$m_0(E) := \sum_{i=1}^{N} l(\mathbf{I}_i)$$

Proposition 10.19. *A function m_0 is one measure on algebra $\mathcal{E}_n$, ie,*

(1) $m_0(\varnothing) = 0$;
(2) *if $\{E_i\}_{i \in \mathbb{N}} \in \mathcal{E}_n$ is a sequence of disjoint sets of pairs (ie, $E_i \cap E_j = \varnothing$ for all $i \neq j$, $i, j = 1, 2, \dots$) and $\bigcup_{i=1}^{\infty} E_i \in \mathcal{E}_n$, then*

$$m_0 \left(\bigcup_{i=1}^{\infty} E_i \right) = \sum_{i=1}^{\infty} m_0(E_i)$$

Proposition 10.20. *Let m_0^* be the outer measure on $(\mathbb{R}^n, \mathcal{P}(\mathbb{R}^n))$ defined by*

$$m_0^*(E) := \inf_{\{E_i\}_{i \in \mathbb{N}}} \left\{ \sum_{i=1}^{+\infty} m_0(E_i) \right\}$$

where:

- $E_i \in \mathcal{E}_n$;
- $E \subseteq \bigcup_{i=1}^{+\infty} E_i$;
- $E \in \mathcal{P}(\mathbb{R}^n)$;

and let m_n be its restriction to $\mathbb{B}_n$ (ie, this is the Borel σ-algebra in $\mathbb{R}^n$). Then based on Theorem 10.4(3), m_n is a measure of the measurable space $(\mathbb{R}^n, \mathbb{B}_n)$ and the triple $(\mathbb{R}^n, \mathbb{B}_n, m_n)$ identifies a measure space.

Proposition 10.21. The measure space $(\mathbb{R}^n, \mathbb{B}_n, m_n)$ is incomplete.

Proposition 10.22. The incomplete measure space $(\mathbb{R}^n, \mathbb{B}_n, m_n)$ is associated to the complete measure space $(\mathbb{R}^n, \widetilde{\mathbb{B}}_n, \widetilde{m}_n)$ where:

- $\widetilde{\mathbb{B}}_n$ is the σ-algebra derived from $\mathbb{B}_n$ by using Equation (10.18), ie,

$$\widetilde{\mathbb{B}}_n = \{E \cup F\}$$

  where:

  - $E \in \mathbb{B}_n$;
  - $F \subseteq D$ for any $D \in \mathcal{D}^{\mathcal{L}_n}$;
  - $\mathcal{D}^{\mathcal{L}_n}$ is the class of the negligibles of $\mathbb{B}_n$;

- $\widetilde{m}_n$ is the completion of the measure m_n derived by using Equation (10.19), ie,

$$\widetilde{m}_n(E \cup F) = m_n(E)$$

Definition 10.33. The members of $\widetilde{\mathbb{B}}_n$ are said to be *Lebesgue measurable sets* of $\mathbb{R}^n$ and $\widetilde{\mathbb{B}}_n$ is said to be the *Lebesgue σ-algebra* in $\mathbb{R}^n$. A measure $\widetilde{m}_n$ is said to be the *Lebesgue measure* in $\mathbb{R}^n$.

Corollary 10.11. A measure $\widetilde{m}_n$ defined on the measurable space $(\mathbb{R}^n, \widetilde{\mathbb{B}}_n)$ is the extension of the measure m_n defined on the measurable space $(\mathbb{R}^n, \mathbb{B}_n)$ from σ-algebra $\mathbb{B}_n$ to σ-algebra $\widetilde{\mathbb{B}}_n$ (see Definition 10.23 and Corollary 10.5), ie, for all $E \in \mathbb{B}_n$ one has

$$\widetilde{m}_n(E) = m_n(E) \tag{10.44}$$

Corollary 10.12. A measure $\widetilde{m}_n$ of Corollary 10.11 is unique (see Theorem 10.4(4)).

10.5.4.2. Properties of Lebesgue measure in $\mathbb{R}^n$
Proposition 10.23. The Lebesgue measure in $\mathbb{R}^n$ holds for the following properties.

(1) Extension of length. *The Lebesgue measure in an interval $\mathbf{I} \subseteq \mathbb{R}^n$ coincides with the value of the length function at that interval, ie,*

$$\widetilde{m}_n(\mathbf{I}) = l(\mathbf{I})$$

(2) Countable additivity. *For any sequence $\{E_i\}_{i\in\mathbb{N}}$ of disjoint pairs of sets belonging to $\tilde{\mathbb{B}}_n$ (ie, $E_i \cap E_j = \varnothing$ for all $i \neq j$, $i, j = 1, 2, \ldots$), one has*

$$\tilde{m}_n\left(\bigcup_{i=1}^{+\infty} E_i\right) = \sum_{i=1}^{+\infty} \tilde{m}_n(E_i)$$

(3) Finite additivity. *For any finite sequence $\{E_i\}_{i=1,2,\ldots,n}$ of disjoint pairs of sets belonging to $\tilde{\mathbb{B}}$ (ie, $E_i \cap E_j = \varnothing$ for all $i \neq j$, $i, j = 1, 2, \ldots, n$), one has*

$$\tilde{m}_n\left(\bigcup_{i=1}^{n} E_i\right) = \sum_{i=1}^{n} \tilde{m}_n(E_i)$$

(4) Monotony. *If $E \subseteq F$, then*

$$\tilde{m}_n(E) \leq \tilde{m}_n(F)$$

(5) *If $E \subseteq F$ and $\tilde{m}_n(E) \leq +\infty$, then*

$$\tilde{m}_n(F) - \tilde{m}_n(E) = \tilde{m}_n(F \backslash E)$$

(6) Continuity from below. *If $\{E_i\}_{i\in\mathbb{N}} \in \tilde{\mathbb{B}}_n$ is a sequence of sets so that $E_1 \subseteq E_2 \subseteq \cdots$, and $E = \bigcup_{i=1}^{\infty} E_i$, one has*

$$\tilde{m}_n(E) = \tilde{m}_n\left(\bigcup_{i=1}^{\infty} E_i\right) = \lim_{i\to+\infty} \tilde{m}_n(E_i)$$

(7) Continuity conditioned from above. *If $\{E_i\}_{i\in\mathbb{N}} \in \tilde{\mathbb{B}}_n$ is a sequence so that $E_1 \supseteq E_2 \supseteq \cdots$, and $\tilde{m}_n(E_1) < +\infty$, one has*

$$\lim_{i\to+\infty} \tilde{m}_n(E_i) = \tilde{m}_n\left(\bigcap_{i=1}^{\infty} E_i\right)$$

(8) Translation invariance. *The Lebesgue measure of interval $\mathbf{I} \subseteq \mathbb{R}^n$ does not change if this interval is translated by $\mathbf{x}$, for all $\mathbf{x} \in \mathbb{R}^n$, ie,*

$$\tilde{m}_n(\mathbf{I}) = \tilde{m}_n(\mathbf{I} + \mathbf{x}), \quad \forall \mathbf{x} \in \mathbb{R}^n$$

Corollary 10.13. *The Lebesgue measure of a point $\mathbf{a} \in \mathbb{R}^n$, is zero, ie,*

$$\tilde{m}_n(\{\mathbf{a}\}) = 0$$

Proposition 10.24. *If μ is a translation-invariant measure on $\mathbb{B}_n$ with the property that $\mu(K) < +\infty$ for any compact set $K \subseteq \mathbb{B}_n$, then a non-negative constant γ exists so that*

$$\mu(E) = \gamma\tilde{m}_n(E), \quad \forall E \in \tilde{\mathbb{B}}_n$$

Based on the finite and countable additivity properties of measure and based on Corollary 10.13, the Lebesgue measure of a finite number or a countable infinity of disjoint points which belong to set $\mathbb{R}^n$ is zero.

More generally, the theorem below holds.

Theorem 10.9. *All of the countable subsets of $\mathbb{R}^n$ have a Lebesgue measure zero.*

Theorem 10.10. *The necessary and sufficient condition so that set $E \in \tilde{\mathbb{B}}_n$ is that two sets $F, G \in \mathbb{B}_n$ exist so that:*

- $F \subseteq E \subseteq G$;
- $\tilde{m}_n(G \backslash F) = 0$.

Proposition 10.25. *Let $\tilde{m}_n$ be the Lebesgue measure in $\mathbb{R}^n$. Then the following propositions hold.*

(1) *Any set $E \in \tilde{\mathbb{B}}_n$ may be approximated by open sets of $\mathbb{R}^n$ so that the difference between the Lebesgue measure of these sets and the Lebesgue measure of E may be reduced arbitrarily, ie, for all $E \in \tilde{\mathbb{B}}_n$ one has*

$$\tilde{m}_n(E) = \inf_{A \in \tau^n} \{\tilde{m}_n(A)\}$$

where:

- $A \supseteq E$;
- A is open in $\mathbb{R}^n$, ie, $A \in \tau^n$, a topology in $\mathbb{R}^n$

Also, if $\tilde{m}_n(E) < \infty$, then

$$\tilde{m}_n(E) = \sup_{K \in \mathcal{K}} \{m_0^*(K)\}$$

where:

- $K \subseteq E$;
- $K \in \mathcal{K}$, the class of the compact sets of $\mathbb{R}^n$

(2) *If $T : \mathbb{R}^n \to \mathbb{R}^n$ is a linear transformation, then for any $E \in \tilde{\mathbb{B}}_n$ one has*

$$\tilde{m}_n(T(E)) = |\det(T)| \tilde{m}_n(E)$$

10.6. LEBESGUE–STIELTJES MEASURE IN $\mathbb{R}$

10.6.1. Construction of the Lebesgue–Stieltjes measure in $\mathbb{R}$

The procedure to construct the Lebesgue–Stieltjes measure in $\mathbb{R}$ is based on four consecutive steps:

(1) identification of function F which belongs to the class of the non-decreasing right continuous monotonous functions defined on $\mathbb{R}$;
(2) extension of function μ_0^F defined on class $\mathcal{I}$ of the intervals of $\mathbb{R}$ to measure μ_0^F defined on the algebra $\mathcal{E}_1$;
(3) shift from measure μ_0^F on algebra $\mathcal{E}_1$ to measure μ^F on the σ-algebra $\mathbb{B}$;
(4) extension, by completion, of measure μ^F from σ-algebra $\mathbb{B}$ to measure $\widetilde{\mu}^F$ on σ-algebra $\widetilde{\mathbb{B}}$.

Notation 10.7. The space of the non-decreasing right continuous monotonous functions defined on $\mathbb{R}$ is denoted by $\chi(\mathbb{R})$.

Definition 10.34. Given $F \in \chi(\mathbb{R})$ and $-\infty \leq a \leq b \leq +\infty$, a function μ_0^F on the intervals of $\mathbb{R}$ is defined as

$$
\begin{aligned}
\mu_0^F((a, b)) &= F(b^-) - F(a) \\
\mu_0^F((a, b]) &= F(b) - F(a) \\
\mu_0^F([a, b)) &= F(b^-) - F(a^-) \\
\mu_0^F([a, b]) &= F(b) - F(a^-)
\end{aligned}
\tag{10.45}
$$

where:

- $F(a^-) = \lim_{x \to a^-} F(x)$;
- $F(b^-) = \lim_{x \to b^-} F(x)$.

Remark 10.4. If $F(x) = x$, then a function μ_0^F coincides with the length function (see Definition 1.63) which is also defined on a class $\mathcal{I}$ of the intervals of $\mathbb{R}$, ie,

$$
\mu_0^F(I) = l(I)
\tag{10.46}
$$

where I is one interval contained in $\mathbb{R}$.

Proposition 10.26. *A function μ_0^F is a continuous function on class $\mathcal{I}$ of the intervals of $\mathbb{R}$.*

Definition 10.35. Let $\mathcal{E}_1$ be the algebra of the elementary sets of $\mathbb{R}$ and let $E \in \mathcal{E}_1$, ie,

$$
E = \bigcup_{i=1}^{N} I_i
$$

where $\{I_i\}_{i=1,2,\dots,N}$ is a sequence of N disjoint pairs of intervals whose length is $l(I_i), i = 1, 2, \dots, N$ Then, a function $\widehat{\mu_0^F} : \mathcal{E}_1 \to [0, +\infty]$ is defined as

$$\widehat{\mu_0^F}(E) := \sum_{i=1}^{N} \mu_0^F(I_i) \tag{10.47}$$

Proposition 10.27. *A function $\widehat{\mu_0^F}$ is one measure on the algebra $\mathcal{E}_1$, ie,*

(1) $\widehat{\mu_0^F}(\varnothing) = 0$;
(2) *if $\{E_i\}_{i\in\mathbb{N}} \in \mathcal{E}_1$ is a sequence of disjoint pairs of sets (ie, $E_i \cap E_j = \varnothing$ for all $i \neq j$, $i, j = 1, 2, \dots$) and $\bigcup_{i=1}^{\infty} E_i \in \mathcal{E}_1$, then*

$$\widehat{\mu_0^F}\left(\bigcup_{i=1}^{\infty} E_i\right) = \sum_{i=1}^{\infty} \widehat{\mu_0^F}(E_i)$$

Remark 10.5. A measure $\widehat{\mu_0^F}$ is the extension (under Equation (10.45)) of a function μ_0^F defined on class $\mathcal{I}$ of the intervals of $\mathbb{R}$ to the elements of algebra $\mathcal{E}_1$; this extension is unique (see in Theorem 10.4(4)).

Proposition 10.28. *Let $(\mu_0^F)^*$ be the outer measure on $(\mathbb{R}, \mathcal{P}(\mathbb{R}))$ defined as*

$$(\mu_0^F)^* := \inf_{\{E_i\}_{i\in\mathbb{N}}} \left\{ \sum_{i=1}^{\infty} \widehat{\mu_0^F}(E_i) \right\} \tag{10.48}$$

where:

- $E_i \in \mathcal{E}_1$;
- $E \subseteq \bigcup_{i=1}^{\infty} E_i$;
- $E \in \mathcal{P}(\mathbb{R})$;

and let μ^F be its restriction to $\mathbb{B}$, ie, for all $E \in \mathbb{B}$ one has

$$\mu^F = (\mu_0^F)^*_{\mathbb{B}} \tag{10.49}$$

Then, based on Theorem 10.4(3), μ^F is a measure on the measurable space $(\mathbb{R}, \mathbb{B})$ and the triple $(\mathbb{R}, \mathbb{B}, \mu^F)$ identifies a measure space.

Proposition 10.29. *The measure space $(\mathbb{R}, \mathbb{B}, \mu^F)$ is incomplete.*

Proposition 10.30. *The incomplete measure space $(\mathbb{R}, \mathbb{B}, \mu^F)$ is associated to the complete measure space $(\mathbb{R}, \widetilde{\mathcal{S}}, \widetilde{\mu}^F)$ where:*

- $\tilde{S}$ is the σ-algebra derived from $\mathbb{B}$ by applying Equation (10.18), ie,

$$\tilde{S} = \{E \cup F\}$$

where:

- $E \in \mathbb{B}$;
- $F \subseteq D$ for any $D \in \mathcal{D}^{\mathcal{L}}$;
- $\mathcal{D}^{\mathcal{L}}$ is the class of the negligibles of $\mathbb{B}$;

- $\tilde{\mu}^F$ is the completion of measure μ^F derived by applying Equation (10.19), ie,

$$\tilde{\mu}^F(E \cup F) = \mu^F(E)$$

Definition 10.36. The elements of $\tilde{S}$ are said to be *Lebesgue–Stieltjes measurable sets* of $\mathbb{R}$ and $\tilde{S}$ is said to be the *Lebesgue–Stieltjes σ-algebra* in $\mathbb{R}$. A measure $\tilde{\mu}^F$ is said to be the *Lebesgue–Stieltjes measure* of $\mathbb{R}$ associated to the function $F \in \chi(\mathbb{R})$.

Corollary 10.14. *A measure $\tilde{\mu}^F$ defined on the measurable space $(\mathbb{R}, \tilde{S})$ is the extension of a measure μ^F defined on the measurable space $(\mathbb{R}, \mathbb{B})$ from σ-algebra $\mathbb{B}$ to σ-algebra $\tilde{S}$ (see Definition 10.23 and Corollary 10.5), ie, for all $E \in \mathbb{B}$ one has*

$$\tilde{\mu}^F(E) = \mu^F(E) \tag{10.50}$$

Corollary 10.15. *A measure $\tilde{\mu}^F$ under Corollary 10.14 is unique (see Theorem 10.4(4)).*

Proposition 10.31. *If $F(x) = x$, then $\tilde{\mu}^F$ coincides with the Lebesgue measure in $\mathbb{R}$ (see Remark 10.4), ie, for all $E \in \tilde{\mathbb{B}}$ one has*

$$\tilde{\mu}^F(E) = \tilde{m}_1(E)$$

therefore, the following equivalence holds:

$$(\mathbb{R}, \tilde{S}, \tilde{\mu}^F) = (\mathbb{R}, \tilde{\mathbb{B}}, \tilde{m}_1) \tag{10.51}$$

Proposition 10.32. *If*

$$F(x) = \mathbf{1}_{[0,+\infty)}(x) \equiv \begin{cases} 1 & \text{if } x \geq 0 \\ 0 & \text{if } x < 0 \end{cases}$$

then the Lebesgue–Stieltjes measure $\tilde{\mu}^F$ is defined on the measurable space $(\mathbb{R}, \mathcal{P}(\mathbb{R}))$. It coincides with the Dirac measured centred at the origin, ie, for all $E \in \mathcal{P}(\mathbb{R})$ one has

$$\tilde{\mu}^F(E) = \delta_0(E) = \begin{cases} 1 & \text{if } 0 \in E \\ 0 & \text{elsewhere} \end{cases} \tag{10.52}$$

Proposition 10.33. *The σ-algebra $\widetilde{\mathcal{S}}$ contains $\mathbb{B}$ by construction and depends on the choice of $F \in \chi(\mathbb{R})$.*

10.6.2. Properties of Lebesgue–Stieltjes measures

Proposition 10.34. *The Lebesgue–Stieltjes measure in an interval $I \subseteq \mathbb{R}$ coincides with the value taken by function μ_0^F defined in Equation (10.45) at that interval, ie,*

$$\widetilde{\mu}^F(I) = \mu_0^F(I) \tag{10.53}$$

Corollary 10.16. *For any interval $I \subseteq \mathbb{R}$, the following equivalence holds:*

$$\mu_0^F(I) = \mu^F(I) \tag{10.54}$$

Proposition 10.35. *The Lebesgue–Stieltjes measure in $\mathbb{R}$ is countably additive, finitely additive, monotonous, continuous from below and continuous conditioned from above.*

Proposition 10.36. *Let F and G be two non-decreasing right continuous functions which belong to $\chi(\mathbb{R})$, ie, then*

$$\mu^F = \mu^G \Leftrightarrow F - G = k, \quad k \text{ a constant}$$

Proposition 10.37. *Let $F \in \chi(\mathbb{R})$ and $x \in \mathbb{R}$. Then*

$$\mu^F(x) = 0 \Leftrightarrow F \text{ continuous in } x$$

Proposition 10.38. *Let $\{F_n(x)\}_{n \in \mathbb{N}}$ be a sequence of functions belonging to $\chi(\mathbb{R})$. If $\sum_{n=1}^{+\infty} F_n(x) = F(x)$, then*

$$\mu^F = \sum_{n=1}^{+\infty} \mu^{F_n}$$

10.7. MEASURABLE FUNCTIONS

10.7.1. Basics

Definition 10.37. Let X and X' be two sets and $f \colon X \to X'$. Also, let $\mathcal{G}' \subseteq \mathcal{P}(X')$. Then the following equivalence holds:

$$f^{-1}(\mathcal{G}') := \{f^{-1}(A') : A' \in \mathcal{G}'\} \tag{10.55}$$

Proposition 10.39. *Let X and X' be two sets and $f : X \to X'$. Then for all $F \in X'$ the following equivalence holds:*

$$f^{-1}(F^c) = [f^{-1}(F)]^c \tag{10.56}$$

and for all $\{F_i\}_{i \in \mathbb{N}} \in X'$ the following equivalence holds:

$$f^{-1}\left(\bigcup_{i=1}^{+\infty} F_i\right) = \bigcup_{i=1}^{+\infty} f^{-1}(F_i) \tag{10.57}$$

Theorem 10.11. *Let X and X' be two sets and $f : X \to X'$. If $\mathcal{M}'$ is a σ-algebra in X', then for all $F \in \mathcal{M}'$ the family of subsets of X defined as*

$$f^{-1}(\mathcal{M}') := \{E \subseteq X : E = f^{-1}(F)\} \tag{10.58}$$

is a σ-algebra in X, defined to be the counter-image *of the σ-algebra M' by f.*

Proposition 10.40. *Let X and X' be two sets and let $f : X \to X'$. Also, let $\mathcal{G}'$ and $\mathcal{H}'$ be two families of subsets of X' so that*

$$\mathcal{G}' \subseteq \mathcal{H}'$$

Then

$$f^{-1}(\mathcal{G}') \subseteq f^{-1}(\mathcal{H}') \tag{10.59}$$

Proposition 10.41. *Let X, X', X'' be sets, let $f : X \to X'$ and $h : X' \to X''$. Also, let $\mathcal{G}''$ be a family of subsets of X''. Then, after defining the compound function, $h(f(X))$, also denoted as $(h \circ f) : X \to X''$, and if (see Definition 10.37).*

$$(h \circ f)^{-1}(\mathcal{G}'') := \{(h \circ f)^{-1}(A'') : A'' \in \mathcal{G}''\}$$

the following equivalence holds:

$$f^{-1}(h^{-1}(\mathcal{G}'')) = (h \circ f)^{-1}(\mathcal{G}'') \tag{10.60}$$

Theorem 10.12. *Let X and X' be sets and let $f : X \to X'$. Also, let $\mathcal{G}'$ be a family of subsets of X' and let $\sigma(\mathcal{G}')$ be the σ-algebra generated by $\mathcal{G}'$. Then, the following equivalence holds:*

$$\sigma(f^{-1}(\mathcal{G}')) = f^{-1}(\sigma(\mathcal{G}')) \tag{10.61}$$

Definition 10.38. A function $f : (X, \mathcal{M}) \to (X', \mathcal{M}')$ is said to be *measurable* if for any set $F \in \mathcal{M}'$ its counter-image through f belongs to $\mathcal{M}$, ie, if

$$f^{-1}(F) \in \mathcal{M}, \quad \forall F \in \mathcal{M}' \tag{10.62}$$

or if

$$f^{-1}(\mathcal{M}') \subseteq \mathcal{M} \tag{10.63}$$

Notation 10.8. The notation below is used to denote that $f : (X, \mathcal{M}) \to (X', \mathcal{M}')$ is a measurable function under Definition 10.38:

$$f \in \mathrm{Meas}((X, \mathcal{M}), (X', \mathcal{M}'))$$

Criterion 10.1 (Measurability of a function). *Let* $(X, \mathcal{M})$ *and* $(X', \mathcal{M}')$ *be two measurable spaces and let* $\mathcal{G}'$ *be a class of subsets of* X'. *Also, let*

$$\mathcal{M}' = \sigma(\mathcal{G}') \tag{10.64}$$

Then, given any function $f : (X, \mathcal{M}) \to (X', \mathcal{M}')$, *the following two statements are equivalent:*

(1) $f \in \mathrm{Meas}((X, \mathcal{M}), (X', \mathcal{M}'))$;
(2) $f^{-1}(\mathcal{G}') \subseteq \mathcal{M}$.

Criterion 10.2 (Measurability of a function of real values). *Let* $(X, \mathcal{M})$ *and* $(\mathbb{R}, \mathbb{B})$ *be two measurable spaces and let be* τ *a topology on* $\mathbb{R}$. *Also, let (see Definition 1.105)*

$$4\mathbb{B} \equiv \sigma(\tau) \tag{10.65}$$

Then, given any function $f : (X, \mathcal{M}) \to (\mathbb{R}, \mathbb{B})$, *the following two statements are equivalent:*

(1) $f \in \mathrm{Meas}((X, \mathcal{M}), (\mathbb{R}, \mathbb{B}))$;
(2) $f^{-1}(\tau) \subseteq \mathcal{M}$.

Proposition 10.42. *Given a function* $f : (\mathbb{R}^n, \mathbb{B}_n) \to (\mathbb{R}, \mathbb{B})$, *if this is continuous, then it is also measurable, ie,*

$$f \in \mathrm{Meas}((\mathbb{R}^n, \mathbb{B}_n), (\mathbb{R}, \mathbb{B}))$$

Proposition 10.43. *The composition of measurable functions is a measurable function.*

Definition 10.39. Let $f : X \to \overline{\mathbb{R}}$. For any $t \in \mathbb{R}$, the *upper level set t of f*, denoted by $lev_{>t}(f)$, is the set defined as follows:

$$lev_{>t}(f) := \{x \in X : f(x) > t\} \tag{10.66}$$

Definition 10.40. Let $f : X \to \overline{\mathbb{R}}$. For any $t \in \mathbb{R}$, the *upper or equal level set t of f*, denoted by $lev_{\geq t}(f)$, is the set defined as follows:

$$lev_{\geq t}(f) := \{x \in X : f(x) \geq t\} \tag{10.67}$$

Definition 10.41. Let $f : X \to \overline{\mathbb{R}}$. For any $t \in \mathbb{R}$, the *lower level set t of f*, denoted by $lev_{<t}(f)$, is the set defined as follows:

$$lev_{<t}(f) := \{x \in X : f(x) < t\} \tag{10.68}$$

Definition 10.42. Let $f : X \to \overline{\mathbb{R}}$. For any $t \in \mathbb{R}$, the *lower or equal level set t of f*, denoted by $lev_{\leq t}(f)$, is the set defined as follows:

$$lev_{\leq t}(f) := \{x \in X : f(x) \leq t\} \tag{10.69}$$

Proposition 10.44. *Let $f : X \to \overline{\mathbb{R}}$. Then:*

- *the upper level set t of f as under Definition 10.39 admits the following representation which is equivalent to Equation (10.66).*

$$lev_{>t}(f) = \{x \in X : x \in f^{-1}((t, +\infty])\} \tag{10.70}$$

- *the upper or equal level set t of f as under Definition 10.40 admits the following representation which is equivalent to Equation (10.67)*

$$lev_{\geq t}(f) = \{x \in X : x \in f^{-1}([t, +\infty])\} \tag{10.71}$$

- *the lower level set t of f as under Definition 10.41 admits the following representation which is equivalent to Equation (10.68)*

$$lev_{<t}(f) = \{x \in X : x \in f^{-1}((-\infty, t])\} \tag{10.72}$$

- *the lower or equal level set t of f as under Definition 10.42 admits the following representation which is equivalent to Equation (10.69)*

$$lev_{\leq t}(f) = \{x \in X : x \in f^{-1}([-\infty, t])\} \tag{10.73}$$

Proposition 10.45. *Let $(X, \mathcal{M})$ be a measurable space and let $f \in$ Meas$(((X, \mathcal{M})), (\overline{\mathbb{R}}, \overline{\mathcal{B}}))$. Then the following relations hold:*

(1) *for all $t \in \mathbb{R}$ one has $lev_{>t}(f) \subseteq \mathcal{M}$;*
(2) *for all $t \in \mathbb{R}$ one has $lev_{\leq t}(f) \subseteq \mathcal{M}$;*
(3) *for all $t \in \mathbb{R}$ one has $lev_{<t}(f) \subseteq \mathcal{M}$;*
(4) *for all $t \in \mathbb{R}$ one has $lev_{\geq t}(f) \subseteq \mathcal{M}$.*

10.7.2. Properties of measurable functions

Proposition 10.46. *Let f, g and $\{f_n\}_{n \in \mathbb{N}}$ be functions which belong to function class* Meas$((X, \mathcal{M}), (\overline{\mathbb{R}}, \overline{\mathbb{B}}))$ *and let α, $\beta \in \mathbb{R}$. Then the functions in the following table also belong to function class* Meas$((X, \mathcal{M}), (\overline{\mathbb{R}}, \overline{\mathbb{B}}))$.

$\alpha f + \beta g$
$\min(f, g)$
$\max(f, g)$
$\|f\|$
$\sup_{n \in \mathbb{N}} f_n$
$\inf_{n \in \mathbb{N}} f_n$
$\lim \sup_{n \to +\infty} f_n$
$\lim \inf_{n \to +\infty} f_n$

Definition 10.43. Let $(X, \mathcal{M})$ be a measurable space, let E be one element of $\mathcal{M}$ and let $f : E \to \overline{\mathbb{R}}$. Then the function $f^\# : \mathcal{M} \to \overline{\mathbb{R}}$ defined as

$$f^\#(x) := \begin{cases} f(x) & \text{if } x \in E \\ 0 & \text{if } x \in E^c \end{cases} \tag{10.74}$$

belongs to the class Meas$((X, \mathcal{M}), (\overline{\mathbb{R}}, \overline{\mathbb{B}}))$ and f is defined as the *restriction of a measurable function*.

Proposition 10.47. *Let $f : E \to \overline{\mathbb{R}}$. The following conditions are equivalent:*

(1) $f \in$ Meas$((E, \mathcal{M}_E), (\overline{\mathbb{R}}, \overline{\mathbb{B}}))$;
(2) $f^\# \in$ Meas$((X, \mathcal{M}), (\overline{\mathbb{R}}, \overline{\mathbb{B}}))$.

10.7.3. Simple functions

Definition 10.44. Given the measurable space $(X, \mathcal{M})$, a function $s : X \to \mathbb{R}$ is said to be a *simple function* if:

(i) $s \in$ Meas$((X, \mathcal{M}), (\mathbb{R}, \mathbb{B}))$;
(ii) s takes a finite number of values, ie,

$$s(x) = \begin{cases} a_1 & \text{if } x \in E_1 \\ a_2 & \text{if } x \in E_2 \\ \vdots \\ a_N & \text{if } x \in E_N \end{cases} \tag{10.75}$$

where $E_i = \{x \in X : s(x) = a_i\}$ for $i = 1, 2, \ldots, N$.

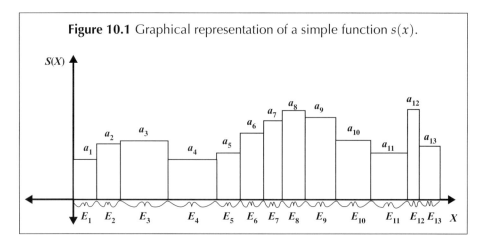

Figure 10.1 Graphical representation of a simple function $s(x)$.

The graphical representation of a generic simple function $s(x)$ is reported in Figure 10.1.

Proposition 10.48. *Let $s : X \to \mathbb{R}$ be a simple function defined on the measurable space $(X, \mathcal{M})$ and let $a_1, a_2, \ldots, a_N$ be the values of s. Then s may be denoted by (ie, simple function standard representation)*

$$s(x) = \sum_{i=1}^{N} a_i \mathbf{1}_{(E_i)}(x) \tag{10.76}$$

where $E_i = \{x \in X : s(x) = a_i\}$.

Theorem 10.13. *Let $(X, \mathcal{M})$ be a measurable space and $f : X \to \mathbb{R}$ be a measurable function. Then the following statements hold:*

(1) *a sequence $\{s_n\}_{n \in \mathbb{N}}$ of simple functions defined in X and of values in $\mathbb{R}$ exists and converges punctually (see Definition 3.10) to f, ie,*

$$\exists \{s_n\}_{n \in \mathbb{N}} \ni' s_n \to f \tag{10.77}$$

(2) *if $f \geq 0$, then a sequence $\{s_n\}_{n \in \mathbb{N}}$ of simple functions defined in X and of values in $[0, +\infty]$ exists, and converges punctually to f from below (see Definition 3.11), ie,*

$$\exists \{s_n\}_{n \in \mathbb{N}} \ni' 0 \leq s_n \uparrow f \tag{10.78}$$

(3) *if f is bounded, then a sequence $\{s_n\}_{n \in \mathbb{N}}$ of simple functions defined in X and of values in $\mathbb{R}$ exists and converges uniformly (see Definition 3.13) to f, ie,*

$$\exists \{s_n\}_{n \in \mathbb{N}} \ni' \{s_n\}_{n \in \mathbb{N}} \overset{uni}{\to} f \tag{10.79}$$

10.8. THE LEBESGUE INTEGRAL (ie, ABSTRACT INTEGRAL)

10.8.1. The Lebesgue integral for simple non-negative functions

Definition 10.45. Let $(X, \mathcal{M}, \mu)$ be a measure space and let $s : X \to [0, +\infty]$, ie, a simple non-negative function, whose standard representation is (see Equation (10.76)) $\sum_{i=1}^{N} a_i \mathbf{1}_{(E_i)}$.

The Lebesgue integral of s on X with respect to μ, denoted by $\int_X s(x) \, d\mu(x)$, is defined as the following quantity:

$$\int_X s(x) \, d\mu(x) := \sum_{i=1}^{N} a_i \mu(E_i) \tag{10.80}$$

and, by convention, $0 \times \infty = 0$.

Notation 10.9. Often, instead of denoting the abstract integral of s on X with respect to μ by $\int_X s(x) \, d\mu(x)$, one may write

$$\int_X s(x) \mu \, (dx)$$

or

$$\int_X s \, d\mu$$

Proposition 10.49. *Let $(X, \mathcal{M}, \mu)$ be a measure space and $s : X \to [0, +\infty]$ be a simple non-negative function. Then, given $E \subseteq X$, the following relation holds:*

$$\int_X s(x) \, d\mu(x) = \int_E s(x) \, d\mu(x) + \int_{X \setminus E} s(x) \, d\mu(x) \tag{10.81}$$

Definition 10.46. Let $(X, \mathcal{M}, \mu)$ be a measure space and let $s : X \to [0, +\infty]$, ie, a simple non-negative function, whose standard representation is

$$s(x) := \sum_{i=1}^{N} a_i \mathbf{1}_{(E_i)}(x)$$

For any $E \in \mathcal{M}$, the abstract integral or Lebesgue integral of s on E with respect to μ, denoted by $\int_E s(x) \, d\mu(x)$, is defined as

$$\int_E s(x) \, d\mu(x) := \sum_{i=1}^{N} a_i \mu(E_i \cap E) \tag{10.82}$$

or

$$\int_E s(x) \, d\mu(x) := \int_X \mathbf{1}_{(E)} s(x) \, d\mu(x) \tag{10.83}$$

and, by convention, $0 \times \infty = 0$.

Remark 10.6. If $s(x) = 1$ for all $x \in E$, $E \in \mathcal{M}$, then

$$\int_E 1 \, d\mu(x) = \mu(E) \tag{10.84}$$

Proposition 10.50. *Let* $(X, \mathcal{M}, \mu)$ *be a measure space, let* E *be a subset of* X *so that* $E \in \mathcal{M}$ *and* $s : E \to [0, +\infty]$, *ie, a simple non-negative function whose standard representation is*

$$s(x) := \sum_{i=1}^{N} a_i \mathbf{1}_{(E_i)}(x)$$

Also, let $(E, \mathcal{M}_E, \mu_E)$ *be a measure space where* μ_E *is the restriction of measure* μ *to set* E *and* $\mathcal{M}_E$ *is the restriction of the* σ-*algebra* $\mathcal{M}$ *to set* E [1].

Then the abstract integral of s *on the subset* E *of* X *with respect to measure* μ *coincides with the abstract integral of* s *on set* E *with respect to measure* μ_E, *ie,*

$$\int_E s(x) \, d\mu(x) = \int_E s(x) \, d\mu_E(x) \tag{10.85}$$

Corollary 10.17. *Let* $(X, \mathcal{M}, \mu)$ *be a measure space, let* E *be a subset of* X *so that* $E \in \mathcal{M}$ *and let* $s : E \to [0, +\infty]$, *ie, a simple non-negative function. Then if* $\mu(E) = 0$, *one has*

$$\int_E s(x) \, d\mu(x) = 0 \tag{10.86}$$

10.8.1.1. Properties of the Lebesgue integral for simple non-negative functions
Proposition 10.51. *Let* $(X, \mathcal{M}, \mu)$ *be a measure space and let* $s : X \to [0, +\infty]$ *and* $t : X \to [0, +\infty]$ *be two simple functions whose standard representation is, respectively,*

$$s(x) := \sum_{i=1}^{N} a_i \mathbf{1}_{(E_i)}(x) \tag{10.87}$$

and

$$t(x) := \sum_{j=1}^{M} b_j \mathbf{1}_{(F_j)}(x) \tag{10.88}$$

Then the following relations hold:

(1) *For all* $c \in [0, +\infty)$, *one has*

$$\int_X c \cdot s(x) \, d\mu(x) = c \cdot \int_X s(x) \, d\mu(x) \tag{10.89}$$

---

[1]Alternatively, μ_E is the measure defined on the σ-algebra $\mathcal{M}_E$ as in Equation (10.5); see Definitions 1.100 and 10.6, Notation 10.1 and Proposition 10.2.

(2) *If $E \in \mathcal{M}$ is a set so that for all $x \in E$ the following holds:*

$$s(x) = 0 \qquad (10.90)$$

  one has

$$\int_E s(x)\, d\mu(x) = 0 \qquad (10.91)$$

(3) *For any pair of sets $E, F \in \mathcal{M}$ so that $E \subseteq F$, one has*

$$\int_E s(x)\, d\mu(x) \leq \int_F s(x)\, d\mu(x) \qquad (10.92)$$

(4) *The following equivalence holds:*

$$\int_X (s(x) + t(x))\, d\mu(x) = \int_X s(x)\, d\mu(x) + \int_X t(x)\, d\mu(x) \qquad (10.93)$$

(5) *If for all $x \in X$ the following holds:*

$$s(x) \leq t(x) \qquad (10.94)$$

  one has

$$\int_X s(x)\, d\mu(x) \leq \int_X t(x)\, d\mu(x) \qquad (10.95)$$

10.8.2. Lebesgue integral for non-negative functions

Definition 10.47. Let $(X, \mathcal{M}, \mu)$ be a measure space and let $f : X \to [0, +\infty]$ be a non-negative function which belongs to the class $\mathrm{Meas}(X, \mathcal{M}), ([0, +\infty], \overline{\mathbb{B}}_{[0,+\infty]})$. The *abstract integral or Lebesgue integral* of f on X with respect to μ, denoted by $\int_X f(x)\, d\mu(x)$, is defined as

$$\int_X f(x)\, d\mu(x) = \sup_{0 \leq s(x) \leq f(x)} \int_X s(x)\, d\mu(x) \qquad (10.96)$$

and, by convention, $0 \times \infty = 0$.

Notation 10.10. Often, instead of denoting the abstract integral of f on X with respect to μ by $\int_X f(x)\, d\mu(x)$, one may write

$$\int_X f(x)\mu\,(dx)$$

or

$$\int_X f\, d\mu$$

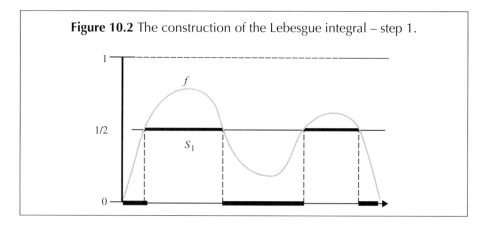

Figure 10.2 The construction of the Lebesgue integral – step 1.

Remark 10.7. Under Definition 10.47, the Lebesgue integral of a measurable non-negative function is a non-negative quantity, ie,

$$\int_X f(x)\, d\mu(x) \geq 0 \qquad (10.97)$$

More specifically, it may be

$$\int_X f(x)\, d\mu(x) = +\infty \qquad (10.98)$$

Remark 10.8 (Intuitive interpretation of the Lebesgue integral). Figures 10.2–10.5 provide an intuitive interpretation about the meaning of Equation (10.96) which defines the Lebesgue integral of a measurable non-negative function f. As a matter of fact, they show that this integral is actually the integral of the boundary of the sequence of simple functions $\{s_n\}_{n\in\mathbb{N}}$, which, under Equation (10.78), is punctually and monotonically convergent from below to function f.

Notation 10.11. Often, given the complete measure space $(\mathbb{R}, \widetilde{\mathbb{B}}, \widetilde{m}_1)$ and given a non-negative function $f : \mathbb{R} \to [0, +\infty]$ which belongs to class $\text{Meas}((\mathbb{R}, \widetilde{\mathbb{B}}), ([0, +\infty], \overline{\mathbb{B}}_{[0,+\infty]}))$, the abstract integral of f on $\mathbb{R}$ with respect to the Lebesgue measure, $\widetilde{m}_1$, is expressed by denoting dx instead of $d\widetilde{m}_1(x)$, ie,

$$\int_{\mathbb{R}} f(x)\, d\widetilde{m}_1(x) \equiv \int_{\mathbb{R}} f(x)\, dx$$

Proposition 10.52. *Let $(X, \mathcal{M}, \mu)$ be a measure space and let $f : X \to [0, +\infty]$ be a non-negative function which belongs to the class* $\text{Meas}((X, \mathcal{M}), ([0, +\infty], \overline{\mathbb{B}}_{[0,+\infty]}))$,

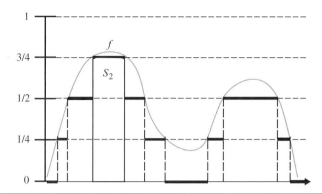

Figure 10.3 The construction of the Lebesgue integral – step 2.

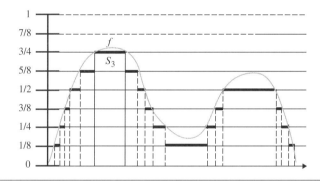

Figure 10.4 The construction of the Lebesgue integral – step 3.

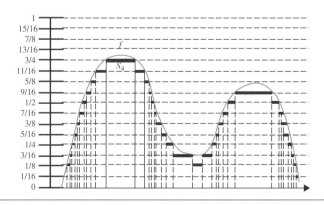

Figure 10.5 The construction of the Lebesgue integral – step 4.

then, given $E \subseteq X$, the following relation holds:

$$\int_X f(x)\, d\mu(x) = \int_E f(x)\, d\mu(x) + \int_{X \setminus E} f(x)\, d\mu(x) \tag{10.99}$$

Definition 10.48. Let $(X, \mathcal{M}, \mu)$ be a measure space and let $f : X \rightarrow [0, +\infty]$ be a non-negative function which belongs to the class $\mathrm{Meas}((X, \mathcal{M}), ([0, +\infty], \overline{\mathbb{B}}_{[0,+\infty]}))$. For any $E \in \mathcal{M}$, the *abstract integral* or *Lebesgue integral of f on E with respect to μ*, denoted by $\int_E f(x)\, d\mu(x)$, is defined as

$$\int_E f(x)\, d\mu(x) := \int_X \mathbf{1}_{(E)}(x) f(x)\, d\mu(x) \tag{10.100}$$

and, by convention, $0 \times \infty = 0$.

Remark 10.9. If $f(x) = 1$ for all $x \in E$, $E \in \mathcal{M}$, then one has

$$\int_E 1\, d\mu(x) = \mu(E) \tag{10.101}$$

Proposition 10.53. *Let $(X, \mathcal{M}, \mu)$ be a measure space, let E be a subset of X so that $E \in \mathcal{M}$ and let $f : E \rightarrow [0, +\infty]$ be a non-negative function which belongs to the class $\mathrm{Meas}((E, \mathcal{M}_E), ([0, +\infty], \overline{\mathbb{B}}_{[0,+\infty]}))$. Also, let $(E, \mathcal{M}_E, \mu_E)$ be the measure space where μ_E is the restriction of measure μ to set E and $\mathcal{M}_E$ is the restriction of the σ-algebra $\mathcal{M}$ to set E [2]. Then the abstract integral of f on subset E of X with respect to measure μ coincides with the abstract integral of f on set E with respect to measure μ_E, ie,*

$$\int_E f(x)\, d\mu(x) = \int_E f(x)\, d\mu_E(x) \tag{10.102}$$

Corollary 10.18. *Let $(X, \mathcal{M}, \mu)$ be a measure space, let E be a subset of X so that $E \in \mathcal{M}$ and let $f : E \rightarrow [0, +\infty]$ be a non-negative function which belongs to the class $\mathrm{Meas}((E, \mathcal{M}_E), ([0, +\infty], \overline{\mathbb{B}}_{[0,+\infty]}))$. Then, if $\mu(E) = 0$, one has*

$$\int_E f(x)\, d\mu(x) = 0 \tag{10.103}$$

---

[2]Alternatively, μ_E is the measure defined on the σ-algebra $\mathcal{M}_E$ as in Equation (10.5); see Definitions 1.100 and 10.6, Notation 10.1 and Proposition 10.2

10.8.2.1. Properties of the Lebesgue integral for non-negative functions

Proposition 10.54. *Let* $(X, \mathcal{M}, \mu)$ *be a measure space and let* $f : X \to [0, +\infty]$ *and* $g : X \to [0, +\infty]$ *be two non-negative functions which belong to the class* $\mathrm{Meas}((X, \mathcal{M}), ([0, +\infty], \overline{\mathbb{B}}_{[0,+\infty]}))$. *Then the following relations hold.*

(1) *For all* $c \in [0, +\infty)$, *one has*

$$\int_X c \cdot f(x)\, d\mu(x) = c \cdot \int_X f(x)\, d\mu(x) \tag{10.104}$$

(2) *If* $E \in \mathcal{M}$ *is a set so that for all* $x \in E$ *the following holds:*

$$f(x) = 0 \tag{10.105}$$

one has

$$\int_E f(x)\, d\mu(x) = 0 \tag{10.106}$$

(3) *For any pair of sets* $E, F \in \mathcal{M}$ *so that* $E \subseteq F$, *one has*

$$\int_E f(x)\, d\mu(x) \le \int_F f(x)\, d\mu(x) \tag{10.107}$$

(4) *The following equivalence holds:*

$$\int_X (f(x) + g(x))\, d\mu(x) = \int_X f(x)\, d\mu(x) + \int_X g(x)\, d\mu(x) \tag{10.108}$$

(5) *If for all* $x \in X$, *the following holds:*

$$f(x) \le g(x) \tag{10.109}$$

one has

$$\int_X f(x)\, d\mu(x) \le \int_X g(x)\, d\mu(x) \tag{10.110}$$

10.8.2.2. Theorems of monotonous convergence

Lemma 10.1 (Fatou's lemma). *Let* $(X, \mathcal{M}, \mu)$ *be a measure space and let* $\{f_n(x)\}_{n \in \mathbb{N}} : X \to [0, +\infty]$ *be a sequence of non-negative functions belonging to the class* $\mathrm{Meas}((X, \mathcal{M}), ([0, +\infty], \overline{\mathbb{B}}_{[0,+\infty]}))$. *If* $\lim \inf_{n \to +\infty} f_n(x)$ *and* $\lim \sup_{n \to +\infty} f_n(x)$ *exist, then the following inequality holds:*

$$\int_X \lim_{n \to +\infty} \inf f_n(x)\, d\mu(x) \le \lim_{n \to +\infty} \inf \int_X f_n(x)\, d\mu(x) \tag{10.111}$$

Theorem 10.14 (Monotonous convergence). *Let $(X, \mathcal{M}, \mu)$ be a measure space and let $\{f_n(x)\}_{n \in \mathbb{N}} : X \to [0, +\infty]$ be a sequence of non-negative functions which belong to the class* $\text{Meas}((X, \mathcal{M}), ([0, +\infty], \overline{\mathbb{B}}_{[0,+\infty]}))$ *and which are punctually and monotonically convergent from below (see Definition 3.11) to a function* $f(x) \in \text{Meas}((X, \mathcal{M}), ([0, +\infty], \overline{\mathbb{B}}_{[0,+\infty]}))$, *ie,*

(i)   *for all $x \in X$, one has $0 \leq f_1(x) \leq f_2(x) \leq \cdots$;*
(ii) $\lim_{n \to +\infty} f_n(x) = f(x)$.

Then the following equivalence holds:

$$\int_X f(x) \, d\mu(x) = \lim_{n \to +\infty} \int_X f_n(x) \, d\mu(x) \tag{10.112}$$

Remark 10.10. Theorem 10.14 states that, under the theorem above, limit and integral operators may be switched.

Corollary 10.19. *Let $(X, \mathcal{M}, \mu)$ be a measure space and let f and g be two non-negative functions which belong to the class* $\text{Meas}((X, \mathcal{M}), ([0, +\infty], \overline{\mathbb{B}}_{[0,+\infty]}))$. *Then the following equivalence holds:*

$$\int_X (f(x) + g(x)) \, d\mu(x) = \int_X f(x) \, d\mu(x) + \int_X g(x) \, d\mu(x) \tag{10.113}$$

Corollary 10.20. *Given the measure space $(X, \mathcal{M}, \mu)$, let $\sum_{n=1}^{+\infty} f_n(x)$ be a series of functions whose general term, $f_n(x)$, is made up of non-negative functions belonging to the class* $\text{Meas}((X, \mathcal{M}), ([0, +\infty], \overline{\mathbb{B}}_{[0,+\infty]}))$. *Let us assume that the series converges to the sum function* $f(x) \in \text{Meas}((X, \mathcal{M}), ([0, +\infty], \overline{\mathbb{B}}_{[0,+\infty]}))$, *ie,*

$$\sum_{n=1}^{+\infty} f_n(x) = f(x) \tag{10.114}$$

Then the following equivalence holds:

$$\int_X f(x) \, d\mu(x) = \sum_{n=1}^{+\infty} \int_X f_n(x) \, d\mu(x) \tag{10.115}$$

10.8.3. Lebesgue integral for any sign function (ie, belonging to space $\mathcal{L}^1(\mu)$)
Definition 10.49. Given a function $f : X \to \mathbb{R}$, the *positive part* and the *negative part of f* are the functions

$$f^+ := \max(f, 0) \quad \text{and} \quad f^- := \max(-f, 0) \tag{10.116}$$

Remark 10.11. The following relations hold:

(1) $f^+ \geq 0$;
(2) $f^- \geq 0$;
(3) $f = f^+ - f^-$;
(4) $|f| = f^+ + f^-$.

Definition 10.50. Let $(X, \mathcal{M}, \mu)$ be a measure space and let $f : X \to \overline{\mathbb{R}}$ be a function belonging to the class $\text{Meas}((X, \mathcal{M}), (\overline{\mathbb{R}}, \overline{\mathcal{B}}))$. The function f is said to be *integrable* (in an abstract sense) *on X with respect to μ* if the following condition holds:

$$\int_X |f(x)| \, d\mu(x) < +\infty \tag{10.117}$$

Definition 10.51. The space $\mathcal{L}^1(X, \mathcal{M}, \mu)$ is defined to be the space of measurable functions which are integrable on the measure space $(X, \mathcal{M}, \mu)$, ie,

$$\mathcal{L}^1(X, \mathcal{M}, \mu) \equiv \left\{ f \text{ measurable } \ni' \int_X |f(x)| \, d\mu(x) < +\infty \right\} \tag{10.118}$$

Notation 10.12. The space $\mathcal{L}^1(X, \mathcal{M}, \mu)$ is also often denoted by $\mathcal{L}^1(\mu)$.

Definition 10.52. Let $(X, \mathcal{M}, \mu)$ be a measure space and let $f : X \to \overline{\mathbb{R}}$ be a function which belongs to the space $\mathcal{L}^1(\mu)$. The quantity below is defined to be the *abstract integral or the Lebesgue integral of f on X with respect to μ*, and is denoted by $\int_X f(x) \, d\mu(x)$:

$$\int_X f(x) \, d\mu(x) = \int_X f^+(x) \, d\mu(x) - \int_X f^-(x) \, d\mu(x) \tag{10.119}$$

where:

- f^+ and f^- are the positive and the negative parts of f, respectively;
- by convention, one has $0 \times \infty = 0$.

The graphical representation of the function f and of the corresponding f^+ and f^- is given in Figure 10.6.

Notation 10.13. Often, instead of $\int_X f(x) \, d\mu(x)$ one may denote the abstract integral of f on X with respect to μ by

$$\int_X f(x) \mu \, (dx)$$

or

$$\int_X f \, d\mu$$

Figure 10.6 Graphical representation of the function f and the corresponding f^+ and f^-.

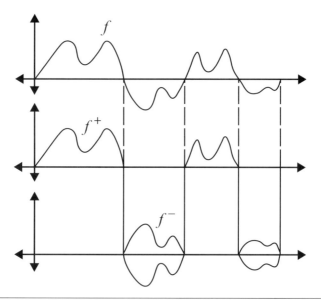

Remark 10.12 (Intuitive interpretation of the Lebesgue integral). In   order   to compute the Lebesgue integral of a measurable function f, of values in $\overline{\mathbb{R}}$ and which belongs to $\mathcal{L}^1(\mu)$, it is first necessary to identify the abstract intervals of the positive and negative parts of f, ie, f^+ and f^-, respectively. Since, by definition, f^+ and f^- are both measurable and non-negative functions, their abstract integral is the integral of the boundary of the two sequences of simple non-negative functions, $\{s_n^+\}_{n \in \mathbb{N}}$ and $\{s_n^-\}_{n \in \mathbb{N}}$, which, under Equation (10.78), are punctually and monotonically convergent from below to functions f^+ and f^-, respectively (see Figures 10.2–10.5). Finally, under Equation (10.119), the abstract integral of f corresponds to the difference between the two abstract integrals quoted above.

Proposition 10.55. *Let* $(X, \mathcal{M}, \mu)$ *be a measure space and let* $f : X \to [0, +\infty]$ *be a function which belongs to the space* $\mathcal{L}^1(\mu)$. *Then, given* $E \subseteq X$, *the following relation holds:*

$$\int_X f(x)\, d\mu(x) = \int_E f(x)\, d\mu(x) + \int_{X \setminus E} f(x)\, d\mu(x) \qquad (10.120)$$

Proposition 10.56. *The Lebesgue integral of any function which belongs to* $\mathcal{L}^1(\mu)$ *never shows the infinite indecision:* $\infty - \infty$.

Remark 10.13. The abstract integral for any sign functions is also defined when at least one of the quantities $\int_X f^+(x)\mu\,(dx)$ and $\int_X f^-(x)\mu\,(dx)$ is finite, under the convention that $0 \times \infty = 0$.

Definition 10.53. Let $(X, \mathcal{M}, \mu)$ be a measure space and let $f : X \to \overline{\mathbb{R}}$ be a function which belongs to $\mathcal{L}^1(\mu)$. For any $E \in \mathcal{M}$, the *abstract integral or Lebesgue integral of f on E with respect to μ*, denoted by $\int_E f(x)\,d\mu(x)$, is defined as

$$\int_E f(x)\,d\mu(x) := \int_X \mathbf{1}_{(E)}(x)f(x)\,d\mu(x) \tag{10.121}$$

under the convention that $0 \times \infty = 0$.

Remark 10.14. If $f(x) = 1$ for all $x \in E$, $E \in \mathcal{M}$, then one has

$$\int_E 1\,d\mu(x) = \mu(E) \tag{10.122}$$

Proposition 10.57. *Let $(X, \mathcal{M}, \mu)$ be a measure space, let E be a subset of X so that $E \in \mathcal{M}$ and let $f : E \to \overline{\mathbb{R}}$ be a function which belongs to $\mathcal{L}^1(\mu_E)$. Also, let $(E, \mathcal{M}_E, \mu_E)$ be a measure space where μ_E is the restriction of measure μ to set E and $\mathcal{M}_E$ is the restriction of the σ-algebra $\mathcal{M}$ to set E [3]. Then the abstract integral of f on the subset E of X with respect to measure μ coincides with the abstract integral of f on set E with respect to measure μ_E, ie,*

$$\int_E f(x)\,d\mu(x) = \int_E f(x)\,d\mu_E(x) \tag{10.123}$$

Corollary 10.21. *Let $(X, \mathcal{M}, \mu)$ be a measure space, let E be a subset of X so that $E \in \mathcal{M}$ and let $f : E \to \overline{\mathbb{R}}$ be a function belonging to $\mathcal{L}^1(\mu_E)$. Then, if $\mu(E) = 0$, one has*

$$\int_E f(x)\,d\mu(x) = 0 \tag{10.124}$$

10.8.3.1. Properties of the Lebesgue integral for any sign functions
Proposition 10.58. *Let $(X, \mathcal{M}, \mu)$ be a measure space and let f and g be two functions which belong to $\mathcal{L}^1(\mu)$. Then the following relations hold:*

(1) *if $E \in \mathcal{M}$ is a set so that for all $x \in E$ the following holds*

$$f(x) = 0 \tag{10.125}$$

---

[3] Alternatively, μ_E is the measure defined on the σ-algebra $\mathcal{M}_E$ as in Equation (10.5); see Definitions 1.100 and 10.6, Notation 10.1 and Proposition 10.2.

one has

$$\int_E f(x) \, d\mu(x) = 0 \tag{10.126}$$

(2) *if for all $x \in X$ the following holds*

$$f(x) \le g(x) \tag{10.127}$$

one has

$$\int_X f(x) \, d\mu(x) \le \int_X g(x) \, d\mu(x) \tag{10.128}$$

10.8.3.2. Properties of the space $\mathcal{L}^1(\mu)$

Proposition 10.59. *The space $\mathcal{L}^1(\mu)$ is a vector space, ie, for all $\alpha, \beta \in \mathbb{R}$ and for all $f, g \in \mathcal{L}^1(\mu)$, one has*

$$\alpha f + \beta g \in \mathcal{L}^1(\mu) \tag{10.129}$$

Proposition 10.60. *The integral operator is a linear functional with regard to the functions which belongs to the vector space $\mathcal{L}^1(\mu)$, ie, for all $\alpha, \beta \in \mathbb{R}$ and for all $f, g \in \mathcal{L}^1(\mu)$, one has*

$$\int_X (\alpha f(x) + \beta g(x)) \, d\mu(x) = \alpha \int_X f(x) \, d\mu(x) + \beta \int_X g(x) \, d\mu(x) \tag{10.130}$$

Proposition 10.61. *Let $f : X \to \overline{\mathbb{R}}$ be a function which belongs to $\mathcal{L}^1(\mu)$. Then the following inequality holds:*

$$\left| \int_X f(x) \, d\mu(x) \right| \le \int_X |f(x)| \, d\mu(x) \tag{10.131}$$

Definition 10.54. Let $(X, \mathcal{M}, \mu)$ be a measure space and let $f : X \to \overline{\mathbb{R}}$ be a function which belongs to $\mathcal{L}^1(\mu)$. Then, the *norm of f in $\mathcal{L}^1(\mu)$*, denoted by $\|f\|$, is defined as

$$\|f\| := \int_X |f(x)| \, d\mu(x) \tag{10.132}$$

Proposition 10.62. *The vector space $\mathcal{L}^1(\mu)$ is not a space norm.*

10.8.3.3. Theorem of the monotonic convergence in the space $\mathcal{L}^1(\mu)$

Proposition 10.63. *Let $(X, \mathcal{M}, \mu)$ be a measure space and let $\{f_n(x)\}_{n \in \mathbb{N}} : X \to [0, +\infty]$ be a sequence of non-negative functions belonging to the class $\text{Meas}((X, \mathcal{M}), ([0, +\infty], \overline{\mathbb{B}}_{[0,+\infty]}))$ which is punctually and monotonically convergent from above (see Definition 3.12) to the function $f(x) \in \mathcal{L}^1(\mu)$, ie,*

(i)   *for all $x \in X$ one has $f_1(x) \geq f_2(x) \geq \cdots \geq 0$;*
(ii) $\lim_{n \to +\infty} f_n(x) = f(x)$.

Also, let

$$f_1(x) \in \mathcal{L}^1(\mu) \tag{10.133}$$

then the following equivalence holds:

$$\int_X f(x)\, d\mu(x) = \lim_{n \to +\infty} \int_X f_n(x)\, d\mu(x) \tag{10.134}$$

10.8.3.4. Space $L^1(\mu)$

Definition 10.55. Given the measure space $(X, \mathcal{M}, \mu)$, the function $f : X \to \mathbb{R}$ is said to *hold property P almost everywhere with respect to μ*, if f satisfies property P at all points of $X \backslash E$, where $\mu(E) = 0$.

Definition 10.56. Given the measure space $(X, \mathcal{M}, \mu)$, functions f and g belonging to $\mathcal{L}^1(\mu)$ are said to be *equal almost everywhere with respect to μ*. This is denoted by writing

$$f = g \text{ almost everywhere} \tag{10.135}$$

or by

$$f \sim g \tag{10.136}$$

if

$$\mu(\{x \in \mathcal{M} : f(x) \neq g(x)\}) = 0 \tag{10.137}$$

Proposition 10.64. *The almost-everywhere equivalence relation between the two functions belonging to the space $\mathcal{L}^1(\mu)$ is an equivalence relation (see Definition 1.33).*

Proposition 10.65. *Given the measure space $(X, \mathcal{M}, \mu)$, let $f : X \to \mathbb{R}$ be a function so that:*

(i) $f \in \mathcal{L}^1(\mu)$;
(ii) $|\int_X f(x)\, d\mu(x)| = \int_X |f(x)|\, d\mu(x)$.

Then f is almost everywhere negative or f is almost everywhere positive with respect to μ, ie,

$$f \sim |f| \quad \text{or} \quad f \sim -|f| \tag{10.138}$$

Definition 10.57. Given a measure space $(X, \mathcal{M}, \mu)$, $L^1(\mu)$ is defined to be the *set of the equivalence classes of the elements of* $\mathcal{L}^1(\mu)$ ie, the *quotient set* (see Definition 1.35) *of* $\mathcal{L}^1(\mu)$ with respect to the *almost everywhere equivalence relation* as in Definition10.56, ie,

$$L^1(\mu) = \frac{\mathcal{L}^1(\mu)}{\sim} = \{[f] : f \in \mathcal{L}^1(\mu)\} \tag{10.139}$$

where $[f]$ is the equivalence class to which function f of $\mathcal{L}^1(\mu)$ belongs, ie, $f \in [f]$.

Definition 10.58. Given $[f]$ in $L^1(\mu)$, *the integral norm* of $[f]$ is the quantity

$$\|f\|_1 := \int_X |f(x)| \, d\mu(x) \tag{10.140}$$

Proposition 10.66. *Given the measure space* $(X, \mathcal{M}, \mu)$, *let f and g be two functions being almost everywhere equal, ie,*

$$f \sim g \tag{10.136}$$

Then f and g have the same integral norm, ie,

$$\|f\|_1 = \|g\|_1 \tag{10.141}$$

10.8.3.4.1. Property of the space $L^1(\mu)$

Proposition 10.67. *The space* $L^1(\mu)$ *is a vector space, ie, for all* $\alpha, \beta \in \mathbb{R}$ *and for all* $[f], [g] \in L^1(\mu)$, *one has*

$$[\alpha f + \beta g] \in L^1(\mu) \tag{10.142}$$

Proposition 10.68. *The integral operator is a linear functional with respect to the elements of the vector space* $L^1(\mu)$, *ie, for all* $\alpha, \beta \in \mathbb{R}$ *and for all* $[f], [g] \in L^1(\mu)$, *one has*

$$\int_X (\alpha f(x) + \beta g(x)) \, d\mu(x) = \alpha \int_X f(x) \, d\mu(x) + \beta \int_X g(x) \, d\mu(x) \tag{10.143}$$

where:

- *f is any element of $[f]$;*
- *g is any element of $[g]$;*
- *$[\alpha f + \beta g]$ is one element of $L^1(\mu)$.*

Proposition 10.69. *Let $[f]$ be an element of $L^1(\mu)$. Then for all $f \in [f]$ the following inequality holds:*

$$\left| \int_X f(x)\, d\mu(x) \right| \leq \int_X |f(x)|\, d\mu(x) \tag{10.144}$$

Proposition 10.70. *The vector space $L^1(\mu)$ is a norm space.*

Theorem 10.15. *Given the measure space $(X, \mathcal{M}, \mu)$, let $\{f_n(x)\}_{n\in\mathbb{N}} : X \to \overline{\mathbb{R}}$ be a sequence of functions belonging to the class $\mathrm{Meas}((X, \mathcal{M}), (\overline{\mathbb{R}}, \overline{\mathbb{B}}))$ so that*

$$\sum_{n=1}^{+\infty} \|f_n(x)\|_1 < +\infty$$

Then the series of functions $\sum_{n=1}^{+\infty} f_n(x)$ is almost everywhere punctually convergent to a function $f(x) \in L^1(\mu)$, and

$$\lim_{N\to+\infty} \left\| f(x) - \sum_{n=1}^{N} f_n(x) \right\|_1 = 0 \tag{10.145}$$

Corollary 10.22. *Let $(X, \mathcal{M}, \mu)$ be a vector space. Then $L^1(\mu)$ is a full vector space norm, ie, a Banach space (see Definition 2.44).*

10.8.4. Theorem of dominated convergence

Theorem 10.16 (Dominated convergence). *Let $(X, \mathcal{M}, \mu)$ be a measure space and let $\{f_n(x)\}_{n\in\mathbb{N}} : X \to \overline{\mathbb{R}}$ be a sequence of functions belonging to the class $\mathrm{Meas}((X, \mathcal{M}), (\overline{\mathbb{R}}, \overline{\mathbb{B}}))$ punctually convergent to the function $f(x) \in \mathrm{Meas}((X, \mathcal{M}), (\overline{\mathbb{R}}, \overline{\mathbb{B}}))$, ie,*

$$\lim_{n\to+\infty} f_n(x) = f(x) \tag{10.146}$$

where $f(x) \in L^1(\mu)$. Also, let $g : X \to \overline{\mathbb{R}}$ be a function which belongs to $L^1(\mu)$ so that for all $n \in \mathbb{N}$ and for all $x \in X$ the following holds:

$$|f_n(x)| \leq g(x) \tag{10.147}$$

Then the following equivalence holds:

$$\int_X f(x)\, d\mu(x) = \lim_{n\to+\infty} \int_X f_n(x)\, d\mu(x) \tag{10.148}$$

Corollary 10.23. *Given the measure space* $(X, \mathcal{M}, \mu)$, *let* $\{f_n(x)\}_{n \in \mathbb{N}}$ *be a sequence of any sign functions belonging to the class* $\text{Meas}((X, \mathcal{M}), (\overline{\mathbb{R}}, \overline{\mathbb{B}}))$ *so that*

$$\sum_{n=1}^{+\infty} \|f_n(x)\|_1 < +\infty$$

Then the following results hold:

(1) *the series of functions* $\sum_{n=1}^{+\infty} f_n(x)$ *is almost everywhere punctually convergent to a function* $f(x)$, *ie,*

$$\sum_{n=1}^{+\infty} f_n(x) \sim f(x)$$

(2) $f(x) \in L^1(\mu)$;
(3) *the integral of the series is equal to the series of the intervals, ie,*

$$\int_X f(x)\, d\mu(x) = \sum_{n=1}^{+\infty} \int_X f_n(x)\, d\mu(x)$$

10.8.5.   Riemann integral and Lebesgue integral

Theorem 10.17. *Let* $f : [a, b] \to \mathbb{R}$ *be a bounded function on the bounded interval* $[a, b] \subseteq \mathbb{R}$. *Then:*

(i) *f is Riemann-integrable on* $[a, b]$ *if and only if the set of the points of discontinuity of f on* $[a, b]$ *has a Lebesgue measure zero;*
(ii) *if f is Riemann-integrable on* $[a, b]$, *then f is also Lebesgue-integrable on* $[a, b]$ *and the two integrals coincide, ie,*

$$\int_a^b f(x)\, dx = \int_a^b f(x)\, d\tilde{m}_1(x)$$

Corollary 10.24. *Let* $f : [a, b] \to \mathbb{R}$ *be a bounded and Riemann-integrable function on the interval* $[a, b]$. *Then, the following hold:*

(1) *the sequence of the abstract intervals of any simple non-negative function of the sequence* $\{s_n^+\}_{n \in \mathbb{N}}$, *which is punctually and monotonically convergent from below (see Equation (10.78)) to the function* f^+, *coincides with the (non-decreasing) sequence of the Riemann lower sums (see Definitions 5.11 and 5.16) of* f^+, *where* $n \in \mathbb{N}$ *identifies a number of points of partition* P_n *of interval* $[a, b]$ *(see Definition 5.14);*

(2) *the sequence of the abstract intervals of any simple non-negative function of the sequence $\{s_n^-\}_{n\in\mathbb{N}}$, which is punctually and monotonically convergent from below (see Equation (10.78)) to the function f^-, coincides with the (non-decreasing) sequence of the Riemann lower sums (see Definitions 5.11 and 5.16) of f^-, where $n \in \mathbb{N}$ identifies a number of points of partition P_n of interval $[a, b]$ (see Definition 5.14);*

(3) *the Lebesgue integral of the boundary of the sequence of simple non-negative functions $\{s_n^+\}_{n\in\mathbb{N}}$, which is punctually and monotonically convergent from below (see Equation (10.78)) to the function f^+, coincides with the boundary for $n \to +\infty$ of the sequence of the lower Riemann sums (see Definitions 5.11 and 5.16) of f^+, ie, (see Definition 5.17) with a boundary for $n \to +\infty$ of the sequence of the upper sums (see Definitions 5.12 and 5.16) of f^+;*

(4) *the Lebesgue integral of the boundary of the sequence of simple non-negative functions $\{s_n^-\}_{n\in\mathbb{N}}$, which is punctually and monotonically convergent from below (see Equation (10.78)) to the function f^-, coincides with the boundary for $n \to +\infty$ of the sequence of the lower Riemann sums (see Definitions 5.11 and 5.16) of f^-, ie, (see Definition 5.17) with the boundary for $n \to +\infty$ of the sequence of the upper sums (see Definitions 5.12 and 5.16) of f^-;*

(5) *the Lebesgue integral of f on $[a, b]$ is equal to the difference between the boundary for $n \to +\infty$ of the sequence of the lower Riemann sums of f^+ and the boundary for $n \to +\infty$ of the sequence of the lower Riemann sums of f^-, or (see Definition 5.17) to the difference between the boundary for $n \to +\infty$ of the sequence of the upper sums of f^+ and the boundary for $n \to +\infty$ of the sequence of the upper sums of f^-.*

Remark 10.15. From a geometrical viewpoint, the main difference between the procedure for computing the Riemann integral and the Lebesgue integral of a function f of values in $\mathbb{R}$ is that the Riemann integral is defined (see Definition 5.17) by the value taken by the boundary for $n \to +\infty$ of the sequence of the lower sums of f, or by the boundary for $n \to +\infty$ of the sequence of the upper sums of f, while the Lebesgue integral is equal to the difference of the integrals of the boundaries of the two sequences, $\{s_n^+\}_{n\in\mathbb{N}}$ and $\{s_n^-\}_{n\in\mathbb{N}}$, which are punctually and monotonically convergent from below to functions f^+ and f^-, respectively.

Theorem 10.18. *Let $f : (a, b) \to \mathbb{R}$ be an unbound function on a bounded interval $(a, b) \subseteq \mathbb{R}$. Then, f is integrable in an abstract sense on (a, b) with respect to the Lebesgue measure $\tilde{m}_1$ if and only if the generalised Riemann integral of f on (a, b) is* *convergent, ie,*

$$f(x) \in \mathcal{L}^1((a,b), \widetilde{\mathbb{B}}_{(a,b)}, \widetilde{m}_1|_{(a,b)}) \Leftrightarrow \int_a^b f(x) \, dx < \infty \tag{10.149}$$

where $\int_a^b f(x) \, dx$ is the generalised Riemann integral of the function f on the interval (a, b).

Theorem 10.19. *Let F be a bounded non-decreasing function whose derivative is equal to F' except for a set having a Lebesgue measure zero. Then the following holds:*

(1) *If A denotes the set of all real numbers t for which $F'(t)$ exists with $0 \le F'(t) < +\infty$, then the Lebesgue measure of set A^c is equal to zero.*

(2) *F' belongs to the class of functions $\mathcal{L}^1(\widetilde{m}_1)$ and for any for all $t_1, t_2 \in \mathbb{R}$ so that $t_1 < t_2$ one has*

$$\int_{t_1}^{t_2} F'(s) \, ds \le F(t_2) - F(t_1) \tag{10.150}$$

(3) *If for all $t \in \mathbb{R}$ one has*

$$F_{ac}(t) := \int_{-\infty}^t F'(s) \, ds \tag{10.151}$$

and

$$F_s(t) := F(t) - F_{ac}(t) \tag{10.152}$$

then one has

$$F'_{ac}(t) = F'(t) \text{ almost everywhere} \tag{10.153}$$

and, therefore,

$$F'_s(t) = 0 \text{ almost everywhere}$$

Consequently, F_s is a singular function under the condition that it is not an identically null function.

Corollary 10.25. *Any function F which satisfies the hypotheses stated in Theorem 10.19 may be expanded as*

$$F(t) := F_s(t) + F_{ac}(t) \tag{10.154}$$

where F_s is said to be the **singular part** *of F and F_{ac} is said to be the* **absolutely continuous part** *of F. And, F_{ac} is a non-decreasing function so that: $F_{ac} \le F$.*

Corollary 10.26. *Let F be a function which satisfies the hypotheses stated in Theorem 10.19. Then, if $t_1 < t_2$, the following holds:*

$$F_s(t_2) - F_s(t_1) = F(t_2) - F(t_1) - \int_{t_1}^{t_2} F'(s) \, ds \ge 0 \tag{10.155}$$

Therefore F_s is also a non-decreasing function and one has $F_s \le F$.

10.9.   RADON–NIKODYM DERIVATIVE

Proposition 10.71. *Let* $(X, \mathcal{M}, \mu)$ *be a measure space and let* $f : X \to [0, +\infty]$ *be a non-negative function which belongs to the class* $\text{Meas}((X, \mathcal{M}), (\overline{\mathbb{R}}, \overline{\mathbb{B}}_{[0,+\infty]}))$. *Then, the function* $\mu_f : \mathcal{M} \to [0, +\infty]$ *defined by*

$$\mu_f(E) := \int_E f(x) \, d\mu(x), \quad \forall E \in \mathcal{M} \tag{10.156}$$

is a measure on $(X, \mathcal{M})$ *and, on this measurable space, the function* $\mu_f(E)$ *is absolutely continuous with respect to* μ.

Theorem 10.20 (Radon–Nikodym). *Let* $(X, \mathcal{M}, \mu)$ *be a measure space and let* ν *be an absolutely continuous measure with respect to* μ. *Then there is one non-negative function* $f : X \to [0, +\infty]$ *only which belongs to the class* $\text{Meas}((X, \mathcal{M}), (\overline{\mathbb{R}}, \overline{\mathbb{B}}_{[0,+\infty]}))$ *so that for all* $E \in \mathcal{M}$ *one has*

$$\int_E d\mu(x) = \int_E f(x) \, d\nu(x) \tag{10.157}$$

and f is said to be the Radon–Nikodym derivative of measure μ with respect to measure ν.

Remark 10.16. In light of Equation (10.101), Equation (10.157) may also be written as

$$\mu(E) = \int_E f(x) \, d\nu(x) \tag{10.158}$$

and is valid for all $E \in \mathcal{M}$.

Corollary 10.27. *The use of the word* derivative *with reference to f is because that function is correctly denoted by writing*

$$f(x) = \frac{d\mu(x)}{d\nu(x)} \tag{10.159}$$

Proposition 10.72. *Let* $(X, \mathcal{M}, \mu)$ *be a measure space and let* $f : X \to [0, +\infty]$ *be the Radon–Nikodym derivative of measure* μ *with respect to measure* ν, *since* ν *is absolutely continuous with respect to* μ. *Also, let* $g : X \to [0, +\infty]$ *be a function belonging to the class* $\text{Meas}((X, \mathcal{M}), (\overline{\mathbb{R}}, \overline{\mathbb{B}}_{[0,+\infty]}))$. *Then for any* $E \in \mathcal{M}$, *one has*

$$\int_E g(x) \, d\mu(x) = \int_E [g(x) \cdot f(x)] \, d\nu(x) \tag{10.160}$$

10.10. INTEGRATION IN PRODUCT SPACES

10.10.1. Basics

Definition 10.59. Given N measurable spaces $(X_1, \mathcal{M}_1), (X_2, \mathcal{M}_2), \ldots,$ $(X_N, \mathcal{M}_N)$, the *class of the rectangles in* $X_1 \times X_2 \times \cdots \times X_N$ is the class of the sets $\mathcal{R}$ defined as

$$\mathcal{R} := \{A_1 \times A_2 \times \cdots \times A_N : A_1 \in \mathcal{M}_1, A_2 \in \mathcal{M}_2, \ldots, A_N \in \mathcal{M}_N\}$$

Definition 10.60. Given the N measurable spaces $(X_1, \mathcal{M}_1), (X_2, \mathcal{M}_2),$ $\ldots, (X_N, \mathcal{M}_N)$, a *rectangle in* $X_1 \times X_2 \times \cdots \times X_N$ is any element $A_1 \times A_2 \times \cdots \times A_N \in \mathcal{R}$.

Definition 10.61. Given the N measurable spaces $(X_1, \mathcal{M}_1), (X_2, \mathcal{M}_2), \ldots,$ $(X_N, \mathcal{M}_N)$, the *product σ-algebra* of the σ-algebras $\mathcal{M}_1, \mathcal{M}_2, \ldots, \mathcal{M}_N$ denoted by $\mathcal{M}_1 \times \mathcal{M}_2 \times \cdots \times \mathcal{M}_N$ is the σ-algebra generated (see Definition 1.103) by the rectangles as in Definition 10.60, or by the σ-algebra generated by $\mathcal{R}$, ie,

$$\mathcal{M}_1 \times \mathcal{M}_2 \times \cdots \times \mathcal{M}_N := \sigma(\mathcal{R})$$

Proposition 10.73 (Associative property of the product of σ-algebras). *Let* $(X_i, \mathcal{M}_i), i = 1, 2, 3,$ *be three measurable spaces. Then the following equivalence holds:*

$$\mathcal{M}_1 \times \mathcal{M}_2 \times \mathcal{M}_3 = \mathcal{M}_1 \times (\mathcal{M}_2 \times \mathcal{M}_3) = (\mathcal{M}_1 \times \mathcal{M}_2) \times \mathcal{M}_3$$

Notation 10.14. Given any point (x, y) in the product space $X \times Y$, if:

- x varies and y is fixed, the following notation is used

$$(x, \underline{y}) \equiv (\cdot, y)$$

- x is fixed and y varies, the following notation is used

$$(\underline{x}, y) \equiv (x, \cdot)$$

Definition 10.62. Let $(X, \mathcal{M})$ and $(Y, \mathcal{N})$ be two measurable spaces and let Q be a subset of the space product $X \times Y$, ie, $Q \in X \times Y$. The *Q-section with respect to $\underline{x}$* (ie, x fixed), denoted by Q_x, is defined as the set

$$Q_x := \{y \in Y : (\underline{x}, y) \in Q\} \tag{10.161}$$

Similarly, the *Q-section with respect to y* (ie, y fixed) denoted by Q_y is the set

$$Q_y := \{x \in X : (x, \underline{y}) \in Q\} \tag{10.162}$$

Definition 10.63. Given two measurable spaces, $(X, \mathcal{M})$ and $(Y, \mathcal{N})$, let $Q \in X \times Y$. Then Q is said to have the *property of sections* if for any $x \in X$ and for any $y \in Y$ one has

$$Q_x \equiv \{y \in Y : (\underline{x}, y) \in Q\} \in \mathcal{N} \quad \text{and} \quad Q_y \equiv \{x \in X : (x, \underline{y}) \in Q\} \in \mathcal{M}$$

Proposition 10.74. *The elements of the σ-algebra product $\mathcal{M} \times \mathcal{N}$ have the property of sections.*

10.10.2. Product measure

Theorem 10.21. *Let $(X, \mathcal{M}, \mu)$ and $(Y, \mathcal{N}, \lambda)$ be two σ-finite measure spaces and let $Q \in X \times Y$. Considering the following points.*

(1) $f_Q(x) : X \mapsto [0, +\infty]$ *so that*

$$f_Q(x) = \lambda(Q_x) \tag{10.163}$$

where $Q_x = \{y \in Y : (\underline{x}, y) \in Q\}$.

(2) $g_Q(y) : Y \mapsto [0, +\infty]$ *so that*

$$g_Q(y) = \mu(Q_y) \tag{10.164}$$

where $Q_y = \{x \in X : (x, \underline{y}) \in Q\}$.

Then $f_Q(x)$ is $\mathcal{M}$-measurable and $g_Q(y)$ is $\mathcal{N}$-measurable, and

$$\int_X f_Q(x)\, d\mu(x) = \int_Y g_Q(y)\, d\lambda(y) \tag{10.165}$$

Corollary 10.28. *Equation (10.165) may also be written as*

$$\int_X \left[\int_Y 1_{(Q)}(x, y)\, d\lambda(y) \right] d\mu(x) = \int_Y \left[\int_X 1_{(Q)}(x, y)\, d\mu(x) \right] d\lambda(y) \tag{10.166}$$

Definition 10.64. Given two σ-finite measure spaces $(X, \mathcal{M}, \mu)$ and $(Y, \mathcal{N}, \lambda)$ and given $Q \in \mathcal{M} \times \mathcal{N}$, then the *product measure* of Q, denoted by $\mu \times \lambda(Q)$, is the function defined as

$$\mu \times \lambda(Q) := \int_X f_Q(x)\, d\mu(x) = \int_Y g_Q(y)\, d\lambda(y) \tag{10.167}$$

or as

$$\mu \times \lambda(Q) := \int_X \left[\int_Y 1_{(Q)}(x, y)\, d\lambda(y) \right] d\mu(x) = \int_Y \left[\int_X 1_{(Q)}(x, y)\, d\mu(x) \right] d\lambda(y)$$
$$\tag{10.168}$$

Remark 10.17. The construction of the product measure holds only for sets which belong to σ-finite measure spaces.

Proposition 10.75. *Given the product measure $\mu \times \lambda$, the following statements hold:*

(i) $\mu \times \lambda$ *is one measure on the product σ-algebra, ie, on $\mathcal{M} \times \mathcal{N}$;*
(ii) $\mu \times \lambda$ *is a σ-finite measure.*

Example 10.1. Given two σ-finite measure spaces $(X, \mathcal{M}, \mu)$ and $(Y, \mathcal{N}, \lambda)$ and given the measure space $(X \times Y, \mathcal{M} \times \mathcal{N}, \mu \times \lambda)$, let $A \times B$ be a rectangle belonging to the product σ-algebra $\mathcal{M} \times \mathcal{N}$.

Under Equation (10.167) the product measure of this rectangle is given by

$$\mu \times \lambda(A \times B) = \int_X f_{A \times B}(x) \, d\mu(x)$$

ie, under Equation (10.163)

$$\mu \times \lambda(A \times B) = \int_X [\lambda((A \times B)_x)] \, d\mu(x) \tag{10.169}$$

Figure 10.7 shows that the section $(A \times B)$ with respect to any $\underline{x}$ (x_1 in Figure 10.7) is defined as

$$\lambda((A \times B)_x) = \lambda(B) \cdot \mathbf{1}_{(A)}(x) \tag{10.170}$$

If right-hand side of Equation (10.170) is replaced by the right-hand side of Equation (10.169) then

$$\mu \times \lambda(A \times B) = \lambda(B)\mu(A) \tag{10.171}$$

Proposition 10.76. *Given the measure spaces $(\mathbb{R}^2, \widetilde{\mathbb{B}} \times \widetilde{\mathbb{B}}, \tilde{m}_1 \times \tilde{m}_1)$ and $(\mathbb{R}^2, \widetilde{\mathbb{B}}_2, \tilde{m}_2)$, the following hold:*

- $\widetilde{\mathbb{B}} \times \widetilde{\mathbb{B}} \subseteq \widetilde{\mathbb{B}}_2$;
- *the product measure $\tilde{m}_1 \times \tilde{m}_1$ and the product measure $\tilde{m}_2$ coincide on $\mathbb{B}_2$;*
- *the measure space $(\mathbb{R}^2, \widetilde{\mathbb{B}}_2, \tilde{m}_2)$ is the completion of the measure space $(\mathbb{R}^2, \widetilde{\mathbb{B}} \times \widetilde{\mathbb{B}}, \tilde{m}_1 \times \tilde{m}_1)$.*

Corollary 10.29. *In general, the measure spaces $(\mathbb{R}^2, \widetilde{\mathbb{B}} \times \widetilde{\mathbb{B}}, \tilde{m}_1 \times \tilde{m}_1)$ and $(\mathbb{R}^2, \widetilde{\mathbb{B}}_2, \tilde{m}_2)$ do not coincide as under the example below.*

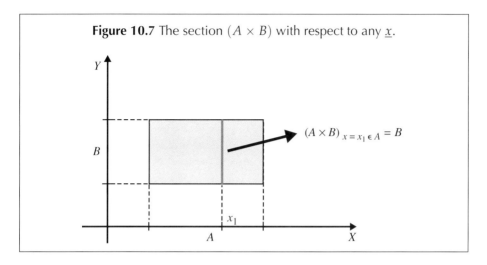

Figure 10.7 The section $(A \times B)$ with respect to any $\underline{x}$.

10.10.3. Integral on product spaces

Definition 10.65. Given a function $f : X \times Y \to \mathbb{R}$, the *positive part* and the *negative part of* f are the functions

$$f^+ := \max(f, 0) \quad \text{and} \quad f^- := \max(-f, 0) \tag{10.172}$$

Definition 10.66. Let $(X \times Y, \mathcal{M} \times \mathcal{N}, \mu \times \lambda)$ be a measure space and let $f : X \times Y \to \mathbb{R}$ be a function belonging to the class $\mathrm{Meas}((X \times Y, \mathcal{M} \times \mathcal{N}),$ $(\overline{\mathbb{R}}, \overline{\mathbb{B}}))$. The function f is said to be *integrable* (in an abstract sense) *on the product space* $X \times Y$ *with respect to the product measure* $\mu \times \lambda$ if the following condition holds:

$$\int_{X \times Y} |f(x, y)| \, d(\mu \times \lambda)(x, y) < +\infty \tag{10.173}$$

Definition 10.67. The space $\mathcal{L}(X \times Y, \mathcal{M} \times \mathcal{N}, \mu \times \lambda)$ is said to be the space of the measurable functions which are integrable on the measure space $(X \times Y, \mathcal{M} \times \mathcal{N}, \mu \times \lambda)$, ie,

$$\mathcal{L}(X \times Y, \mathcal{M} \times \mathcal{N}, \mu \times \lambda)$$

$$\equiv \left\{ f \text{ measurable } \ni' \int_{X \times Y} |f(x, y)| \, d(\mu \times \lambda)(x, y) < +\infty \right\} \tag{10.174}$$

Notation 10.15. The space $\mathcal{L}(X \times Y, \mathcal{M} \times \mathcal{N}, \mu \times \lambda)$ may also be denoted as $\mathcal{L}(\mu \times \lambda)$.

Definition 10.68. Let $(X \times Y, \mathcal{M} \times \mathcal{N}, \mu \times \lambda)$ be a measure space and let $f : X \times Y \to \mathbb{R}$ be a function belonging to the space $\mathcal{L}(\mu \times \lambda)$. The equivalence below is defined as the *abstract integral* or *Lebesgue integral of f on $X \times Y$ with respect to the product measure $\mu \times \lambda$* and is denoted by $\int_{X \times Y} f(x, y)\, d(\mu \times \lambda)(x, y)$:

$$\int_{X \times Y} f(x, y)\, d(\mu \times \lambda)(x, y) = \int_{X \times Y} f^+(x, y)\, d(\mu \times \lambda)(x, y)$$
$$- \int_{X \times Y} f^-(x, y)\, d(\mu \times \lambda)(x, y) \qquad (10.175)$$

where:

- f^+ and f^- are the positive and the negative parts of f, respectively;
- by convention, $0 \times \infty = 0$.

Notation 10.16. Often, instead of writing $\int_{X \times Y} f(x, y)\, d(\mu \times \lambda)(x, y)$ to denote the abstract integral of f on $X \times Y$ with respect to $\mu \times \lambda$, one may use either

$$\int_{X \times Y} f(x, y)\mu \times \lambda\, (d(x, y))$$

or

$$\int_{X \times Y} f\, d(\mu \times \lambda)$$

10.10.3.1. Fubini–Tonelli theorem
Theorem 10.22. *Let $(X, \mathcal{M}, \mu)$ and $(Y, \mathcal{N}, \lambda)$ be two σ-finite measure spaces. Then the following hold.*

(1) Tonelli. *If $f : X \times Y \to [0, +\infty]$ is a non-negative function which belongs to the class $\mathrm{Meas}((X \times Y, \mathcal{M} \times \mathcal{N}), (\overline{\mathbb{R}}, \overline{\mathbb{B}}_{[0,+\infty]}))$, then*

$$\int_{X \times Y} f(x, y)\, d(\mu \times \lambda)(x, y) = \int_X d\mu(x) \int_Y f(x, y)\, d\lambda(y)$$
$$= \int_Y d\lambda(y) \int_X f(x, y)\, d\mu(x) \qquad (10.176)$$

(2) Fubini. *Let $f \in \mathcal{L}(\mu \times \lambda)$, ie, $\int_{X \times Y} |f(x, y)|\, d(\mu \times \lambda)(x) < +\infty$. Then*

$$f(x, \underline{y}) \in \mathcal{L}^1(\mu) \quad \text{for any y with respect to λ} \quad \text{and}$$
$$f(\underline{x}, y) \in \mathcal{L}^1(\lambda) \quad \text{for any x with respect to μ} \qquad (10.177)$$

and

$$\int_{X \times Y} f(x, y)\, d(\mu \times \lambda)(x, y) = \int_X d\mu(x) \int_Y f(x, y)\, d\lambda(y)$$
$$= \int_Y d\lambda(y) \int_X f(x, y)\, d\mu(x) \qquad (10.178)$$

Definition 10.69. Integrals

$$\int_X d\mu(x) \int_Y f(x,y)\,d\lambda(y) \quad \text{and} \quad \int_Y d\lambda(y) \int_X f(x,y)\,d\mu(x)$$

as in the second and third members of Equations (10.176) and (10.178) are said to be *iterated integrals*

Notation 10.17. The iterated integral $\int_X d\mu(x) \int_Y f(x,y)\,d\lambda(y)$ is often denoted by $\int_X (\int_Y f(x,y)\,d\lambda(y))\,d\mu(x)$.

Notation 10.18. The iterated integral $\int_Y d\lambda(y) \int_X f(x,y)\,d\mu(x)$ is also often denoted by: $\int_Y (\int_X f(x,y)\,d\mu(x))\,d\lambda(y)$.

Remark 10.18. Theorem 10.22 states under which conditions it is possible to determine $\int_{X\times Y} f(x,y)\,d(\mu\times\lambda)(x,y)$, ie, the abstract integral of a function defined on the product space (see Definition 10.66), by computing the iterated integrals defined in Definition 10.69.

Remark 10.19. The Tonelli theorem is not applicable to non-constant sign functions, as shown by the following example.

Example 10.2. Consider the measurable space $(\mathbb{R}^2, \mathbb{B}\times\mathbb{B})$. Let:

- Q be a subset of $\mathbb{R}^2$ defined as

$$Q := [0,1)\times[0,1)$$

- $f:\mathbb{R}^2\to\mathbb{R}$ be a function defined as

$$f(x,y) = \sum_{i=0}^{+\infty} \mathbf{1}_{(Q+(i,i))}(x,y) - \sum_{i=0}^{+\infty} \mathbf{1}_{(Q+(i+1,i))}(x,y) \qquad (10.179)$$

The function $f(x,y)$ as in Equation (10.179) does not have a constant sign. In fact, if one expands the right-hand side of Equation (10.179), the expression is

$$f(x,y) = \mathbf{1}_{[0,1)\times[0,1)}(x,y) - \mathbf{1}_{[1,2)\times[0,1)}(x,y) + \mathbf{1}_{[1,2)\times[1,2)}(x,y)$$
$$- \mathbf{1}_{[2,3)\times[1,2)}(x,y) + \cdots$$

Therefore, this function does not satisfy one of the conditions set in Theorem 10.22 (under Tonelli). Specifically, below a demonstration is given that the iterated integrals in the second and third element of Equation (10.176) are different; these integrals, in this case in point, are respectively

$$\int_{\mathbb{R}} dm_1(x) \int_{\mathbb{R}} f(x, y) \, dm_1(y) \qquad (10.180)$$

and

$$\int_{\mathbb{R}} dm_1(y) \int_{\mathbb{R}} f(x, y) \, dm_1(x) \qquad (10.181)$$

In fact, as Figure 10.8 shows, for any y fixed in $\mathbb{R}$ one has

$$\int_{\mathbb{R}} f(x, y) \, dm_1(x) = 0 \qquad (10.182)$$

while for any x fixed in $\mathbb{R}$, one has

$$\int_{\mathbb{R}} f(x, y) \, dm_1(y) = \mathbf{1}_{[0,1)}(x) \qquad (10.183)$$

Under Equations (10.182) and (10.126), it can be derived that the iterated integral as in Equation (10.180) can be written as

$$\int_{\mathbb{R}} dm_1(y) \int_{\mathbb{R}} f(x, y) \, dm_1(x) = 0$$

Under Equations (10.183) and (6.1) it can be derived that the iterated integral as in Equation (10.181) is

$$\int_{\mathbb{R}} dm_1(x) \int_{\mathbb{R}} f(x, y) \, dm_1(y) = 1$$

Also, Figure 10.8 shows that

$$\int_{X \times Y} |f(x, y)| \, d(m_1 \times m_1)(x, y) = +\infty$$

and then $f \notin \mathcal{L}(m_1 \times m_1)$, ie, the necessary condition for integrability required by Theorem 10.22 (under Fubini) is not satisfied.

Remark 10.20. Example 10.2 shows that the existence of iterated integrals, ie,

$$\int_{Y} d\lambda(y) \int_{X} f(x, y) \, d\mu(x)$$

and

$$\int_{X} d\mu(x) \int_{Y} f(x, y) \, d\lambda(y)$$

implies that neither of these integrals are equal nor does f belong to the space $\mathcal{L}(\mu \times \lambda)$.

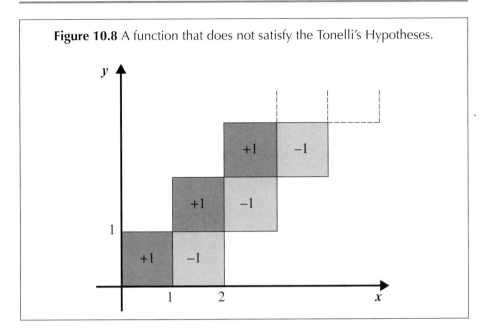

Figure 10.8 A function that does not satisfy the Tonelli's Hypotheses.

Remark 10.21. In general, the existence and the equivalence of the iterated intervals does not imply that f belongs to $\mathcal{L}(\mu \times \lambda)$ and, then, that they are equal to the integral $\int_{X \times Y} f(x, y) \, d(\mu \times \lambda)(x, y)$ which is the first member of Equation (10.178).

10.10.3.1.1. Riemann integral and Lebesgue integral

Theorem 10.23. *Let $f : [a, b] \times [c, d] \to \mathbb{R}$ be a bounded function on a bounded interval $[a, b] \times [c, d] \subseteq \mathbb{R}^2$. Then:*

(i) *f is Riemann-integrable on $[a, b] \times [c, d]$ if and only if the set of points of discontinuity of f on $[a, b] \times [c, d]$ has a Lebesgue measure zero;*

(ii) *if f is Riemann-integrable on $[a, b] \times [c, d]$, then f is also Lebesgue-integrable on $[a, b] \times [c, d]$ and the two integrals coincide, ie,*

$$\int_a^b \int_c^d f(x, y) \, dy \, dx = \int_a^b \int_c^d f(x, y) \, d(\tilde{m}_1 \times \tilde{m}_1)(x, y) \qquad (10.184)$$

Corollary 10.30. *Let $f : [a, b] \times [c, d] \to \mathbb{R}$ be a function which belongs to the space $\mathcal{L}(\tilde{m}_1 \times \tilde{m}_1)$. Then the following hold.*

(1) *The Lebesgue integral of f on the space $[a, b] \times [c, d]$ with respect to the measure product $\tilde{m}_1 \times \tilde{m}_1$ coincides with the iterated integral of f, computed with respect to the measure $\tilde{m}_1|_{[c,d]}(y)$, and after with respect to the measure $\tilde{m}_1|_{[a,b]}(x)$. Such a*

iterated integral coincides with the Riemann integral of f on a region $[a, b] \times [c, d]$ computed with the vertical integration criterion (see Criterion 5.2), ie,

$$\int_a^b \int_c^d f(x, y) \, d(\tilde{m}_1 \times \tilde{m}_1)(x, y) = \int_a^b \left(\int_c^d f(x, y) \, d\tilde{m}_1(y) \right) d\tilde{m}_1(x)$$

$$= \int_a^b \left(\int_c^d f(x, y) \, d(y) \right) dx$$

(2) *The Lebesgue integral of f on the space $[a, b] \times [c, d]$ with respect to the measure product $\tilde{m}_1 \times \tilde{m}_1$ coincides with the iterated integral of f, computed with respect to the measure $\tilde{m}_1|_{[a,b]}(x)$, and after with respect to the measure $\tilde{m}_1|_{[c,d]}(y)$. Such an iterated integral coincides with the Riemann integral of f on a region $[a, b] \times [c, d]$ computed with the vertical integration criterion (see Criterion 5.2), ie,*

$$\int_a^b \int_c^d f(x, y) \, d(\tilde{m}_1 \times \tilde{m}_1)(x, y) = \int_c^d \left(\int_a^b f(x, y) \, d\tilde{m}_1(x) \right) d\tilde{m}_1(y)$$

$$= \int_c^d \left(\int_a^b f(x, y) \, d(x) \right) dy$$

Theorem 10.24. *Let $f : (a, b) \times (c, d) \to \mathbb{R}$ be an unbound function on a bounded interval $(a, b) \times (c, d) \subseteq \mathbb{R}^2$. Then f is integrable in an abstract sense on $(a, b) \times (c, d)$ with respect to the product measure $\tilde{m}_1 \times \tilde{m}_1$ if and only if the generalised Riemann integral of f on $(a, b) \times (c, d)$ is convergent, ie,*

$$f(x, y) \in \mathcal{L}((a, b) \times (c, d), \tilde{\mathbb{B}}_{(a,b)} \times \tilde{\mathbb{B}}_{(a,b)}, \tilde{m}_1 \times \tilde{m}_1|_{(a,b) \times (c,d)})$$

$$\Updownarrow \qquad\qquad\qquad (10.185)$$

$$\int_a^b \int_c^d f(x, y) \, dy \, dx < \infty$$

where $\int_a^b \int_c^d f(x, y) \, dy \, dx$ is the generalised Riemann integral of function f on the interval $(a, b) \times (c, d)$.

Probability theory

11.1. BASICS

Definition 11.1. Given a set Ω and its σ-algebra $\mathcal{M}$, the *probability space* is defined as the measurable space which contains a probability measure (see Definition 10.21). It is denoted by the triple $(\Omega, \mathcal{M}, P)$.

Definition 11.2. Let $\{\mathcal{F}_t\}_{t\geq 0}$ be a filtration with respect to a non-null Ω space (ie, $\{\mathcal{F}_t\}_{t\geq 0}$ is a family of growing σ-algebras of subsets in a non-null Ω space; see Definition 1.102) which belongs to the probability space $(\Omega, \mathcal{M}, P)$. Then the quadruple $(\Omega, \mathcal{M}, \{\mathcal{F}_t\}_{t\geq 0}, P)$ is said to be the *filtered probability space* with respect to filtration $\{\mathcal{F}_t\}_{t\geq 0}$.

Definition 11.3. Let $(\Omega, \mathcal{M}, P)$ be a probability space and let $A \in \mathcal{M}$. The *probability of A*, denoted by $P(A)$, is defined as the following quantity:

$$P(A) := \int_A dP(\omega) \tag{11.1}$$

Corollary 11.1. *The following relation holds:*

$$P(A) \equiv P(\{\omega : \omega \in A\})$$
$$\equiv \sum_{\omega \in A} P(\omega)$$

11.2. PROBABILITY MEASURES AND FUNCTIONS

Definition 11.4. Let $(\Omega, \mathcal{M})$ be a measurable space and let P and $\widetilde{P}$ be two probability measures defined on that space. The probability measure $\widetilde{P}$ is said to be *absolutely continuous with respect to probability measure P* if for any $E \in \mathcal{M}$ so that $P(E) = 0$ one has

$$\widetilde{P}(E) = 0 \tag{11.2}$$

Definition 11.5. Let $(\Omega, \mathcal{M})$ be a measurable space and let P and $\widetilde{P}$ be two probability measures defined on that space. Probability measures P and $\widetilde{P}$ are said to be *equivalent* if

$$P(E) = 0 \Leftrightarrow \tilde{P}(E) = 0, \quad \forall E \in \mathcal{M} \tag{11.3}$$

Remark 11.1. Under Definitions 11.4 and 11.5, a probability measure P defined on a measurable space $(\Omega, \mathcal{M})$ may also be absolutely continuous (or equivalent) with respect to a non-probability measure provided that this non-probability measure is defined on the same measurable space and satisfies the same conditions as under Equation (11.2) (or under Equation (11.3)).

Definition 11.6. Let $(\Omega, \mathcal{M}, P)$ be a probability space. A *cumulative density function* or *cumulated distribution function (CDF)* of P is the function $F_P : \mathbb{R} \to [0, 1]$ so that

$$F_P(t) := P((-\infty, t]) \tag{11.4}$$

The definition above gives a first result for CDF uniqueness.

Proposition 11.1. *If $F_P = F_{P'}$, then*

$$P = P'$$

Theorem 11.1. *Let F_P be the CDF with respect to the probability measure P. Then we have the following.*

(1) *F_P is a non-decreasing function. Therefore, for any t it admits a left boundary*

$$F_P(t-) := \lim_{s \to t-} F_P(s)$$

and a right boundary

$$F_P(t+) := \lim_{s \to t+} F_P(s)$$

and:

$$F_P(t-) \leq F_P(t) \leq F_P(t+)$$

(2) *F_P is right continuous, ie,*

$$F_P(t+) = F_P(t), \quad \forall t$$

(3) *One has*

$$\lim_{t \to -\infty} F_P(t) = 0$$

and

$$\lim_{t \to +\infty} F_P(t) = 1$$

Corollary 11.2. *Under Theorem 11.1(1) and (2), F_P belongs to the class of functions $\chi(\mathbb{R})$ (see Definition 10.7).*

Theorem 11.2. *Let $F : \mathbb{R} \to \mathbb{R}$ be a non-decreasing right continuous function with $F(-\infty) = 0$ and $F(+\infty) = 1$. Then there is one probability P only defined on $\mathbb{B}(\mathbb{R})$ so that*

$$F_P = F$$

Definition 11.7. The function $S_P(t) : \mathbb{R} \to [0, 1]$ is defined to be the *survivor function* of P so that

$$S_P(t) := 1 - F_P(t) = P((t, +\infty)) \tag{11.5}$$

11.2.1. Types of probability measures

Definition 11.8. A probability measure P of values in $\mathbb{R}$ is said to be *discrete* if a countable set E exists so that

$$P(E) = 1$$

Proposition 11.2. *Let $E = \{t_i\}_{i \in \mathbb{N}}$ be a sequence of real values and let P be a discrete probability measure so that $P(E) = 1$. Also, let $P(t_i) = p_i$, then for all $B \in \mathbb{B}$ the following relations hold:*

$$P(B) = \sum_{i=1}^{\infty} p_i \delta_{t_i}(B) \tag{11.6}$$

$$F_P(t) = \sum_{i=1}^{\infty} p_i \delta_{t_i}((-\infty, t]) \tag{11.7}$$

where δ_{t_i} is the Dirac measure centred at t_i (see Definition 10.18) or the non-centred Kronecker delta (see Definition 6.2);

$$F_P(t) = \sum_{i=1}^{\infty} p_i \mathbf{1}_{(t_i \leq t)}, \quad \forall t \in \mathbb{R} \tag{11.8}$$

where $\mathbf{1}_{(t_i \leq t)}$ is the index function (see Definition 6.3);

$$F_P(t) = \sum_{i=1}^{\infty} p_i (1 - \theta_{t_i}(t)) \tag{11.9}$$

where θ_{t_i} is the non-centred Heaviside function (see Definition 6.4).

Corollary 11.3. *If P is a discrete probability measure of real values, then only the members of set $E = \{t_i\}_{i \in \mathbb{N}}$ will have a non-null probability. Their probability is determined by*

$$P(t_i) = F_P(t_i) - F_P(t_i-) = \Delta_{F_P}(t_i) \tag{11.10}$$

It follows that the CDF of a discrete probability measure grows only by jumps which have a width $P(t_i) = p_i$ at points t_i.

Definition 11.9. A probability measure P of values in $\mathbb{R}$ is said to be *absolutely continuous with respect to the Lebesgue measure* $\tilde{m}_1$, if a function $f_P : \mathbb{R} \to \mathbb{R}^+$ exists, also called the *probability density function (PDF) of P*, so that $f_P \in L^1(\tilde{m}_1)$ and for any interval $(a, b]$ one has

$$P((a, b]) = \int_a^b f_P(t) \, d\tilde{m}_1(t) \tag{11.11}$$

where $\int_a^b f_P(t) \, d\tilde{m}_1(t)$ is the Lebesgue integral.

Proposition 11.3. *If f_P is a Riemann-integrable function on $(a, b]$, then the right-hand side of Equation (11.11) coincides with the Riemann integral of function f_P on $(a, b]$ (see Theorem 10.17), ie,*

$$P((a, b]) = \int_a^b f_P(t) \, d\tilde{m}_1(t) = \int_a^b f_P(t) \, dt$$

Remark 11.2. If measure $\tilde{m}_1$ is discrete, then the right-hand side of Equation (11.11) coincides with the Riemann–Stieltjes integral of function f_P on $(a, b]$ (see Section 5.3.3):

$$P((a, b]) = \int_a^b dF_P(t)$$

Definition 11.10. Let P be a probability measure of values in $\mathbb{R}$ which is absolutely continuous with respect to the Lebesgue measure $\tilde{m}_1$ and whose PDF is equal to f_P. Then the CDF of P is defined as

$$F_P(t) = \int_{-\infty}^t f_P(s) \, ds, \quad \forall t \in \mathbb{R} \tag{11.12}$$

Proposition 11.4. *If f_p is the PDF of a probability measure P of values in $\mathbb{R}$, which is absolutely continuous with respect to the Lebesgue measure $\tilde{m}_1$, then the following holds:*

$$\int_{-\infty}^{+\infty} f_p(s) \, ds = 1 \tag{11.13}$$

Corollary 11.4. *The probability measure P is absolutely continuous with respect to the Lebesgue measure if and only if a function $f : \mathbb{R} \to \mathbb{R}^+$ exists so that*

$$\int_{-\infty}^{+\infty} f(s)\, ds = 1 \tag{11.14}$$

and

$$F_P(t) = \int_{-\infty}^{t} f(s)\, ds, \quad \forall t \in \mathbb{R} \tag{11.15}$$

Function f coincides with the PDF P with respect to the Lebesgue measure as under Definition 11.9, ie,

$$f = f_P \tag{11.16}$$

Theorem 11.3. *If P is an absolutely continuous probability measure with respect to the Lebesgue measure, then F_P is continuous and differentiable. Its derivative coincides with the PDF of P with respect to the Lebesgue measure, ie,*

$$F_P'(t) = f_P(t) \quad almost\ everywhere \tag{11.17}$$

Also, for any $a, b \in \mathbb{R}$, $-\infty \le a \le b \le +\infty$, the following holds:

$$F_P(b) - F_P(a) = \int_a^b f_P(s)\, ds \tag{11.18}$$

Definition 11.11. A probability measure P of values in $\mathbb{R}$ is said to be *singular* if its CDF F_P is identically non-null and its derivative F_P' (exists and is) equal to zero almost everywhere.

11.2.1.1. Relations between types of probability measures

Proposition 11.5. *Any discrete probability measure is singular. Specifically, discrete probability measures coincide with singular probability measures which have a segment continuous CDF.*

Remark 11.3. Singular probability functions also exist, which in spite of singularity, have a continuous CDF.

Proposition 11.6. *For singular probability measures with a segment continuous CDF F_P or for discrete probability measures, under the condition that the interval of integration has at least one point of discontinuity, the following relations hold:*

$$\int_{t_1}^{t_2} F_P'(s)\, ds < F_P(t_2) - F_P(t_1) \tag{11.19}$$

Also, one has

$$\int_{t_1}^{t_2} \mathrm{d}F_P(s) = F_P(t_2) - F_P(t_1) \tag{11.20}$$

where $\int_{t_1}^{t_2} \mathrm{d}F_P(s)$ is the Riemann–Stieltjes integral (see Theorem 10.19).

Remark 11.4. The inequality in Equation (11.19) corresponds to the inequality as in Equation (10.150) provided that it is a strict inequality.

Theorem 11.4. *Any probability measure P of values in $\mathbb{R}$ has one representation only, ie,*

$$P = a_{\mathrm{d}} P_{\mathrm{d}} + a_{\mathrm{ac}} P_{\mathrm{ac}} + a_{\mathrm{s}} P_{\mathrm{s}} \tag{11.21}$$

where $a_{\mathrm{d}} \geq 0, a_{\mathrm{ac}} \geq 0, a_{\mathrm{s}} \geq 0, a_{\mathrm{d}} + a_{\mathrm{ac}} + a_{\mathrm{s}} = 1$, P_{d} is a discrete probability measure, P_{ac} is an absolutely continuous probability measure and P_{s} is a singular probability measure with a continuous CDF.

Remark 11.5. By using the representation of any probability measure P given by Equation (11.21), one may derive:

- the discrete probability measures (ie, the singular probability measures with a segment continuous CDF), if $a_{\mathrm{ac}} = a_{\mathrm{s}} = 0$;
- the absolutely continuous probability measures, if $a_{\mathrm{d}} = a_{\mathrm{s}} = 0$;
- the singular probability measures with continuous CDF, if $a_{\mathrm{d}} = a_{\mathrm{ac}} = 1$.

It is clear that any "mixture"/combination of the three fundamental types of probability measures quoted above can be derived under the condition that at least two of the three coefficients $a_{\mathrm{d}}, a_{\mathrm{ac}}$ and a_{s} in the right-hand side of Equation (11.21) are non-null.

11.3. CONDITIONAL PROBABILITIES AND INDEPENDENCE

Definition 11.12 (Bayes' rule). Let:

- $\{\Omega, \Im, P\}$ be a probability space;
- A and B be two events defined on $\{\Omega, \Im, P\}$, ie, $A \in \Im$ and $B \in \Im$;
- $P(A) > 0$.

The probability measure P_E defined on $\mathcal{M}$ is said to be the *conditioned probability given E*, ie,

$$P_E(F) := \begin{cases} \dfrac{P(E \cap F)}{P(E)} & \text{if } P(E) \neq 0 \\ 0 & \text{if } P(E) = 0 \end{cases} \qquad \forall F \in \mathcal{M} \tag{11.22}$$

Remark 11.6. The conditioned probability given E is usually denoted by writing $P(\cdot|E)$.

We now give some properties of conditional probabilities:

(1) $0 \le P(B|A) \le 1$;
(2) if $B \supseteq A$, then $P(B|A) = 1$;
(3) $P(A|A) = 1$;
(4) $P(A|A^c) = 0$;
(5) if B and C are compatible events, ie, $B \cap C = \emptyset$, then

$$P(B \cup C|A) = P(B|A) + P(C|A) \tag{11.23}$$

(6) if $B \cap C \ne \emptyset$, then $P(B \cup C|A) = P(B|A) + P(C|A) - P(B \cap C|A)$;
(7) if $B \subseteq C$, then $P(B|A) \le P(C|A)$.

Corollary 11.5 (Compound probability rule). *Equation (11.22) allows an analytic expression to be derived to compute $P(A \cap B)$ when $P(B|A)$ and $P(A)$ are known:*

$$P(A \cap B) = P(A) \cdot P(B|A) \tag{11.24}$$

Corollary 11.6. *If Equation (11.24) is extended to the case of three events, one also has*

$$P(A \cap B \cap C) = P(A) \cdot P(B|A) \cdot P(C|A \cap B)$$

Corollary 11.7. *In general, in the case of $n + 1$ events, one has*

$$P(A_1 \cap A_2 \cap \cdots \cap A_{n+1}) = P(A_1) \cdot P(A_2|A_1) \cdot P(A_3|A_1 \cap A_2)$$
$$\cdots P(A_{n+1}|A_1 \cap A_2 \cap \cdots \cap A_n)$$

where $P(A_1 \cap A_2 \cap \cdots \cap A_n) > 0$ *and* $P(A_1) > P(A_1 \cap A_2) > P(A_1 \cap A_2 \cap A_3) > \cdots > P(A_1 \cap A_2 \cap \cdots \cap A_n) > 0$.

Proposition 11.7. *If $B_1, B_2, \ldots$ are events incompatible in pairs, ie, $B_i \cap B_j = \emptyset$ for all $i \ne j$, then*

$$P\left(\bigcup_{i=1}^{\infty} B_i|A\right) = \sum_{i=1}^{\infty} P(B_i|A)$$

Theorem 11.5 (Theorem of total probabilities). *Let the following hold.*

- Let $A_1, A_2, \ldots, A_n$ be n events incompatible in pairs, ie, $A_i \cap A_j = \emptyset$ for all $i \ne j \in n, \ni'$:

(1) $\Omega = \bigcup_{i=1}^{n} A_i$;

(2) *with at least one event having a positive probability.*

- *Let B be any other event defined on the same probability space.*

Then

$$P(B) = \sum_{i=1}^{n} P(A_i) \cdot P(B|A_i) \tag{11.25}$$

Theorem 11.6 (Bayes' theorem). *Let the following hold.*

- *Let $A_1, A_2, \ldots, A_n$ be n events incompatible in pairs, ie, $A_i \cap A_j = \varnothing$ for all $i \neq j \in n, \ni':$*

(1) $\Omega = \bigcup_{i=1}^{n} A_i$;

(2) *each of them has a positive probability.*

- *Let B be any other event defined on the same probability space.*
  Then

$$P(A_i|B) = \frac{P(A_i) \cdot P(B|A_i)}{\sum_{i=1}^{n} P(A_i) \cdot P(B|A_i)} \tag{11.26}$$

11.3.1. Independent events

Definition 11.13. Let:

- $\{\Omega, \Im, P\}$ be a probability space;
- A and B be two events defined on $\{\Omega, \Im, P\}$, ie, $A \in \Im$ and $B \in \Im$;
- $P(A) > 0$.

It is said that *event B is independent of event A* with respect to probability measure P of the considered probability space if and only if the following equivalence holds:

$$P(B|A) = P(B) \tag{11.27}$$

Remark 11.7. The definition above states that the occurrence of event A does not lead to any improvement of information about the occurrence of B, or the probability of event B remains unchanged after knowing that event A occurred.

Remark 11.8. Similarly, it is said that *event A is independent of event B* with respect to probability measure P of the considered probability space if and only if the following equivalence holds:

$$P(A|B) = P(A) \quad \text{where } P(B) > 0 \tag{11.28}$$

Definition 11.14. Let:

- $\{\Omega, \Im, P\}$ be a probability space;
- A and B be two events defined on $\{\Omega, \Im, P\}$, ie, $A \in \Im$ and $B \in \Im$;
- $P(A) \cdot P(B) > 0$.

It is said that the *two events A and B are independent* if and only if Equations (11.27) and (11.28) hold at the same moment, ie, if and only if

$$P(B|A) = P(B), \quad P(A|B) = P(A) \tag{11.29}$$

Theorem 11.7. *Equation (11.29) is equivalent to*

$$P(A \cap B) = P(A) \cdot P(B) \tag{11.30}$$

Definition 11.15. Let A, B and C be three events; they are *mutually independent* if and only if all four of the following conditions hold:

(1) $P(A \cap B) = P(A) \cdot P(B)$;
(2) $P(A \cap C) = P(A) \cdot P(C)$;
(3) $P(B \cap C) = P(B) \cdot P(C)$;
(4) $P(A \cap B \cap C) = P(A) \cdot P(B) \cdot P(C)$.

Remark 11.9. If conditions (1), (2) and (3) hold only, but not (4), the three events are *independent in pairs*, but they are not mutually independent.

Remark 11.10. If three events are mutually independent, then they are also independent in pairs. The opposite is not true.

Definition 11.16. In general, one has

- $\{\Omega, \Im, P\}$, a probability space;
- $A_1, A_2, \ldots, A_n$, n events defined on $\{\Omega, \Im, P\}$.

They are said to be *mutually independent* if and only if

$$P(A_1 \cap A_2 \cap \cdots \cap A_n) = P(A_1) \cdot P(A_2) \cdots P(A_n) \tag{11.31}$$

ie,

$$P\left(\bigcap_{i=1}^{n} A_i\right) = \prod_{i=1}^{n} P(A_i)$$

for any permutation of the integers $(1, 2, \ldots, n)$.

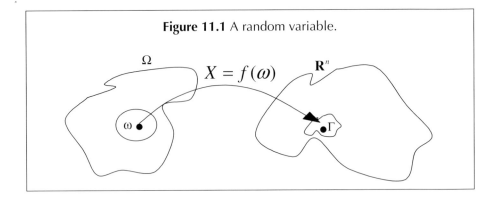

Figure 11.1 A random variable.

11.4. RANDOM VARIABLES

Definition 11.17. Given a set of elementary events $\omega_1, \omega_2, \omega_3, \omega_4, \ldots, \omega_n$ which compose a set Ω, let $(\Omega, \Im, P)$ be a probability space. A function which builds the mapping $X : \Omega \to \mathbb{R}$, ie, which assigns for all $\omega \in \Omega$ a value $X(\omega)$ of $\mathbb{R}$ and which is measurable by $(\Omega, \Im)$ in $(\mathbb{R}, \mathbb{B}(\mathbb{R}))$, is defined as a *random variable* on $(\Omega, \Im, P)$. The notation below holds:

$$X^{-1}(\Gamma) \doteq \{\omega \in \Omega : X(\omega) \in \Gamma\} \in \Im$$

It reads: the pre-images of X (ie, the inverse of function), defined as the value ω which belongs to set Ω when the value of function X evaluated at ω belongs to set Γ, belong to $\Im$ (see Figure 11.1).

Remark 11.11. If Γ is a subset of $\mathbb{R}$, then the *σ-algebra* generated by Γ on the topological space $(\mathbb{R}, \Gamma)$ is a *Borel σ-algebra* on $\mathbb{R}$, ie, $\mathbb{B}(\mathbb{R})$. More generally, it is said that $\Gamma \in \mathbb{B}(\mathbb{R})$.

Alternatively, given K elementary events $\omega_1, \omega_2, \ldots, \omega_k$, X cannot have more than K different values. This means that for any ω_j where $j = 1, 2, \ldots, K$, x assigns a real value, as x_l, where $l = 1, 2, \ldots, L$ with $L \leq K$ since X cannot map a number of events larger than those which compose the probability space Ω. These values are denoted as $x_1, \ldots, x_L$, where $L \leq K$, and without loss of generality one assumes that $x_1 < \cdots < x_L$.

It is clear from the above that given an elementary event ω_j, its probability is equivalent to the probability taken by the corresponding value of the random variable X, ie, x_l. Formally, considering that $x_l = f(\omega_j)$, one has that $P(\omega_j) = P(f(\omega_j) = x_l) = P(x_l)$. This probability is defined as p_l, ie, $P(\omega_j) = P(x_l) = p_l$.

Remark 11.12. If several elementary events ω_j are mapped with the same real value of the random variable X, ie, $f(\omega_1) = x_2$, $f(\omega_{10}) = x_2$, the union of all of the elementary events ω_i so that $f(\omega_i) = x_m$ (in the example above $i = 1, 10$ and $m = 2$) may be defined as the set of X and it is denoted by c_l. Hence, it may be said that any random variable X generates a full partition of Ω in a set c_l, with $l = 1, 2, \ldots, L$, where $P(\omega_i) = P(c_l)$ and c_l is the set of X so that $f(\omega_i) = x_m$.

Definition 11.18. If the probability space Ω is finite, there will be *discrete random variables*; if the probability space Ω is infinite, then there will be *continuous random variables*.

Notation 11.1. In the following, $\mathbb{B} \doteq \mathbb{B}(\mathbb{R})$ and $\mathbb{B}_k \doteq \mathbb{B}(\mathbb{R}^k)$ will also be used.

Proposition 11.8. *Let $(\Omega, \mathcal{M}, P)$ be a probability space and let $X : \Omega \to \mathbb{R}$ be a random variable. Then the function $P_X : \mathbb{B} \to [0, 1]$ defined as*

$$P_X(E) \doteq P(X^{-1}(E)), \quad \forall E \in \mathbb{B} \tag{11.32}$$

is a probability measure on the measurable space $(\mathbb{R}, \mathbb{B})$ and, therefore, the triple $(\mathbb{R}, \mathbb{B}, P_X)$ identifies a probability space.

Definition 11.19. A probability measure P_X defined on the measurable space $(\mathbb{R}, \mathbb{B})$ is said to be the *(probability) distribution* of the random variable X.

Proposition 11.9. *Given the random variable $X : (\Omega, \mathcal{M}, P) \to (\mathbb{R}, \mathbb{B}, P_X)$, the family of sets defined as*

$$\sigma(X) \doteq \{X^{-1}(E) : E \in \mathbb{B}\} \tag{11.33}$$

is a σ-algebra on Ω and is called the σ-algebra generated by X; it reads: the σ-algebra generated by X is equal to the counter- images of X of the set of E where E is a Borel set. Alternatively, Equation (11.33) may be written as

$$X^{-1}(E) \in \sigma(X) \tag{11.34}$$

Remark 11.13. The expression (11.33) which defines the σ-algebra generated by the random variable $X : (\Omega, \mathcal{M}, P) \to (\mathbb{R}, \mathbb{B}, P_X)$ may also be written as

$$\sigma(X) \doteq \{\omega : X(\omega) \in E\}, \quad \forall E \in \mathbb{B} \tag{11.35}$$

Corollary 11.8. *The σ-algebra generated by the random variable X is the smallest σ-algebra with respect to this random variable that is measurable.*

Definition 11.20. Let $(\Omega, \mathcal{M}, P)$ be a probability space and $X_1, X_2, \ldots, X_N$ some random variables on Ω. Then $X_1, X_2, \ldots, X_N$ are said to be *independent with respect to P* if their generated σ-algebras, ie, $\sigma(X_1), \sigma(X_2), \ldots, \sigma(X_N)$, are independent with respect to P (see Definition 10.9).

Proposition 11.10. *Given the probability space* $(\Omega, \mathcal{M}, P)$, *let* $X : (\Omega, \mathcal{M}, P) \to (\mathbb{R}, \mathbb{B}, P_X)$ *be a random variable and let* $A \subseteq \Omega$. *Then, the following relation holds:*

$$A \subseteq \mathcal{M} \tag{11.36}$$

Proposition 11.11. *Given the probability space* $(\Omega, \mathcal{M}, P)$ *and the random variable* $X : (\Omega, \mathcal{M}, P) \to (\mathbb{R}, \mathbb{B}, P_X)$, *let* $A \in \Omega$ *so that*

$$X(A) = E \tag{11.37}$$

Then one has

$$E \subseteq \mathbb{B} \tag{11.38}$$

and the probability *of E is given by the following quantity:*

$$P_X(E) = P(A) \tag{11.39}$$

which represents the sum of the probabilities for the random variable X to take each of the values contained in set E.

Proposition 11.12. *The probability of E, ie, $P_X(E)$, may be expressed as*

$$P_X(E) = \int_E dP_X(x) \tag{11.40}$$

Corollary 11.9. *The probability of E, ie, $P_X(E)$, may also be expressed as*

$$P_X(E) = \int_A dP(\omega) \tag{11.41}$$

where $A = X^{-1}(E)$.

11.4.1. Random vectors

Definition 11.21. Let $(\Omega, \mathcal{M}, P)$ be a probability space and let $\mathbf{X} : \Omega \to \mathbb{R}^k$, $\mathbf{X} = (X_1, X_2, \ldots, X_k)$, be a function measurable by $(\Omega, \mathcal{M})$ in $(\mathbb{R}^k, \mathbb{B}(\mathbb{R}^k))$. Then $\mathbf{X}$ is defined to be the *k-dimensional random vector* or *k-dimensional random variable*.

Proposition 11.13. *Let* $(\Omega, \mathcal{M}, P)$ *be a probability space and let* $\mathbf{X} : \Omega \to \mathbb{R}^k$ *be a k-dimensional random vector,* $\mathbf{X} = (X_1, X_2, \ldots, X_k)$. *Then the function* $P_{\mathbf{X}} : \mathbb{B}_k \to [0, 1]$ *defined by*

$$P_{\mathbf{X}}(E) = P(\mathbf{X}^{-1}(E)), \quad \forall E \in \mathbb{B}_k$$

is the probability measure on the measurable space $(\mathbb{R}^k, \mathbb{B}_k)$ *and the triple* $(\mathbb{R}^k, \mathbb{B}_k, P_{\mathbf{X}})$ *identifies a probability space.*

Remark 11.14. The demonstration of this proposition is absolutely analogous to that of Proposition 11.8.

Definition 11.22. The probability measure $P_{\mathbf{X}}$ defined on the measurable space $(\mathbb{R}^k, \mathbb{B}_k)$ is said to be the *joint (probability) distribution* of $X_1, X_2, \ldots, X_k$, or the *distribution of the random vector* $\mathbf{X}$.

Proposition 11.14. *Given the k-dimensional random vector* $\mathbf{X} : (\Omega, \mathcal{M}, P) \to (\mathbb{R}^k, \mathbb{B}, P_{\mathbf{X}})$ *ie,* $\mathbf{X} = (X_1, X_2, \ldots, X_k)$, *the set family defined as*

$$\sigma(\mathbf{X}) \doteq \{\mathbf{X}^{-1}(\mathbf{E}) : \mathbf{E} \in \mathbb{B}_k\} \tag{11.42}$$

or as

$$\sigma(\mathbf{X}) \doteq \{(X_1^{-1}(E_1), \ldots, X_k^{-1}(E_k)) : E_1, \ldots, E_k \in \mathbb{B}\} \tag{11.43}$$

is a σ-*algebra on* Ω *and is called the* σ-algebra generated by the random vector $\mathbf{X}$.

Remark 11.15. Expressions (11.42) and (11.43) which define the σ-algebra generated by the k-dimensional random vector $\mathbf{X} : (\Omega, \mathcal{M}, P) \to (\mathbb{R}^k, \mathbb{B}, P_{\mathbf{X}})$ may also be written as

$$\sigma(\mathbf{X}) \doteq \{\omega : X_1(\omega) \in E_1, X_2(\omega) \in E_2, \ldots, X_k(\omega) \in E_k\}, \quad \forall E_1, E_2, \ldots, E_k \in \mathbb{B} \tag{11.44}$$

Corollary 11.10. *The* σ-algebra generated by the k-dimensional random vector $\mathbf{X}$ is the smallest σ-algebra with respect to which this random vector is measurable.

11.4.2. Probability functions of a random variable

Proposition 11.8 shows that any random variable $X : (\Omega, \mathcal{M}) \to (\mathbb{R}, \mathbb{B})$ is paired off to a distribution (see Definition 11.19) as well as to a CDF and a survivor distribution.

Definition 11.23. Given a random variable $X : (\Omega, \mathcal{M}, P) \to (\mathbb{R}, \mathbb{B}, P_X)$:

(1) the *CDF* of X is defined as

$$F_X(x) \doteq P_X((-\infty, x]) = P(\{X \le x\}) \tag{11.45}$$

(2) the *survivor distribution* of X is defined as

$$S_X(x) \doteq 1 - F_X(x) = P_X((x, +\infty)) = (P(\{X > x\})) \tag{11.46}$$

Remark 11.16. The definition of the CDF and the survivor function of a k-dimensional random vector $\mathbf{X} = (X_1, X_2, \ldots, X_k)$ is analogous.

Remark 11.17. The CDF of a random variable X may be expanded (see Equation (11.45)):

$$F_X(x) \doteq P(\{\omega \in \Omega : X(\omega) \le x\}) = P_X(X(\omega) \le x) \tag{11.47}$$

which has to be interpreted as the probability that, in a set of elementary events ω, the real value which is assigned to the random variable X is lower than or equal to a specific value x, $-\infty \le x \le +\infty$.

Remark 11.18. Similarly, the survivor function of a random variable X may be similarly expanded (see Equation (11.46)):

$$S_X(x) \doteq 1 - F_X(x) = P(\{\omega \in \Omega : X(\omega) > x\}) = P_X(X(\omega) > x) \tag{11.48}$$

Proposition 11.15. *Let* $X : (\Omega, \mathcal{M}, P) \to (\mathbb{R}, \mathbb{B}, P_X)$ *be a random variable having distribution* P_X *and CDF* F_X. *Then, for any* $a, b \in \mathbb{R}$, $-\infty \le a < b \le +\infty$, *the following relations hold:*

$$P_X(a < X \le b) = F_X(b) - F_X(a)$$
$$P_X(a \le X \le b) = F_X(b) - F_X(a-)$$
$$P_X(a \le X < b) = F_X(b-) - F_X(a-)$$
$$P_X(a < X < b) = F_X(b-) - F_X(a)$$

where:

- $F_X(a-) = F_X(a) - P_X(a)$;
- $F_X(b-) = F_X(b) - P_X(b)$.

Probability measures P_X *generated* (in the sense of Proposition 11.8) by a random variable $X : (\Omega, \mathcal{M}, P) \to (\mathbb{R}, \mathbb{B}, P_X)$ are broken down into discrete, absolutely continuous and singular probability measures as in Definitions 11.8, 11.9 and 11.11, respectively

Then the following definition may be derived.

Definition 11.24. The random variable $X : (\Omega, \mathcal{M}, P) \to (\mathbb{R}, \mathbb{B}, P_X)$ is said to be a *discrete random variable* if its distribution function P_X is discrete, ie, if a countable set $E = \{x_1, x_2, \ldots, x_j, \ldots\}$ exists so that

$$P_X(E) = 1$$

Proposition 11.16. *Let* $X : (\Omega, \mathcal{M}, P) \to (\mathbb{R}, \mathbb{B}, P_X)$ *be a discrete random variable and let us assume, without loss of generality, that the elements of E of Definition 11.24 are set in a growing sequence, ie, $x_1 \leq x_2 \leq \cdots \leq x_j \leq \cdots$. Then F_X, ie, the CDF of X, can be written as*

$$F_X(x_l) = \sum_{j=1}^{l} P_X(x_j), \quad \forall x_l \in E \tag{11.49}$$

Notation 11.2. One may denote

$$P_X(x_j) = p_j \tag{11.50}$$

and

$$x_l = x \tag{11.51}$$

so that Equation (11.49) becomes

$$F_X(x) = \sum_{j=1}^{l} p_j, \quad \forall x \in E \tag{11.52}$$

Definition 11.25. The random variable $X : (\Omega, \mathcal{M}, P) \to (\mathbb{R}, \mathbb{B}, P_X)$ with respect to the Lebesgue measure $\tilde{m}_1$ is said to be an *absolutely continuous random variable* if its distribution function P_X is absolutely continuous, ie, if

$$P_X(E) = \int_E f_X(x) \, d\tilde{m}_1(x), \quad \forall E \in \mathbb{B} \tag{11.53}$$

and function f is said to be the *PDF of P_X*.

Remark 11.19. Based on Proposition (11.3), Equation (11.53) may be equally written as

$$P_X(E) = \int_E f_X(x) \, dx, \quad \forall E \in \mathbb{B} \tag{11.54}$$

Theorem 11.8. *If $X : (\Omega, \mathcal{M}, P) \to (\mathbb{R}, \mathbb{B}, P_X)$ is an absolutely continuous random variable, then F_X is continuous and differentiable. Its derivative coincides with the PDF of P_X (with respect to the Lebesgue measure), ie,*

$$F'_X(x) = f_X(x) \tag{11.55}$$

and, for any $a, b \in \mathbb{R}, -\infty \le a \le b \le +\infty$, the following holds:

$$F_X(b) - F_X(a) = \int_a^b f_X(s)\, ds \tag{11.56}$$

or

$$F_X(x) = \int_{-\infty}^x f_X(t)\, dt \tag{11.57}$$

Proposition 11.17. *If the probability measure P_X defined on $(\mathbb{R}, \mathbb{B})$ is absolutely continuous with respect to the Lebesgue measure and has a PDF f_X, then the following equivalence holds:*

$$\int_E dP_X(x) = \int_E f_X(x)\, dx, \quad \forall E \in \mathbb{B} \tag{11.58}$$

Corollary 11.11. *The following equivalence can be derived from Equation (11.58):*

$$dP_X = f_X\, dx \tag{11.59}$$

or, equally, based on Proposition 11.3,

$$dP_X = f_X\, d\tilde{m}_1 \tag{11.60}$$

Corollary 11.12. *The following equivalence also holds:*

$$\int_A dP(\omega) = \int_E f_X(x)\, dx, \quad \forall E \in \mathbb{B} \tag{11.61}$$

Theorem 11.9. *If a distribution P_X of the random variable $X : (\Omega, \mathcal{M}) \to (\mathbb{R}, \mathbb{B})$ admits density f_X with respect to the Lebesgue measure, then:*

(1) *for any function $g : \mathbb{R} \to [0, +\infty)$, to be integrable with respect to the probability measure P_X, one has*

$$\int_{\mathbb{R}} g(x)\, dP_X(x) = \int_{\mathbb{R}} g(x) f_X(x)\, d\tilde{m}_1 \tag{11.62}$$

(2) *for any function $g : \mathbb{R} \to \mathbb{R}$, g belonging to $\mathcal{L}^1(P_X)$, one has*

$$\int_{\mathbb{R}} g(x)\, dP_X(x) = \int_{\mathbb{R}} g(x) f_X(x)\, d\tilde{m}_1 \qquad (11.63)$$

Definitions 11.24 and 11.25 show how the concept of density function of probability measure P_X "*generated*" by a random variable X is applied only to absolutely continuous random variables. It was demonstrated (see Equation (11.55)) that in absolutely continuous random variables, F_X is a continuous and differentiable function whose derivative is equal to f_X. However, the following proposition holds which allows one to extend the concept of the density function of P_X with respect to the Lebesgue measure to discrete random variables.

Proposition 11.18. *Let $X : (\Omega, \mathcal{M}, P) \to (\mathbb{R}, \mathbb{B}, P_X)$ be a discrete random variable, then the CDF may be represented as*

$$F_X(x) = \sum_{j \in \mathbb{R}} p_j (1 - \theta(x_j - x)) \qquad (11.64)$$

where $\theta(x)$ is the Heaviside function (see Notation 6.4).

Proposition 11.19. *Let $X : (\Omega, \mathcal{M}, P) \to (\mathbb{R}, \mathbb{B}, P_X)$ be a discrete random variable, then the CDF may be denoted as*

$$F_X(x) = \sum_{j \in \mathbb{R}} p_j \mathbf{1}_{(x_j \leq x)} \qquad (11.65)$$

where $\mathbf{1}_{(x_j \leq x)}$ is the index function (see Definition 6.3).

Remark 11.20. Clearly $F_X(x)$ is a constant left segment continuous function with jumps of width p_j when $x_j \leq x$.

Proposition 11.20. *Let $X : (\Omega, \mathcal{M}, P) \to (\mathbb{R}, \mathbb{B}, P_X)$ be a discrete random variable, then the PDF may be denoted as*

$$f_X(x) = \sum_{j \in R} p_j \delta(x_j - x) \qquad (11.66)$$

where $\delta(x)$ is the discrete version of the Dirac delta (Kroneker delta; see Definition 6.4).

Remark 11.21. A probability function of a random variable may be used to study phenomena described by other random variables and the corresponding probability functions may be derived.

Example 11.1. The random variable which describes the number of events x which occur in a time interval $[0, t]$ is defined to be Poisson random variable, ie, $X \sim \text{Poisson}(\lambda t)$, and its PDF is $f_X(t) = ((\lambda t)^x / x!)e^{-\lambda t}$ where λt represents the mean of occurrence of events in the time interval $[0, t]$.

It can be derived that the probability that no event occurs in interval $[0, t]$ is

$$P(X = 0) = \frac{(\lambda t)^0}{0!}e^{-\lambda t} = e^{-\lambda t}$$

This is required if one needs to study the random variable T which describes the time interval $[0, t]$, or simply t, required for an event to occur.

Two methods may be used to derive the probability functions of T.

(1) The probability that the random variable X is equal to zero (ie, that in the interval t no event occurred) is equivalent to the probability that the random variable T is higher than t (ie, that a longer time than t is required for the occurrence of an event), ie,

$$F_T(t) = P(T \leq t) = 1 - P(T > t) = 1 - e^{-\lambda t}$$

(2) The probability that the random variable T is smaller or equal to t is equal to the probability that the random variable X is higher or equal to one, ie,

$$P(T \leq t) = P(X = 1) + P(X = 2) + P(X = 3) + \cdots = P(X \geq 1)$$

if one considers Equation (4.4) one may then compute the PDF by deriving $F_T(t)$ with respect to t, ie,

$$f_T(t) = \frac{d}{dt}F_T(t) = \lambda e^{-\lambda t}$$

The random variable T with a probability density function $\lambda e^{-\lambda t}$ is defined to be exponential with parameter λ and is denoted by: $T \sim \exp(\lambda)$ where λ^{-1} represents the average time interval between one event and another. This is also called the inter-arrival time.

Based on the observations made for the example above, the following useful proposition may be derived.

Proposition 11.21. *Given a random variable X distributed as a Poisson, ie, $X \sim$ Poisson(λt) and its PDF $f_X(t) = ((\lambda t)^x / x!)e^{-\lambda t}$, which describes the number of events x which occur in an interval $[0, t]$ and where λt represents the mean of occurrence of events in the time interval $[0, t]$, the random variable T, which describes*

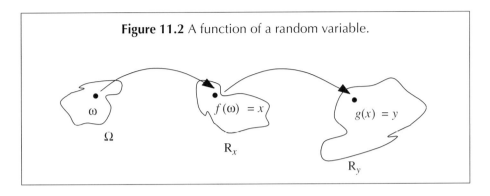

Figure 11.2 A function of a random variable.

the time interval $[0, t]$, or simply t, required for an event x to occur is defined as an exponential, ie, $T \sim \exp(\lambda)$, with its PDF $f_T(t) = \lambda e^{-\lambda t}$ where λ^{-1} represents the average time elapsed between one event and another, or also called the inter-arrival time.

Definition 11.26. A random variable Z distributed according to the normal law is denoted as

$$Z \sim N(0, 1)$$

Definition 11.27. A random variable X distributed according the normal law is denoted as

$$X \sim N(\mu, \sigma^2)$$

Proposition 11.22. *The normal random variable X can be represented in terms of standard normal random variable Z as*

$$\frac{X - \mu}{\sigma} = Z$$

11.4.3. Probability distribution for a random variable function

The random variable Y is defined as a function of a random variable X, ie, $Y = g(X)$; then $Y = g(f(\omega))$ (see Figure 11.2).

Example 11.2. If the random variables $T_1, T_2, T_3, \ldots, T_n$ are independent and identically distributed as discrete exponentials with a parameter λ, ie, $T_i \sim \exp(\lambda)$, $f_T(t) = \lambda e^{-\lambda t}$ for $t \geq 0$, the random variable T_i describes the time t for an event to occur, or time t between two consecutive events, ie, the inter-arrival time.

Then let $Y_n = \sum_{i=1}^{n} T_i$ be defined. The PDF $f_Y(y)$ is then derived.

A random variable Y_n describes the time t for the occurrence of n events $(n \in N)$ or time t between n pairs of consecutive events, since it is the summation of n exponential random variables. In order to derive the CDF and then the PDF one should recall that the random variable which describes the number of n events, where n is an integer, which occur in the time interval t described by an exponential random variable, is distributed as a Poisson random variable with an average occurrence in the time interval t equal to λt, ie, $\xi \sim \text{Poisson}(\lambda t)$ with $f_\xi(t) = ((\lambda t)^n / n!) e^{-\lambda t}$.

It can be that by the construction of Y_n, the related CDF, ie, $F_{Y_n}(t) = P(Y_n \leq t)$, represents the probability that a shorter or equal time at interval $[0, t]$, or t, is enough for the occurrence of at least n events.

Therefore, there are two ways to derive the Y_n probability functions, ie, by following by analogy the procedure of Example 11.1.

(1) The probability that the random variable ξ is smaller than or equal to $(n - 1)$ (ie, in the interval t, $(n - 1)$ events occur) is equal to the probability that the random variable Y_n is higher than t (ie, that a time longer than t is needed for the occurrence of at least n events), ie,

$$P(\xi \leq n - 1) = P(Y_n > t) = \sum_{j=0}^{n-1} \frac{(\lambda t)^j}{j!} e^{-\lambda t}$$

Since the CDF was defined as $F_X(x) = P(X \leq x)$, one may derive the CDF of the random variable T:

$$F_{Y_n}(t) = 1 - \sum_{j=0}^{n-1} \frac{(\lambda t)^j}{j!} e^{-\lambda t} \tag{11.67}$$

(2) The probability that the random variable Y_n is smaller than or equal to t (ie, that n events surely occur in interval t) is equivalent to the probability that the random variable ξ is higher than or equal to n (ie, that in interval t at least n events occur), ie,

$$F_{Y_n}(t) = \sum_{j=n}^{\infty} \frac{(\lambda t)^j}{j!} e^{-\lambda t} \tag{11.68}$$

Recalling Equation (4.4), ie, $\sum_{j=0}^{\infty}((\lambda t)^j / j!) = e^{\lambda t}$, then $\sum_{j=0}^{\infty}((\lambda t)^j / j!)e^{-\lambda t} = 1$; using this result, Equation (11.67) corresponds to (11.68), ie,

$$f_{Y_n}(t) = \frac{\lambda^n e^{-\lambda t} t^{n-1}}{(n - 1)!} \quad \text{where } n, t > 0 \tag{11.69}$$

This PDF is the density of an Erlang random variable with parameters n, λ.

One may conclude that given the random variable $T_1, T_2, T_3, \ldots, T_n$, the PDF of a function of a random variable defined as $Y_n = \sum_{i=1}^{n} T_i$ is distributed as an Erlang with parameters (n, λ), ie, $Y_n \sim \text{Erlang}(n, \lambda)$. This PDF shows the distribution of time necessary so that n events occur. Hence, based on Proposition 11.21, the random variable which describes the occurrence of events in the time interval t is distributed as $\text{Poisson}(\lambda t)$.

Based on the considerations of Example 11.2, the following useful proposition is derived.

Proposition 11.23. *Given a sequence of random variables $T_1, T_2, T_3, \ldots, T_n$ independent and identically distributed as a discrete exponential with a parameter λ, ie, $T_i \sim \exp(\lambda)$, $f_T(t) = \lambda e^{-\lambda t}$ for $t \geq 0$, which describe the time t for the occurrence of an event, or time t between two consecutive events (ie, the inter-arrival time), the random variable $Y_n = \sum_{i=1}^{n} T_i$, which describes the time t for the occurrence of n events or time t between the occurrence of n pairs of consecutive events, is defined as an Erlang, ie, $Y_n \sim \text{Erlang}(n, \lambda)$ for $n \in N$,*

$$f_{Y_n}(t) = \frac{\lambda^n e^{-\lambda t} t^{n-1}}{(n-1)!} \quad \text{where } n, t > 0$$

This proposition also holds by using the definition of a random variable Y_n as a base.

The observations above may also be extended to the case where the sequence of random variables $T_1, T_2, T_3, \ldots, T_n$ are independent and identically distributed as a continuous discrete exponential with parameter λ, ie, $T_i \sim \exp(\lambda)$. In this case, the following proposition holds.

Proposition 11.24. *Given a sequence of random variables $T_1, T_2, T_3, \ldots, T_n$ independent and identically distributed as a continuous exponential with a parameter λ, ie, $T_i \sim \exp(\lambda)$, $f_T(t) = \lambda e^{-\lambda t}$ for $t \geq 0$, which describe the time t for the occurrence of an event, or time t between two consecutive events (ie, the inter-arrival time), the random variable $Y_n = \sum_{i=1}^{n} T_i$, which describes the time t for the occurrence of n events or time t between n pairs of consecutive events is defined as a gamma, ie, $Y_n \sim \text{gamma}(n, \lambda)$ for $n \in \mathbb{R}$,*

$$f_{Y_n}(t) = \frac{\lambda^n e^{-\lambda t} t^{n-1}}{\Gamma(n)} \quad \text{where } n, t > 0.$$

This proposition clearly also holds by starting from the definition of a random variable Y_n.

The following useful corollary is derived from the demonstration above.

Corollary 11.13. *Given a random variable* $X \sim \text{gamma}(n, \lambda)$ *for* $n \in \mathbb{R}$, *ie,*

$$f_X(t) = \frac{\lambda^n e^{-\lambda t} t^{n-1}}{\Gamma(n)} \quad \text{where } n, t > 0$$

if the same random variable is defined only for $n \in \mathbb{N}$, *then* $X \sim \text{Erlang}(n, \lambda)$, *ie,*

$$f_X(t) = \frac{\lambda^n e^{-\lambda t} t^{n-1}}{(n-1)!} \quad \text{where } n, t > 0$$

Example 11.3. Let the random variable $X \sim N(\mu, \sigma^2)$, ie,

$$f_X(x) = \frac{1}{\sigma\sqrt{2\pi}} e^{-(x-\mu)^2/2\sigma^2}$$

$x \in (-\infty; +\infty)$ and $Y = |X|$. The PDF of Y is derived by applying the symmetry property of a normal distribution and of the absolute value function, ie,

$$f_Y(y) = \frac{2}{\sigma\sqrt{2\pi}} e^{-(y-\mu)^2/2\sigma^2} \quad \text{where } y \in [0; +\infty)$$

Theorem 11.10. *Given the CDF* $F_X(x)$ *and its PDF* $f_X(x)$, *the PDF of* $Y = g(X)$, *ie,* $f_Y(y)$ *where* g *is a monotonous function, is denoted as*

$$f_Y(y) = f_X(g^{-1}(y)) \cdot \left| \frac{1}{g'(g^{-1}(y))} \right| \tag{11.70}$$

Corollary 11.14. *If* g *is a monotonous growing function, it is denoted as*

$$f_Y(y) = f_X(g^{-1}(y)) \cdot \frac{1}{g'(g^{-1}(y))} \tag{11.71}$$

Example 11.4. Let the random variable $X \sim N(\mu, \sigma^2)$ as in Definition 11.27 and $Y = e^X$. The PDF of Y is derived as $Y = g(x) = e^X$, hence $x = g^{-1}(y) = \ln(y)$; since this is an exponential monotonous growing function Equation (11.71) may be used

$$f_Y(y) = f_X(g^{-1}(y)) \cdot \frac{1}{g'(g^{-1}(y))} \tag{11.71}$$

whence

$$f_Y(y) = \frac{1}{y \cdot \sigma\sqrt{2\pi}} e^{-(\ln(y)-\mu)^2/2\sigma^2}$$

In this last expression, one may recognise the PDF of a lognormal random variable. In fact, if

$$X \sim N(\mu, \sigma^2)$$

and $Y = e^X$, then

$$Y \sim \text{Log } N(e^{\mu + \sigma^2/2}, e^{\mu + \sigma^2/2} \cdot (e^{\sigma^2} - 1))$$

Theorem 11.11 (Gillespie). *Given the CDF $F_X(x)$ and its PDF $f_X(x)$, the PDF of $Y = g(X)$, ie, $f_Y(y)$, is given by the following expression:*

$$f_Y(y) = \int_{-\infty}^{+\infty} \delta(y - g(x)) f_X(x) \, dx$$

where δ is the non-centred delta function (see Notation 6.3).

Theorem 11.12 (Central limit). *Let X_i, for $i = 1, 2, \ldots N$, be N independent and identically distributed random variables with a mean equal to μ and a variance equal to σ^2 and let Y_N be defined as*

$$Y_N = \frac{\sum_{i=0}^{N}(X_i - \mu)}{\sqrt{N}} \tag{11.72}$$

it can be derived that $E(Y_N) = 0$, $\text{VAR}(Y_N) = \sigma^2$ for $N \to \infty$ and one has

$$Y_N \sim N(0, \sigma^2)$$

11.5. RADON–NIKODYM DERIVATIVE

Theorem 11.13 (Radon–Nikodym theorem for probability measures). *Let $(\Omega, \mathcal{M}, P)$ be a probability space. If $\widetilde{P}$ is an absolutely continuous probability measure with respect to P as under Definition 11.4, then there is one non-negative random variable only $\Lambda : (\Omega, \mathcal{M}) \to (\mathbb{R}, \mathbb{B})$ so that for all $A \in \mathcal{M}$ one has*

$$\int_A dP = \int_A \Lambda \, d\widetilde{P} \tag{11.73}$$

and Λ is said to be the Radon–Nikodym *derivative of the probability measure P with respect to the probability measure $\widetilde{P}$.*

Remark 11.22. In light of Equation (11.1), Equation (11.73) may also be written as

$$P(A) = \int_A \Lambda \, d\widetilde{P} \tag{11.74}$$

valid for all $A \in \mathcal{M}$.

Corollary 11.15. *The use of the word* derivative *with reference to* Λ *is due to the fact that, typically, this random variable is correctly denoted by writing*

$$\Lambda = \frac{dP}{d\widetilde{P}} \tag{11.75}$$

Theorem 11.14 (Bayes' theorem). *Equation (11.73) implies the condition*

$$E^P[Y] = E^{\widetilde{P}}[\Lambda \cdot Y] \tag{11.76}$$

for any random variable Y, where one has $E^{\widetilde{P}}|\Lambda \cdot Y| < \infty$.

Proposition 11.25. *Let* $X : (\Omega, \mathcal{M}) \to (\mathbb{R}, \mathbb{B})$ *and* $Y : (\Omega, \mathcal{M}) \to (\mathbb{R}, \mathbb{B})$ *be two random variables which have P_X and P_Y, respectively. If P_X and P_Y are two equivalent probability measures, then the random variable $\Lambda_{X,Y}$, ie, the Radon–Nikodym derivative of P_X with respect to P_Y, may be expressed as*

$$\Lambda_{X,Y} = \frac{dP_X}{dP_Y} \tag{11.77}$$

or as

$$\Lambda_{X,Y} = \frac{f_X}{f_Y} \tag{11.78}$$

where f_X and f_Y represent the density functions of P_X and of P_Y, respectively, with respect to the Lebesgue measure.

11.6. MOMENTS
11.6.1. Expected value and variance of random variables
Definition 11.28. The expected value or the first moment or mean of the random variable X denoted by $E(X)$ is the number defined by

$$E(X) = \sum_x x f_X(x)$$

if X is discrete, and by

$$E(X) = \int_{-\infty}^{+\infty} x f_X(x) \, dx$$

if X is continuous.

Proposition 11.26. *If X is a random variable with PDF $f_X(x)$ and $Y = g(X)$, then*

$$E(Y) = \sum_y y f_Y(y) = \sum_x g(x) f_X(x)$$

if X is discrete, and

$$E(Y) = \int_{-\infty}^{+\infty} y f_Y(y) \, dy = \int_{-\infty}^{+\infty} g(x) f_X(x) \, dx$$

if X is continuous.

Definition 11.29. Given X a random variable with a mean μ and given r a positive integer, the rth non-centred moment of X is defined to be the expected value of the function $g(X) = X^r$, ie,

$$\mu_r = E(X^r)$$

Definition 11.30. Given X a random variable with a mean μ and given r a positive integer, the rth centred moment of X is defined to be the expected value of function $g(X) = (X - \mu)^r$, ie,

$$\bar{\mu}_r = E[(X - \mu)^r]$$

Theorem 11.15. *The following relation exists between the centred and non-centred moments:*

$$\bar{\mu}_r = \sum_{h=0}^{r} (-1)^h \binom{r}{h} \mu^h \mu_{r-h} \tag{11.79}$$

where $\binom{r}{h}$ is the binomial coefficient.

Remark 11.23. The centred moment is equal to the non-centred moment, ie, $\mu_1 = \bar{\mu}_1$. The first moment is denoted by μ.

Definition 11.31. The second centred moment of X, ie, $E[(X - \mu)^2]$, is also defined as the variance and is denoted by σ^2.

Proposition 11.27. *Variance may also be computed by the relation below:*

$$\sigma^2 = \mu_2 - (\mu_1)^2 \tag{11.80}$$

or by using Notation 11.23

$$\sigma^2 = \mu_2 - (\bar{\mu}_1)^2$$

Definition 11.32. Given two random variables X and Y, whose expected values are μ_X and μ_Y respectively, the covariance between X and Y, denoted by $\text{cov}(X, Y)$ is defined as the quantity

$$\text{cov}(X, Y) = E[(X - \mu_X) \cdot (Y - \mu_Y)] \tag{11.81}$$

Proposition 11.28. *Covariance between the two random variables X and Y may be also expressed as*

$$\text{cov}(X, Y) = E(X \cdot Y) - \mu_X \cdot \mu_Y$$

11.6.1.1. Expected value and variance of random vectors

Definition 11.33. The vector of the expected values of each random variable $X_i, i = 1, 2, \ldots, n$, which constitutes the vector $\underline{X}$ is defined to be the expected value or first moment or mean of the n-dimensional random vector $\underline{X} = [X_1 \quad X_2 \quad \cdots \quad X_n]$ and is denoted by $E(\underline{X})$, ie,

$$E(\underline{X}) = [E(X_1) \quad E(X_2) \quad \cdots \quad E(X_n)]$$
$$= \left[\sum_{x_1} x_1 f_{X_1}(x_1) \quad \sum_{x_2} x_2 f_{X_2}(x_2) \quad \cdots \quad \sum_{x_n} x_n f_{X_n}(x_n) \right]$$

if X_i are discrete random variables, or by

$$E(\underline{X}) = [E(X_1) \quad E(X_2) \quad \cdots \quad E(X_n)]$$
$$= \left[\int_{-\infty}^{+\infty} x_1 f_{X_1}(x_1)\, dx_1 \quad \int_{-\infty}^{+\infty} x_2 f_{X_2}(x_2)\, dx_2 \quad \cdots \quad \int_{-\infty}^{+\infty} x_n f_{X_n}(x_n)\, dx_n \right]$$

if X_i are continuous random variables.

Definition 11.34. Given the n-dimensional random vector $\underline{X} = [X_1 X_2 \cdots X_n]$ with an expected value equal to $\underline{\mu}$, the symmetric positive semi-definite matrix below is defined to be the *variance–covariance matrix* of $\underline{X}$ and is denoted by Σ, ie,

$$\Sigma = E[(\underline{X} - \underline{\mu})^2]$$
$$= E[(\underline{X} - \underline{\mu})(\underline{X} - \underline{\mu})^{\text{T}}] \tag{11.82}$$

Proposition 11.29. *The variance–covariance matrix of $\underline{X}$ may also be expressed as*

$$\Sigma = E[\underline{X}\underline{X}^{\text{T}}] - \underline{\mu}\underline{\mu}^{\text{T}}$$

Remark 11.24. The usual representation of the variance–covariance matrix of a n-dimensional random vector $\underline{X} = [X_1 \quad X_2 \quad \cdots \quad X_n]$ is

$$\Sigma = \begin{bmatrix} \sigma_1^2 & \text{cov}(X_1, X_2) & \cdots & \text{cov}(X_1, X_n) \\ \text{cov}(X_2, X_1) & \sigma_2^2 & \cdots & \text{cov}(X_2, X_n) \\ \vdots & \vdots & \vdots & \vdots \\ \text{cov}(X_n, X_1) & \text{cov}(X_n, X_2) & \cdots & \sigma_n^2 \end{bmatrix}$$

Definition 11.35. Given two n-dimensional random vectors $\underline{X}$ and $\underline{Y}$, whose expected values correspond to vectors $\underline{\mu}_X$ and $\underline{\mu}_Y$ respectively, the covariance matrix between $\underline{X}$ and $\underline{Y}$, denoted by $\text{cov}(\underline{X}, \underline{Y})$, is defined to be the matrix

$$\text{cov}(\underline{X}, \underline{Y}) = E[(\underline{X}^T - \underline{\mu}_X^T) \cdot (\underline{Y} - \underline{\mu}_Y)] \tag{11.83}$$

Proposition 11.30. *The covariance matrix between two random vectors $\underline{X}$ and $\underline{Y}$ may also be expressed as*

$$\text{cov}(\underline{X}, \underline{Y}) = E(\underline{X}^T \cdot \underline{Y}) - \underline{\mu}_X^T \cdot \underline{\mu}_Y$$

Remark 11.25. The covariance matrix $\text{cov}(\underline{X}, \underline{Y})$ between two random vectors $\underline{X}$ and $\underline{Y}$ may also expanded as

$$\text{cov}(\underline{X}, \underline{Y}) = \begin{bmatrix} \sigma_{X_1 Y_1} & \sigma_{X_1 Y_2} & \cdots & \sigma_{X_1 Y_n} \\ \sigma_{X_2 Y_1} & \sigma_{X_2 Y_2} & \cdots & \sigma_{X_2 Y_n} \\ \vdots & \vdots & \vdots & \vdots \\ \sigma_{X_n Y_1} & \sigma_{X_n Y_2} & \cdots & \sigma_{X_n Y_n} \end{bmatrix}$$

where

$$\sigma_{X_i Y_j} = \text{cov}(X_i, Y_j), i = 1, 2, \ldots, n; j = 1, 2, \ldots, n.$$

Remark 11.26. In order to compute the covariance matrix between two random vectors they do not necessarily need to have the same dimension.

As an example, to compute the covariance matrix between a n-dimensional random vector $\underline{X}$ and a m-dimensional random vector $\underline{Y}$, with $n \neq m$, the covariance matrix would be a rectangular symmetric matrix of order $n \times m$, ie,

$$\text{cov}(\underline{X}, \underline{Y}) = \begin{bmatrix} \sigma_{X_1 Y_1} & \sigma_{X_1 Y_2} & \cdots & \sigma_{X_1 Y_n} \\ \sigma_{X_2 Y_1} & \sigma_{X_2 Y_2} & \cdots & \sigma_{X_2 Y_n} \\ \vdots & \vdots & \vdots & \vdots \\ \sigma_{X_m Y_1} & \sigma_{X_m Y_2} & \cdots & \sigma_{X_m Y_n} \end{bmatrix}$$

11.6.1.2. Expected value and variance properties
11.6.1.2.1. Expected value and random variable variance properties

(1) If $X = \mathbf{1}_A$, then $E(X) = P(A)$.
(2) If $Z = X + Y$, then

$$E(Z) = E(X) + E(Y)$$

and

$$\text{VAR}(Z) = \text{VAR}(X + Y) = \text{VAR}(X) + \text{VAR}(Y) + 2\,\text{cov}(X, Y)$$

(3) If $Z = aX$, then

$$E(Z) = aE(X)$$

and

$$\text{VAR}(Z) = a^2 \, \text{VAR}(X)$$

(4) If X and Y are two independent random variables, then the following relation below holds:

$$E(X \cdot Y) = E(X) \cdot E(Y)$$

that is

$$\text{cov}(X, Y) = 0$$

and

$$\text{VAR}(X + Y) = \text{VAR}(X) + \text{VAR}(Y)$$

11.6.1.2.2. Expected value and random vector variance properties

(1) If $\underline{Z} = \underline{X} + \underline{Y}$, then

$$E(\underline{Z}) = E(\underline{X}) + E(\underline{Y})$$

and

$$\begin{aligned}
\text{VAR}(\underline{Z}) = \text{VAR}(\underline{X} + \underline{Y}) &= \text{VAR}(\underline{X}) + \text{VAR}(\underline{Y}) + 2\,\text{cov}(\underline{X}, \underline{Y}) \\
&= \text{VAR}(\underline{X}) + \text{VAR}(\underline{Y}) + 2[E(\underline{X}^\text{T} \cdot \underline{Y}) - (E(\underline{X}))^\text{T} \cdot E(\underline{Y})]
\end{aligned}$$

(2) If $\underline{Z} = \underline{a}^\text{T}\underline{X}$, then

$$E(\underline{Z}) = E(\underline{a}^\text{T}\underline{X}) = \underline{a}^\text{T}E(\underline{X})$$

and

$$\text{VAR}(\underline{Z}) = \underline{a}^\text{T}\Sigma\underline{a} \qquad\qquad (11.84)$$

where Σ is the variance–covariance matrix of the random vector $\underline{X}$, ie, $\Sigma = \text{VAR}(\underline{X})$.

Remark 11.27. $E(\underline{Z})$ may also be denoted by

$$E(\underline{Z}) = \sum_{i=1}^{n} a_i E(X_i)$$

and $\text{VAR}(\underline{Z})$ may also be denoted by

$$\text{VAR}(\underline{Z}) = \sum_{i=1}^{n}\sum_{j=1}^{n} a_i a_j \sigma_{ij}$$

where:

$$\sigma_{ij} = \begin{cases} \sigma_i^2 & \text{if } i = j \\ \text{cov}(X_i, X_j) & \text{if } i \neq j \end{cases}$$

(3) If X and Y are two independent random vectors, then the following relation holds:

$$E(\underline{X}^{\mathrm{T}} \cdot \underline{Y}) = (E(\underline{X}))^{\mathrm{T}} \cdot E(\underline{Y})$$

that is

$$\mathrm{cov}(\underline{X}, \underline{Y}) = \mathbf{0}$$

and

$$\mathrm{VAR}(\underline{X} + \underline{Y}) = \mathrm{VAR}(\underline{X}) + \mathrm{VAR}(\underline{Y})$$

11.6.2. Conditioned expected value

11.6.2.1. Expected value conditioned to a random vector

Theorem 11.16. *Let* $(\Omega, \mathcal{M}, P)$ *be a probability space and let* $X : (\Omega, \mathcal{M}, P) \to (\mathbb{R}, \mathbb{B}, P_X)$ *be a random variable with* $E(|X|) < \infty$, *ie,* $X \in \mathcal{L}^1(\Omega, \mathcal{M}, P)$, *and* $\mathbf{Y} : (\Omega, \mathcal{M}, P) \to (\mathbb{R}^n, \mathbb{B}_n, P_{\mathbf{Y}})$ *be a n-dimensional random vector. Then only one random variable exists:*

$$U = E(X|\mathbf{Y}) \tag{11.85}$$

which is said to be the conditioned expected value *(or conditioned expectation) of* X *given* $\mathbf{Y}$ *which satisfies the following properties:*

(i) *a function* $g : \mathbb{R}^n \to \mathbb{R}$ *exists so that* $U = g(\mathbf{Y})$;

(ii) *for any set* $A \in \mathbb{B}_n$, *the* partial averaging property *holds, ie,*

$$\int_A E(X|\mathbf{Y}) \, dP = \int_A X \, dP \tag{11.86}$$

Proposition 11.31. *If* $\widetilde{U}$ *is another random variable with the same properties as* U, *then*

$$\widetilde{U} = U$$

that is

$$P(\{\omega : \widetilde{U}(\omega) = U(\omega)\}) = 1$$

11.6.2.1.1. Properties of the expected value conditioned to a random vector

(1) one has

$$E[E(X|\mathbf{Y})] = E(X) \tag{11.87}$$

(2) If X is independent of $\mathbf{Y}$, then

$$E(X|\mathbf{Y}) = E(X) \tag{11.88}$$

and, specifically, if $X = c$, c constant, one has

$$E(c|\mathbf{Y}) = c \tag{11.89}$$

(3) *Linearity*:
$$E(aX_1 + bX_2|\mathbf{Y}) = aE(X_1|\mathbf{Y}) + bE(X_2|\mathbf{Y}) \tag{11.90}$$

(4) *Positiveness*: if $X \geq 0$ almost everywhere, then
$$E(X|\mathbf{Y}) \geq 0 \tag{11.91}$$

(5) *Jensen inequality*: if $\phi : \mathbb{R} \to \mathbb{R}$ is convex and $E|\phi(X)| < \infty$, then
$$E[\phi(X)|\mathbf{Y}] \geq \phi[E(X|\mathbf{Y})] \tag{11.92}$$

(6) *Tower property*: let $X : (\Omega, \mathcal{M}, P) \to (\mathbb{R}, \mathbb{B}, P_X)$, $\mathbf{Y} : (\Omega, \mathcal{M}, P) \to (\mathbb{R}^n, \mathbb{B}_n, P_\mathbf{Y})$ and $\mathbf{Z} : (\Omega, \mathcal{M}, P) \to (\mathbb{R}^n, \mathbb{B}_n, P_\mathbf{Z})$ be a random variable and two n-dimensional random vectors, respectively, then
$$E[E(X|\mathbf{Y}, \mathbf{Z})|\mathbf{Y}] = E[E(X|\mathbf{Y})|\mathbf{Y}, \mathbf{Z}] = E(X|\mathbf{Y}) \tag{11.93}$$

Since Y is a subset of Y, Z, set Y, Z contains more information than Y. If one estimates X on the basis of information contained in Y, Z, and then estimates the estimator derived on the basis of information contained in Y, then one would obtain the same result as if X had been estimated directly on the basis of information contained in Y.

(7) *Bring out what is known from the expected value*: if W is an random variable function on a random vector $\mathbf{Y}$, ie, $W := h(\mathbf{Y})$, then
$$E[X \cdot W|\mathbf{Y}] = W \cdot E(X|\mathbf{Y}) \tag{11.94}$$

Proposition 11.32. *By using Equation (11.85), Equation (11.86) may equally be expressed as*
$$E[E(X|\mathbf{Y}) \cdot \mathbf{1}_{\{\mathbf{Y} \in A\}}] = E(X \cdot \mathbf{1}_{\{\mathbf{Y} \in A\}}), \quad \forall A \in \mathbb{B}_n \tag{11.95}$$

Lemma 11.1. *If $Z = h(\mathbf{Y})$ is any random variable and $E[|Z(\omega) \cdot E(X(\omega)|\mathbf{Y})|] < \infty$, then*
$$E[Z \cdot E(X|\mathbf{Y})] = E[Z \cdot X]$$

11.6.2.2. Expected value conditioned to a σ-algebra
Theorem 11.17. *Let $(\Omega, \mathcal{M}, P)$ be a probability space and let $\mathcal{G}$ be a sub-σ-algebra of $\mathcal{M}$. Also, let $X : (\Omega, \mathcal{M}, P) \to (\mathbb{R}, \mathbb{B}, P_X)$ be a random variable with $E(|X|) < \infty$, ie, $X \in \mathcal{L}^1(\Omega, \mathcal{M}, P)$. Then, there is only one random variable*
$$Y = E(X|\mathcal{G}) \tag{11.96}$$

which is said to be the conditioned expected value of X with respect to $\mathcal{G}$, *which satisfies the following properties:*

(i) Y is measurable with respect to $\mathcal{G}$;

(ii) for any set $A \in \mathcal{G}$, the partial averaging property holds, ie,

$$\int_A Y \, dP = \int_A X \, dP \tag{11.97}$$

Proposition 11.33. *If $\widetilde{Y}$ is another random variable with the same properties as Y, then*

$$\widetilde{Y} = Y$$

that is,

$$P(\{\omega : \widetilde{Y}(\omega) = Y(\omega)\}) = 1$$

11.6.2.2.1.   Properties of the expected value conditioned to a σ-algebra

(1) one has

$$E[E(X|\mathcal{G})] = E[X] \tag{11.98}$$

(2) If X is measurable with respect to $\mathcal{G}$, then

$$E(X|\mathcal{G}) = X \tag{11.99}$$

(3) *Linearity*:

$$E(\alpha_1 X_1 + \alpha_2 X_2 | \mathcal{G}) = \alpha_1 E(X_1|\mathcal{G}) + \alpha_2 E(X_2|\mathcal{G}) \tag{11.100}$$

(4) *Positiveness*: if $X \geq 0$ almost everywhere, then

$$E(X|\mathcal{G}) \geq 0 \tag{11.101}$$

(5) *Jensen inequality*: if $\phi : \mathbb{R} \to \mathbb{R}$ is convex and $E|\phi(X)| < \infty$, then

$$E[\phi(X)|\mathcal{G}] \geq \phi[E(X|\mathcal{G})] \tag{11.102}$$

(6) *Tower property*: if $\mathcal{H}$ is a sub-σ-algebra of $\mathcal{G}$ then

$$E[E(X|\mathcal{G})|\mathcal{H}] = E[E(X|\mathcal{H})|\mathcal{G}] = E[X|\mathcal{H}] \tag{11.103}$$

Since $\mathcal{H}$ is sub-σ-algebra of $\mathcal{G}$, $\mathcal{G}$ contains more information than $\mathcal{H}$. If one estimates X on the basis of information contained in $\mathcal{G}$ and then estimates the estimator derived on the basis of information contained in $\mathcal{H}$, then one would obtain the same result as if X had been estimated directly on the basis of information contained in $\mathcal{H}$.

(7) *Bring out what is known from the expected value*: if Z is measurable with respect to $\mathcal{G}$, then

$$E(ZX|\mathcal{G}) = Z \cdot E(X|\mathcal{G}) \tag{11.104}$$

Proposition 11.34. *By using Equation (11.96), Equation (11.97) may be equally expressed as*

$$E[\mathbf{1}_A \cdot E(X|\mathcal{G})] = E[\mathbf{1}_A \cdot X], \quad \forall A \in \mathcal{G} \tag{11.105}$$

Lemma 11.2. *Let Z be a $\mathcal{G}$-measurable random variable and $E[|Z(\omega) \cdot E(X(\omega)|\mathcal{G})|] < \infty$ then*

$$E[Z \cdot E(X|\mathcal{G})] = E[Z \cdot X] \tag{11.106}$$

11.7. PROBABILITY GENERATING FUNCTION

Definition 11.36. Let X be a discrete non-negative random variable with probability density function $p_i = P(X = x_i)$, $i = 1, 2, 3, \ldots$, then a *probability generating function* is a function X denoted as $\Pi_X(z)$, or as $\Pi(z)$, determined as the expected value for the quantity z^X:

$$\Pi_X(z) = E(z^X) = \langle z^X \rangle = \sum_i p_i z^{x_i} = \sum_x p_x z^x \tag{11.107}$$

for all z so that summation is convergent.

Theorem 11.18. *The rth derivative of $\Pi_X(z)$ for the value of $z = 1$ has the relation with the rth non-centred moments of the random variable X as follows[1]:*

$$\begin{aligned}
\frac{d^r}{dz^r} \Pi(z)\bigg|_{z=1} &= E[X(X-1)(X-2)\cdots(X-r+1)] \\
&= E[(X^2 - X)(X-2)\cdots(X-r+1)] \\
&= E[(X^3 - 3X^2 + 2X)\cdots(X-r+1)] \\
&\quad\vdots
\end{aligned} \tag{11.108}$$

Remark 11.28. Then the mean and the variance of a discrete random variable X are derived from above, ie,

$$E(X) = \mu = \Pi'(1) \tag{11.109}$$

$$\text{VAR}(X) = \sigma^2 = \mu_2 - (\mu)^2 = \Pi''(1) + \Pi'(1) - [\Pi'(1)]^2 \tag{11.110}$$

In the demonstration of Theorem 11.18, $\Pi'(1) = \mu$ and $\Pi''(1) = \mu_2 - \mu$.

---

[1]When making multiplications of Equation (11.108) by using additive properties of the expected value, one will obtain a summation where the addendums will be all the non-centred moments of order r.

Theorem 11.19. *Let X and Y be two independent random variables, then the proba-bility generating function of the sum X+Y, $\Pi_{X+Y}(z)$, is given by*

$$\Pi_{X+Y}(z) = \Pi_X(z)\Pi_Y(z) \qquad (11.111)$$

11.8. MOMENT GENERATING FUNCTION

Definition 11.37. Given X, a random variable, and t, a real variable, function X, denoted by $M_X(t)$ or by $M(t)$, is defined to be the *moment generating function* and is determined to be the expected value of the quantity e^{tX}:

$$M_X(t) = E(e^{tX}) = \langle e^{tX} \rangle$$

$$= \begin{cases} \sum_x e^{tx} p_x & \text{if } X \text{ is a discrete random variable} \\ \int_{-\infty}^{+\infty} e^{tx} f(x)\, dx & \text{if } X \text{ is a continuous random variable} \end{cases}$$

Intuition 11.1. *When X is a discrete random variable, M(t) coincides with the probability generating function for $z = e^t$. See Definition 11.11(7).*

Intuition 11.2. *When X is a continuous random variable, M(t) coincides with the bilateral Laplace transform of the PDF f, $\mathcal{L}$. See Definition 9.3.*

Theorem 11.20. *The rth derivative of $M_X(t)$ for a value of $t = 0$ will represent the rth non-centred moment of the random variable X:*

$$\mu_r = \frac{d^r}{dt^r} M(t)|_{t=0} \qquad (11.112)$$

Remark 11.29. Then the mean and the variance of a random variable X is derived from above:

$$E(X) = \mu = \frac{d}{dt} M(t)\Big|_{t=0} = M'(0) \qquad (11.113)$$

$$\text{VAR}(X) = \sigma^2 = M''(0) - [M'(0)]^2 \qquad (11.114)$$

Remark 11.30. Then, the moment generating function may not exist, if there is no existence of all distribution moments.

Example 11.5. If $X \sim N(\mu, \sigma^2)$, ie,

$$f_X(x) = \frac{1}{\sigma\sqrt{2\pi}} e^{-(x-\mu)^2/2\sigma^2}$$

the first, second, third and fourth moment of X are derived by using the moment generating function.

First, the moment generating function must be derived for X:

$$M_X(t) = E(e^{tX}) = \int_{-\infty}^{+\infty} e^{tx} f(x)\, dx$$

$$= e^{(t^2\sigma^2/2)+\mu t} \tag{11.115}$$

To compute the four non-centred moments one may use (see Equation (11.112))

$$\mu_1 = \mu$$
$$\mu_2 = \mu^2 + \sigma^2$$
$$\mu_3 = \mu^3 + 3\mu\sigma^2$$
$$\mu_4 = \mu^4 + 6\mu^2\sigma^2 + 3\sigma^4$$

To compute the first centred moment, Notation 11.23 is sufficient, ie, $\mu_1 = \mu$, then

$$\bar{\mu}_1 = \mu$$

to compute moments of higher order, one may use Equation (11.79), ie,

$$\bar{\mu}_2 = \sigma^2$$
$$\bar{\mu}_3 = 0$$
$$\bar{\mu}_4 = 3\sigma^4$$

Theorem 11.21. *Given X and Y, two independent random variables, the moment generating function of the sum $X + Y$, $M_{X+Y}(t)$, is*

$$M_{X+Y}(t) = M_X(t)M_Y(t)$$

Theorem 11.22. *Given X a random variable with the moment generating function $M_X(t)$ and letting $Y = aX + b$, then*

$$M_Y(t) = e^{bt} M_X(at)$$

11.9. CHARACTERISTIC FUNCTION

Sometimes it is not possible to determine the moment generating function. However, the characteristic function may be used to compute moments.

Definition 11.38. Given X a random variable and t a real variable, the function of X denoted by $C_X(t)$, or $C(t)$, is defined to be the *characteristic function*. It is the expected value of the quantity e^{itX}, where $i = \sqrt{-1}$:

$$C_X(t) = E(e^{itX}) = \begin{cases} \sum_x e^{itx} p(x) & \text{if } X \text{ is a discrete random variable} \\ \int_{-\infty}^{+\infty} e^{itx} f(x)\, dx & \text{if } X \text{ is a continuous random variable} \end{cases}$$

Definition 11.39. Given X a continuous random variable and t a real variable, the *characteristic function* is a function of X denoted by $C_X(t)$, or by $C(t)$, and is determined as:

$$C_X(t) = M_X(it)$$

Remark 11.31. When X is a discrete random variable, $C(t)$ coincides with the *probability generating function* for $z = e^{it}$. See Definition 11.11(7).

Remark 11.32. When X is a continuous random variable, $C(t)$ coincides with the *Fourier transform* of PDF f, $\mathcal{F}$. See Definition 9.4.

Remark 11.33. Based on Equation (7.8), ie, $e^{itX} = \cos(tX) + i\sin(tX)$, then

$$C_X(t) = E(e^{itX}) = E(\cos(tX)) + iE(\sin(tX)) \tag{11.116}$$

Theorem 11.23. *The characteristic function always exists.*

Theorem 11.24. *The rth derivative of $C_X(t)$ for a value of $t = 0$ will represent the rth non-centred moment of the random variable X, ie,*

$$\mu_r = i^{-r} \frac{d^r}{dt^r} C(t) \Big|_{t=0} \tag{11.117}$$

Example 11.6. Consider $X \sim N(\mu, \sigma^2)$. By using the characteristic function, the first four non-centred moments of X are derived.

First, one has to identify the expression of the characteristic function of X. By using Definition 11.39 one has $C_X(t) = M_X(it)$, and under Example 11.5 one has

$$M_X(t) = e^{t^2\sigma^2/2 + \mu t} \tag{11.115}$$

then one has $M_X(it) = e^{i^2 t^2 \sigma^2/2 + i\mu t}$,

$$C_X(t) = e^{i\mu t - t^2\sigma^2/2} \tag{11.118}$$

It is now possible to compute the first four non-centred moments of X. See Example 11.5.

Theorem 11.25. *If the random variable has the characteristic function $C_X(t)$, then the random variable $Y = aX + b$, with a and b constant, has the characteristic function $C_Y(t) = e^{itb} C_X(at)$*

Corollary 11.16. *Let X be a random variable and let $Y = aX + b$, be a random variable, then the characteristic functions are as follows:*

$$C_Y(t) = \int_{-\infty}^{+\infty} e^{it(ax+b)} f(x)\, dx$$

11.9.1. Characteristic function and probability function

Notation 11.3. The characteristic function and the PDF may be equally denoted, respectively, as follows:

$$C_X(t) = \tilde{f}_j(t) \quad \text{and} \quad f_X(x) = f(x)$$

Theorem 11.26. *Let μ be a probability measure with a characteristic function $\tilde{f}_j$. For $-\infty < a < b < +\infty$, the following relation holds, which is also said to be the inverse Levy formula:*

$$\frac{\mu(a,b) + \mu[a,b]}{2} = \frac{1}{2\pi} \lim_{T \to \infty} \int_{-T}^{T} \frac{e^{-ita} - e^{-itb}}{it} \tilde{f}_j(t)\, dt \tag{11.119}$$

Theorem 11.27. *Let x be a random variable, let f and $\tilde{f}$ be the PDF and the characteristic function, respectively. The following relation holds:*

$$f(x) = \frac{1}{2\pi} \int_{-\infty}^{+\infty} e^{-itx} \tilde{f}(t)\, dt \tag{11.120}$$

Example 11.7. Let $X \sim N(0; \sigma^2)$ and, then, let $f_X(x) = \frac{1}{\sqrt{2\pi}\sigma} e^{-x^2/2\sigma^2}$ and $C_X(t) = e^{-\sigma^2 t^2/2}$ (see Example 11.6), then the following relation holds:

$$\frac{1}{\sqrt{2\pi}\sigma} e^{-x^2/2\sigma^2} = \frac{1}{2\pi} \int_{-\infty}^{+\infty} e^{-itx} e^{-t^2\sigma^2/2}\, dt$$

Corollary 11.17. *Let x be a random variable, let F and $\tilde{f}$ be the CDF and the characteristic function. The following relation holds. Actually, this is another version of the inverse Levy formula:*

$$F(b) - F(a) = \frac{1}{2\pi} \int_{-\infty}^{+\infty} \frac{e^{-ita} - e^{-itb}}{it} \tilde{f}(t)\, dt \tag{11.121}$$

Corollary 11.18. *Defining x as a random variable, P_j its PDF and $\tilde{f}_j$ its characteristic function, the following relation holds:*

$$P_j(x \leq a) = 1 - \frac{1}{2\pi} \lim_{T \to \infty} \int_{-T}^{T} \frac{e^{-ita}}{it} \tilde{f}_j(t)\, dt \tag{11.122}$$

$$P_j(x > a) = \frac{1}{2\pi} \lim_{T \to \infty} \int_{-T}^{T} \frac{e^{-ita}}{it} \tilde{f}_j(t)\, dt \tag{11.123}$$

Corollary 11.19. *Defining x as a random variable, P_j its PDF and $\tilde{f}_j$ its characteristic function, the following relation holds:*

$$P_j(x > a) = \frac{1}{2} - \frac{1}{2\pi} \lim_{T \to \infty} \int_{0}^{T} \frac{e^{ita}\tilde{f}_j(-t) - e^{-ita}\tilde{f}_j(t)}{it}\, dt \tag{11.124}$$

Corollary 11.20. *Defining x as a random variable, P_j its PDF and $\tilde{f}_j$ its characteristic function, the following relation holds:*

$$P_j(x > a) = \frac{1}{2} + \frac{1}{\pi} \int_{0}^{\infty} \Im\left[\frac{e^{-ita}\tilde{f}_j(t)}{t}\right] dt \tag{11.125}$$

Corollary 11.21. *Defining x as a random variable, P_j its PDF and $\tilde{f}_j$ its characteristic function, the following relation holds:*

$$P_j(x > a) = \frac{1}{2} + \frac{1}{\pi} \int_{0}^{\infty} \Re\left[\frac{e^{-ita}\tilde{f}_j(t)}{it}\right] dt \tag{11.126}$$

Remark 11.34. The theorems and corollaries above evidently also hold for the conditioned probability measures.

11.10. CUMULANT GENERATING FUNCTION

Definition 11.40. Given a random variable and t a real variable, the *cumulant generating function* denoted by $K_X(t)$, or by $K(t)$, is the function which represents the logarithm of the moment generating function:

$$K_X(t) = \ln M_X(t) \tag{11.127}$$

or

$$K_X(t) = t\kappa_1 + \frac{t^2}{2!}\kappa_2 + \frac{t^3}{3!}\kappa_3 + \frac{t^4}{4!}\kappa_4 + o(t^5) \tag{11.128}$$

where κ are defined to be the cumulants.

Intuition 11.3. *Definition 11.40 shows the Maclaurin expansion of the function* $K_X(t)$ *($f(0) = 0$ since $\ln(M(0)) = \ln 1 = 0$). Hence, the rth derivative of $K_X(t)$ for a value of $t = 0$ will represent the rth cumulant of random variable X:*

$$\kappa_r = \frac{d^r}{dt^r} K(t)\Big|_{t=0} = K^r(0) \tag{11.129}$$

Definition 11.41. Given a random variable and t a real variable, the *cumulant generating function* X, denoted by $K_X(t)$, or by $K(t)$, is the function which represents the logarithm of the moment generating function:

$$K_X(it) = \ln C_X(t) \tag{11.130}$$

or

$$K_X(it) = it\kappa_1 + \frac{(it)^2}{2!}\kappa_2 + \frac{(it)^3}{3!}\kappa_3 + \frac{(it)^4}{4!}\kappa_4 + o(t^5) \tag{11.131}$$

where κ are defined to be the cumulants

Intuition 11.4. *Definition 11.131 shows the Maclaurin expansion of the function* $K_X(t)$ *(clearly, $f(0) = 0$ since $\ln(C(0)) = \ln 1 = 0$). Hence, the rth derivative of $K_X(t)$ for a value of $t = 0$ will represent the rth cumulant of random variable X:*

$$\kappa_r = i^{-r}\frac{d^r}{dt^r}K(it)\Big|_{t=0} = K^r(0) \tag{11.132}$$

11.10.1. Relations between κ_r and μ_r via the moment generating function

$\kappa_1 = \dfrac{d}{dt}K(t)\big|_{t=0}$

$$\kappa_1 = \mu_1 \tag{11.133}$$

$\kappa_2 = \dfrac{d^2}{dt^2}K(t)\big|_{t=0}$

$$\kappa_2 = \mu_2 - (\mu_1)^2 = \sigma^2 \tag{11.134}$$

$\kappa_3 = \dfrac{d^3}{dt^3}K(t)\big|_{t=0}$

$$\kappa_3 = \mu_3 - 3\mu_1\mu_2 + 2(\mu_1)^3 \tag{11.135}$$

$\kappa_4 = \dfrac{d^4}{dt^4}K(t)\big|_{t=0}$

$$\kappa_4 = -6(\mu_1)^4 + 12(\mu_1)^2\mu_2 - 3(\mu_2)^2 - 4\mu_1\mu_3 + \mu_4 \tag{11.136}$$

$\kappa_5 = \dfrac{d^5}{dt^5}K(t)\big|_{t=0}$

$$\kappa_5 = 24[\mu_1]^5 - 60[\mu_1]^3\mu_2 + 20[\mu_1]^2\mu_3 - 10\mu_2\mu_3 + 30\mu_1[\mu_2]^2 - 5\mu_1\mu_4 + \mu_5 \tag{11.137}$$

11.10.2. Relations between κ_r and μ_r via the characteristic function

$$i\kappa_1 = \frac{d}{dt}K(it)\big|_{t=0}$$

$$\kappa_1 = \mu_1 \tag{11.138}$$

$$i^2\kappa_2 = \frac{d^2}{dt^2}K(it)\big|_{t=0}$$

$$\kappa_2 = \mu_2 - (\mu_1)^2 \tag{11.139}$$

As in Section 11.10.1 the cumulants below are computed.

11.10.2.1. Relations between κ_r and $\bar{\mu}_r$

With respect to the first centred moment, given relation (11.133), ie, $\kappa_1 = \mu_1$, and recalling Remark 11.23, the relation below is derived:

$$\kappa_1 = \bar{\mu}_1 = \mu \tag{11.140}$$

With respect to the second centred moment, given relation (11.134), ie, $\kappa_2 = \mu_2 - (\mu_1)^2$, the relation below is derived by using Equation (11.80):

$$\kappa_2 = \bar{\mu}_2 = \sigma^2 \tag{11.141}$$

With respect to the third centred moment, given relation (11.135), ie, $\kappa_3 = \mu_3 - 3\mu_1\mu_2 + 2(\mu_1)^3$, the relation below is derived by using Equation (11.79):

$$\bar{\mu}_3 = \mu_3 - 3\mu\mu_2 + 2\mu^3 \tag{11.142}$$

Hence,

$$\kappa_3 = \bar{\mu}_3 \tag{11.143}$$

With respect to the fourth centred moment, given relation (11.136) and using Equation (11.80) one has

$$\kappa_4 = -3(\bar{\mu}_2)^2 - 4\mu\mu_3 + \mu_4 - 3\mu^4 + 6\mu^2\mu_2 \tag{11.144}$$

using Equation (11.79) one has

$$\bar{\mu}_4 = \mu_4 - 4\mu\mu_3 + 6\mu^2\mu_2 - 3\mu^4 \tag{11.145}$$

combining Equations (11.144) and (11.145) one has the following relation for κ_4:

$$\kappa_4 = \bar{\mu}_4 - 3(\bar{\mu}_2)^2 = \bar{\mu}_4 - 3\sigma^4$$

With respect to the fifth centred moment, using Equation (11.79) one has

$$\bar{\mu}_5 = \mu_5 - 5\mu\mu_4 + 10\mu^2\mu_3 - 10\mu^3\mu_2 + 4\mu^5 \tag{11.146}$$

given relation (11.137) and using Equation (11.80) one has

$$\kappa_5 = \bar{\mu}_5 - 10\bar{\mu}_3\bar{\mu}_2$$

12.1. STOCHASTIC PROCESS

12.1.1. Introduction

Let $\omega \in \Omega$ be a set of elementary events, T a finite set and $(\Omega, \mathcal{F}, P)$ a probability space. For all $t \in T$, a random variable X_t exists which builds the mapping $X_t : \Omega \to \mathbb{R}$.

Definition 12.1. Given a probability space (see Definition 11.1) $(\Omega, \mathcal{F}, P)$, a *stochastic process* is a parametrised collection of random variables

$$\{X_t\}_{t \in T} \tag{12.1}$$

defined on probability space $(\Omega, \mathcal{F}, P)$ of values in $\mathbb{R}$ where T is the parameter space.

Definition 12.2. If T is an interval of $\mathbb{R}$, $\{X_t\}_{t \in T}$ is said to be a *continuous stochastic process.*

Definition 12.3. If T is a subset of $\mathbb{N}$, $\{X_t\}_{t \in T}$ is said to be a *discrete stochastic process.*

Definition 12.4. For all $\omega \in \Omega$, functions X_t which leads from T to $\mathbb{R}$, ie, $X_t : T \to \mathbb{R}$, are said to be the *trajectories* of X_t.

Remark 12.1. Alternatively, the trajectory represents the values of X_t by varying t.

Remark 12.2. Sometimes a stochastic process $\{X_t\}_{t \in T}$ of real values defined on a probability space $(\Omega, \mathcal{F}, P)$ which has the space of parameters T is also denoted by

$$X_t(\omega) : T \times \Omega \to \mathbb{R}$$

which is extended with respect to Equation (12.1), and where:

- the product set $T \times \Omega$ is the "domain" of the stochastic process, and the product σ-algebra $\mathbb{B}|_T \times \mathcal{F}$ is paired off to that set;
- the set of real numbers $\mathbb{R}$ is the "codomain" of the stochastic process, and the Borel σ-algebra on $\mathbb{R}$ is paired off to that set, ie, $\mathbb{B}$.

Remark 12.3. If the stochastic process is defined as $\{X_t\}_{t\in[0,\infty)}$, its "domain" is the product set $[0, \infty) \times \Omega$ and the product σ-algebra $\mathbb{B}|_{[0,\infty)} \times \mathcal{F}$ is paired off to that set.

Definition 12.5. The stochastic process $\{X_t\}_{t\in[0,\infty)}$ defined on the probability space $(\Omega, \mathcal{F}, P)$ and of values in $\mathbb{R}$ is defined as *measurable* if it is measurable with respect to the product σ-algebra: $\mathbb{B}|_{[0,+\infty)} \times \mathcal{F}$, ie, if

$$\{(t, \omega) : X_t(\omega) \in A\} \in \mathbb{B}|_{[0,+\infty)} \times \mathcal{F} \tag{12.2}$$

for any $A \in \mathbb{B}$, or if the function

$$X_t(\omega) : ([0, +\infty) \times \Omega, \mathbb{B}|_{[0,+\infty)} \times \mathcal{F}) \to (\mathbb{R}, \mathbb{B}) \tag{12.3}$$

is measurable.

Definition 12.6. Let $\{X_t\}_{t\in T}$ be a stochastic process defined in the probability space $(\Omega, \mathcal{F}, P)$. Then $\sigma(X_1, X_2, \ldots, X_k)$ is defined as the *σ-algebra generated by the random variables* (see Equations (11.33) and (11.35)) $X_1, X_2, \ldots, X_k$.

Notation 12.1. The equation $\sigma(X_1, X_2, \ldots, X_k) \doteq \sigma(X_s; 1 \leq s \leq k)$ holds.

Remark 12.4. Notation 12.1 means that $\sigma(X_s; 0 \leq s \leq t)$ is the smallest σ-algebra which contains all of the sets of the type

$$\{\omega : X_{t_1}(\omega) \in E_1, \ldots, X_{t_k}(\omega) \in E_k\}$$

where:

- $t_j \leq t$;
- $E_j \subset \mathbb{R}$ are the Borel sets, $j \leq k = 1, 2, \ldots$.

Definition 12.7. Let:

- $\{X_t\}_{t \in T}$ be a stochastic process defined on the probability space $(\Omega, \Im, P)$;
- $\sigma(X_0, X_1, \ldots, X_k)$ be the σ-algebra generated by the random variables $X_0, X_1, \ldots, X_k$; then a *filtration* of $\{X_t\}_{t \in T}$, denoted by $\{\mathcal{F}_t\}_{t \geq 0}$, is said to be the family of the σ-algebras generated as follows (see Definition 1.102):

$$\sigma(X_0) = \mathcal{F}_0$$
$$\sigma(X_0, X_1) = \mathcal{F}_1$$
$$\vdots$$
$$\sigma(X_0, X_1, \ldots, X_k) = \mathcal{F}_k$$
$$\vdots$$
$$\sigma(X_s; 0 \leq s \leq t) = \mathcal{F}_t$$

so that $\mathcal{F}_0 \subset \mathcal{F}_1 \subset \cdots \subset \mathcal{F}_k \cdots \subset \mathcal{F}_t$.

Definition 12.8. Given the filtered probability space $(\Omega, \Im, \{\mathcal{F}_t\}_{t \geq 0}, P)$, the stochastic process $\{X_t\}_{t \in T}$ is said to be *adapted to* $\{\mathcal{F}_t\}_{t \geq 0}$ if any X_t is $\mathcal{F}_t$-measurable, ie, if for all t, knowing information contained in $\mathcal{F}_t$, one knows the value of X_t.

Definition 12.9. A *natural filtration* of process $\{X_t\}_{t \in [0,\infty)}$ is the smallest filtration with respect to which the stochastic process is adapted. It is denoted by $\mathbb{F}^X = \{\mathcal{F}_t^X\}_{t \in [0,\infty)}$ where $\mathcal{F}_t^X = \sigma(X_s; 0 \leq s \leq t)$. Therefore, it corresponds to the filtration generated by the process itself[1].

Definition 12.10. A m-dimensional vector of stochastic processes is defined to be a *m-dimensional vector stochastic process*, ie,

$$\mathbf{X}_t := (X_{1,t}, X_{2,t}, \ldots, X_{m,t})$$

12.1.2. Random time

Definition 12.11. Given a probability space $(\Omega, \mathcal{F}, P)$, a $\mathcal{F}$-measurable random variable which has values in $[0, +\infty]$ is defined to be a *continuous random time* τ.

Definition 12.12. Given a probability space $(\Omega, \mathcal{F}, P)$, a $\mathcal{F}$-measurable random variable which has values in $\{0, 1, 2, \ldots\} \cup \{+\infty\}$ is defined to be a *discrete random time* τ.

---

[1] Alternatively, the natural filtration of a stochastic process represents the set of information which characterises it.

Definition 12.13. Given the probability space $(\Omega, \mathcal{F}, P)$ and its filtration $\mathbb{F} = \{\mathcal{F}_t\}_{t \in [0,\infty)}$, the continuous random time τ is said to be a *continuous stopping time* with respect to the filtration $\mathbb{F} = \{\mathcal{F}_t\}_{t \in [0,\infty)}$ if, for any $t \geq 0$, one has

$$\{\tau \leq t\} = \{\omega : \tau(\omega) \leq t\} \in \mathcal{F}_t \tag{12.4}$$

This means that for any $t \geq 0$, if one observes information contained in $\mathcal{F}_t$, one may say whether the event $\{\tau \leq t\}$ occurred or not.

Remark 12.5. If $\tau(\omega) = \infty$ for any $\omega \in \Omega$, then the event $\{\tau \leq t\}$ never occurs.

Example 12.1. Let $\{X_t\}_{t \in [0,\infty)}$ be a stochastic process of real values and continuous trajectories, defined on the probability space $(\Omega, \mathcal{F}, P)$ and adapted to the filtration $\mathbb{F} = \{\mathcal{F}_t\}_{t \in [0,\infty)}$. The *first passage time* of process $\{X_t\}_{t \in [0,\infty)}$ for level $a \in \mathbb{R}$, ie, time t when for the first time process $\{X_t\}_{t \in [0,\infty)}$ has value a, is a random time so that

$$\tau_a := \inf\{t > 0 : X_t = a\}$$

It is also a stopping time with respect to the filtration $\mathbb{F} = \{\mathcal{F}_t\}_{t \in [0,\infty)}$ since for any t one has

$$\{\omega : \tau_a \leq t\} = \left\{\omega : \sup_{0 \leq s \leq t} X_s \geq a\right\} \in \mathcal{F}_t$$

and it reads: event $\tau_a \leq t$, ie, the random time of first passage of process X_t for level a occurring before time t, is equivalent to event $\sup_{0 \leq s \leq t} X_s \geq a$, ie, the highest value taken by process X_t within time t has been higher or equal to a; this last event surely belongs to $\mathcal{F}_t$ since by hypothesis $\{X_t\}_{t \in [0,\infty)}$ is adapted to the filtration $\mathbb{F} = \{\mathcal{F}_t\}_{t \in [0,\infty)}$, and then event $\{\tau_a \leq t\}$ also belongs to $\mathcal{F}_t$. It can be derived that τ_a is a stopping time with respect to the given filtration.

Definition 12.14. Consider a probability space $(\Omega, \mathcal{F}, P)$ and its discrete filtration $\mathbb{F} = \{\mathcal{F}_n\}_{n \in \mathbb{N}}$. A random discrete time τ is said to be a *discrete stopping time* with respect to the filtration $\mathbb{F} = \{\mathcal{F}_n\}_{n \in \mathbb{N}}$ if, for any $n = 0, 1, 2, \ldots, \infty$, one has

$$\{\tau = n\} = \{\omega : \tau(\omega) = n\} \in \mathcal{F}_n \tag{12.5}$$

This means that for any $n = 0, 1, 2, \ldots, \infty$, if one observes information contained in $\mathcal{F}_n$ one may say whether event $\{\tau = n\}$ occurred or not.

Proposition 12.1. *The condition stated in Equation (12.5) is equal to the following condition:*

$$\{\tau \leq n\} = \{\omega : \tau(\omega) \leq n\} \in \mathcal{F}_n \tag{12.6}$$

for any $n = 0, 1, 2, \ldots, \infty$.

Definition 12.15. Given $\{X_t\}_{t\in[0,\infty)}$ a stochastic process of real values which has continuous trajectories, defined on the probability space $(\Omega, \mathcal{F}, P)$ and adapted to filtration $\mathbb{F} = \{\mathcal{F}_t\}_{t\in[0,\infty)}$ and τ, the continuous stopping time with respect to this same filtration, the *stopped process*, denoted by $\{X_t^\tau\}_{t\in[0,\infty)}$, is the stochastic process expressed as follows:

$$\{X_t^\tau\}_{t\in[0,\infty)} := \{X_{\min(t,\tau)}\}_{t\in[0,\infty)}$$

12.1.3. Martingale

Definition 12.16. A stochastic process $\{X_t\}_{t\in[0,\infty)}$ defined on a filtered probability space $(\Omega, \mathcal{F}, \{\mathcal{F}_t\}_{t\in[0,\infty)}, P)$ and adapted to the filtration $\{\mathcal{F}_t\}_{t\in[0,\infty)}$ is said to be the *martingale* with respect to that filtration (and to probability measure P) if

$$E(|X_t|) < \infty, \quad \forall t \tag{12.7}$$

and

$$E(X_t|\mathcal{F}_s) = X_s, \quad \forall s \leq t \tag{12.8}$$

Remark 12.6. Equation (12.8) may also be expressed as

$$E(X_t - X_s|\mathcal{F}_s) = E(\Delta X_t|\mathcal{F}_s) = 0, \quad \forall 0 \leq s < t < \infty \tag{12.9}$$

where $\Delta X_t = X_t - X_s$.

Remark 12.7. Equation (12.8) may also be expressed, in light of the concept of the conditioned expected value of a σ-algebra (see Equation (11.97)), as

$$\int_A X_t \, dP = \int_A X_s \, dP, \quad \forall 0 \leq s < t < \infty \tag{12.10}$$

for any $A \in \mathcal{F}_s$.

Definition 12.17. A stochastic process $\{X_t\}_{t\in[0,\infty)}$ which satisfies the conditions stated in the definition above, but holding (instead of Equation (12.8))

$$E(X_t|\mathcal{F}_s) \leq X_s, \quad \forall s \leq t \tag{12.11}$$

is said to be a *super-martingale* with respect to the filtration $\{\mathcal{F}_t\}_{t\in[0,\infty)}$ (and to probability measure P).

Remark 12.8. Equation (12.11) may also be expressed as

$$E(X_t - X_s|\mathcal{F}_s) = E(\Delta X_t|\mathcal{F}_s) \leq 0, \quad \forall 0 \leq s < t < \infty \tag{12.12}$$

where $\Delta X_t = X_t - X_s$.

Definition 12.18. A stochastic process $\{X_t\}_{t\in[0,\infty)}$ which satisfies the conditions stated in the definition above, but holding (instead of Equation (12.11))

$$E(X_t|\mathcal{F}_s) \geq X_s, \quad \forall s \leq t \tag{12.13}$$

is said to be a *sub-martingale* with respect to the filtration $\{\mathcal{F}_t\}_{t\in[0,\infty)}$ (and to probability measure P).

Remark 12.9. Equation (12.13) may also be expressed as

$$E(X_t - X_s|\mathcal{F}_s) = E(\Delta X_t|\mathcal{F}_s) \geq 0, \quad \forall 0 \leq s < t < \infty \tag{12.14}$$

where $\Delta X_t = X_t - X_s$.

Corollary 12.1. *Any martingale is a super-martingale and a sub-martingale at the same moment.*

Corollary 12.2. *If X is a super-martingale, then $-X$ is a sub-martingale. The opposite is also true.*

Proposition 12.2. *The expected value of:*

- *a martingale is constant, ie,*

$$E(X_t) = E(X_s), \quad \forall 0 \leq s < t < \infty \tag{12.15}$$

- *a martingale is non-growing, ie,*

$$E(X_t) \leq E(X_s), \quad \forall 0 \leq s < t < \infty \tag{12.16}$$

- *a sub-martingale is non-decreasing, ie,*

$$E(X_t) \geq E(X_s), \quad \forall 0 \leq s < t < \infty \tag{12.17}$$

Definition 12.19. Let $\mathcal{S}$ the set of the stopping time with respect to the filtration $\mathbb{F} = \{\mathcal{F}_t\}_{t\in[0,\infty)}$ with respect to a non-null Ω set which belongs to the probability space $(\Omega, \mathcal{F}, P)$. The stochastic process $\{X_t\}_{t\in[0,\infty)}$, defined on $(\Omega, \mathcal{F}, P)$, is said to be a *local martingale* if a growing sequence of stopping time $\{\tau_n\}_{n=0}^{\infty} \subset \mathcal{S}$ exists so that

$$\lim_{n\to+\infty} \tau_n = \infty$$

and that for all $n \in \mathbb{N}$ the stopped process $\{X_t^{\tau_n}\}_{t\in[0,\infty)}$ is a martingale with respect to the filtration $\mathbb{F} = \{\mathcal{F}_t\}_{t\in[0,\infty)}$.

Proposition 12.3. *Any martingale is also a local martingale. The opposite is not necessarily true.*

Proposition 12.4. *Any positive local martingale is a super-martingale.*

12.1.4. Brownian motion

Definition 12.20. The *standard Brownian motion* is a stochastic process defined on a probability space $(\Omega, \mathcal{F}, P)$ and denoted by $\{W_t\}_{t \in [0,\infty)}$ which has the following properties:

(1) $W_0 = 0$;
(2) $(W_t - W_s) \frown N(0, (t - s))$;
(3) $(W_{t_2} - W_{t_1})$ is independent from $(W_{t_3} - W_{t_2})$ where intervals $[t_3 - t_2)$ and $[t_2 - t_1)$ do not superimpose;
(4) the strong Markov Property holds, ie, $P(W_{s+t} \in c \mid W_t = x, W_{t-1} = y) = P(W_{s+t} \in c \mid W_t = x)$;
(5) is a function continuous in time, ie, for any fixed ω, one has $\{W_t\}_{t \in [0,\infty)}$ for $t \geq 0 \because W_t$ is continuous, ie, $P((\omega) \because t \to W_t(\omega) \text{ is continuous}) = 1$.

Corollary 12.3. *Based on properties (1) and (2) of Definition 12.20, the following relation holds:*

$$(W_t - W_0) = (W_t - 0) = W_t$$

and

$$W_t \frown N(0, t)$$

It can be derived that the standard Brownian motion considered at any time t is distributed according to a normal probability law of a zero expected value and variance t.

Definition 12.21. A *n-dimensional standard Brownian motion*, denoted by $\mathbf{W}_t = (W_{1,t} W_{2,t} \ldots W_{n,t})$ is a *n*-component vector stochastic process and each component is a one-dimensional standard Brownian motion (see Definition 12.20).

Definition 12.22. The set $\{\mathcal{F}_t^W\}_{t \in [0,\infty)}$ of the σ-algebras generated by a standard Brownian motion W_t constitutes the *natural filtration* generated by this stochastic process.

Remark 12.10. The natural filtration of the Brownian motion is often denoted as

$$\{\mathcal{F}_t^W\}_{t \in [0,\infty)} : \mathcal{F}_t^W = \sigma(W_s, 0 \leq s \leq t)$$

Corollary 12.4. *The following properties hold:*

(1) $s \leq t \to \mathcal{F}_s^W \subseteq \mathcal{F}_t^W$;
(2) W_t is $\mathcal{F}_t^W$-measurable for any t;

(3) *for* $t \leq t_1 \leq \cdots \leq t_n$, *increments* $W_{t_1} - W_t, W_{t_2} - W_{t_1}, \ldots, W_{t_1} - W_{t_{n-1}}$ *are independent of* $\mathcal{F}_t^W$.

Theorem 12.1. *The differential process of two Brownian motions, ie,* $W_{t+s} - W_t = \Delta W_t \triangleq B_s$ *where* $0 \leq s \leq \infty$, *is a Brownian motion.*

Corollary 12.5. *The process* ΔW_t *may be defined as*

$$W_{t+s} - W_t = \Delta W_t \triangleq \varepsilon \sqrt{\Delta t}$$

where $\varepsilon \sim N(0, 1)$.

Proposition 12.5. *The standard Brownian is a martingale with respect to its natural filtration* $\{\mathcal{F}_t^W\}_{t \in [0,\infty)}$, *ie, for any* $0 \leq s < t$

$$E(W_t | \mathcal{F}_s^W) = W_s \quad \text{almost surely} \tag{12.18}$$

Remark 12.11. In light of Proposition 12.3, since the standard Brownian motion is a martingale, it is also a local martingale.

Proposition 12.6. *Let* $\{W_t\}_{t \in [0,\infty)}$ *be a standard Brownian motion defined on the probability space* $(\Omega, \mathcal{F}, P)$ *and* $\{\mathcal{F}_t^W\}_{t \in [0,\infty)}$ *be its natural filtration. Also, let* $\vartheta < \infty$. *Then the exponential stochastic process* Z_t *defined as*

$$Z_t := e^{\vartheta W_t - (1/2)\vartheta^2 t} \tag{12.19}$$

is a martingale with respect to $\{\mathcal{F}_t^W\}_{t \in [0,\infty)}$.

12.1.4.1. Variation of Brownian motion

Theorem 12.2. *The* quadratic variation *of the Brownian motion on the interval* $[0, T]$ *partitioned as* $\Pi = \{t_0, t_1, t_2, t_3, t_4, \ldots, t_n\}$ *is equal to* T, *ie,*

$$\langle f \rangle(T) = \lim_{\|\Pi\| \to 0} \sum_{k=0}^{n-1} |W_{t_{k+1}} - W_{t_k}|^2 = T \tag{12.20}$$

Corollary 12.6. *Since the Brownian motion has a quadratic variation different than zero, it is not differentiable (see also Theorem 5.7).*

Theorem 12.3. *The first variation of Brownian motion on the interval* $[0, T]$ *partitioned as* $\Pi = \{t_0, t_1, t_2, t_3, t_4, \ldots, t_n\}$ *is infinite, ie,*

$$\mathrm{FV}_{[0,T]}(f) = \lim_{\|\Pi\| \to 0} \sum_{k=0}^{n-1} |W_{t_{k+1}} - W_{t_k}| = +\infty \tag{12.21}$$

12.1.4.2. Correlated Brownian motions

Theorem 12.4. *Let* $\begin{bmatrix} W_t \\ Y_t \end{bmatrix}$ *be a two-dimensional vector stochastic process formed by two independent Brownian motions W_t and Y_t, defined on the probability space $(\Omega, \mathcal{F}, P)$, ie,*

$$\begin{bmatrix} W_t \\ Y_t \end{bmatrix} \sim N\left(\mathbf{0}, \Sigma' = \begin{bmatrix} t & 0 \\ 0 & t \end{bmatrix}\right) \tag{12.22}$$

Defining

$$U^{\mathrm{T}} = \begin{bmatrix} 1 & 0 \\ \rho_{WZ} & \sqrt{(1 - \rho_{WZ}^2)} \end{bmatrix} \tag{12.23}$$

the operation

$$U^{\mathrm{T}} \begin{bmatrix} W_t \\ Y_t \end{bmatrix} \tag{12.24}$$

returns two Brownian motions $\begin{bmatrix} W_t \\ Z_t \end{bmatrix}$ defined on the probability space $(\Omega, \mathcal{F}, P)$ and correlated according to a linear correlation coefficient equal to ρ_{WZ}, ie,

$$\begin{bmatrix} W_t \\ Z_t \end{bmatrix} \sim N\left(\mathbf{0}, \Sigma = \begin{bmatrix} t & \rho_{WZ}t \\ \rho_{WZ}t & t \end{bmatrix}\right) \tag{12.25}$$

where

$$\begin{bmatrix} W_t \\ Z_t \end{bmatrix} = \begin{bmatrix} W_t \\ \rho_{WZ}W_t + (\sqrt{1 - \rho_{WZ}^2})Y_t \end{bmatrix} \tag{12.26}$$

Theorem 12.5. *Let* $\begin{bmatrix} W_t \\ Z_t \end{bmatrix}$ *be a two-dimensional vector stochastic process formed by two Brownian motions W_t and Z_t, defined on the probability space $(\Omega, \mathcal{F}, P)$ and correlated according to a linear correlation coefficient equal to ρ_{WZ}, ie,*

$$\begin{bmatrix} W_t \\ Z_t \end{bmatrix} \sim N\left(\mathbf{0}, \Sigma = \begin{bmatrix} t & \rho_{WZ}t \\ \rho_{WZ}t & t \end{bmatrix}\right) \tag{12.25}$$

then the two-dimensional vector stochastic process $\begin{bmatrix} W_t \\ Y_t \end{bmatrix}$ defined as

$$\begin{bmatrix} W_t \\ Y_t \end{bmatrix} = \begin{bmatrix} W_t \\ -\dfrac{\rho_{WZ}}{\sqrt{(1-\rho_{WZ}^2)}}W_t + \dfrac{1}{\sqrt{(1-\rho_{WZ}^2)}}Z_t \end{bmatrix}$$

or as

$$\begin{bmatrix} W_t \\ Y_t \end{bmatrix} = (U^{\mathrm{T}})^{-1} \begin{bmatrix} W_t \\ Z_t \end{bmatrix} \tag{12.27}$$

where

$$(U^{\mathsf{T}})^{-1} = \begin{bmatrix} \dfrac{1}{\rho_{WZ}} & 0 \\[2mm] -\dfrac{\rho_{WZ}}{\sqrt{(1-\rho_{WZ}^2)}} & \dfrac{1}{\sqrt{(1-\rho_{WZ}^2)}} \end{bmatrix}$$

is a process composed of two Brownian processes W_t and Y_t, defined on the probability space $(\Omega, \mathcal{F}, P)$, which are independent between them and governed by following the bivariate normal probability law:

$$\begin{bmatrix} W_t \\ Y_t \end{bmatrix} \sim N\left(\mathbf{0}, \Sigma' = \begin{bmatrix} t & 0 \\ 0 & t \end{bmatrix}\right) \tag{12.22}$$

Remark 12.12. Given the two-dimensional vector stochastic process $\begin{bmatrix} W_t \\ Z_t \end{bmatrix}$ and $\begin{bmatrix} W_t \\ Z_t \end{bmatrix}$ identified in Theorems 12.4 and 12.5, matrices $(U)^{-1}$ and $(U^{\mathsf{T}})^{-1}$ are the inverse of matrices U and U^{T}, respectively.

Corollary 12.7. *Theorems 12.4 and 12.5 are not applied to Brownian motions only but also to their increments. In light of Theorem 12.1, the differential process of two Brownian motions is a Brownian motion[2]. Therefore, we have the following.*

(1) *W_t and Z_t are two standard Brownian motions correlated according to a correlation coefficient equal to ρ_{WZ}. ΔW_t and ΔZ_t are also two standard Brownian motions correlated according to a correlation coefficient equal to ρ_{WZ}. The two-dimensional vector stochastic process $\begin{bmatrix} \Delta W_t \\ \Delta Z_t \end{bmatrix}$ may be expressed as*

$$\begin{bmatrix} \Delta W_t \\ \Delta Z_t \end{bmatrix} = \begin{bmatrix} \Delta W_t \\ \rho_{WZ}\Delta W_t + (\sqrt{1 - \rho_{WZ}^2})\Delta Y_t \end{bmatrix} \tag{12.28}$$

where ΔW_t and ΔY_t are two independent Brownian motions.

(2) *W_t and Y_t are two independent standard Brownian motions, ΔW_t and ΔY_t are also two independent standard Brownian motions and the two-dimensional stochastic process $\begin{bmatrix} \Delta W_t \\ \Delta Y_t \end{bmatrix}$ may be expressed as*

$$\begin{bmatrix} \Delta W_t \\ \Delta Y_t \end{bmatrix} = \begin{bmatrix} \Delta W_t \\ -\dfrac{\rho_{WZ}}{\sqrt{(1-\rho_{WZ}^2)}}\Delta W_t + \dfrac{1}{\sqrt{(1-\rho_{WZ}^2)}}\Delta Z_t \end{bmatrix} \tag{12.29}$$

where ΔW_t and ΔZ_t are two correlated Brownian motion according to a correlation coefficient equal to ρ_{WZ}.

---

[2]Here the *increment of the Brownian motion* and the *differential process of a Brownian motion* are used equivalently.

Theorem 12.6. *Let W_t and Z_t be two Brownian motions correlated according to a correlation coefficient $\rho_{WZ} \in [-1, 1]$. Then, on the interval $[0, T]$ with a partition $\Pi = \{t_0, t_1, \ldots, t_n\}$, the following relation holds:*

$$\lim_{\|\Pi\| \to 0} \sum_{k=0}^{n-1} (W_{t_{k+1}} - W_{t_k})(Z_{t_{k+1}} - Z_{t_k}) = \rho_{WZ} T \qquad (12.30)$$

12.1.5. Wiener process

Definition 12.23. For $s \to 0$ in Definition 12.20(5), $\to \Delta W_t \to dW_t$ and, then, one may define in the continuous time $dW_t \triangleq \varepsilon \sqrt{dt}$ and, hence, its distribution follows:

$$dW_t \sim N(0, \sqrt{dt})$$

ie, a *Wiener process*.

Definition 12.24. The process

$$dX = adt + bdW_t \qquad (12.31)$$

is said to be a *generalised Wiener process*. It holds the following distributive property:

$$dX \curvearrowright N(adt, b\sqrt{dt})$$

Definition 12.25. The product of two Wiener processes is denoted as

$$dW_{1,t}\, dW_{2,t}$$
$$d\langle W_{1,t}, W_{2,t} \rangle$$

Theorem 12.7. *The square of a Wiener process dW_t, also called the* differential representation of a Brownian motion, *is given by*

$$dW_t\, dW_t = dt \qquad (12.32)$$

Theorem 12.8. *The product of two correlated Wiener processes according to a correlation coefficient $\rho_{w_1,w_2} \in [-1, 1]$ is given by*

$$dW_{1,t}\, dW_{2,t} = \rho_{w_1,w_2}\, dt \qquad (12.33)$$

Corollary 12.8. *The product of two independent Wiener processes is given by*

$$dW_{1,t}\, dW_{2,t} = 0$$

Theorem 12.9. *Let dW_t and dZ_t be two correlated Wiener processes according to a correlation coefficient equal to ρ_{WZ}, and let dW_t and dY_t be two independent Wiener processes, then the two-dimensional vector Wiener process $\begin{bmatrix} dW_t \\ dZ_t \end{bmatrix}$ may be expressed as*

$$\begin{bmatrix} dW_t \\ dZ_t \end{bmatrix} = \begin{bmatrix} dW_t \\ \rho_{WZ}\, dW_t + \left(\sqrt{1 - \rho_{WZ}^2} \right) dY_t \end{bmatrix} \qquad (12.34)$$

12.1.5.1. Itô's algebra

Proposition 12.7. *Let W_t and Z_t be two one-dimensional standard Brownian motions, then one has:*

(1) $(dW_t)^2 = dt$;

(2) $dt \cdot dt = (dt)^2$; $(dt)^2$ *is one infinitesimal order higher than dt, therefore equations where it may be algebraically summed to a term in dt may be neglected and then considered equal to zero;*

(3) $dW_t \cdot dt = \sqrt[2]{dt} \cdot dt = (dt)^{3/2}$; $(dt)^{3/2}$ *is one infinitesimal order higher than dt, therefore equations where it may be algebraically summed to a term in dt may be neglected and then considered equal to zero.*

(4) *One has*

$$dW_t \cdot dZ_t = \begin{cases} 0 & \text{independence} \\ \rho_{WZ}\, dt & \text{correlation according to a} \\ & \text{correlation coefficient equal to } \rho_{WZ} \end{cases}$$

12.1.6. Poisson process

Definition 12.26. A process $\{N_t, t \geq 0\}$ is a Poisson process with intensity λ, $\lambda > 0$, if:

(1) $N_{t=0} = 0$;

(2) the process has stationary and independent increments;

(3) the number of events in any interval of length t is distributed as a Poisson random variable, with mean λt, ie, $E[N_t] = \lambda t$, and with a PDF as

$$P[N_{t+s} - N_s = n] = e^{-\lambda t} \frac{(\lambda t)^n}{n!}$$

Remark 12.13. The definition of the Poisson process, and especially property (2), allows one to define easily the diffusive Poisson process dN_t where $E[dN_t] = \lambda\, dt$.

12.2. ITÔ INTEGRAL

12.2.1. Basics

Definition 12.27. One can define $V = V(0, T)$ as the class of the stochastic processes:

$$f_t(\omega) : [0, T] \times \Omega \to \mathbb{R}$$

so that:

(1) $f_t(\omega)$ is $\mathbb{B}|_{[0,T]} \times \mathcal{F}$-measurable, where $\mathbb{B}|_{[0,T]}$ is the Borel σ-algebra restricted to interval $[0, T]$ and $\mathcal{F}$ is the σ-algebra of the probability space $(\Omega, \mathcal{F}, P)$ onto which the standard Brownian motion is defined;

(2) $f_t(\omega)$ is $\mathcal{F}_t^W$-measurable, ie, $f_t(\omega)$ is adapted with respect to $\{\mathcal{F}_t^W\}_{t \in [0,T]}$, ie, to natural filtration generated by the standard Brownian motion $\{W_t\}_{t \in [0,T]}$;

(3) $f_t(\omega)$ belongs to the space $L^2([0, T] \times \Omega)$, ie, the space of the stochastic processes X_t which satisfy the condition

$$E\left[\int_0^T [X_t(\omega)]^2 \, dt\right] < \infty \qquad (12.35)$$

12.2.2. Construction of the Itô integral

In this section, the following integral is defined:

$$I_t(f)(\omega) \equiv \int_0^t f_s(\omega) \, dW_s, \quad t \in [0, T] \qquad (12.36)$$

for a class of processes f wide enough, where W_t is the standard Brownian motion defined on the probability space $(\Omega, \mathcal{F}, P)$ to which natural filtration $\{\mathcal{F}_t^W\}_{t \in [0,T]}$ is associated. In general, $f_t(\omega)$ is a stochastic process (it may also be a deterministic process), which, by hypothesis, is dependent only from the process W_s with $s \leq t$.

Formally, this is to require that $f_t(\omega)$ is $\mathcal{F}_t^W$-measurable for any $t \in [0, T]$, ie, the process $f_t(\omega)$ is adapted with respect to natural filtration of the Brownian motion, ie, $\{\mathcal{F}_t^W\}_{t \in [0,T]}$. Intuitively, this means that the value of $f_t(\omega)$ is known when all of the information of the Brownian motion is known until time t, ie, when $\{W_s\}_{s \leq t}$ is known.

In order to define the Itô integral of the process $f_t(\omega)$, one is also required to satisfy the other hypotheses. Synthetically, all of the hypotheses are stated in the conditions of belonging of $f_t(\omega)$ to the class of the processes $V(0, T)$ (see Definition 12.27).

For the process which belongs to class $V(0, T)$, the procedure followed to define the Itô integral is based on three steps:

(1) the integral of a given class of process ϕ (ie, simple processes) is defined;
(2) it is demonstrated that any process $f \in \mathcal{V}(0, T)$ may be approximated (in the appropriate sense) by a sequence of simple processes $\{\phi_t^n(\omega)\}_{n\in\mathbb{N}}$;
(3) $\int_0^t f_s(\omega)\, dW_s$ is defined as a boundary – in $L^2([0, T] \times \Omega)$ – of $\int_0^t \phi_s^n(\omega)\, dW_s$ when $\{\phi_t^n(\omega)\}_{n\in\mathbb{N}}$ tends to $f_t(\omega)$ (always in the appropriate sense).

12.2.2.1. Itô integral for a simple process

Definition 12.28. Consider a partition $0 = t_0 \leq t_1 \leq \cdots \leq t_r = T$ of the interval $[0, T]$ and assume that for any $j = 0, 1, \ldots, n$, a $\mathcal{F}_{t_j}$-measurable random variable exists so that

$$a_j(\omega) : \Omega \to [-K, K] \tag{12.37}$$

where K is a positive and finite constant. Then the stochastic process may be defined as $\phi_t(\omega) : [0, T] \times \Omega \to [-K, K]$ by writing

$$\phi_t(\omega) := a_j(\omega), \quad \forall t \in (t_j, t_{j+1}], \ \forall j = 0, 1, \ldots, r - 1 \tag{12.38}$$

or (see Proposition 10.48)

$$\phi_t(\omega) := \sum_{j=0}^{r-1} a_j(\omega) \cdot \mathbf{1}_{(t_j, t_{j+1}]} \tag{12.39}$$

for $t_j < t \leq t_{j+1}$ and for any $j = 0, 1, \ldots, n - 1$.

This bounded and left continuous stochastic process is said to be a *simple process*.

Definition 12.29. The Itô integral of a simple process $\phi_t(\omega)$ is

$$I_t(\phi)(\omega) \equiv \int_0^t \phi_s(\omega)\, dW_s := \sum_{j=0}^{r-1} a_j(\omega)(W_{t_{j+1}} - W_{t_j}) \tag{12.40}$$

for $t_j < t \leq t_{j+1}$ and for any $j = 0, 1, \ldots, n - 1$.

12.2.2.1.1. Properties of the Itô integral for a simple process

Proposition 12.8. *If ϕ_1 and ϕ_2 are simple processes, then the following equivalences hold:*

(1)

$$\int_0^t (\phi_{1,s}(\omega) + \phi_{2,s}(\omega))\, dW_s = \int_0^t \phi_{1,s}(\omega)\, dW_s + \int_0^t \phi_{2,s}(\omega)\, dW_s \tag{12.41}$$

(2)

$$\int_0^t c\phi_{1,s}(\omega)\, dW_s = c\int_0^t \phi_{1,s}(\omega)\, dW_s \tag{12.42}$$

(3)

$$E\left(\left(\int_0^t \phi_{1,s}(\omega)\, dW_s\right)^2\right) = E\left(\int_0^t (\phi_{1,s}(\omega))^2\, ds\right) \tag{12.43}$$

and

$$E\left(\int_0^t \phi_{1,s}(\omega)\, dW_s \cdot \int_0^t \phi_{2,s}(\omega)\, dW_s\right) = E\left(\int_0^t \phi_{1,s}(\omega) \cdot \phi_{2,s}(\omega)\, ds\right) \tag{12.44}$$

(4)

$$E\left[\int_s^{t'} \phi_{1,u}(\omega)\, dW_u \middle| \mathcal{F}_t^W\right] = \int_s^t \phi_{1,u}(\omega)\, dW_u, \quad 0 \le s \le t \le t' \le T \tag{12.45}$$

(5)

$$E\left(\int_0^t \phi_{1,s}(\omega)\, dW_s\right) = 0 \tag{12.46}$$

12.2.2.2. Itô integral for a generic integrand process

Theorem 12.10. Let $f_t(\omega)$ be a process which belongs to class $\mathcal{V}(0, T)$, as in Definition 12.27, then a sequence of simple processes $\{\phi_t^n(\omega)\}_{n\in\mathbb{N}}$ exists which approximates $f_t(\omega)$ in $L^2([0, T] \times \Omega)$, ie,

$$\lim_{n\to+\infty} E\left[\int_0^T |\phi_t^n(\omega) - f_t(\omega)|^2\, dt\right] = 0 \tag{12.47}$$

for any $0 \le T < \infty$.

Theorem 12.11. Let:

- $f_t(\omega) : [0, T] \times \Omega \to \mathbb{R}$ be a stochastic process which belongs to class $\mathcal{V}(0, T)$ as under Definition 12.27;
- $\{\phi_t^n(\omega)\}_{n\in\mathbb{N}}$ be a sequence of simple processes which approximate $f_t(\omega)$ as under Equation (12.47).

then the sequence $\{I_t(\phi^n)(\omega)\}_{n\in\mathbb{N}}$, ie, the sequence of the Itô integrals of the sequence of simple processes:

(1) is a Cauchy sequence in $L^2([0, T] \times \Omega)$;

(2) is convergent in $L^2([0, T] \times \Omega)$ to a stochastic process denoted by $I_t(f)(\omega)$ or by $I_t(f)$, ie,

$$\lim_{n \to +\infty} E\left[\int_0^T |I_t(\phi^n)(\omega) - I_t(f)(\omega)|^2 \, dt\right] = 0$$

for any $0 \leq T < \infty$.

Theorem 12.11 allows the following definition to be stated.

Definition 12.30. Let $f_t(\omega)$ be a process which belongs to the class $\mathcal{V}(0, T)$ and $\{\phi_t^n(\omega)\}_{n \in \mathbb{N}}$ a sequence of simple processes which approximate $f_t(\omega)$ as under Equation (12.47). Then the Itô integral of the process $f_t(\omega)$ is defined as

$$I_t(f)(\omega) \equiv \int_0^t f_s(\omega) \, dW_s := \lim_{n \to +\infty} \int_0^t \phi_s^n(\omega) \, dW_s, \quad 0 \leq t \leq T \qquad (12.48)$$

being the limit intended in $L^2([0, T] \times \Omega)$.

Remark 12.14. Equation (12.48) may also be written as

$$I(f)(\omega) \equiv \int_s^t f_u(\omega) \, dW_u := \lim_{n \to +\infty} \int_s^t \phi_u^n(\omega) \, dW_u, \quad 0 \leq s \leq t \leq T \qquad (12.49)$$

12.2.2.2.1. Itô integral properties
Proposition 12.9. *Let $f_t(\omega)$ be any process which belongs to the class $\mathcal{V}(0, T)$. Then the following properties hold.*

(1) *For any $0 \leq s \leq t \leq T$, the Itô integral of the process $f_t(\omega)$, ie, the quantity*

$$\int_s^t f_u(\omega) \, dW_u$$

is a $\mathcal{F}_t^W$-measurable random variable and is a continuous function of its upper integration boundary.

(2) *The following equivalence holds:*

$$\int_s^t f_u(\omega) \, dW_u = \int_s^v f_u(\omega) \, dW_u + \int_v^t f_u(\omega) \, dW_u, \quad 0 \leq s \leq v \leq t \leq T$$

(3) *If $g_t(\omega)$ is another process which belongs to class $\mathcal{V}(0, T)$, then*

$$\int_s^t f_u(\omega) \, dW_u \pm \int_s^t g_u(\omega) \, dW_u = \int_s^t (f_u(\omega) \pm g_u(\omega)) \, dW_u$$

with $0 \leq s \leq t \leq T$.

(4) *Let $c \in \mathbb{R}$, then*

$$\int_s^t c \cdot f_u(\omega) \, dW_u = c \cdot \int_s^t f_u(\omega) \, dW_u, \quad 0 \leq s \leq t \leq T$$

(5) *Itô isometry:*

$$E\left[\left(\int_s^t f_u(\omega) \, dW_u\right)^2\right] = E\left[\int_s^t (f_u(\omega))^2 \, du\right], \quad 0 \leq s \leq t \leq T \quad (12.50)$$

whence, if $f_t(\omega) = f(t)$, ie, if $f_t(\omega)$ is a deterministic function, one has

$$E\left[\left(\int_s^t f_u(\omega) \, dW_u\right)^2\right] = \int_s^t |f(u)|^2 \, du, \quad 0 \leq s \leq t \leq T \quad (12.51)$$

(6) *Itô integral of the process $f_t(\omega)$ is a martingale with respect to the natural filtration of the standard Brownian motion $\mathbf{F}^W = \{\mathcal{F}_t^W\}_{t \in [0,T]}$, ie, for any $0 \leq s \leq t \leq t' \leq T$, one has*

$$E\left[\int_s^{t'} f_u(\omega) \, dW_u \middle| \mathcal{F}_t^W\right] = \int_s^t f_u(\omega) \, dW_u, \quad 0 \leq s \leq t \leq t' \leq T \quad (12.52)$$

(7) *The expected value of an Itô integral is equal to zero, ie,*

$$E\left[\int_s^t f_u(\omega) \, dW_u\right] = 0, \quad 0 \leq s \leq t \leq T \quad (12.53)$$

12.3. ITÔ PROCESSES

Definition 12.31. The class $\mathcal{W}_{\mathcal{H}} = \mathcal{W}_{\mathcal{H}}(0, T)$ is defined to be the class of the stochastic processes:

$$f_t(\omega) : [0, T] \times \Omega \to \mathbb{R}$$

so that:

(1) $f_t(\omega)$ is $\mathbb{B}|_{[0,T]} \times \mathcal{F}$-measurable, where $\mathbb{B}|_{[0,T]}$ is the Borel σ-algebra restricted to the interval $[0, T]$ and $\mathcal{F}$ is the σ-algebra of the probability space $(\Omega, \mathcal{F}, P)$ where the standard Brownian motion is defined;

(2) a growing family of σ-algebras exists $\{\mathcal{H}_t\}_{t \in [0,T]}$ so that

- W_t is a martingale with respect to $\{\mathcal{H}_t\}_{t \in [0,T]}$;
- $f_t(\omega)$ is $\mathcal{H}_t$-measurable, ie, $f_t(\omega)$ is adapted with respect to $\{\mathcal{H}_t\}_{t \in [0,T]}$;

(3) $f_t(\omega)$ is a stochastic process which satisfies the condition

$$P\left[\int_0^T [X_t(\omega)]^2 \, dt < \infty\right] = 1$$

Notation 12.2. In the following, any reference to event ω in the notation of the stochastic processes will be omitted, ie,

$$X_t(\omega) = X_t$$

Definition 12.32. Let $W_t, t \in [0, T]$, be a standard Brownian motion on $(\Omega, \mathcal{F}, P)$. The *stochastic integral* or the *one-dimensional Itô process* is the stochastic process X_t defined on $(\Omega, \mathcal{F}, P)$ by

$$X_t = X_0 + \int_0^t u_s \, ds + \int_0^t v_s \, dW_s, \quad 0 \le t \le T < \infty \tag{12.54}$$

where:

- u is $\mathcal{H}_t$−measurable for any $t \in [0, T]$;
- $P\left(\int_0^t |u_s| \, ds < +\infty; \forall t \in [0, T] \right) = 1$;
- $v \in \mathcal{W}_{\mathcal{H}}(0, T)$, specifically $P\left[\int_0^T v_t^2 \, dt < \infty \right] = 1$.

Definition 12.33. If X_t is a one-dimensional Itô process, then X_t is said to hold a *stochastic differential* or *stochastic differential equation* (SDE) given by

$$dX_t = u_t \, dt + v_t \, dW_t \tag{12.55}$$

where the member u_t is said to be the *drift* of the stochastic differential and the member v_t is said to be the *diffusion* (coefficient) of the stochastic differential.

Remark 12.15. The expression in differential form of an Itô process, given by Equation (12.55), shows how the Itô processes are actually a generalisation of the generalised Wiener processes (see Equation (12.31)), because in the Itô processes, the drift and the diffusion terms may not necessarily be either constant or deterministic, but they may even be stochastic processes.

Proposition 12.10. *If X_t is an Itô process whose stochastic differential has a drift equal to zero, then X_t is a martingale with respect to the natural filtration of the standard Brownian motion $\mathbb{F}^W = \{\mathcal{F}_t^W\}_{t \in [0,T]}$.*

Definition 12.34. Let $W_t = (W_{1,t}, W_{2,t}, \ldots, W_{n,t})^{\mathrm{T}}$ be a standard n-dimensional Brownian motion defined on the probability space $(\Omega, \mathcal{F}, P)$. Then the *multi-dimensional stochastic integral* or the *multi-dimensional Itô process* is the m-dimensional vector process $\mathbf{X}_t = (X_{1,t}, X_{2,t}, \ldots, X_{m,t})$ defined on $(\Omega, \mathcal{F}, P)$ as

$$\mathbf{X}_t = \mathbf{X}_0 + \int_0^t \boldsymbol{\mu}_{X_s} \, ds + \int_0^t \mathbf{V}_{X_s} \, d\mathbf{W}_s \tag{12.56}$$

where:

- μ_{X_t} is a m-dimensional vector of the following type:

$$\mu_{X_t} = \begin{bmatrix} \mu_{X_{1,t}} \\ \mu_{X_{2,t}} \\ \vdots \\ \mu_{X_{m,t}} \end{bmatrix}$$

and any of its members is $\mathcal{H}_t$-measurable and $P(\int_0^t |\mu_{X_i}(s,\omega)|\,ds < +\infty; \forall t \in [0,T]) = 1$, for all $i = 1, 2, \ldots, m$;

- V_{X_t} is a matrix of the order $m \times n$ of the type (where every single element is $v_{i;j,t}$):

$$V_{X_t} = \begin{bmatrix} v_{1;1,t} & v_{1;2,t} & \cdots & v_{1;n,t} \\ v_{2;1,t} & v_{2;2,t} & \cdots & v_{2;n,t} \\ \vdots & \vdots & \vdots & \vdots \\ v_{m;1,t} & \cdots & \cdots & v_{m;n,t} \end{bmatrix}$$

every element belongs to class $\mathcal{W}_{\mathcal{H}}(0,T)$ and, specifically,

$$P\left(\int_0^t (v_{i;j,s})^2\,ds < +\infty \ \forall t \in [0,T] \right) = 1, \quad \forall i = 1, 2, \ldots, m, \ \forall j = 1, 2, \ldots, n$$

Remark 12.16. Equation (12.56) may be also expanded as

$$\begin{bmatrix} X_{1,t} \\ X_{2,t} \\ \vdots \\ X_{m,t} \end{bmatrix} = \begin{bmatrix} X_{1,0} \\ X_{2,0} \\ \vdots \\ X_{m,0} \end{bmatrix} + \begin{bmatrix} \int_0^t \mu_{X_1}(s,\omega)\,ds \\ \int_0^t \mu_{X_2}(s,\omega)\,ds \\ \vdots \\ \int_0^t \mu_{X_m}(s,\omega)\,ds \end{bmatrix} + \begin{bmatrix} \sum_{j=1}^n [\int_0^t v_{1;j,s}\,dW_j] \\ \sum_{j=1}^n [\int_0^t v_{2;j,s}\,dW_j] \\ \vdots \\ \sum_{j=1}^n [\int_0^t v_{m;j,s}\,dW_j] \end{bmatrix} \quad (12.57)$$

Definition 12.35. If X_t is a multi-dimensional Itô process, then X_t is said to hold the *multi-dimensional stochastic differential* or *the vector SDE* given by

$$d\mathbf{X}_t = \mu_{X_t}\,dt + V_{X_t}\,d\mathbf{W}_t \quad (12.58)$$

which corresponds to a system of m (one-dimensional) stochastic differentials:

$$\begin{cases} dX_{1,t} = \mu_{X_{1,t}}\,dt + \sum_{j=1}^n v_{1;j,t}\,dW_{j,t} \\ \qquad \vdots \\ dX_{m,t} = \mu_{X_{m,t}}\,dt + \sum_{j=1}^n v_{m;j,t}\,dW_{j,t} \end{cases} \quad (12.59)$$

where any stochastic differential $dX_{i,t}$ $(i = 1, 2, \ldots, m)$ holds a *drift* equal to $\mu_{X_{i,t}}$ and a vector of *diffusion coefficients* $(v_{i;1,t}, v_{i;2,t}, \ldots, v_{i;n,t})$ associated to the corresponding standard Brownian motions.

12.4. ITÔ'S LEMMA

12.4.1. Uni-dimensional case

Theorem 12.12 (Itô's lemma). *Let X_t be an Itô process with a stochastic differential:*

$$dX_t = u_t \, dt + v_t \, dW_t \tag{12.55}$$

Also, let

$$g_t(X_t) : [0, +\infty) \times \mathbb{R} \to \mathbb{R}$$

be a function with a continuous first derivative with respect to t and with continuous first and second derivatives with respect to X_t.

Then the stochastic process $Y_t = g(t, X_t)$ continues to be a one-dimensional Itô process whose stochastic differential is given by

$$dY_t = \frac{\partial}{\partial t} g_t(X_t) \, dt + \frac{\partial}{\partial x} g_t(X_t) \, dX_t + \frac{1}{2} \frac{\partial^2}{\partial x^2} g_t(X_t) \, (dX_t)^2 \tag{12.60}$$

where (see Proposition 12.7)

$$(dW_t)^2 = dt \quad and \quad (dt)^2 = dt \, dW_t = 0$$

ie,

$$dY_t = \left[\frac{\partial}{\partial t} g_t(X_t) + \frac{\partial}{\partial x} g_t(X_t) u_t + \frac{1}{2} \frac{\partial^2}{\partial x^2} g_t(X_t) v_t^2 \right] dt + \left[\frac{\partial}{\partial x} g_t(X_t) v_t \right] dW_t \tag{12.61}$$

Corollary 12.9 (Representation of the integral form of Itô's lemma).
The stochastic differential stated in Equation (12.61) corresponds to the following representation of the integral form of the Itô process Y_t:

$$Y_t = g_t(X_t) = g_0(X_0) + \int_0^t \left[\frac{\partial}{\partial s} g_s(X_s) + \frac{\partial}{\partial x} g_s(X_s) u_s + \frac{1}{2} \frac{\partial^2}{\partial x^2} g_s(X_s) v_s^2 \right] ds$$

$$+ \int_0^t \frac{\partial}{\partial x} g_s(X_s) v_s \, dW_s \tag{12.62}$$

If t_0 is an arbitrary point which belongs to $[0, t)$, Equation (12.62) becomes

$$Y_t = g_t(X_t) = g_{t_0}(X_{t_0}) + \int_{t_0}^t \left[\frac{\partial}{\partial s} g_s(X_s) + \frac{\partial}{\partial x} g_s(X_s) u_s + \frac{1}{2} \frac{\partial^2}{\partial x^2} g_s(X_s) v_s^2 \right] ds$$

$$+ \int_{t_0}^t \frac{\partial}{\partial x} g_s(X_s) v_s \, dW_s \tag{12.63}$$

12.4.2. Two-dimensional case

Theorem 12.13. *Let* $\mathbf{X}_t = (X_{1,t}, X_{2,t})$ *be a two-dimensional Itô process dependent on a two-dimensional standard Brownian motion* $\mathbf{W}_t = (W_{1,t}, W_{2,t})$, *where* $W_{1,t}$ *and* $W_{2,t}$ *are two standard Brownian motions correlated according to a correlation coefficient* $\rho_{1,2} \in [-1, 1]$. *The stochastic differential of* $\mathbf{X}_t$ *is then (see Equation (12.59))*

$$dX_{1,t} = \mu_{X_{1,t}} \, dt + v_{1;1,t} \, dW_{1,t} + v_{1;2,t} \, dW_{2,t}$$
$$dX_{2,t} = \mu_{X_{2,t}} \, dt + v_{2;1,t} \, dW_{1,t} + v_{2;2,t} \, dW_{2,t}$$

(12.64)

Also, let

$$\mathbf{g}_t(\mathbf{X}_t) \equiv \begin{bmatrix} g_{1,t}(X_{1,t}, X_{2,t}) \\ g_{2,t}(X_{1,t}, X_{2,t}) \end{bmatrix} : [0, +\infty) \times \mathbb{R}^2 \to \mathbb{R}^2$$

a function (this is a vector function of a vector) having a continuous first derivative with respect to t and having continuous pure and mixed first- and second-order derivatives with respect to $X_{1,t}$ *and to* $X_{2,t}$. *Then, the stochastic process*

$$\mathbf{Y}_t = (Y_{1,t}, Y_{2,t}) = \begin{bmatrix} g_{1,t}(X_{1,t}, X_{2,t}) \\ g_{2,t}(X_{1,t}, X_{2,t}) \end{bmatrix} = \mathbf{g}_t(\mathbf{X}_t)$$

continues to be a two-dimensional Itô process whose stochastic differential is given by simplifying the notation[3] from

$$dY_1 = \frac{\partial g_1}{\partial t} \, dt + \frac{\partial g_1}{\partial x_1} \, dX_1 + \frac{\partial g_1}{\partial x_2} dX_2$$
$$+ \frac{1}{2} \left[\frac{\partial^2 g_1}{\partial x_1^2} (dX_1)^2 + 2 \frac{\partial^2 g_1}{\partial x_1 \partial x_2} dX_1 \, dX_2 + \frac{\partial^2 g_1}{\partial x_2^2} (dX_2)^2 \right]$$
$$dY_2 = \frac{\partial g_2}{\partial t} \, dt + \frac{\partial g_2}{\partial x_1} \, dX_1 + \frac{\partial g_2}{\partial x_2} \, dX_2$$
$$+ \frac{1}{2} \left[\frac{\partial^2 g_2}{\partial x_1^2} (dX_1)^2 + 2 \frac{\partial^2 g_2}{\partial x_1 \partial x_2} dX_1 \, dX_2 + \frac{\partial^2 g_2}{\partial x_2^2} (dX_2)^2 \right]$$

(12.65)

ie, by using (12.64) in (12.65), and by simplifying (see Proposition 12.7) and by using a further simplified notation one has[4]

---

[3] For $i = 1, 2$: $Y_{i,t} = Y_i$; $X_{i,t} = X_i$; $g_{i,t}(X_{1,t}, X_{2,t}) = g_i$).
[4] For any $i, j = 1, 2$: $\mu_{X_{i,t}} = \mu_{X_i}$; $v_{i;j,t} = v_{i,j}$; $W_{i,t} = W_i$.

$$dY_1 = \left[\frac{\partial g_1}{\partial t} + \frac{\partial g_1}{\partial x_1} \mu_{X_1} + \frac{\partial g_1}{\partial x_2} \mu_{X_2} + \frac{1}{2} \frac{\partial^2 g_1}{\partial x_1^2} (v_{1,1}^2 + v_{1,2}^2 + 2 v_{1,1} v_{1,2} \rho_{1,2}) \right.$$

$$+ \frac{1}{2} \frac{\partial^2 g_1}{\partial x_2^2} (v_{2,1}^2 + v_{2,2}^2 + 2 v_{2,1} v_{2,2} \rho_{1,2})$$

$$\left. + \frac{\partial^2 g_1}{\partial x_1 \partial x_2} (v_{1,1} v_{2,1} + v_{1,2} v_{2,2} + (v_{1,1} v_{2,2} + v_{2,1} v_{1,2}) \rho_{1,2}) \right] dt$$

$$+ \left[\frac{\partial g_1}{\partial x_1} v_{1,1} + \frac{\partial g_1}{\partial x_2} v_{2,1} \right] dW_1 + \left[\frac{\partial g_1}{\partial x_1} v_{1,2} + \frac{\partial g_1}{\partial x_2} v_{2,2} \right] dW_2$$

$$dY_2 = \left[\frac{\partial g_2}{\partial t} + \frac{\partial g_2}{\partial x_1} \mu_{X_1} + \frac{\partial g_2}{\partial x_2} \mu_{X_2} + \frac{1}{2} \frac{\partial^2 g_2}{\partial x_1^2} (v_{1,1}^2 + v_{1,2}^2 + 2 v_{1,1} v_{1,2} \rho_{1,2}) \right.$$

$$+ \frac{1}{2} \frac{\partial^2 g_2}{\partial x_2^2} (v_{2,1}^2 + v_{2,2}^2 + 2 v_{2,1} v_{2,2} \rho_{1,2})$$

$$\left. + \frac{\partial^2 g_2}{\partial x_1 \partial x_2} (v_{1,1} v_{2,1} + v_{1,2} v_{2,2} + (v_{1,1} v_{2,2} + v_{2,1} v_{1,2}) \rho_{1,2}) \right] dt$$

$$+ \left[\frac{\partial g_2}{\partial x_1} v_{1,1} + \frac{\partial g_2}{\partial x_2} v_{2,1} \right] dW_1 + \left[\frac{\partial g_2}{\partial x_1} v_{1,2} + \frac{\partial g_2}{\partial x_2} v_{2,2} \right] dW_2$$

(12.66)

12.4.3. General case

Theorem 12.14. Let $X_t = (X_{1,t}, X_{2,t}, \ldots, X_{m,t})$ be a m-dimensional Itô process which depends on a standard n-dimensional Brownian motion $W_t = (W_{1,t}, W_{2,t}, \ldots, W_{n,t})$, where $W_{i,t}$ and $W_{j,t}$ are two standard Brownian motions correlated according to a correlation coefficient (this correlation coefficient will be clearly equal to one if $i = j$) $\rho_{i,j} \in [-1, 1]$, $i = 1, 2, \ldots, n$, $j = 1, 2, \ldots, n$. Therefore, the stochastic differential of X_t is (see Equation (12.59))

$$\begin{cases} dX_{1,t} = \mu_{X_{1,t}} \, dt + \sum_{j=1}^{n} v_{1;j,t} \, dW_{j,t} \\ \quad \vdots \\ dX_{m,t} = \mu_{X_{m,t}} \, dt + \sum_{j=1}^{n} v_{m;j,t} \, dW_{j,t} \end{cases}$$

(12.59)

In addition,

$$\mathbf{g}_t(\mathbf{X}_t) \equiv \begin{bmatrix} g_{1,t}(X_{1,t}, X_{2,t}, \ldots, X_{m,t}) \\ g_{2,t}(X_{1,t}, X_{2,t}, \ldots, X_{m,t}) \\ \vdots \\ g_{p,t}(X_{1,t}, X_{2,t}, \ldots, X_{m,t}) \end{bmatrix} : [0, +\infty) \times \mathbb{R}^m \to \mathbb{R}^p$$

a function (this is a vector function of a vector) with a continuous first derivative with respect to t and continuous pure and mixed first- and second-order derivatives with respect to $X_{1,t}, X_{2,t}, \ldots, X_{m,t}$. Then the stochastic process

$$\mathbf{Y}_t = (Y_{1,t}, Y_{2,t}, \ldots, Y_{p,t}) = \begin{bmatrix} g_{1,t}(X_{1,t}, X_{2,t}, \ldots, X_{m,t}) \\ g_{2,t}(X_{1,t}, X_{2,t}, \ldots, X_{m,t}) \\ \vdots \\ g_{p,t}(X_{1,t}, X_{2,t}, \ldots, X_{m,t}) \end{bmatrix} = \mathbf{g}_t(\mathbf{X}_t)$$

is a p-dimensional Itô process whose stochastic differential is given by simplifying the notation[5] by

$$dY_h = \frac{\partial g_h}{\partial t}\, dt + \sum_{i=1}^{m} \frac{\partial g_h}{\partial x_i}\, dX_i + \frac{1}{2} \sum_{j=1}^{m} \sum_{i=1}^{m} \frac{\partial^2 g_h}{\partial x_i \partial x_j}\, dX_i\, dX_j, \quad h = 1, 2, \ldots, p \tag{12.67}$$

ie, using (12.64) in (12.65), and by using some simplifications (see Proposition 12.7) and a further simplified notation one has[6]

$$dY_h = \left[\frac{\partial g_h}{\partial t} + \sum_{i=1}^{m} \frac{\partial g_h}{\partial x_i} \mu_{X_i} + \frac{1}{2} \sum_{j=1}^{m} \sum_{i=1}^{m} \frac{\partial^2 g_h}{\partial x_i \partial x_j} (\mathbf{V} \cdot \mathbf{V}^{\mathsf{T}})_{i,j} \right] dt$$

$$+ \sum_{i=1}^{m} \frac{\partial g_h}{\partial x_i} \left(\sum_{q=1}^{m} v_{i,q} dW_{q,t} \right), \quad h = 1, 2, \ldots, p \tag{12.68}$$

where $(\mathbf{V} \cdot \mathbf{V}^{\mathsf{T}})_{i,j}$ is the element which belongs to the ith row and the jth column of the square matrix $\mathbf{V} \cdot \mathbf{V}^{\mathsf{T}}$, since $\mathbf{V}$ is the matrix, of the order of $m \times n$, of the diffusion coefficients of the m-dimensional Itô process $\mathbf{X}_t = (X_1, X_2, \ldots, X_m)$ with respect to the standard n-dimensional Brownian motion $\mathbf{W}_t = (W_1, W_2, \ldots, W_n)$.

12.4.4. Leibniz rule

Theorem 12.15. *Let X_t and Y_t be two one-dimensional Itô processes with a stochastic differential equal to*

$$dX_t = \mu_{1,t}\, dt + \sigma_{1,t}\, dW_t \tag{12.69}$$

and

$$dY_t = \mu_{2,t}\, dt + \sigma_{2,t}\, dW_t \tag{12.70}$$

respectively.

Then the product of these two processes, ie, the function $g_t(X_t, Y_t) = X_t \cdot Y_t$, continues to be an Itô one-dimensional process whose stochastic differential is

---

[5]For any $h = 1, 2, \ldots$: $Y_{h,t} = Y_h$; $X_{h,t} = X_h$; $g_{h,t}(X_{1,t}, X_{2,t}) = g_h$.
[6]In particular: $\mu_{X_i,t} = \mu_{X_i}$; $v_{i;q,t} = v_{i,q}$; $W_{i,t} = W_i$; $(\mathbf{V} \cdot \mathbf{V}^{\mathsf{T}})_{i;j,t} = (\mathbf{V} \cdot \mathbf{V}^{\mathsf{T}})_{i,j}$.

given by

$$dg_t(X_t, Y_t) = d(X_t \cdot Y_t) = Y_t \cdot dX_t + X_t \cdot dY_t + dY_t \cdot dX_t \tag{12.71}$$

ie,

$$dg_t(X_t, Y_t) = d(X_t \cdot Y_t) = (Y_t\mu_{1,t} + X_t\mu_{2,t} + \sigma_{1,t}\sigma_{2,t})\, dt + (Y_t\sigma_{1,t} + X_t\sigma_{2,t})\, dW_t \tag{12.72}$$

Remark 12.17. The Leibniz rule (see Theorem 12.13) can be derived from the application of Itô's lemma to the Itô two-dimensional process given by (X_t, Y_t), where $g_t(X_t, Y_t)$ is a vector function of real values and where:

• the vector of the drift coefficients is

$$\mu = \begin{bmatrix} \mu_{1,t} \\ \mu_{2,t} \end{bmatrix}$$

• the matrix of the diffusion coefficients is

$$V = \begin{bmatrix} \sigma_{1,t} \\ \sigma_{2,t} \end{bmatrix}$$

Corollary 12.10. *The general formula of stochastic integration by parts is derived from Equation (12.71), ie,*

$$\int_0^t X_s \cdot dY_s = X_t \cdot Y_t - X_0 \cdot Y_0 - \int_0^t Y_s \cdot dX_s - \int_0^t dY_s \cdot dX_s \tag{12.73}$$

Example 12.2. Let X_t be a two-dimensional Itô process with a stochastic differential

$$dX_{k,t} = \mu_{X_{k,t}}\, dt + \sigma_{X_{k,t}}\, dW_t, \quad k = 1, 2 \tag{12.74}$$

where the drift and diffusion coefficients may also be stochastic processes. Then, the following equivalences can be derived from Equation (12.74):

$$\mu_X = \begin{bmatrix} \mu_{X_{1,t}} \\ \mu_{X_{2,t}} \end{bmatrix}, \quad V_X = \begin{bmatrix} \sigma_{X_{1,t}} \\ \sigma_{X_{2,t}} \end{bmatrix}$$

Considering the function (this is a vector function of real values) $g_t(X_t) = X_{1,t}/X_{2,t}$, where the process $X_{2,t}$ is assumed to always be different from zero. By applying the Leibniz rule (see Equation (12.71)) one may determine the stochastic differential of the one-dimensional Itô process defined as

$$Y_t = g_t(\mathbf{X}_t) = \frac{X_{1,t}}{X_{2,t}}$$

Actually, this is the Itô algebra (see Proposition 12.7):

$$dY = \left[\frac{\mu_{X_1}}{X_2} - \frac{(\sigma_{X_1}\sigma_{X_2} + X_1\mu_{X_2})}{(X_2)^2} + \frac{X_1\sigma_{X_2}^2}{(X_2)^3}\right]dt + \left[\frac{\sigma_{X_1}}{X_2} - \frac{X_1\sigma_{X_2}}{(X_2)^2}\right]dW$$

Corollary 12.11. *Let X_t be an Itô process whose stochastic differential is equal to*

$$dX_t = \mu_t\, dt + \sigma_t\, dW_t \tag{12.75}$$

If the integrand function is deterministic in an Itô integral, ie, it is a function of the variable t only and it is differentiable, then the following equivalence holds:

$$d(f_t \cdot X_t) = f_t\, dX_t + \frac{d}{dt}f_t X_t\, dt \tag{12.76}$$

ie, by using the representation in the integral form:

$$\int_0^t f_s\, dX_s = f_t X_t - f_0 X_0 - \int_0^t \frac{d}{ds}f_s X_s\, ds \tag{12.77}$$

Example 12.3. Let X_t be an Itô process with a stochastic differential

$$dX_t = \mu\, dt + \sigma\, dW_t \tag{12.78}$$

and let B_t be a function t described by the following ODE:

$$dB_t = \mu B_t\, dt \tag{12.79}$$

The solution of (12.79) is (see Theorem 8.1)

$$B_t = e^{\mu t}$$

Consider a function $g_t(X_t) = X_t/B_t$, where B_t is assumed to always be different than zero. By applying the Leibniz rule (see Corollary 12.11) one may determine the stochastic differential of the one-dimensional Itô process defined as

$$Y_t = g_t(X_t) = \frac{X_t}{B_t}$$

Also, one will have

$$dY_t = d\frac{X_t}{B_t} = X_t\left(-\frac{\mu}{B_t}\right)dt + \frac{1}{B_t}(\mu\, dt + \sigma\, dW_t)$$

Corollary 12.12. *If the integrand function is deterministic in an Itô integral, ie, it is a function of the variable t only, and it is differentiable, then the following relation holds:*

$$d(f_t \cdot W_t) = f_t \, dW_t + \frac{d}{dt} f_t W_t \, dt \tag{12.80}$$

ie, by using the representation in the integral form:

$$\int_0^t f_s \, dW_s = f_t W_t - \int_0^t \frac{d}{ds} f_s W_s \, ds \tag{12.81}$$

12.5. GIRSANOV THEOREM

Definition 12.36. Let $W_t, t \in [0, T]$, be a standard Brownian motion on the filtered probability space $(\Omega, \mathcal{F}, \{\mathcal{F}_t\}_{t \in [0,T]}, P)$. Also, let $\vartheta < \infty$. Then the U_t is defined in differential form:

$$dU_t := \vartheta \, dW_t \tag{12.82}$$

Definition 12.37. The *exponential Doléans* of the process U_t, denoted by $\mathcal{E}_t(U)$, is the stochastic exponential of U_t, ie, the solution of the following SDE:

$$d\mathcal{E}_t(U) = \mathcal{E}_t(U) \, dU_t = \mathcal{E}_t(U)\vartheta \, dW_t \tag{12.83}$$

under the initial condition

$$\mathcal{E}_0(U) = 1 \tag{12.84}$$

Proposition 12.11. *The exponential Doléans of the process U_t, ie, the solution of Equation (12.83) with the initial condition provided by Equation (12.84) is*

$$\mathcal{E}_t(U) = e^{\vartheta W_t - (1/2)\vartheta^2 t} \tag{12.85}$$

Theorem 12.16 (Girsanov). *Let $W_t, t \in [0, T]$, be a standard Brownian motion of the filtered probability space $(\Omega, \mathcal{F}, \{\mathcal{F}_t\}_{t \in [0,T]}, P)$. For any constant $\vartheta < \infty$, consider the following exponential local martingale (and super-martingale; see Proposition 12.4):*

$$Z_t := e^{(\vartheta W_t - (\vartheta^2/2)t)}, \quad 0 \le t \le T \tag{12.86}$$

If Z_t is a martingale with respect to the filtration $\{\mathcal{F}_t\}_{t \in [0,T]}$ and to probability measure P, then, for any $A \in \mathcal{F}_T$,

$$Q(A) := E^P(Z_T \cdot \mathbf{1}_A) \tag{12.87}$$

is a probability measure of the measurable space $(\Omega, \mathcal{F}_T)$ and, under such a probability measure, the stochastic process

$$\widetilde{W}_t = W_t - \vartheta t \tag{12.88}$$

is a standard Brownian motion.

Theorem 12.17. *The quantity Z_t is a martingale with respect to filtration $\{\mathcal{F}_t\}_{t\in[0,T]}$ and to the probability measure P.*

Corollary 12.13. *For any $t \in [0, T]$, the random variable*

$$Z_t := e^{(\vartheta W_t - (\vartheta^2/2)t)}$$

is the Radon–Nikodym derivative of the probability measure Q with respect to the equivalent probability measure (see Equation (11.3)) P on the measurable space $(\Omega, \mathcal{F}_t)$, ie,

$$\frac{dQ}{dP} = e^{(\vartheta W_t - (\vartheta^2/2)t)} \quad \text{on } (\Omega, \mathcal{F}_t) \tag{12.89}$$

Remark 12.18. Theorem 12.16 continues also to hold if $\widetilde{W}_t$ is a process defined differently than in Equation (12.88). For example, if $\widetilde{W}_t$ is defined as

$$\widetilde{W}_t = \sigma W_t - \vartheta t$$

obviously, if both the members of the equation are divided by σ, a new process $\widetilde{\widetilde{W}}_t$ is obtained to be defined as

$$\widetilde{\widetilde{W}}_t = \frac{\widetilde{W}_t}{\sigma} = W_t - \frac{\vartheta}{\sigma}t$$

which is a standard Brownian motion under Q, and in that case the Radon–Nikodym derivative of Q with respect to P on the measurable space $(\Omega, \mathcal{F}_t)$ will be

$$\frac{dQ}{dP} = e^{((\vartheta/\sigma)W_t - (1/2)(\vartheta/\sigma)^2 t)}$$

Theorem 12.18 (Girsanov II). *Let W_t, $t \in [0, T]$, be a standard Brownian motion on the filtered probability space $(\Omega, \mathcal{F}, \{\mathcal{F}_t\}_{t\in[0,T]}, P)$. For any measurable process ϑ_t, $t \in [0, T]$, adapted to filtration $\{\mathcal{F}_t\}_{t\in[0,T]}$ and so that $E(e^{(1/2)\int_0^t \vartheta_s^2\, ds}) < \infty$, consider the following exponential local martingale (and super-martingale; see Proposition 12.4):*

$$Z_t := e^{(\int_0^t \vartheta_s\, dW_s - (1/2)\int_0^t \vartheta_s^2\, ds)}, \quad 0 \le t \le T \tag{12.90}$$

If Z_t is a martingale with respect to the filtration $\{\mathcal{F}_t\}_{t\in[0,T]}$ and to probability measure P, then, for any $A \in \mathcal{F}_T$,

$$Q(A) := E^P(Z_T \cdot \mathbf{1}_A) \tag{12.91}$$

is a probability measure on the measurable space $(\Omega, \mathcal{F}_T)$ and, under that stochastic probability process,

$$\widetilde{W}_t = W_t - \int_0^t \vartheta_s\, ds \tag{12.92}$$

is a standard Brownian motion.

Theorem 12.19. *The quantity Z_t is a martingale with respect to the filtration $\{\mathcal{F}_t\}_{t\in[0,T]}$ and to probability measure P.*

Corollary 12.14. *For any $t \in [0, T]$, the random variable.*

$$Z_t := e^{\left(\int_0^t \vartheta_s \, dW_s - (1/2) \int_0^t \vartheta_s^2 \, ds\right)}$$

is the Radon–Nikodym derivative of the probability measure Q with respect to the equivalent probability measure (see Equation (11.3)) P on the measurable space $(\Omega, \mathcal{F}_t)$, ie,

$$\frac{dQ}{dP} \equiv e^{\left(\int_0^t \vartheta_s \, dW_s - (1/2) \int_0^t \vartheta_s^2 \, ds\right)} \quad on \ (\Omega, \mathcal{F}_t) \tag{12.93}$$

12.6. FEYNMAN–KAC FORMULA

12.6.1. The formula in $\mathbb{R}^1$

Notation 12.3. The notation $f_t(X_t) := f(t, X_t)$ will be used below.

Theorem 12.20. *In $\mathbb{R}^1$, let $X_t^{s,x}$ ($X_t^{s,x}$ may also be written as $X_t|X_s = x$) be the solution to the equation*

$$dX_t = b(t, X_t) \, dt + \sigma(t, X_t) \, dB_t, \quad s < t \le T \tag{12.94}$$
$$X_s = x$$

with b and σ being continuous functions with continuous and bounded first- and second-order derivatives (with respect to x). Also, let $f : \mathbb{R} \to \mathbb{R}$ be a continuous function with continuous and bounded first- and second-order derivatives and $g(s, x)$ a continuous function from $\mathbb{R}_+ \times \mathbb{R}$ to $\mathbb{R}$ with continuous first- and second-order derivatives (with respect to x). Then the function

$$v(s, x) = E\left[f(X_T)e^{\int_s^T g(t,X_t) \, dt}\middle| X_s = x\right], \quad 0 \le s \le T \tag{12.95}$$

satisfies the equation

$$v_s' + b(s, x)v_x' + \tfrac{1}{2}\sigma^2(s, x)v_{xx}'' + g(s, x)v(s, x) = 0 \tag{12.96}$$

with the final condition $\lim_{s\to T} v(s, x) = f(X_T)$.

12.6.2. The formula in $\mathbb{R}^2$

12.6.2.1. Independent Brownian motions

Theorem 12.21. In $\mathbb{R}^2$, let $X_t^{s,x}$ and $Y_t^{s,y}$ be the solutions to the following SDEs:

$$dX_t = a(t, X_t)\, dt + \sigma_{11}(t, X_t)\, dB_{1,t} + \sigma_{12}(t, X_t)\, dB_{2,t}, \quad s < t \leq T \qquad (12.97)$$

$$X_s = x$$

and

$$dY_t = b(t, Y_t)\, dt + \sigma_{21}(t, Y_t)\, dB_{1,t} + \sigma_{22}(t, Y_t)\, dB_{2,t}, \quad s < t \leq T \qquad (12.98)$$

$$Y_s = y$$

with $a, b, \sigma_{11}, \sigma_{12}, \sigma_{21}, \sigma_{22}$ being continuous functions with continuous and bounded first- and second-order derivatives (with respect to x and y)[7]. $B_{1,t}$ and $B_{2,t}$ are two independent one-dimensional standard Brownian motions. Also, in $\mathbb{R}^2$, let $f : \mathbb{R}^2 \to \mathbb{R}$ be a continuous function with continuous and bounded first- and second-order derivatives and let $g(s, x, y)$ be a continuous function from $\mathbb{R}_+ \times \mathbb{R}^2$ to $\mathbb{R}$ with continuous first- and second-order derivatives (with respect to x and y). Then the function

$$v(s, x, y) = E\left[f(X_T, Y_T) e^{\int_s^T g(t, X_t, Y_t)\, dt} \,\Big|\, X_s = x, Y_s = y \right], \quad 0 \leq s \leq T \qquad (12.99)$$

satisfies the equation

$$v_s' + a v_x' + b v_y' + \tfrac{1}{2}(\sigma_{11}^2 + \sigma_{12}^2) v_{xx}'' + \tfrac{1}{2}(\sigma_{21}^2 + \sigma_{22}^2) v_{yy}''$$

$$+ (\sigma_{11}\sigma_{21} + \sigma_{12}\sigma_{22}) v_{xy}'' + g(s, x, y) v(s, x, y) = 0 \qquad (12.100)$$

with the final condition $\lim_{s \to T} v(s, x, y) = f(X_T, Y_T)$.

12.6.2.2. Correlated Brownian motions

Theorem 12.22. In $\mathbb{R}^2$, let $X_t^{s,x}$ and $Y_t^{s,y}$ be the solution to the following SDEs:

$$dX_t = a(t, X_t)\, ds + \sigma_{11}(t, X_t)\, dB_{1,t} + \sigma_{12}(s, X_t)\, dB_{2,t}, \quad s < t \leq T \qquad (12.101)$$

$$X_s = x$$

and

$$dY_t = b(t, Y_t)\, dt + \sigma_{21}(t, Y_t)\, dB_{1,t} + \sigma_{22}(t, Y_t)\, dB_{2,t}, \quad s < t \leq T \qquad (12.102)$$

$$Y_s = y$$

---

[7]In the following, the arguments of the coefficients of the SDEs will be omitted to streamline the narrative.

with a, b, σ_{11}, σ_{12}, σ_{21}, σ_{22} being continuous functions with continuous and bounded first- and second-order derivatives (with respect to x and y)[8]. $B_{1,t}$ and $B_{2,t}$ are two one-dimensional standard motions with correlation so that $dB_{1,t} \cdot dB_{2,t} = \rho_{B_1,B_2} \cdot dt$. Also, in $\mathbb{R}^2$, let $f : \mathbb{R}^2 \to \mathbb{R}$ be a continuous function with continuous and bounded first- and second-order derivatives and let $g(s, x, y)$ be a continuous function from $\mathbb{R}_+ \times \mathbb{R}^2$ to $\mathbb{R}$ continuous first- and second-order derivatives (with respect to x and y). Then the function

$$v(s, x, y) = E\left[f(X_T, Y_T)e^{\int_s^T g(t,X_t,Y_t)\,dt} \middle| X_s = x, Y_s = y\right], \quad 0 \le s \le T \quad (12.103)$$

satisfies the equation

$$v'_s + av'_x + bv'_y + v''_{xy}((\sigma_{11}\sigma_{21} + \sigma_{12}\sigma_{22}) + (\sigma_{11}\sigma_{22} + \sigma_{12}\sigma_{21})\rho_{B_1,B_2})$$
$$+ \tfrac{1}{2}v''_{xx}(\sigma_{11}^2 + \sigma_{12}^2 + 2\sigma_{11}\sigma_{12}\rho_{B_1,B_2}) + \tfrac{1}{2}v''_{yy}(\sigma_{21}^2 + \sigma_{22}^2 + 2\sigma_{21}\sigma_{22}\rho_{B_1,B_2})$$
$$+ g(s, x, y)v(s, x, y) = 0 \quad (12.104)$$

with the final condition $\lim_{s \to T} v(t, x, y) = f(X_T, Y_T)$.

12.6.3.   The formula in $\mathbb{R}^n$

Theorem 12.23. In $\mathbb{R}^n$, let $X_s^{t,x}$ be the solution to the equation

$$dX_s = b(s, X_s)\,ds + \sigma(s, X_s)\,dZ_s, \quad t < s \le T \quad (12.105)$$
$$X_t = x$$

with b and σ being continuous and bounded first- and second-order derivatives (with respect to x). Also, in $\mathbb{R}^n$, let $f : \mathbb{R}^n \to \mathbb{R}$ be a continuous function with continuous and bounded first- and second-order derivatives and let $g(t, x)$ be a continuous function from $\mathbb{R}_+ \times \mathbb{R}^n$ to $\mathbb{R}$ with continuous first- and second-order derivatives (with respect to x). Then the function

$$v(t, x) = E\left[f(X_T)e^{\int_t^T g(s,X_s)\,ds} \middle| X_t = x\right], \quad 0 \le t \le T \quad (12.106)$$

satisfies the equation

$$v'_t + \sum_{i=1}^n b_i(t, x)v'_{x_i} + \frac{1}{2}\sum_{i,j=1}^n (\sigma\sigma')_{ij}v''_{x_ix_j} + g(t, x)v(t, x) = 0 \quad (12.107)$$

with the final condition $\lim_{t \to T} v(t, x) = f(X_T)$.

---

[8]In the following, the arguments of the coefficients of the SDEs will be omitted to streamline the narrative.

Stochastic differential equations

13.1. GEOMETRIC BROWNIAN MOTIONS
13.1.1. Constant coefficient geometric Brownian motion

Theorem 13.1. *Let W_t be a one-dimensional standard Brownian motion. The Cauchy problem defined in the SDE below as an initial condition, ie,*

$$dX_t = aX_t\,dt + bX_t\,dW_t \tag{13.1}$$
$$X_s = x$$

together with the stochastic integral

$$X_t = x + \int_s^t aX_u\,du + \int_s^t bX_u\,dW_u \tag{13.2}$$

is an Itô process said to be a Constant coefficient geometric Brownian motion. *This process has the following solution:*

$$X_t = xe^{b(W_t - W_s) + (a - b^2/2)(t-s)}, \quad 0 \le s \le t < \infty \tag{13.3}$$

Remark 13.1. Provided that one considers the initial positive condition, X_s, the geometric Brownian motion is a stochastic process whose values are always positive.

13.1.1.1. Logarithm transformation of the geometric Brownian motion

Theorem 13.2. *Let W_t be a one-dimensional standard Brownian motion and let X_t be a constant coefficient geometric Brownian motion with a stochastic differential given by Equation (13.1). Let the process Y_t be defined as*

$$Y_t = \ln X_t \tag{13.4}$$

then the Cauchy problem defined by the following SDE as an initial condition, ie,

$$dY_t = \left(a - \frac{b^2}{2}\right)dt + b\,dW_t \tag{13.5}$$
$$Y_s = \ln x$$

has the solution

$$Y_t = \ln x + \left(a - \frac{b^2}{2} \right)(t - s) + b(W_t - W_s) \tag{13.6}$$

Proposition 13.1. *The process*

$$dY_t = \left(a - \frac{b^2}{2} \right) dt + b \, dW_t$$

where $Y_t = \ln X_t$ is distributed as

$$\ln \frac{X_t}{X_{t-dt}} \sim N\left(\left(a - \frac{b^2}{2} \right) dt, b\sqrt{dt} \right)$$

13.1.1.2. Confidence interval for a geometric Brownian motion

Proposition 13.2. *Let $Z \sim N(0,1)$ and let X_t be a constant coefficient geometric Brownian motion as in Equation (13.1), then the relation below holds:*

$$P(X_{t-s}e^{\min} \leq X_t \leq X_{t-s}e^{\max}) = \varkappa$$

where:

- *$\varkappa$ is the probability;*
- *$\max = bz_{\varkappa/2}\sqrt{t-s} + (a - b^2/2)(t-s)$;*
- *$\min = b(-z_{\varkappa/2})\sqrt{t-s} + (a - b^2/2)(t-s)$;*
- *$\pm z_{\varkappa/2}$ are the boundaries of the random variable Z which define the probability.*

13.1.2. Variable coefficient geometric Brownian motion

Theorem 13.3. *Let W_t be a one-dimensional standard Brownian motion. The Cauchy problem defined by the following SDE as an initial condition, ie,*

$$dX_t = a_t X_t \, dt + b_t X_t \, dW_t \tag{13.7}$$
$$X_s = x$$

is an Itô process said to be a variable coefficient geometric Brownian motion. *This process has the following solution:*

$$X_t = xe^{\int_s^t b_u \, dW_u + \int_s^t (a_u - b_u^2/2) \, du}, \quad 0 \leq s \leq t < \infty \tag{13.8}$$

13.2. ORNSTEIN–UHLENBECK PROCESSES

When a process is occurring which submits the Brownian motion to an elastic force q, a mean-reverting process is occurring:

$$dX_t = -qX_t \, dt + \sigma \, dW_t, \quad q, \sigma > 0 \tag{13.9}$$

Generalising this SDE, one gets to the *Ornstein–Uhlenbeck arithmetic diffusion process*:

$$dX_t = q(\mu - X_t) \, dt + \sigma \, dW_t, \quad q, \sigma > 0 \tag{13.10}$$

This model is *mean-reverting*, since the value of X_t tends to move elastically to the mean value μ: in fact, if X_t is lower than μ, the member in dt will be positive and will have the effect of causing X_{t+dt} to approach μ, if, in contrast, X_t is higher than μ, the member in dt will be negative, but will tend to reduce the difference between X_{t+dt} and μ.

Proposition 13.3. *The solution to the SDE (13.10), ie, of the following Cauchy problem*

$$dX_t = q(\mu - X_t) \, dt + \sigma \, dW_t, \quad q, \sigma > 0$$
$$X_0 = x \tag{13.11}$$

is given by

$$X_t = \sigma W_t - \sigma \int_0^t q e^{-q(t-\tau)} W_\tau \, d\tau + x e^{-qt} - \mu e^{-qt} + \mu$$

Proposition 13.4. *Given the process*

$$dX_t = q(\mu - X_t) \, dt + \sigma \, dW_t \tag{13.10}$$

where $X_0 = x$, one has the following distribution for X_t:

$$X_t \sim N\left((x - \mu)e^{-qt} + \mu; \sqrt{\frac{\sigma^2}{2q}(1 - e^{-2qt})}\right) \tag{13.12}$$

Corollary 13.1. *In order to generalise the distributive properties with reference to any constant initial condition identified at time s, with $s < t$ equal to X_s, Equation (13.12) may be also written as*

$$X_t \sim N\left((X_s - \mu)e^{-q(t-s)} + \mu; \sqrt{\frac{\sigma^2}{2q}(1 - e^{-2q(t-s)})}\right) \tag{13.13}$$

Corollary 13.2. *Given a Ornestein–Uhlenbeck process as*

$$dX_t = (\alpha - \theta X_t)\, dt + \sigma\, dW_t, \quad q, \sigma > 0 \tag{13.14}$$

where X_s is the initial value, one has the following distribution for X_t

$$X_t \sim N\left(\left(X_s - \frac{\alpha}{\theta}\right)e^{-\theta(t-s)} + \frac{\alpha}{\theta}; \sqrt{\frac{\sigma^2}{2\theta}(1 - e^{-2\theta(t-s)})}\right) \tag{13.15}$$

13.2.1. Confidence intervals for a Ornestein–Uhlenbeck process

Proposition 13.5. *Let $Z \sim N(0,1)$ and let X_t be an Ornestein–Uhlenbeck process as indicated in (13.10), then the following relation holds:*

$$P(X_s e^{-q(t-s)} + \min \leq X_t \leq X_s e^{-q(t-s)} + \max) = \varkappa$$

where:

- *$\varkappa$ is the probability;*
- *$\max = \mu + z_{\varkappa/2}\sqrt{(\sigma^2/2q)(1 - e^{-2q(t-s)})} - \mu e^{-q(t-s)}$;*
- *$\min = \mu - z_{\varkappa/2}\sqrt{(\sigma^2/2q)(1 - e^{-2q(t-s)})} - \mu e^{-q(t-s)}$;*
- *$\pm z_{\varkappa/2}$ are the boundaries of the random variable Z which define the probability.*

Corollary 13.3. *If the predictive dynamics of the model are $(t - s) = 1$, ie, $s = t - 1$, then redefining consistently $t = t + 1$ and $s = t$, one has*

$$P\left(\mu - z_{\varkappa/2}\sqrt{\frac{\sigma^2}{2q}(1 - e^{-2q})} + (X_t - \mu)e^{-q}\right.$$

$$\left. \leq X_{t+1} \leq \mu + z_{\varkappa/2}\sqrt{\frac{\sigma^2}{2q}(1 - e^{-2q})} + (X_t - \mu)e^{-q}\right) = \varkappa \tag{13.16}$$

Proposition 13.6. *Let $Z \sim N(0,1)$ and let X_t be an Ornestein–Uhlenbeck process as in Equation (13.14), then the following relation holds:*

$$P(X_s e^{-\theta(t-s)} + \min \leq X_t \leq X_s e^{-\theta(t-s)} + \max) = \varkappa$$

where:

- *$\varkappa$ is the probability;*
- *$\max = z_{\varkappa/2}\sqrt{(\sigma^2/2\theta)(1 - e^{-2\theta(t-s)})} - (\alpha/\theta)e^{-\theta(t-s)} + \alpha/\theta$;*
- *$\min = -z_{\varkappa/2}\sqrt{(\sigma^2/2\theta)(1 - e^{-2\theta(t-s)})} - (\alpha/\theta)e^{-\theta(t-s)} + \alpha/\theta$;*

- $\pm z_{\varkappa/2}$ are the boundaries of the random variable Z which define the probability.

Corollary 13.4. *If the predictive dynamics of this model are $(t - s) = 1$, ie, $s = t - 1$, then redefining consistently $t = t + 1$ and $s = t$, one has*

$$P\left(-z_{\varkappa/2}\sqrt{\frac{\sigma^2}{2\theta}(1 - e^{-2\theta})} + \left(X_t - \frac{\alpha}{\theta}\right)e^{-\theta} + \frac{\alpha}{\theta}\right.$$
$$\left. \leq X_{t+1} \leq z_{\varkappa/2}\sqrt{\frac{\sigma^2}{2\theta}(1 - e^{-2\theta})} + \left(X_t - \frac{\alpha}{\theta}\right)e^{-\theta} + \frac{\alpha}{\theta}\right) = \varkappa$$

Part III

Finance

Actuarial calculus

14.1. CAPITALISATION REGIMES

In a financial context, a recurrent issue is the valorisation of a capital available today at a given future date. In order to analyse this problem, it is necessary to state some preliminarily concepts described in the following. The first of these concepts is *capitalisation*.

Definition 14.1. *Capitalisation* at time t ($t \geq 0$) of an initial capital C is the value this capital will have at the end of a time interval which begins at the current date (denoted by 0) and ends at date t.

Definition 14.2. A *capitalisation factor* is the function $m(t)$, where t is the maturity date of an investment or a loan beginning at time 0, which, multiplied by the value of the initial capital C, returns the value of the capital at date t.

The capitalisation factor must be a continuous function of its argument t, and must satisfy the following two conditions:

$$m(0) = 1 \tag{14.1}$$

and

$$m'(t) \geq 0 \tag{14.2}$$

Definition 14.3. Let C be the initial capital of an investment or a loan and let $m(t)$ be its capitalisation factor, $t \in [0, T]$ (either $t \in [0, T)$ or $t \in [0, +\infty)$). Then

$$M(C, t) = m(t) \cdot C \tag{14.3}$$

(depending only on C and t) is said to be the *capitalisation factor of the initial capital C with respect to time horizon $[0, t]$; it is computed with respect to the capitalisation factor $m(t)$.*

Definition 14.4. Defining C as the initial capital of an investment or a loan, the *interest per unit of the initial capital, denoted by I_t, is*

$$I_t = \frac{M(C, t) - C}{C} \tag{14.4}$$

or

$$I_t = m(t) - 1 \tag{14.5}$$

Remark 14.1. The link between Equations (14.4) and (14.5) is made by (14.3). Then

$$I_t = \frac{M(C,t) - C}{C} = \frac{m(t) \cdot C - C}{C} = m(t) - 1$$

Definition 14.5. The *(unit) interest rate* or *yield rate*, denoted by i, is the interest per unit of initial capital of an investment or a loan which has a duration of a unit length, ie,

$$i = I_1 = m(1) - 1 \tag{14.6}$$

Definition 14.6. The *capitalisation regime is a family of capitalisation factors* $\{f(t,a)\}$ which is dependent on time and on another parameter a which varies inside a given set A.

Definition 14.7. The *capitalisation law of* a capitalisation regime $\{f(t,a)\}$ is a given capitalisation function $\{f(t,\bar{a})\}$ with $\bar{a} \in A$ ($\bar{a}$ fixed).

Definition 14.8. The *simple* or *linear interest rate capitalisation regime* is a financial regime whose capitalisation factor is

$$m(t,a) = 1 + at, \quad t \geq 0, \ a > 0 \tag{14.7}$$

Remark 14.2. Based on the above definition, the interest rate at maturity in the time interval is directly proportional to that time interval and to the initial capital C.

In light of Equation (14.6), for the simple interest rate capitalisation regime, the unit interest rate coincides with the variable a in (14.7), ie,

$$i = a \tag{14.8}$$

Definition 14.9. The *compounded interest capitalisation regime in discrete time* is a financial regime whose capitalisation factor can be written as:

$$m(t,a) = (1+a)^t, \quad t \geq 0, \ a > 0 \tag{14.9}$$

Remark 14.3. In light of Equation (14.6), for this capitalisation regime the unit interest rate coincides with the variable a inside (14.9), ie,

$$i = a \tag{14.10}$$

Proposition 14.1. *Assuming that, under a compounded interest capitalisation regime in discrete time, interest is computed at every n^{th} moment of the unit length period; then, formula (14.9) of the compounded interest capitalisation factor in discrete time becomes*

$$m(t, a, n) = \left(1 + \frac{a}{n}\right)^{nt} \tag{14.11}$$

Definition 14.10. A *continuously compounded* or *exponential interest rate capitalisation regime* is a capitalisation regime whose capitalisation can be written as

$$m(t, a) = e^{at} \tag{14.12}$$

Definition 14.11. Coefficient a of Equation (14.12) represents the *instantaneous interest rate intensity* or *the interest rate force*.

Remark 14.4. In this financial regime, the unit interest rate is given by the following formula:

$$i = e^a - 1 \tag{14.13}$$

or the instantaneous interest rate intensity may be written as

$$a = \ln(1 + i) \tag{14.14}$$

Notation 14.1. The instantaneous interest rate intensity is often denoted by the greek letter δ.

Theorem 14.1. *The continuously compounded interest rate capitalisation regime is a limit case of the discrete time compounded interest rate capitalisation regime, ie,*

$$\lim_{n \to +\infty} \left(1 + \frac{a}{n}\right)^{nt} = e^{at} \tag{14.15}$$

where n is the number of sub-periods of every period of unit length.

Proof. The demonstration of the equivalence between Equations (14.12) and (14.15) is provided by making the number of sub-periods n in (14.11) tend to infinity. This can be derived directly from the application of the remarkable limit identified in Theorem 3.3 and at Corollary 3.1. □

Proposition 14.2. *The capitalisation factor in a continuously compounded capitalisation regime is described by the following ODE:*

$$dm(t, a) = a \cdot m(t, a)\, dt \tag{14.16}$$

Proof. The solution to Equation (14.16) is directly determined by using the integration factor e^{at}, (see Theorem 8.1). □

Corollary 14.1. *If $a = a(t)$, the capitalisation factor in a continuously compounded capitalisation regime is given by*

$$m(t, a(t)) = e^{\int_0^t a(s)\, ds} \tag{14.17}$$

Remark 14.5. By construction, the unit interest rate given by a continuous capitalisation regime, ie,

$$i = e^a - 1 \tag{14.13}$$

is always higher than the unit interest rate of the compounded capitalisation regime in discrete time, ie,

$$i = a \tag{14.10}$$

Definition 14.12. A *hyperbolic interest rate capitalisation regime* is a capitalisation regime which has the following capitalisation factor:

$$m(t) = \frac{1}{1 - at}, \quad 0 \le t < \frac{1}{a}, a > 0 \tag{14.18}$$

Remark 14.6. The limit on the values of t is necessary in order to comply with the definition of the capitalisation factor (see condition (14.2)). Its applicability is limited to short maturity.

Remark 14.7. In this financial regime, the interest rate is given by the following formula:

$$i = \frac{a}{1 - a} \tag{14.19}$$

where a is defined as the unit discount rate.

14.2. DISCOUNT REGIME

The previous section focused on how to compute the final value of a capital available at the current date at a given future date. However, the issue is often the opposite: how to evaluate a future capital at the current date. This problem is known in the literature as the discount of a future capital. In order to study this issue, it is necessary to outline some preliminarily concepts, such as the *"present value"*.

Definition 14.13. The *present value* is the value taken at the current date (denoted by 0) by a final capital C which will be available at a future date $t(t \geq 0)$.

Definition 14.14. The *discount factor* is the function $v(t)$, where t is the future date when a given capital C is available multiplied by C which returns the value of this capital at the current date (denoted by 0). The discount factor must be a continuous function of its argument t, and must satisfy the following two conditions:

$$v(0) = 1 \tag{14.20}$$

and

$$v'(t) \leq 0 \tag{14.21}$$

Definition 14.15. Let C be the final capital of an investment or a loan, and let $v(t)$ be its discount factor $t \in [0, T]$ (either $t \in [0, T)$, or $t \in [0, +\infty)$). Then

$$V(C, t) = v(t) \cdot C \tag{14.22}$$

(which depends only on C and t) is said to be the *discount value of the final capital C with respect to time horizon $[0, t]$ computed according to discount factor $v(t)$.*

Definition 14.16. Defining C as the final capital of an investment or a loan, the *discount per unit of final capital*, denoted by D_t, is

$$D_t = \frac{C - V(C, t)}{C} \tag{14.23}$$

or

$$D_t = 1 - v(t) \tag{14.24}$$

Remark 14.8. The link between Equations (14.23) and (14.24) is made by (14.22). Then

$$D_t = \frac{C - V(C, t)}{C} = \frac{C - v(t) \cdot C}{C} = 1 - v(t)$$

Definition 14.17. The *(unit) discount rate*, denoted by d, is the discount per unit of final capital with respect to an investment or a loan which lasts for a period of unit length, ie,

$$d = D_1 = 1 - v(1) \tag{14.25}$$

Definition 14.18. The *discount regime* is the family of discount factors $\{v(t, a)\}$. This depends on time and on another parameter a which varies inside a given set A.

Definition 14.19. A *discount law* belonging to the regime $\{v(t,a)\}$ is a given discount function $\{v(t,\bar{a})\}$ with $\bar{a} \in A$ ($\bar{a}$ fixed).

Definition 14.20. A *simple discount regime* is a capitalisation regime having a discount factor as

$$v(t,a) = \frac{1}{1+at}, \quad t \geq 0, a > 0 \tag{14.26}$$

Remark 14.9. In light of Equation (14.25), in the simple interest discount regime, the unit discount rate coincides with the variable a of the following function, as in Equation (14.26), ie,

$$d = \frac{a}{1+a} \tag{14.27}$$

Definition 14.21. A *compounded discount regime in discrete time* is a discount regime whose discount factor is

$$v(t,a) = (1+a)^{-t}, \quad t \geq 0, a > 0 \tag{14.28}$$

Remark 14.10. In light of Equation (14.25), in this capitalisation regime, the unit discount rate coincides with the following function of the variable a as in Equation (14.28), ie,

$$d = \frac{a}{1+a} \tag{14.29}$$

Definition 14.22. A *continuously compounded* or *exponential discount regime* is any discount regime whose discount factor is

$$v(t,a) = e^{-at} \tag{14.30}$$

Proposition 14.3. *The discount factor of a continuously compounded discount regime is described by the following ODE:*

$$dv(t,a) = -a \cdot v(t,a)\, dt \tag{14.31}$$

Proof. The solution to Equation (14.16) is immediate by using the integration factor e^{at} (see Theorem 8.1). □

Corollary 14.2. *If $a = a(t)$, the discount factor in a continuously compounded discount regime is given by*

$$v(t,a(t)) = e^{-\int_0^t a(s)\, ds} \tag{14.32}$$

Remark 14.11. In this financial regime the unit discount rate is given by the following formula:

$$d = 1 - e^{-a} \tag{14.33}$$

ie, the instantaneous interest rate intensity may be denoted by

$$a = -\ln(1 + d) \tag{14.34}$$

Theorem 14.2. *The continuously compounded discount regime is the limit case of compounded discount regime in discrete time, ie,*

$$\lim_{n \to +\infty} \left(1 + \frac{a}{n}\right)^{-nt} = e^{-at} \tag{14.35}$$

where n is the number of sub-periods of every period of unit length.

Proof. The demonstration can be derived from the demonstration of Theorem 14.1. □

Remark 14.12. By construction, the unit interest rate given by a continuous discount regime, ie,

$$d = 1 - e^{-a} \tag{14.33}$$

is always higher than the unit interest rate of the compounded capitalisation regime in discrete time, ie,

$$d = \frac{a}{1 + a} \tag{14.29}$$

Definition 14.23. A *commercial discount rate* is a discount regime which has the following capitalisation factor:

$$v(t) = 1 - at, \quad 0 \le t < \frac{1}{a}, \ a > 0 \tag{14.36}$$

Remark 14.13. The limit on the values of t is necessary in order to comply with the definition of the discount factor (see condition (14.21)). It may only be applied to short maturities.

Remark 14.14. In this discount regime, the unit discount rate is given by the following formula:

$$d = a$$

14.3. DISCOUNTING AND CAPITALISATION

Proposition 14.4. *The relation below holds between the capitalisation and the discount factors:*

$$v(t) = \frac{1}{m(t)} \tag{14.37}$$

Definition 14.24. If $m(t)$ is a capitalisation factor, then the *conjugate discount factor of* $m(t)$ is denoted by

$$v(t) = \frac{1}{m(t)}$$

Definition 14.25. The *discount regimes conjugated or associated* to the simple interest capitalisation regime, to the compounded interest rate in discrete time, to the exponential or hyperbolic interest rate are the discount regimes whose discount factor corresponds to the reciprocal of these capitalisation factors. For these capitalisation regimes, the relation identified at (14.37) holds where its right-hand side is specified with (14.7), with (14.9), with (14.12) and with (14.18), respectively.

Proposition 14.5. *Given the ODEs which describe the continuously compounded capitalisation and discount factors:*

$$dm(t, a) = a(t) \cdot m(t, a)\, dt, \quad dv(t, a) = -a(t) \cdot v(t, a)\, dt$$

then

$$\frac{1}{m(t, a(t))} = v(t, a(t)) = e^{-\int_0^t a(s)\, ds}$$

$$m(t, a(t)) = \frac{1}{v(t, a(t))} = e^{\int_0^t a(s)\, ds}$$

and

$$d\frac{1}{m(t, a)} = -a(t) \cdot \frac{1}{m(t, a)}\, dt$$

$$d\frac{1}{v(t, a)} = a(t) \cdot \frac{1}{v(t, a)}\, dt$$

Proposition 14.6. *Let i and d be the unit interest rate and the unit discount rate for a given financial capitalisation and/or discount regime, then the following relation holds:*

$$d = \frac{i}{1 + i}$$

ie,

$$i = \frac{d}{1 - d}$$

Equity derivatives models

15.1. INTRODUCTION

In the financial markets, the most widespread pricing models are based on the fundamental assumption that markets are frictionless, ie,

(1) investors are price takers;
(2) they all have access to the same set of information;
(3) there is no transaction cost or fee;
(4) assets are perfectly divisible and liquid;
(5) there is no limit to credit exposure by the bank;
(6) interest rates for loans and borrowing are identical.

The models below are not listed on the basis of their publication dates, but on the need to provide a sound and consistent overview of the derivative pricing methods.

15.2. PRICING MODELS FOR EUROPEAN OPTIONS

15.2.1. Pricing in a uniperiodical context

The essential issue concerning the pricing model is the payoff definition at contingent claim maturity.

Then, an outline is provided on how to price a typical European-type path independent contingent claim: the call, whose maturity payoff is defined by[1]

$$g(S_T) = (S_T - K)^+ \triangleq \max\{S_T - K, 0\}$$

ie,

$$g(S_T) = \begin{cases} S_T - K & \text{if } S_T > K \text{ the option is exercised} \\ 0 & \text{if } S_T \leq K \text{ the option is abandoned} \end{cases}$$

---

[1] In the case of a put

$$g(S_T) = (K - S_T)^+ \triangleq \max\{K - S_T, 0\}$$

ie,

$$g(S_T) = \begin{cases} K - S_T & \text{if } S_T < K \text{ the option is exercised} \\ 0 & \text{if } S_T \geq K \text{ the option is abandoned} \end{cases}$$

In order to price the derivative above on a uniperiodical spot market at time $t = 0$, the main problem is estimating the value of the random variable S at time $T = 1$ (S_T). This final value may be a random variable on the probability space $\Omega = \{w_1, w_2\}$ with a probability measure P so that $P(w_1) + P(w_2) = 1$.

Formally, S_T is a function $S_T : \Omega \longrightarrow R_+$ and, then, the *payoff* for the *call* at time $T = 1$: $X = C_T = (S_T - K)^+$ becomes

$$C_T(w) = \begin{cases} C^u = (S^u - K)^+ & \text{if } w = w_1 \\ C^d = (S^d - K)^+ & \text{if } w = w_2 \end{cases}$$

Intuitively, the option price is given by the expected value under measure P of its discounted payoff, ie,

$$C_0 = E_P((1 + r)^{-1} C_T) = (1 + r)^{-1} \cdot [P(w_1)(S^u - K)^+ + P(w_2)(S^d - K)^+]$$
$$(15.1)$$

Obviously, the value depends on the probability measure P. This may come from subjective estimations and then be derived from hypotheses made by investors about market evolution trends. The aim here is to demonstrate that only one probability measure exists which may satisfy the equivalence (15.1). This type of measure has clear characteristics.

15.2.1.1. The method of portfolio replication

Intuitively, a contingent claim price, as defined in the section above, is equal to the value of a portfolio which exactly replicates its payoff at maturity. Therefore, the idea is to build up a portfolio ϕ at time $t = 0$ which exactly replicates the payoff of the option at time T—which for the sake of simplicity is still considered as uniperiodical[2].

The portfolio of an investor who has a short position in a European option is $\phi = \phi_0 = (\alpha_0, \beta_0)$. Specifically, let α_0 be the number of investors' shares at time $t = 0$ and β_0 money deposited in/borrowed from a bank at interest rate r.

Let $V_t(\phi)$ be the (payoff) value of this portfolio at time $t = 0$ and $t = T$. It can be derived that the value process $V(\phi)$ is:

(i) $V_0(\phi) = \alpha_0 S_0 + \beta_0$;
(ii) $V_T(\phi) = \alpha_0 S_T + \beta_0(1 + r)$.

---

[2]This method is similar to the Sharpe–Rendleman–Bartter model, although the authors originally worked on a free-arbitrage model for the dynamic analysis of the interest rates.

For the above, the portfolio exactly replicates the option when $V_T(\phi) = C_T$, ie,

$$V_T(\phi)(\omega) = \begin{cases} V^u(\phi) = \alpha_0 S^u + (1+r)\beta_0 = C^u & \text{if } \omega = \omega_1 \\ V^d(\phi) = \alpha_0 S^d + (1+r)\beta_0 = C^d & \text{if } \omega = \omega_2 \end{cases} \tag{15.2}$$

The solution of this system gives the value of α_0, β_0 which allows to determine the replication portfolio of the option at time $t = T$. Also, based on the expression at point i. These values may be used to determine $V_0(\phi)$ and, then, to identify the price of call C_0 since $V_0(\phi) = C_0$.

The values of α_0, β_0 to solve the system are:

- $\alpha_0 = (C^u - C^d)/(S^u - S^d)$;
- $\beta_0 = (C^d S^u - C^u S^d)/((S^u - S^d)(1+r))$;

whence

$$C_0 = V_0(\phi) = \alpha_0 S_0 + \beta_0 = \frac{C^u - C^d}{S^u - S^d} S_0 + \frac{C^d S^u - C^u S^d}{(S^u - S^d)(1+r)} \tag{15.3}$$

Given the construction conditions, this value is also defined to be the manufacturing cost. It is important to outline that for a call, the value of α is always greater than zero and β is always less than zero. In other words[3], $\alpha \in R_+$, $\beta \in R_-$.

From the above, this model requires the following information in order to determine the price of a European option, ie,

(1) the payoff of the call at time $t = T$;
(2) the values of the share at time $t = 0, T$;
(3) the interest rate r.

Cashflows provided by the model are defined as follows:

- at time $t = 0$

$$\left\{ \begin{array}{ll} \text{sale of the option} & C_0 \\ \alpha_0 \text{ shares bought} & -\alpha_0 S_0 \\ \text{cash deposited/borrowed} & -\beta_0 \end{array} \right\} \ni' V_0(\phi) - C_0 = 0$$

- at time $t = T$

$$\left\{ \begin{array}{ll} \textit{payoff} \text{ from option} & -C_T \\ \alpha_0 \text{ shares sold} & +\alpha_0 S_T \\ \text{cash drawn/paid back} & +(1+r)\beta_0 \end{array} \right\} \ni' V_T(\phi) - C_T = 0$$

---

[3] For a *put* one has always: (i) $\alpha \in R_-$; (ii) $\beta \in R_+$.

No indication about the investors' preference is required; in fact, the authors define their price as a rational price.

In addition, if $V_0(\phi) \neq C_0$ there is a possibility of *arbitrage*[4].

For this reason $V_0(\phi) = C_0$ is also defined to be a no-arbitrage price. The price determined by using this method has two characteristics:

(1) it is not affected by the investors' preferences;
(2) it is arbitrage-free.

Then, the price is defined to be the *arbitrage price in a risk-neutral economy*.

This model is easy to implement in the presence of very simple contingent claims. In the case of complex derivatives, the pricing method determined by replication is particularly difficult to implement. Hence, a method must be developed in order to obtain to the same result, ie, determine a price having the same characteristics but that is easier to compute.

15.2.1.2. The martingale method

The probability method for contingent claim pricing is based on the notion of martingale, which intuitively represents the probabilities for fair play. The use of the martingale method for derivative pricing requires one to determine a probability measure P^* equivalent to P. P^* with respect to P has to describe the stochastic process which identifies the discounted evolution trend of the price of the underlying S^* to be defined as:

(i) $S_0^* = S_0$;
(ii) $S_T^* = (1+r)^{-1}S_T$.

It is said that S^* follows a martingale measure P^*. More simply S^* is said to be P^*-martingale, under the equivalence

$$S_0^* = E_{P^*}(S_T^*) \tag{15.4}$$

---

[4]An arbitrage is the possibility provided by the market to combine the products offered in order to generate a risk-free profit. Formally, two forms of arbitrage exist: *strong arbitrage* and *weak arbitrage*.

An arbitrage is *weak* when a portfolio ϕ exists so that

(1) $V_0(\phi) - X = 0$;
(2) $V_T(\phi) - X_T \geq 0$;
(3) $P(V_T(\phi) > 0) > 0$.

An arbitrage is *strong*, when a portfolio ϕ exists so that:

(1) $V_0(\phi) - X < 0$ and
(2) $V_T(\phi) - X_T \geq 0$.

Equation (15.4) is expanded in order to determine this measure:

$$S_0^* = E_{P^*}(S_T^*) = (1+r)^{-1} \cdot [P^*(w_1)S^u + P^*(w_2)S^d]$$
(15.5)

since

$$P^*(w_1) + P^*(w_2) = 1$$
$$P^*(w_2) = 1 - P^*(w_1)$$

Equation (15.5) may also be written as

$$S_0^* = (1+r)^{-1} \cdot [P^*(w_1)S^u + (1 - P^*(w_1))S^d]$$
(15.6)

The solution to Equation (15.6) determines the *unique* solution for the value of $P^*(w_1)$ and $P^*(w_2)$:

(i) $P^*(w_1) = ((1+r)S_0 - S^d)/(S^u - S^d)$;
(ii) $P^*(w_2) = (S^u - (1+r)S_0)/(S^u - S^d)$.

As under Section 15.2.1, the option price is intuitively given by the expected value under a given probability measure (15.1) and, in the section above, the correct price for any contingent claim was determined by using the portfolio replication method.

Proposition 15.1. *P^* is the probability measure which satisfies Equation (15.1) and then gives the contingent claim price determined by using the portfolio replication method.*

Intuition 15.1. *Intuitively, the above may be demonstrated by simplifying Equation (15.1) and considering only the positive part of the maximum function:*

$$= (1+r)^{-1} \cdot [P(w_1)S^u + P(w_2)S^d - K]$$

Defining $-(1+r)^{-1} \cdot K = Y$ as a generic constant, Equation (15.1) may be written as

$$C_0 = (1+r)^{-1} \cdot [P(w_1)S^u + P(w_2)S^d] + Y$$

Hence, the probabilistic component of the option price is equal to that of the price of the underlying; in additional it is clear that at time $t = 0$, the discounted option price $C_0^* = C_0$.

If $C_0^* = C_0$ and if the probabilistic component is the same, then obviously, if P^* is the martingale probability measure which allows one to verify the equivalence

$$S_0^* = E_{P^*}(S_T^*)$$

then, intuitively, P^* is the unique probability measure which solves Equation (15.1):

$$C_0^* = (1+r)^{-1} \cdot [P^*(\omega_1)S^u + P^*(\omega_2)S^d] + Y$$

whence

$$C_0^* = C_0 = E_{P^*}((1+r)^{-1}C_T) = E_{P^*}(C_T^*) \tag{15.7}$$

ie, P^* is also a martingale probability measure for the option.

Proof. For an explicit demonstration one may compare the result of Equation (15.7) with Equation (15.3). Expanding (15.7) one obtains

$$C_0^* = (1+r)^{-1} \cdot [P^*(\omega_1)C^u + (1 - P^*(\omega_1))C^d]$$

by replacing the probability measures and simplifying

$$C_0^* = \frac{(C^u - C^d)S_0}{S^u - S^d} + \frac{C^d S^u + C^u S^d}{(S^u - S^d)(1+r)}$$

which is equal to Equation (15.3). ☐

Therefore, the martingale method proves effective when computing the *arbitrage price* of any contingent claim *in a risk-neutral economy* as defined under Section 15.2.1.

These results may be generalised beyond the uniperiodical time horizon. It will be demonstrated that the coincidence above between the portfolio replication method and the martingale method is valid anyway.

15.2.2. Pricing in a multiperiodical context: the binomial model (Cox–Ross–Rubinstein)

Consider the *set* of dates, $0, 1, \ldots, T$, and two assets, a risky asset S and a risk-free asset B, such as a government bond (or a saving account), which generates an interest $r \geq 0$ in the time period $[t, t+1]$. These two securities may then be represented via two stochastic processes, ie,

(i) $B_t = (1+r)^t = \hat{r}^t$ for all $t \leq T$;
(ii) $S_{t+1} = S_t \tilde{\xi}_{t+1}$;

where:

- $\tilde{\xi}_{t+1} \in \{u, d\}$ for all $t \leq T - 1$;
- $d < \hat{r} < u$;
- $S_0 > 0$;

- ξ_t are random variables independent and identically distributed on the probability space $(\Omega, \Im, P)$;
- $\Im$ is the σ-algebra of all of the possible subsets of Ω, ie, $\Im = 2^{\Omega}$ or $\Im = \sigma(\Omega)$, and P is the *set* of the probability measures which satisfy property $P\{\xi_t = u\} = p = 1 - P\{\xi_t = d\}$ for all $t \leq T$.

Since Ω is defined by all of the possible values that the random variable ξ_t may take, then $\Im = \sigma(\Omega) = \sigma(\xi_0, \xi_1, \ldots, \xi_t)$, for all $t \leq T$, and given the definition of process S, one has $\sigma(\xi_0, \xi_1, \ldots, \xi_t) = \sigma(S_0, S_1, \ldots, S_t)$, for all $t \leq T$.

One can define $\sigma(S_0, S_1, \ldots, S_t)$ as the natural filtration of process S and denote it by $\Im^S = (\Im_t^S)_{t \leq T}$. In other words, the filtration of a stochastic process represents the set of the information of this process. From the above, $\Im = \Im^S$.

Based on the characteristics of process S under point (ii) S_t may be written as

$$S_t = S_0 \prod_{j=1}^{t} \xi_j, \quad \forall t \leq T$$

and, similarly, by applying Proposition 3.2

$$S_t = S_0 \cdot e^{\sum_{j=1}^{t} \zeta_j}, \quad \forall t \leq T$$

where ζ_t are again independent and identically distributed on the probability space $(\Omega, \Im, P)$, ie, $P\{\zeta_t = \ln u\} = p = 1 - P\{\zeta_t = \ln d\}$ for all $t \leq T$. Hence, process S is often called an exponential random walk.

15.2.2.1. Portfolio replication

As under Section 15.2.1.1, let one assume that a short investor's position is replicated on a call. In this case, since this is a multiperiodical horizon, the replication portfolio ϕ at time $T - 1$ is defined by assuming that it exactly replicates the call payoff at time $T(C_T)$:

$$V_T(\phi) = \alpha_{T-1}S_T + \beta_{T-1}\hat{r} = C_T = (S_T - K)^+ \tag{15.8}$$

Since $S_T = S_{T-1}\xi_T$, expression (15.8) may also be written $V_T(\phi) = \alpha_{T-1}S_{T-1}\xi_T + \beta_{T-1}\hat{r} = C_T = (S_{T-1}\xi_T - K)^+$. Since ξ_T may take two values only, u and d, then, as under Section 1.2, the following system is determined:

$$V_T(\phi)(\xi) = \begin{cases} V_T^u(\phi) = \alpha_{T-1}uS_{T-1} + \hat{r}\beta_{T-1} = (S_{T-1}u - K)^+ & \text{if } \xi_T = u \\ V_T^d(\phi) = \alpha_{T-1}dS_{T-1} + \hat{r}\beta_{T-1} = (S_{T-1}d - K)^+ & \text{if } \xi_T = d \end{cases}$$

This system has one solution only:

- $\alpha_{T-1} = ((S_{T-1}u - K)^+ - (S_{T-1}d - K)^+)/S_{T-1}(u - d);$
- $\beta_{T-1} = (u(S_{T-1}d - K)^+ - d(uS_{T-1} - K)^+)/\hat{r}(u - d);$

and, by definition, the portfolio value at time $T - 1$ is equal to the call value at time $T - 1$:

$$V_{T-1}(\phi) = \alpha_{T-1}S_{T-1} + \beta_{T-1} = C_{T-1} \tag{15.9}$$

By replacing the values of α_{T-1} and β_{T-1} in Equation (15.9), one obtains

$$V_{T-1}(\phi) = \frac{(S_{T-1}u - K)^+ - (S_{T-1}d - K)^+}{S_{T-1}(u - d)} S_{T-1}$$
$$+ \frac{u(S_{T-1}d - K)^+ - d(uS_{T-1} - K)^+}{\hat{r}(u - d)}$$
$$= \hat{r}^{-1}\left[\frac{(\hat{r} - d)(S_{T-1}u - K)^+}{(u - d)} + \frac{(u - \hat{r})(S_{T-1}d - K)^+}{(u - d)}\right]$$

defining

$$p_* = \frac{(\hat{r} - d)}{(u - d)} \tag{15.10}$$

$$1 - p_* = \frac{(u - \hat{r})}{(u - d)} \tag{15.11}$$

since $V_{T-1}(\phi) = C_{T-1}$, one gets the call value at time $T - 1$:

$$V_{T-1}(\phi) = C_{T-1} = \hat{r}^{-1}[p_*(S_{T-1}u - K)^+ + (1 - p_*)(S_{T-1}d - K)^+] \tag{15.12}$$

This procedure is iterated to define the value of the replication portfolio at time $T - 1$ and, then, to identify the call value at time $T - 2$, ie,

$$V_{T-1}(\phi) = \alpha_{T-2}S_{T-1} + \beta_{T-2}\hat{r} = C_{T-1}$$

Hence, by using properties of process S, S_{T-1} may be replaced by $\xi_{T-1}S_{T-2}$ in the above expression:

$$V_{T-1}(\phi) = \alpha_{T-2}\xi_{T-1}S_{T-2} + \beta_{T-2}\hat{r} = C_{T-1} \tag{15.13}$$

Since Equation (15.12) gives the values of C_{T-1}, Equation (15.13) may also be written as

$$\alpha_{T-2}\xi_{T-1}S_{T-2} + \beta_{T-2}\hat{r} = \hat{r}^{-1}[p_*(S_{T-1}u - K)^+ + (1 - p_*)(S_{T-1}d - K)^+]$$

by using the properties of process S, S_{T-1} may be replaced by $\xi_{T-1}S_{T-2}$, in the right-hand side of the expression above and, then, the value of C_{T-1} is amended (right-hand side of the expression above) as

$$C_{T-1} = \hat{r}^{-1}[p_*(\zeta_{T-1}S_{T-2}u - K)^+ + (1 - p_*)(\zeta_{T-1}S_{T-2}d - K)^+] \qquad (15.14)$$

Then the new system which gives the values of α_{T-2} and β_{T-2} may be defined as

$$V_{T-1}(\phi)(\zeta) = \begin{cases} V_{T-1}^u(\phi) = \alpha_{T-2}uS_{T-2} + \hat{r}\beta_{T-2} = C_{T-1}^u & \text{if } \zeta_{T-1} = u \\ V_{T-1}^d(\phi) = \alpha_{T-2}dS_{T-2} + \hat{r}\beta_{T-2} = C_{T-1}^d & \text{if } \zeta_{T-1} = d \end{cases} \qquad (15.15)$$

The system (15.15) has the following solution:

$$\alpha_{T-2} = \frac{C_{T-1}^u - C_{T-1}^d}{S_{T-2}(u - d)} \qquad (15.16)$$

$$\beta_{T-2} = \frac{uC_{T-1}^d - dC_{T-1}^u}{\hat{r}(u - d)} \qquad (15.17)$$

where, by using Equation (15.14), one obtains the values for C_{T-1}^u and C_{T-1}^d:

$$C_{T-1}^u = \hat{r}^{-1}[p_*(S_{T-2}u^2 - K)^+ + (1 - p_*)(S_{T-2}ud - K)^+] \qquad (15.18)$$

$$C_{T-1}^d = \hat{r}^{-1}[p_*(S_{T-2}ud - K)^+ + (1 - p_*)(S_{T-2}d^2 - K)^+] \qquad (15.19)$$

Also, the portfolio value at time $T - 2$ is defined to be equal to the call value at time $T - 2$:

$$V_{T-2}(\phi) = \alpha_{T-2}S_{T-2} + \beta_{T-2} = C_{T-2} \qquad (15.20)$$

By replacing Equations (15.16) and (15.17) in Equation (15.20) one obtains

$$C_{T-2} = \frac{C_{T-1}^u - C_{T-1}^d}{S_{T-2}(u - d)}S_{T-2} + \frac{uC_{T-1}^d - dC_{T-1}^u}{\hat{r}(u - d)}$$

by using Equations (15.10) and (15.11) one has

$$= \frac{1}{\hat{r}}(p_*C_{T-1}^u + (1 - p_*)C_{T-1}^d)$$

by replacing (15.18) and (15.19) and simplifying, one obtains

$$C_{T-2} = \frac{1}{\hat{r}^2}[p_*^2(S_{T-2}u^2 - K)^+ + 2p_*(1 - p_*)(S_{T-2}ud - K)^+$$
$$+ (1 - p_*)^2(S_{T-2}d^2 - K)^+] \qquad (15.21)$$

This procedure is iterated to define the value of portfolio replication at time $T - 2$ and, then, to identify the call value at time $T - 3$:

$$V_{T-2}(\phi) = \alpha_{T-3}S_{T-2} + \beta_{T-3}\hat{r} = C_{T-2}$$

Hence, by using the properties of process S one may replace S_{T-2} of the expression above by $\xi_{T-2}S_{T-3}$:

$$V_{T-2}(\phi) = \alpha_{T-3}\xi_{T-2}S_{T-3} + \beta_{T-3}\hat{r} = C_{T-2} \tag{15.22}$$

Since Equation (15.21) gives the value of C_{T-2}, Equation (15.22) may also be written as

$$\alpha_{T-3}\xi_{T-2}S_{T-3} + \beta_{T-3}\hat{r} = \frac{1}{\hat{r}^2}[p_*^2(S_{T-2}u^2 - K)^+ + 2p_*(1 - p_*)(S_{T-2}ud - K)^+$$
$$+ (1 - p_*)^2(S_{T-2}d^2 - K)^+]$$

by using the properties of process S, one may replace S_{T-2} by $\xi_{T-1}S_{T-2}$ in the right-hand side of the expression above and, then, the value of C_{T-2} may also be written (right-hand side of the expression above) as

$$C_{T-2} = \frac{1}{\hat{r}^2}[p_*^2(\xi_{T-2}S_{T-3}u^2 - K)^+ + 2p_*(1 - p_*)(\xi_{T-2}S_{T-3}ud - K)^+$$
$$+ (1 - p_*)^2(\xi_{T-2}S_{T-3}d^2 - K)^+] \tag{15.23}$$

Hence, a new system may be defined which gives the values of α_{T-3} and of β_{T-3}:

$$V_{T-2}(\phi)(\xi) = \begin{cases} V_{T-2}^u(\phi) = \alpha_{T-3}uS_{T-3} + \hat{r}\beta_{T-3} = C_{T-2}^u & \text{if } \xi_T = u \\ V_{T-2}^d(\phi) = \alpha_{T-3}dS_{T-3} + \hat{r}\beta_{T-3} = C_{T-2}^d & \text{if } \xi_T = d \end{cases}$$

whose solution is

$$\alpha_{T-3} = \frac{C_{T-2}^u - C_{T-2}^d}{S_{T-3}(u - d)} \tag{15.24}$$

$$\beta_{T-3} = \frac{uC_{T-2}^d - dC_{T-2}^u}{\hat{r}(u - d)} \tag{15.25}$$

where, by using Equation (15.23), one obtains the following values for C_{T-1}^u and C_{T-1}^d:

$$C_{T-2}^u = \frac{1}{\hat{r}^2}[p_*^2(S_{T-3}u^3 - K)^+ + 2p_*(1 - p_*)(S_{T-3}u^2d - K)^+$$
$$+ (1 - p_*)^2(S_{T-3}ud^2 - K)^+] \tag{15.26}$$

$$C_{T-2}^d = \frac{1}{\hat{r}^2}[p_*^2(S_{T-3}du^2 - K)^+ + 2p_*(1 - p_*)(S_{T-3}d^2u - K)^+$$
$$+ (1 - p_*)^2(S_{T-3}d^3 - K)^+] \tag{15.27}$$

Also, the portfolio value at time $T - 3$ is defined to be equal to the call value at time $T - 3$:

$$V_{T-3}(\phi) = \alpha_{T-3}S_{T-3} + \beta_{T-3} = C_{T-3} \tag{15.28}$$

By replacing Equations (15.24) and (15.25) in Equation (15.28), one obtains

$$C_{T-3} = \frac{C^u_{T-2} - C^d_{T-2}}{S_{T-3}(u - d)}S_{T-3} + \frac{uC^d_{T-2} - dC^u_{T-2}}{\hat{r}(u - d)}$$

by using Equations (15.10) and (15.11) one has

$$C_{T-3} = \frac{1}{\hat{r}}(p_*C^u_{T-2} + (1 - p_*)C^d_{T-2})$$

by replacing (15.26) and (15.27) and simplifying, one obtains

$$C_{T-3} = \frac{1}{\hat{r}^3}[p_*^3(S_{T-3}u^3 - K)^+ + 3p_*^2(1 - p_*)(S_{T-3}u^2d - K)^+$$
$$+ 3p_*(1 - p_*)^2(S_{T-3}ud^2 - K)^+ + (1 - p_*)^3(S_{T-3}d^3 - K)^+] \tag{15.29}$$

Based on results of Equations (15.12), (15.21) and (15.29), the formula which gives the value of a European call at any time $t = T - m$ may be generalised[5]:

$$C_{T-m} = \frac{1}{\hat{r}^m} \sum_{j=0}^{m} \binom{m}{j} p_*^j (1 - p_*)^{m-j} (u^j d^{m-j} S_{T-m} - K)^+ \tag{15.30}$$

for $m = 1, \ldots, T$.

In order to get rid of the maximum function from that formula, one defines

$$a = \inf\{j \in N^+ \mid S_{T-m}u^j d^{m-j} - K > 0\}$$

Hence, Equation (15.30) may also be written as

$$C_{T-m} = \frac{1}{\hat{r}^m} \sum_{j=a}^{m} \binom{m}{j} p_*^j (1 - p_*)^{m-j} (u^j d^{m-j} S_{T-m} - K)$$

hence, by simplifying, one has

$$C_{T-m} = \frac{S_{T-m}}{\hat{r}^m} \sum_{j=a}^{m} \binom{m}{j} (p_*u)^j [(1 - p_*)d]^{m-j} - \frac{K}{\hat{r}^m} \sum_{j=a}^{m} \binom{m}{j} p_*^j (1 - p_*)^{m-j}$$

---

[5] We recall the formula to bring a binomial to the power of n: $(a + b)^n = \sum_{k=0}^{n} \binom{n}{k} a^k b^{n-k}$.

and bringing $\hat{r}^m$ inside the first summation and considering that $(1 - p_*)d = 1 - p_* u$, one obtains

$$C_{T-m} = S_{T-m} \sum_{j=a}^{m} \binom{m}{j} \left(p_* \frac{u}{\hat{r}} \right)^j \left(1 - p_* \frac{u}{\hat{r}} \right)^{m-j} - \frac{K}{\hat{r}^m} \sum_{j=a}^{m} \binom{m}{j} p_*^j (1 - p_*)^{m-j}$$

(15.31)

The resulting value, by repeating the same procedure as in Section 15.2.1.1, gives the *arbitrage price in a risk-neutral economy.*

15.2.2.2. The martingale probability measure

As under Section 15.2.1.2, the use of the martingale method for derivative pricing requires one to determine a probability measure P^* equivalent to P. However, P^* with respect to P must describe a stochastic process which identifies the discounted evolution trend of the price of the underlying S^* to be defined as:

(i) $S_0^* = S_0$;
(ii) $S_T^* = (1 + r)^{-T} S_T$.

It is said that S^* follows the martingale measure P^* or, simply, S^* is said to be a P^*-martingale, when, with respect to its natural filtration $\mathfrak{I}^S$, the following equivalence holds:

$$S_t^* = E_{P^*}(S_{t+1}^* \mid \mathfrak{I}_t^S), \quad \forall t \leq T - 1$$

The expression above is expanded as follows to determine the martingale measure:

$$\hat{r}^{-t} S_t = E_{P^*}(\hat{r}^{-(t+1)} \xi_{t+1} S_t \mid \mathfrak{I}_t^S)$$

simplifying, one has

$$\hat{r} = E_{P^*}(\xi_{t+1} \mid S_0, S_1, \ldots, S_t)$$

given the distributive characteristics of ξ_{t+1}, one has

$$\hat{r} = u p_* + (1 - p_*)d$$

solving by p_* one obtains the value of p_* as in (15.10) and the (15.11).

Intuition 15.2. *In Section 15.2.1.2, it was demonstrated that the martingale measure p_* of S^* is the same as the* contingent claim *whose* payoff is defined on S^*, then the probability measure determined above may also satisfy the following equivalence which gives the call price at time $t = T - m$ with a maturity at time T for $m = 1, \ldots, T$:*

$$C_{T-m}^* = E_{P^*}(\hat{r}^{-m}(S_T - K)^+ \mid \mathfrak{I}_{T-m}^S), \quad \forall m \leq T$$

(15.32)

Proposition 15.2. *The contingent claim price as under Equation (15.32) computed as the expected discounted value under the martingale measure p_* is equal to the price determined by using the portfolio replication method as under Equation (15.31).*

Proof. Given Equation (15.32) and using the definition of process S, one has

$$C^*_{T-m} = E_{P^*}(\hat{r}^{-m}(S_{T-m}\xi_{T-m+1}\xi_{T-m+2,...,}\xi_T - K)^+ \mid \Im^S_{T-m}), \quad \forall m \leq T$$

$\hat{r}^{-m}$ is a constant and, then, it may be taken out of the brackets; S_{T-m} is adapted to $\Im^S_{T-m}$ and $\xi_{T-m+1}\xi_{T-m+2,...,}\xi_T$ are independent from $\Im^S_{T-m}$. Hence,

$$C^*_{T-m} = \hat{r}^{-m}E_{P^*}((S_{T-m}\xi_{T-m+1}\xi_{T-m+2,...,}\xi_T - K)^+), \quad \forall m \leq T$$

Considering that $\xi_{T-m+1}, \xi_{T-m+2}, \ldots, \xi_T$ are independent and identically distributed random variables so that:

(1) $E(\xi_t) = up_* + (1 - p_*)d$;
(2) $E(\xi_0\xi_1\xi_2, \ldots, \xi_t) = E(\xi_0)E(\xi_1)E(\xi_2), \ldots, E(\xi_t)$;

one obtains

$$C^*_{T-m} = \hat{r}^{-m}\sum_{j=0}^{m}\binom{m}{j}p_*^j(1 - p_*)^{m-j}(u^j d^{m-j}S_{T-m} - K)^+, \quad \forall m \leq T$$

which is nothing but expression (15.30). This, except for the definition of $a = \inf\{j \in N^+ \mid S_{T-m}u^j d^{m-j} - K > 0\}$, coincides with Equation (15.31). $\square$

It may be generalised that the martingale method and the portfolio replication method give the same result. Consequently, one may conclude that the pricing of any European-type path-independent contingent claim may be made, without any loss of generality, by using the martingale method, which is more flexible and effective.

The binomial model usually works for discrete time units. It may be easily represented by the binomial tree. Concerning discrete models, the infinitesimal reduction of the time unit turns the model from a discrete to a continuous model.

15.2.2.3.   Implementation of the Cox–Ross–Rubinstein model

In the following, a description of the procedure to implement the Cox–Ross–Rubinstein (CRR) model on a spreadsheet with respect to a European call option is given.

Figure 15.1 Entering the option parameters.

	A	B	C	D	E	F
1						
2		K=	50			
3		So	50			
4		n	20	r=	5%	
5				σ=	30%	
6		T	1			
7						
8						

Figure 15.2 Determining the time interval of every step.

	A	B	C	D	E	F
1						
2		K=	50			
3		So	50			
4		n	20	r=	5%	
5		ΔT	=C6/C4	σ=	30%	
6		T	1			
7						
8						

First, the option parameters must be entered (see Figure 15.1):

- the price of the underlying at time zero, ie, 50 here;
- the option strike price, ie, K, 50 here;
- maturity, ie, T, one year here;
- the interest rate, ie, r or rate, 5% per annum here;
- volatility, ie, σ or sigma, 30% per annum here;
- the number of the steps, ie, n, 20 here.

Then, the time interval of every step is determined by making the model computation, ie, ΔT or delta t as in Figure 15.2. The discount factor is determined, ie, discount as in Figure 15.3. Next, the values of u and d are determined

Figure 15.3 Determining the discount factor.

	A	B	C	D	E	F
1		discount=	=EXP(deltat*-rate)			
2		K=	50			
3		So	50			
4		n	20	r=	5%	
5		ΔT	0,05	σ=	30%	
6		T	1			
7						
8						

Figure 15.4 Determining the values of u and d.

	A	B	C	D	E	F
1		discount=	0,9975031	u=	1,069	
2		K=	50	d=	0,935	
3		So	50			
4		n	20	r=	5%	
5		ΔT	0,05	σ=	30%	
6		T	1	=1/u		
7						
8				=EXP(sigma*RADQ(deltat))		

as in Figure 15.4. After determining the values of u and d, the probabilities to move from the top to the bottom of the binomial tree are computed. The formula is given in Figure 15.5. Finally, the values of the underlying are determined (ie, S_T). The value at time zero is projected down to maturity by using quantities u and d as in Figure 15.6. After determining this quantity, the derivative payoff at maturity is computed. In this case, the formula $\max(S_T - k, 0)$ is applied to time step 20 (see Figure 15.7). A step-back procedure is used to complete the tree. For every node, the discounted value of the mean weighed by p and q of the quantity is reported in the two successive nodes (see Figure 15.8). Then the tree is completed by following this numerical procedure to obtain to

Figure 15.5 The formula for determining the probabilities to move from the top to the bottom of the binomial tree.

	A	B	C	D	E	F	G	H	I	J
1		discount=	0,9975031	u=	1,069				p=	0,502
2		K=	50	d=	0,935				q=	0,498
3		So	50							
4		n	20	r=	5%				=1-p	
5		ΔT	0,05	σ=	30%					
6		T	1							
7							=(EXP(rate*deltat)-d)/(u-d)			
8										

Figure 15.6 Projecting the value at time zero down to maturity by using quantities u and d.

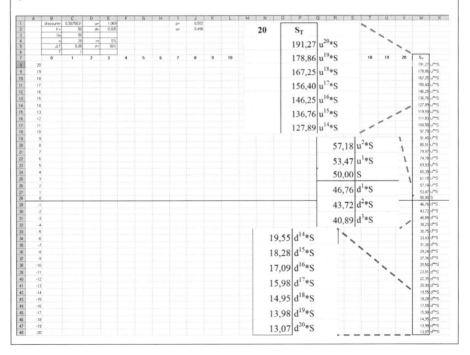

Figure 15.7 Computing the derivative payoff at maturity (in this case, the formula $\max(S_T - k, 0)$ is applied to time step 20).

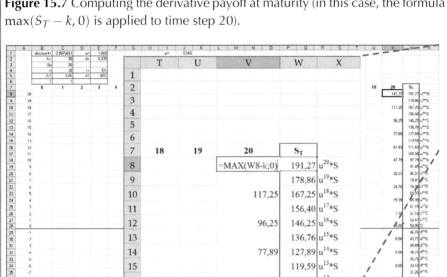

Figure 15.8 Using a step-back procedure to complete the tree.

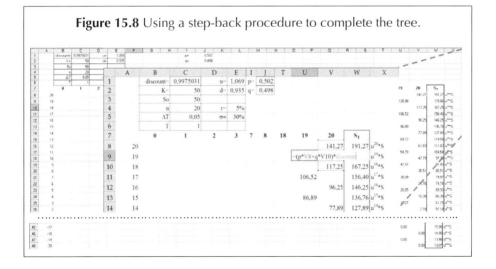

279

Figure 15.9 Completing the tree by the following numerical procedure outlined in the text. The European call option price cell is indicated by the dark arrow on the left.

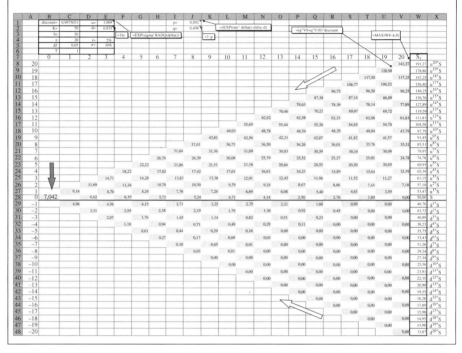

the European call option price cell indicated by the dark arrow on the left in Figure 15.9.

15.2.3. The Black–Scholes–Merton model

In this section, some derivations of the famous Black–Scholes–Merton (BSM) formula are studied. First, the formula is simply derived as the definition of the CRR model in continuous time. In other words, the BSM pricing method is only an asymptotic procedure of the CRR model. Eventually, some direct derivations of this model are explored.

15.2.3.1. The asymptotic solution of the CRR model

Let the time horizon of a contingent claim be $[0, T]$ to be partitioned in n sub-intervals:

$$I_j = [j\Delta_n, (j+1)\Delta_n] \quad \text{for } j = 0, \ldots, n-1$$

where $\Delta_n = T/n$ and $n = 2^k$.

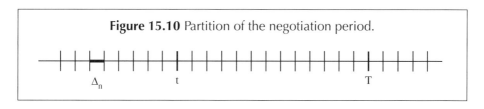

Figure 15.10 Partition of the negotiation period.

The stochastic processes determined is Section 15.2.2 become:

(i) $B_{j\Delta_n} = (1 + r_n)^j = \hat{r}_n^j$, for all $j = 0, \ldots, n$;

(ii) $S_{(j+1)\Delta_n} = \xi_{n,j+1} S_{j\Delta_n}$, for all $j = 0, \ldots, n - 1$;

where r_n is the interest rate along the time horizon I_j, for all n, $\xi_{n,j}$ is a random variable whose values are defined on a set which has two members: $\{u_n, d_n\}$.

Under the conditions above, $\xi_{n,j}$ are independent and identically distributed random variables on the probability space $(\Omega_n, \Im_n, P_n)$, where $\Im_n$ is the σ-algebra of all of the possible subsets of Ω_n, ie, $\Im_n = 2^{\Omega_n} = \sigma(\Omega_n)$, and P_n is the set of probability measures which satisfy the following property:

$$P_n\{\xi_{n,j} = u_n\} = p = 1 - P_n\{\xi_{n,j} = d_n\}, \quad \forall j = 1, \ldots, n$$

Also, let an asymptotic behaviour of r_n, u_n, d_n be defined as follows with $r \geq 0$ and $\sigma > 0$:

- $1 + r_n = e^{r\Delta_n}$;
- $u_n = e^{\sigma\sqrt{\Delta_n}}$;
- $d_n = u_n^{-1}$;

then, $m_n(t) \triangleq (T - t)/\Delta_n$ for all $n \in N$ is defined as the number of negotiation periods $(T - t)$ taking as Δ_n the numeraire (see Figure 15.10).

By using new notation, the formula (15.31) may also be written as

$$C_t = S_t \sum_{j=a_n(t)}^{m_n(t)} \binom{m_n(t)}{j} \left(p_* \frac{u_n}{\hat{r}_n} \right)^j \left(1 - p_* \frac{u_n}{\hat{r}_n} \right)^{m_n(t)-j}$$

$$- \frac{K}{\hat{r}_n^{m_n(t)}} \sum_{j=a_n(t)}^{m_n(t)} \binom{m_n(t)}{j} p_*^j (1 - p_*)^{m_n(t)-j} \tag{15.33}$$

where $a_n(t) = \inf\{j \in N^+ \mid S_{T-m_n(t)} u_n^j d_n^{m_n(t)-j} - K > 0\}$.

Proposition 15.3. *The following expression holds*

$$\lim_{n\to\infty} S_t \sum_{j=a_n(t)}^{m_n(t)} \binom{m_n(t)}{j}\left(p_*\frac{u_n}{\widehat{r}_n}\right)^j\left(1 - p_*\frac{u_n}{\widehat{r}_n}\right)^{m_n(t)-j}$$

$$- \frac{K}{\widehat{r}_n^{m_n(t)}} \sum_{j=a_n(t)}^{m_n(t)} \binom{m_n(t)}{j}p_*^j(1 - p_*)^{m_n(t)-j}$$

$$= S_t N(d_1) - Ke^{-r(T-t)}N(d_2) \tag{15.34}$$

where

$$d_1 = \frac{\ln(S_t/K) + (r + \sigma^2/2)(T - t)}{\sigma\sqrt{T - t}} \tag{15.35}$$

$$d_2 = \frac{\ln(S_t/K) + (r - \sigma^2/2)(T - t)}{\sigma\sqrt{T - t}} \tag{15.36}$$

$$N(x) = \frac{1}{\sqrt{2\pi}} \int_{-\infty}^{x} e^{-u^2/2}\, du$$

Proof. In order to make this demonstration, it may be helpful to study the behaviour for $n \to \infty$, or for $\Delta_n \to 0$ of some expressions. The first limit is

$$\lim_{n\to\infty} p_* = \lim_{n\to\infty} \frac{\widehat{r}_n - d_n}{u_n - d_n} = \lim_{\Delta_n\to 0} \frac{e^{r\Delta_n} - e^{-\sigma\sqrt{\Delta_n}}}{e^{\sigma\sqrt{\Delta_n}} - e^{-\sigma\sqrt{\Delta_n}}}$$

$$= \lim_{x\to 0} \frac{e^{rx^2} - e^{-\sigma x}}{e^{\sigma x} - e^{-\sigma x}} \quad \text{(simplifying by } \sqrt{\Delta_n} = x\text{, one has)}$$

Since this is an indeterminate form $0/0$, by using the *De l'Hospital* rule, one has

$$\lim_{n\to\infty} p_* = \tfrac{1}{2} \tag{15.37}$$

The second limit is

$$\lim_{n\to\infty} p_*\frac{u_n}{\widehat{r}_n} = \lim_{n\to\infty} \frac{\widehat{r}_n - d_n}{u_n - d_n}\frac{u_n}{\widehat{r}_n} = \lim_{\Delta_n\to 0} \frac{e^{r\Delta_n} - e^{-\sigma\sqrt{\Delta_n}}}{e^{\sigma\sqrt{\Delta_n}} - e^{-\sigma\sqrt{\Delta_n}}}\frac{e^{\sigma\sqrt{\Delta_n}}}{e^{r\Delta_n}}$$

$$= \lim_{x\to 0} \frac{e^{rx^2} - e^{-\sigma x}}{e^{\sigma x} - e^{-\sigma x}}\frac{e^{\sigma x}}{e^{rx^2}} \quad \text{(simplifying by } \sqrt{\Delta_n} = x\text{)}$$

$$= \lim_{x\to 0} \frac{1 - e^{-\sigma x - rx^2}}{1 - e^{-2\sigma x}} \quad \text{(simplifying again)}$$

Since this is an indeterminate form $0/0$, by using the De l'Hospital rule, one has

$$\lim_{n\to\infty} p_*\frac{u_n}{\widehat{r}_n} = \frac{1}{2} \tag{15.38}$$

The third limit is

$$\lim_{x \to 0} \frac{2\sigma x}{1 - e^{-2\sigma x}}$$

Since this is an indeterminate form $0/0$, by using the De l'Hospital rule, one has

$$\lim_{x \to 0} \frac{2\sigma x}{1 - e^{-2\sigma x}} = 1 \tag{15.39}$$

The fourth limit is

$$\lim_{n \to \infty} m_n(t) \sqrt{\Delta_n} \left(1 - 2p_* \frac{u_n}{\widehat{r}_n} \right)$$

$$= \lim_{n \to \infty} \frac{(T-t)}{\sqrt{\Delta_n}} \left(1 - 2p_* \frac{u_n}{\widehat{r}_n} \right)$$

(by substituting the definition of $m_n(t)$ and simplifying $\sqrt{\Delta_n}$)

$$= \lim_{n \to \infty} \frac{(T-t)}{\sqrt{T/n}} \left(1 - 2 \frac{e^{r\Delta_n} - e^{-\sigma\sqrt{\Delta_n}}}{e^{\sigma\sqrt{\Delta_n}} - e^{-\sigma\sqrt{\Delta_n}}} \frac{e^{\sigma\sqrt{\Delta_n}}}{e^{r\Delta_n}} \right)$$

(substituting the definition of Δ_n, of p_* and of $\widehat{r}_n, d_n, u_n$)

$$= \lim_{x \to 0} - \frac{(T-t)}{x} \left(\frac{e^{-2\sigma x} + 1 - 2e^{-\sigma x - rx^2}}{2\sigma x} \frac{2\sigma x}{1 - e^{-2\sigma x}} \right)$$

(defining $\sqrt{\Delta_n} = x$ more simply and simplifying again)

The left member of the original limit is further expanded and using Equation (15.39) one obtains

$$\lim_{n \to \infty} m_n(t) \sqrt{\Delta_n} \left(1 - 2p_* \frac{u_n}{\widehat{r}_n} \right) = \lim_{x \to 0} - \frac{(T-t)}{x} \left(\frac{e^{-2\sigma x} + 1 - 2e^{-\sigma x - rx^2}}{2\sigma x} \right)$$

Since this is an indeterminate form $0/0$, by applying the De l'Hospital rule twice, one has

$$\lim_{n \to \infty} m_n(t) \sqrt{\Delta_n} \left(1 - 2p_* \frac{u_n}{\widehat{r}_n} \right) = -(T-t) \left(\frac{r}{\sigma} + \frac{\sigma}{2} \right) \tag{15.40}$$

The fifth limit is

$$\lim_{n \to \infty} m_n(t) \sqrt{\Delta_n} (1 - 2p_*)$$

$$= \lim_{n \to \infty} \frac{(T-t)}{\sqrt{T/n}} \left(1 - 2 \frac{e^{r\Delta_n} - e^{-\sigma\sqrt{\Delta_n}}}{e^{\sigma\sqrt{\Delta_n}} - e^{-\sigma\sqrt{\Delta_n}}} \right)$$

(replacing the definition of $m_n(t)$, Δ_n, p_* and of $\widehat{r}_n, d_n, u_n$)

$$= \lim_{x \to 0} (T-t) \left(\frac{e^{\sigma x} + e^{-\sigma x} - 2e^{rx^2}}{x e^{\sigma x} - x e^{-\sigma x}} \right) \quad \text{(simplifying by } \sqrt{\Delta_n} = x)$$

Since this is an indeterminate form $0/0$, by applying the De l'Hospital rule twice, one has

$$\lim_{n \to \infty} m_n(t) \sqrt{\Delta_n}(1 - 2p_*) = (T - t) \left(\frac{\sigma}{2} - \frac{r}{\sigma} \right) \tag{15.41}$$

In order to continue this demonstration, it may be useful to identify an expression more easy to manipulate for the term $a_n(t)$. For this purpose, by using the definition of $a_n(t)$, ie,

$$a_n(t) = \inf\{j \in N^+ \mid S_{T-m_n(t)} u_n^j d_n^{m_n(t)-j} - K > 0\}$$

it becomes clear that the value of j which returns a trivial solution to the expression $S_{T-m_n(t)} u_n^j d_n^{m_n(t)-j} - K$ is equal to $a_n(t)$. Then the value of j has to be determined, and considering the logarithm of the expression inside inf one obtains

$$j = \frac{\ln(K/S_t) + m_n(t)\sigma\sqrt{\Delta_n}}{2\sigma\sqrt{\Delta_n}}$$

and, then

$$a_n(t) = \frac{\ln(K/S_t) + m_n(t)\sigma\sqrt{\Delta_n}}{2\sigma\sqrt{\Delta_n}} \tag{15.42}$$

In order to provide further demonstration, the structure of formula (15.34) is considered. As S_t and K are invariant when computing the limit, it will be sufficient to demonstrate that:

(1) $\lim_{n \to \infty} \sum_{j=a_n(t)}^{m_n(t)} \binom{m_n(t)}{j} \left(p_* \frac{u_n}{\hat{r}_n} \right)^j \left(1 - p_* \frac{u_n}{\hat{r}_n} \right)^{m_n(t)-j} \overset{?}{=} N(d_1)$;

(2) $\lim_{n \to \infty} \sum_{j=a}^{m} \binom{m_n(t)}{j} p_*^j (1 - p_*)^{m_n(t)-j} \overset{?}{=} N(d_2)$;

(3) $\lim_{n \to \infty} \frac{1}{\hat{r}_n^{m_n(t)}} \overset{?}{=} e^{-r(T-t)}$.

Point (1). One recalls the expression

$$\sum_{j=a_n(t)}^{m_n(t)} \binom{m_n(t)}{j} \left(p_* \frac{u_n}{\hat{r}_n} \right)^j \left(1 - p_* \frac{u_n}{\hat{r}_n} \right)^{m_n(t)-j} ; \quad P\{a_n(t) \le \gamma_n \le m_n(t)\},$$

with the random variable γ_n distributed as

$$\gamma_n \sim \text{bin}\left(p_* \frac{u_n}{\hat{r}_n}, m_n(t) \right)$$

Then $P\{a_n(t) \le \gamma_n \le m_n(t)\}$ is determined since the limit at point (1) above is the asymptotic measure of that probability, ie,

$$\lim_{n \to \infty} \sum_{j=a_n(t)}^{m_n(t)} \binom{m_n(t)}{j} \left(p_* \frac{u_n}{\hat{r}_n} \right)^j \left(1 - p_* \frac{u_n}{\hat{r}_n} \right)^{m_n(t)-j} \overset{a}{=} P\{a_n(t) \le \gamma_n \le m_n(t)\} \tag{15.43}$$

Standardising this random variable

$$\tilde{\gamma}_n = \frac{\gamma_n - E_p(\gamma_n)}{\sqrt{VAR(\gamma_n)}} = \frac{\gamma_n - p_*(u_n/\hat{r}_n)m_n(t)}{\sqrt{p_*(u_n/\hat{r}_n)(1 - p_*(u_n/\hat{r}_n))m_n(t)}}$$

for $n \to \infty$ the sequence of random variables $\tilde{\gamma}_n$ converges in distribution under the theorem of the central limit to the standardised normal random variable. Hence,

$$P\{a_n(t) \le \gamma_n \le m_n(t)\} = P\left\{ \frac{a_n(t) - E_p(\gamma_n)}{\sqrt{VAR(\gamma_n)}} \le \tilde{\gamma}_n \le \frac{m_n(t) - E_p(\gamma_n)}{\sqrt{VAR(\gamma_n)}} \right\}$$

To determine the asymptotic probability $\overset{a}{P}$ as under Equation (15.43) it is necessary to study the limit at the boundaries of interval for $n \to \infty$, ie,

$$\begin{cases} \lim_{n\to\infty} \dfrac{m_n(t) - E_p(\gamma_n)}{\sqrt{VAR(\gamma_n)}} \\ \lim_{n\to\infty} \dfrac{a_n(t) - E_p(\gamma_n)}{\sqrt{VAR(\gamma_n)}} \end{cases}$$

For the first limit, one has

$$\lim_{n\to\infty} \frac{m_n(t) - E_p(\gamma_n)}{\sqrt{VAR(\gamma_n)}} = \lim_{n\to\infty} \frac{\sqrt{(1 - p_*(u_n/\hat{r}_n))m_n(t)}}{\sqrt{p_*(u_n/\hat{r}_n)}}$$

or

$$= \begin{cases} \lim_{n\to\infty} \dfrac{m_n(t) - E_p(\gamma_n)}{\sqrt{VAR(\gamma_n)}} = \infty \\ \ \diagdown \end{cases} \tag{15.44}$$

For the second limit, one has

$$\lim_{n\to\infty} \frac{a_n(t) - E_p(\gamma_n)}{\sqrt{VAR(\gamma_n)}} = \lim_{n\to\infty} \frac{a_n(t) - p_*(u_n/\hat{r}_n)m_n(t)}{\sqrt{p_*(u_n/\hat{r}_n)(1 - p_*(u_n/\hat{r}_n))m_n(t)}}$$
$$= \lim_{n\to\infty} \frac{\ln(K/S_t) + \sigma m_n(t)\sqrt{\Delta_n}(1 - 2p_*(u_n/\hat{r}_n))}{2\sigma\sqrt{\Delta_n}\sqrt{p_*(u_n/\hat{r}_n)(1 - p_*(u_n/\hat{r}_n))m_n(t)}}$$
(by Equation (15.42))

For simplicity this limit is rearranged, ie,

$$\lim_{n\to\infty} \frac{a_n(t) - E_p(\gamma_n)}{\sqrt{VAR(\gamma_n)}} = \lim_{n\to\infty} \frac{\ln(K/S_t) + \sigma \cdot \lim_{n\to\infty} m_n(t)\sqrt{\Delta_n}(1 - 2p_*(u_n/\hat{r}_n))}{2\sigma\sqrt{\Delta_n}\sqrt{p_*(u_n/\hat{r}_n)(1 - p_*(u_n/\hat{r}_n))m_n(t)}}$$

the numerator shows the result of (15.40), hence

$$\lim_{n\to\infty} \frac{a_n(t) - E_p(\gamma_n)}{\sqrt{\mathrm{VAR}(\gamma_n)}} = \lim_{n\to\infty} \frac{\ln(K/S_t) - (r + \sigma^2/2)(T - t)}{2\sigma\sqrt{p_*(u_n/\hat{r}_n)(1 - p_*(u_n/\hat{r}_n))(T - t)}}$$

Based on results (15.37) and (15.38), one obtains

$$= \left\{ \lim_{n\to\infty} \frac{a_n(t) - E_p(\gamma_n)}{\sqrt{\mathrm{VAR}(\gamma_n)}} = \frac{\ln(K/S_t) - (r + \sigma^2/2)(T - t)}{\sigma\sqrt{(T - t)}} \right. \tag{15.45}$$

Therefore, for $n \to \infty$ the asymptotic probability $\overset{a}{P}$ as under Equation (15.43)

$$\overset{a}{P}\left\{ \frac{a_n(t) - E_p(\gamma_n)}{\sqrt{\mathrm{VAR}(\gamma_n)}} \le \tilde{\gamma}_n \le \frac{m_n(t) - E_p(\gamma_n)}{\sqrt{\mathrm{VAR}(\gamma_n)}} \right\}$$

may also be written by substituting the results derived in Equation (15.44) and (15.45) as

$$\overset{a}{P}\left\{ \frac{\ln K/S_t - (r + \sigma^2/2)(T - t)}{\sigma\sqrt{(T - t)}} \le \tilde{\gamma}_n < \infty \right\}$$

By using the definition of d_1 given by Equation (15.35) and by using the symmetry feature of the normal random variable, one has

$$\overset{a}{P}\{-d_1 \le \tilde{\gamma}_n < \infty\} = \overset{a}{P}\{\tilde{\gamma}_n < d_1\} = \frac{1}{\sqrt{2\pi}} \int_{-\infty}^{d_1} e^{-\tilde{\gamma}^2/2} d\tilde{\gamma} = N(d_1)$$

$$\therefore \lim_{n\to\infty} \sum_{j=a_n(t)}^{m_n(t)} \binom{m_n(t)}{j} \left(p_* \frac{u_n}{\hat{r}_n}\right)^j \left(1 - p_* \frac{u_n}{\hat{r}_n}\right)^{m_n(t)-j} = N(d_1)$$

Point (2). One recalls the expression

$$\sum_{j=a_n(t)}^{m_n(t)} \binom{m_n(t)}{j} p_*^j (1 - p_*)^{m_n(t)-j}; \quad P\{a_n(t) \le \lambda_n \le m_n(t)\},$$

with the random variable λ_n distributed as

$$\lambda_n \sim \mathrm{bin}(p_*, m_n(t))$$

By a similar procedure as for point (1), $P\{a_n(t) \le \lambda_n \le m_n(t)\}$ is determined, since the limit at point (2) is the asymptotic measure of this probability, ie,

$$\lim_{n\to\infty} \sum_{j=a_n(t)}^{m_n(t)} \binom{m_n(t)}{j} \left(p_* \frac{u_n}{\hat{r}_n}\right)^j \left(1 - p_* \frac{u_n}{\hat{r}_n}\right)^{m_n(t)-j} = \overset{a}{P}\{a_n(t) \le \lambda_n \le m_n(t)\}$$

$$\tag{15.46}$$

The random variable is standardised, to obtain, under the theorem of the central limit, that:

$$\tilde{\lambda}_n = \frac{\lambda_n - E_p(\lambda_n)}{\sqrt{\mathrm{VAR}(\lambda_n)}} = \frac{\lambda_n - p_* m_n(t)}{\sqrt{p_*(1 - p_*)m_n(t)}} \overset{a}{\sim} N(0, 1)$$

Hence,

$$P\{a_n(t) \le \lambda_n \le m_n(t)\} = P\left\{ \frac{a_n(t) - p_* m_n(t)}{\sqrt{p_*(1 - p_*)m_n(t)}} \le \tilde{\lambda}_n \le \frac{m_n(t) - p_* m_n(t)}{\sqrt{p_*(1 - p_*)m_n(t)}} \right\}$$

To determine the asymptotic probability $\overset{a}{P}$ under Equation (15.46) it is necessary to study the limit of the two boundaries of the interval for $n \to \infty$, ie,

$$\begin{cases} \lim_{n \to \infty} \dfrac{m_n(t) - p_* m_n(t)}{\sqrt{p_*(1 - p_*)m_n(t)}} \\[2em] \lim_{n \to \infty} \dfrac{a_n(t) - p_* m_n(t)}{\sqrt{p_*(1 - p_*)m_n(t)}} \end{cases}$$

to obtain, for the first limit,

$$= \begin{cases} \lim_{n \to \infty} \dfrac{m_n(t) - p_* m_n(t)}{\sqrt{p_*(1 - p_*)m_n(t)}} = \infty \\[2em] \end{cases} \tag{15.47}$$

and for the second limit

$$\lim_{n \to \infty} \frac{a_n(t) - p_* m_n(t)}{\sqrt{p_*(1 - p_*)m_n(t)}}$$

$$= \lim_{n \to \infty} \frac{\ln(K/S_t) + \sigma(T - t)(\sigma/2 - r/\sigma)}{2\sigma\sqrt{\Delta_n}\sqrt{p_*(1 - p_*)m_n(t)}}$$

(by using (15.42) and then (15.41))

$$= \frac{\ln K/S_t - (r - \sigma^2/2)(T - t)}{\sigma\sqrt{(T - t)}}$$

(based on the results of Equations (15.37) and (15.38))

or

$$= \begin{cases} \\ \lim_{n \to \infty} \dfrac{a_n(t) - p_* m_n(t)}{\sqrt{p_*(1 - p_*)m_n(t)}} = \dfrac{\ln K/S_t - (r - \sigma^2/2)(T - t)}{\sigma\sqrt{(T - t)}} \end{cases} \tag{15.48}$$

Similarly as above, for $n \to \infty$, the asymptotic probability $\overset{a}{P}$ as under Equation (15.46), ie,

$$P\left\{ \frac{a_n(t) - p_* m_n(t)}{\sqrt{p_*(1 - p_*)m_n(t)}} \leq \tilde{\lambda}_n \leq \frac{m_n(t) - p_* m_n(t)}{\sqrt{p_*(1 - p_*)m_n(t)}} \right\}$$

may be expressed by replacing the results derived in Equations (15.47) and (15.48) as

$$\overset{a}{P}\left\{ \frac{\ln(K/S_t) - (r - \sigma^2/2)(T - t)}{\sigma\sqrt{(T - t)}} \leq \tilde{\lambda}_n < \infty \right\}$$

By using the definition of d_2 given by Equation (15.36) and the characteristics of symmetry of the normal, one obtains

$$\overset{a}{P}\{-d_2 \leq \tilde{\lambda}_n < \infty\} = \overset{a}{P}\{\tilde{\lambda}_n < d_1\} = \frac{1}{\sqrt{2\pi}} \int_{-\infty}^{d_2} e^{-\tilde{\lambda}^2/2} d\tilde{\lambda} = N(d_2)$$

$$\therefore \lim_{n \to \infty} \sum_{j=a}^{m} \binom{m_n(t)}{j} p_*^j (1 - p_*)^{m_n(t)-j} = N(d_2)$$

Point (3). One has

$$\lim_{n \to \infty} \frac{1}{\hat{r}_n^{m_n(t)}} = \lim_{n \to \infty} \hat{r}_n^{-m_n(t)} = \lim_{n \to \infty} (1 + r_n)^{-m_n(t)}$$

based on the construction characteristics of the process

$$\lim_{\Delta_n \to 0} e^{-r\Delta_n m_n(t)} = \lim_{\Delta_n \to 0} e^{-r\Delta_n \frac{T-t}{\Delta_n}} = e^{-r(T-t)}$$

$$\therefore \lim_{n \to \infty} \frac{1}{\hat{r}_n^{m_n(t)}} = e^{-r(T-t)} \qquad \square$$

Finally, the BSM model may be derived from the CRR model after determining a correct definition of the asymptotic behaviour of the critical parameters of the model u_n, d_n, r_n. Based on the above, it becomes clear that formula (15.34) gives, in the continuous time, the *arbitrage price in a risk-neutral economy*. This means that a contingent claim replication strategy ϕ exists in the continuous time which gives the same results.

15.2.3.2. The portfolio replication method and the martingale probability measure

In Sections 15.2.1 and 15.2.2, a demonstration was given that the contingent claim price is equal to the portfolio value which exactly replicates its payoff at maturity. Therefore, the methodological approach used up to now consisted of building a portfolio ϕ at time $t = 0$ which replicates exactly the payoff of this option at time T. In the following, a demonstration is given that this approach is also true under hypothesis that the interval $[0, T]$ is continuous.

A strategy is defined:

$$\phi = \phi_t = (\phi_t^1, \phi_t^2)$$

The portfolio value at time t is defined for an investor with a short position in a derivative, ie,

$$V_t = \phi_t^1 S_t + \phi_t^2 B_t \tag{15.49}$$

Substantially, let ϕ_t^1 be the number of shares held at time t and ϕ_t^2 be the money deposited to/borrowed from a bank at interest rate r. It is clear that ϕ_t^1, ϕ_t^2 are stochastic processes on the probability space $(\Omega, \Im, P)$.

15.2.3.2.1. The stochastic process of S Let the behaviour of S in time be described by a SDE:

$$dS_t = \mu S_t \, dt + \sigma S_t \, dW_t \tag{15.50}$$

where:

- μ is the yield rate of S;
- σ is the diffusion rate of S;
- W_t, where $t \in [0, T]$, is the one-dimensional Brownian motion defined on the filtered probability space $(\Omega, \Im^W, P)$ with $\Im = \Im^W$.

Equation (15.50) may also be expressed as an Itô stochastic integral for all $t \in [0, T]$:

$$S_t = S_0 + \int_0^t \mu S_u \, du + \int_0^t \sigma S_u \, dW_u$$

Theorem 15.1. *A solution to Equation (15.50), for $t \leqslant u$, is*

$$S_u = S_t \cdot e^{(\mu - \sigma^2/2) \, dt + \sigma \, dW_t} \tag{15.51}$$

which describes in continuous time the price behaviour of any security S. By using this solution, one may simulate the path that any security may have in the future by using only the current position of this security (see Figure 15.11).

Proof. In the following, a demonstration that Equation (15.51) is actually the solution of Equation (15.50) is given. By applying the Itô's rule to Equation (15.50) one obtains

$$dS = \frac{dS}{dt} \, dt + \frac{dS}{dW} \, dW_t + \frac{1}{2} \frac{d^2 S}{dW^2} \, dt \tag{15.52}$$

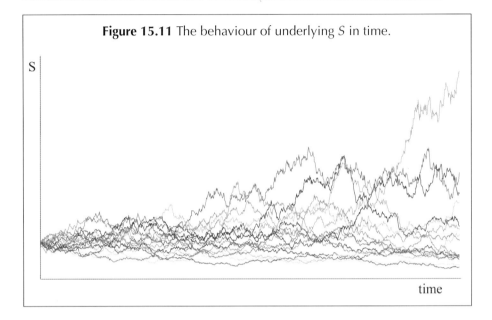

Figure 15.11 The behaviour of underlying S in time.

S

time

Substituting the derivatives inside Equation (15.52), one obtains

$$dS = \left(\mu - \frac{\sigma^2}{2} \right) S \, dt + \sigma \, dW_t + \frac{1}{2} \sigma^2 S \, dt$$

simplifying, one has

$$dS = \mu S \, dt + \sigma S \, dW$$

Based on the above, Equation (15.51) is the only possible solution to Equation (15.50). □

The set of information contained in the Brownian motion $\Im_t^W$ is the same as that inside the behaviour of security $\Im_t^S$. This is because the random variable S_t for any invertible function $f : R \to R_+$ is $S_t = f(W_t)$. In probabilistic terms, this coincidence of information may be expressed as $\Im_t^W = \Im_t^S$, and it reads that the filtration of W is the same as of S. This is important because it allows to impose characteristics onto parameters, ie, $\sigma \{ W_u \mid u \le t \} = \sigma \{ S_u \mid u \le t \}$.

In addition, this is a Markovian process, ie, the future value of S is exclusively determined on the base of its current value. This comes from Equation (15.51) and from the fact that, by definition, the Brownian motion has the Markov property.

Proposition 15.4. *The conditional expected value under probability measure p of the stochastic process is equal to*

$$E_p(S_u \mid \Im_t) = S_t \cdot e^{\mu(u-t)} \tag{15.53}$$

Proof. Given the equivalence between $\Im_t = \Im_t^S$, one has

$$E_p(S_u \mid \Im_t) = E_p(S_u \mid \Im_t^S)$$

given the definition of $\Im_t^S$ and using Equation (15.52), one has

$$E_p(S_u \mid \Im_t) = S_t \cdot E_p(e^{(\mu-\sigma^2/2)\,dt+\sigma\,dW_t} \mid S_t)$$

since $(W_u - W_t)$ is independent from S_t, one has

$$E_p(S_u \mid \Im_t) = S_t \cdot E_p(e^{(\mu-\sigma^2/2)(u-t)+\sigma(W_u-W_t)})$$

since $e^{(\mu-\sigma^2/2)(u-t)}$ is a constant, and recalling the moment generating function $\varphi(t)$ of a normal random variable, one has

$$E_p(S_u \mid \Im_t) = S_t \cdot e^{(\mu-\sigma^2/2)(u-t)} \cdot e^{(u-t)(\sigma^2/2)}$$

simplifying, one has (15.53). □

Corollary 15.1. *This model satisfies the property of lognormality in share price probability distribution, or the normality of logarithms for security yield rates, ie,*

$$\ln \frac{S_t}{S_s} \sim N\left(\left(\mu - \frac{\sigma^2}{2}\right) dt, \sigma\sqrt{dt}\right)$$

where $dt = (t - s)$. Graphically, parameters μ and σ may then be interpreted as the drift and volatility of the logarithmic returns of S, respectively (see Figure 15.12).

Proof. Considering the natural logarithm of solution (15.51), one obtains

$$\ln S_t - \ln S_s = \left(\mu - \frac{\sigma^2}{2}\right) dt + \sigma\, dW_t$$

One recalls here the generalised Wiener process defined in Definition 12.24 and, then, one may say that

$$\ln S_t - \ln S_s \sim N\left(\left(\mu - \frac{\sigma^2}{2}\right) dt, \sigma\sqrt{dt}\right) \qquad \square$$

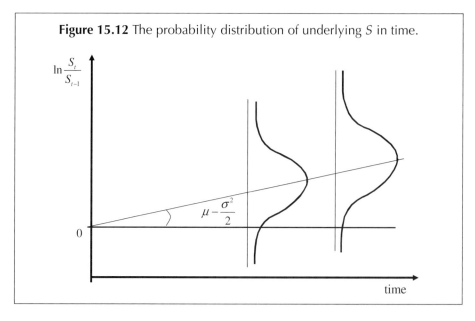

Figure 15.12 The probability distribution of underlying S in time.

15.2.3.2.2. The stochastic process of B (or saving account process) It is assumed that the behaviour of process B in time, which describes the price for a government bond (or a saving account), is described by a differential equation which represents capitalisation by a continuously compounded interest rate for all $t \in [0, T]$, ie,

$$dB_t = rB_t \, dt \tag{15.54}$$

whose solution is

$$B_t = e^{rt} \tag{15.55}$$

See Proposition 14.2.

15.2.3.2.3. The stochastic process of V (or the replication portfolio process) As in Sections 15.2.1 and 15.2.2 the contingent claim replication portfolio must show the same value at any moment of interval $[0, T]$, to avoid the possibility of arbitrage. Then, the strategy $\phi = \phi_t = (\phi_t^1, \phi_t^2)$ has to be self-financing.

Definition 15.1. A strategy ϕ_t is defined to be *self-financing* if the portfolio value $V(\phi)$, for all $t \in [0, T]$, equal to

$$V_t(\phi) = \phi_t^1 S_t + \phi_t^2 B_t \tag{15.56}$$

satisfies the following equation below, ie,

$$V_t(\phi) = V_0(\phi) + \int_0^t \phi_u^1 \, dS_u + \int_0^t \phi_u^2 \, dB_u \tag{15.57}$$

where the intervals have to be clearly defined; for this purpose, it is sufficient that they converge in the sense of L_2 ie,

$$P\left\{\int_0^T |\phi_u^1|^2 \, dS_u < \infty\right\} = 1, \quad P\left\{\int_0^T |\phi_u^2| \, dB_u < \infty\right\} = 1$$

15.2.3.2.4. Discounted processes
Definition 15.2. One can define the *discounted processes* as $S_t^* \triangleq S_t / B_t$ and $V_t^* \triangleq V_t / B_t$.

Then their SDEs are derived; for S_t^*, one has

$$dS_t^* = d\frac{S_t}{B_t}$$

The form of Itô's lemma derived from the Leibniz rule is applied (see Corollary 12.11 and, in particular, Example 12.3):

$$d\frac{S_t}{B_t} = dS_t^* = -r\frac{S_t}{B_t} \, dt + \frac{1}{B_t}(\mu S_t \, dt + \sigma S_t \, dW_t)$$

$$\text{(by using the definition of } S_t^*\text{)}$$

$$= -rS_t^* \, dt + \mu S_t^* \, dt + \sigma S_t^* \, dW_t$$

which is equal to

$$dS_t^* = (\mu - r)S_t^* \, dt + \sigma S_t^* \, dW_t \tag{15.58}$$

whose solution, as in Theorem 15.1 for Equation (15.50), is with $u \geq t$:

$$S_u^* = S_t^* \cdot e^{(\mu - r - \sigma^2/2) \, dt + \sigma \, dW_t} \tag{15.59}$$

for V_t^*. Rearranging Equation (15.57) in its differential form, one obtains

$$dV_t(\phi) = \phi_t^1 \, dS_t + \phi_t^2 \, dB_t, \quad \forall t \in [0, T]$$

This SDE describes the continuous behaviour of the replication portfolio $V(\varphi)$ value. Then, the SDE of the discounted portfolio is derived:

$$dV_t^*(\phi) = d\frac{V_t}{B_t} = V_t \, d\frac{1}{B_t} + \frac{1}{B_t} \, dV_t$$

Substituting the definitions of dV_t, dS_t and dB_t, one obtains

$$dV_t^*(\phi) = [(\mu - r)S_t^* + \sigma S_t^* \, dW_t]\phi_t^1$$

By using Equation (15.58), one obtains

$$dV_t^* = \phi_t^1 \, dS_t^* \tag{15.60}$$

15.2.3.2.5. The martingale measure p^*

Theorem 15.2. *A martingale measure p^* exists that is equivalent to p for S^*, ie, S^* is a martingale under measure p^*. A measure p^* exists, hence it is true that*

$$E_{p^*}(S_u^* \mid S_t^*) = S_t^*$$

Proof. Given the conditions:

(1) $dS_t^* = (\mu - r)S_t^* \, dt + \sigma S_t^* \, dW_t$;
(2) $S_u^* = S_t^* \cdot e^{(\mu - r - \sigma^2/2) \, dt + \sigma \, dW_t}$, where $u \geq t$;
(3) $E_p(S_u^* \mid \Im_t) = E_p(S_u^* \mid S_t)$ or S^* has the Markov property;
(4) $(W_u - W_t) \sim N(0, u - t)$ is the standard Brownian motion.

Defining

$$\frac{r - \mu}{\sigma} W_t \triangleq u_t$$

The exponential Doléans is given by

$$\varepsilon_t(u) = \varepsilon_t \left(\frac{r - \mu}{\sigma} W_t \right) = e^{(((r-\mu)/\sigma)W_t - (1/2)((r-\mu)/\sigma)^2 t)}$$

The mean is

$$E(\varepsilon_t(u)) = E(e^{(((r-\mu)/\sigma)W_t - (1/2)((r-\mu)/\sigma)^2 t)})$$

$$= e^{-(1/2)((r-\mu)/\sigma)^2 t} E(e^{((r-\mu)/\sigma)W_t})$$

recalling expression of the moment generating function $\varphi(t)$ of a normal random variable, one has:

$$E(\varepsilon_t(u)) = e^{-(1/2)((r-\mu)/\sigma)^2 t} e^{(1/2)((r-\mu)/\sigma)^2 t} = 1$$

Then the Radon–Nikodym derivative is defined as

$$\frac{dP^*}{dP} = \varepsilon_t(u)$$

The Girsanov theorem (see Theorem 12.16) states that if:

(1) W_t is the standard Brownian motion;
(2) $E(\varepsilon_t(u)) = 1$;

then the change in the probability measure defined by

$$\frac{dP^*}{dP} = e^{(((r-\mu)/\sigma)W_t - (1/2)((r-\mu)/\sigma)^2 t)}$$

is that, also, $W_t^* = W_t - ((r - \mu)/\sigma)t$ is a standard Brownian motion under p^*.

Based on the above, without any loss of generality, one may rearrange Equation (15.58) under the new probability measure P^*, ie, based on the standard Brownian motion W_t^*. To this end, W_t^* is rearranged in differential terms, ie,

$$dW_t^* = dW_t - \frac{r - \mu}{\sigma} dt$$

Substituting dW_t in Equation (15.58), one obtains

$$dS_t^* = (\mu - r)S_t^* \, dt + \sigma S_t^* \left(dW_t^* + \frac{r - \mu}{\sigma} \, dt \right)$$

simplifying, one has

$$dS_t^* = \sigma S_t^* \, dW_t^* \tag{15.61}$$

The solution to this SDE, derivable in the same way as Equation (15.51), is (for all $u \geq t$)

$$S_u^* = S_t^* \cdot e^{-(\sigma^2/2) \, dt + \sigma \, dW_t^*} \tag{15.62}$$

Based on this equation, it is easy to demonstrate that S^* is a martingale under measure p^*:

$$E_{p^*}(S_u^* \mid S_t^*) \overset{?}{=} S_t^*$$

substituting Equation (15.62) one obtains

$$E_{p^*}(S_t^* \cdot e^{-(\sigma^2/2) \, dt + \sigma \, dW_t^*} \mid S_t^*) \overset{?}{=} S_t^*$$

simplifying, one has

$$E_{p^*}(e^{-(\sigma^2/2)(u-t)+\sigma(W_u^*-W_t^*)} \mid S_t^*) \overset{?}{=} 1$$

Based on the independence properties of $(W_u^* - W_t^*)$, one obtains

$$E_{p^*}(e^{\sigma(W_u^*-W_t^*)}) \overset{?}{=} e^{(\sigma^2/2)(u-t)}$$

recalling the expression of a moment generating function $\varphi(t)$ of a normal random variable, one has

$$e^{(\sigma^2/2)(u-t)} = e^{(\sigma^2/2)(u-t)} \qquad \qquad \square$$

Theorem 15.3. *Under the probability measure p^*, the process which governs S is represented by the following SDE:*

$$dS_t = rS_t \, dt + \sigma S_t \, dW_t^* \tag{15.63}$$

Proof. One recalls the definition of S_t^* and computes its derivative:

$$dS_t^* = d\left(\frac{S}{B}\right) = S_t \, d\frac{1}{B_t} + \frac{1}{B_t} \, dS_t$$

Equation (15.61) is recalled and by substituting the definition of dS_t and of S_t^*, one has

$$\frac{1}{B_t} r S_t \, dt + \frac{1}{B_t} \sigma S_t \, dW_t^* = \frac{1}{B_t} \mu S_t \, dt + \frac{1}{B_t} \sigma S_t \, dW_t$$

simplifying, one has

$$r S_t \, dt + \sigma S_t \, dW_t^* = dS_t \qquad \square$$

Corollary 15.2. *Under the probability measure p^* the $\ln S_t$ distribution is*

$$\ln S_t \backsim N\left(\ln S_s + \left(r - \frac{\sigma^2}{2}\right)(t - s), \sigma\sqrt{(t - s)}\right)$$

Proof. A similar demonstration is provided in Corollary 15.1. $\qquad \square$

Theorem 15.4. *Under the same martingale measure p^*, where S^* is a martingale, V^* is also a martingale.*

Proof. The differential Equation (15.60), ie,

$$V_t^* = V_0^* + \int_0^t \phi_u^1 \, dS_u^* \qquad (15.64)$$

given

$$P\left\{\int_0^t |\phi_u^1|^2 \, dS_u^* < \infty\right\} = 1,$$

then, the stochastic integral converges in the sense of L_2 and given that any stochastic integral which converges is a martingale, then V^* is also a martingale under measure p^*. $\qquad \square$

This leads to an important result in terms of continuous time contingent claim X pricing. This result is similar to that derived in Sections 15.2.1 and 15.2.2 for discrete time. Given a contingent claim X for which a replication portfolio exists, considering it was demonstrated that the portfolio and the underlying discounted processes (V^* and S^*, respectively) are martingales under measure p^*, based on the equivalence between the contingent claim X and portfolio V, the discounted process of the contingent claim X (defined as $X^* \triangleq B_T^{-1}X$) is also a martingale under the same probability measure p^*. Then, the current contingent claim price under the no-arbitrage condition, $\pi_t(X)$, since this is a

p^*-martingale, coincides with its expected value under p^*, ie,

$$\pi_0(X) = E_{P^*}(X^* \mid \Im_t)$$

and, using the definition of X^* and expressing pricing at a generic time t, one has

$$\pi_t(X) = B_t E_{P^*}(B_T^{-1} X \mid \Im_t) \tag{15.65}$$

15.2.3.2.6.   The pricing of a European call option
Proposition 15.5. *In the case of a European call option, a self-financing replication portfolio exists which is a martingale under the same measure p^* of process S^*.*

Proof. The demonstration is broken down into three parts:

(i)   the call discounted payoff has the same martingale measure p^* as the discounted process of the underlying S^*;
(ii)   a replication portfolio ϕ_t of a European call exists;
(iii) this portfolio is self-financing.

Part (i). Given a European call whose payoff at maturity is

$$X_T = (S_T - K)^+$$

Then the discounted payoff is defined as

$$X_T^* = \frac{(S_T - K)^+}{B_T}$$

Let

$$X_T^* = X_0^* + \int_0^T h_u \, dS_u^* \tag{15.66}$$

where h_u is that

$$P\left\{ \int_0^t |h_u|^2 \, dS_u^* < \infty \right\} = 1,$$

then the stochastic integral converges in the sense of L_2 and given that any stochastic integral which converges is a martingale, then, $X^{*\cdot}$ is also a martingale under measure p^*.

Part (ii). If $X^{*\cdot}$ is a martingale, then $E_{p^*} X_T^* = E_{p^*} X_0^* = X_0^*$, hence Equation (15.66) may also be written as

$$X_T^* = E_{p^*} X_T^* + \int_0^T h_u \sigma S_t^* \, dW_t^*$$

Based on the theorem of martingale representation if X^* is a martingale and converges in the sense of L_2 then one predictable process $\theta_u = h_u \sigma S_u^{*}$ [6] exists only which converges in the sense of L_2 so that

$$X_T^* = E_{p^*} X_T^* + \int_0^T \theta_u \, dW_u^*$$

$$X_T^* = E_{p^*} X_T^* + \int_0^T h_u \, dS_u^* \tag{15.67}$$

$$X_T^* = X_0^* + \int_0^T h_u \, dS_u^*$$

If $\phi_u^1 = h_u$, then Equation (15.64) coincides with Equation (15.66), ie, one replication portfolio exists only so that its value is equal to the contingent claim value.

Then the call ϕ_t replication portfolio is determined. In order to do this the value of ϕ_t^2 has to be computed. Using Equation (15.49), substituting $\phi_t^1 = h_t$ and solving by ϕ_t^2, one obtains

$$\phi_t^2 = \frac{V_t - \phi_t^1 S_t}{B_t}$$

Using the definition of V_t^* and of S_t^* one obtains

$$\phi_t^2 = V_t^* - \phi_t^1 S_t^*$$

hence, unique replication portfolio exists, ie,

$$\phi_t = (\phi_t^1, \phi_t^2) = (h_t, V_t^* - h_t S_t^*) \tag{15.68}$$

Part (iii). In the following, in order to solve arbitrage problems, a demonstration is required that this portfolio is self-financing, that is, it must be verified that this strategy satisfies Definition 15.1, ie,

$$V_t(\phi) \overset{?}{=} V_0(\phi) + \int_0^t \phi_u^1 \, dS_u + \int_0^t \phi_u^2 \, dB_u, \quad \forall t \in [0, T]$$

whose differential expression is

$$dV_t(\phi) \overset{?}{=} \phi_t^1 \, dS_t + \phi_t^2 \, dB_t, \quad \forall t \in [0, T]$$

---

[6] A sequence A_n is *predictable* if $A_n = f_n(x_0, x_1, \ldots, x_{n-1})$. A predictable process has to be fed with information up to the period just before the current period to make a forecast for the future. A sequence A_n is *adaptable* if $A_n = f_n(x_0, x_1, \ldots, x_{n-1}, x_n)$. An adaptable process requires information up to the current period to make a forecast for the future. Then, any predictable process is adaptable. The reverse is not true.

the right member (right-hand side), ie, $\phi_t^1 \, dS_t + \phi_t^2 \, dB_t$ and the left member (left-hand side), ie, $dV_t(\phi)$, are studied separately in order to demonstrate the equivalence.

In the right member, substituting strategy (15.68), one has

$$\phi_t^1 \, dS_t + \phi_t^2 \, dB_t = \phi_t^1 \, dS_t + \phi_t^2 \, dB_t = h_t \, dS_t + (V_t^* - h_t S_t^*) \, dB_t,$$

by using the relation given by Equation (15.54), ie, $dB_t = rB_t \, dt$,

$$\phi_t^1 \, dS_t + \phi_t^2 \, dB_t = h_t \, dS_t + (V_t - h_t S_t)r \, dt \tag{15.69}$$

For the left member, given that $V_t = B_t V_t^*$, one has

$$dV_t(\phi) = d(B_t V_t^*)$$

Then the Leibniz rule is applied and, as was demonstrated for Definition 15.2, the third term of this expression is equal to zero. This coincides with the product derivation rule, whence

$$dV_t(\phi) = B_t \, dV_t^* + V_t^* \, dB_t$$

By using the relation given by Equation (15.54), ie, $dB_t = rB_t \, dt$ and based on Equation (15.60) and on the definition of V_t^* given by Definition 15.2, one has

$$dV_t(\phi) = B_t \phi_t^1 \, dS_t^* + V_t r \, dt$$

based on the definition of S_t^* given inside Definition 15.2 the Leibniz rule is applied and, as was demonstrated in Definition 15.2, the third term of the derivation is equal to zero. Then this computation coincides with the product derivation rule, whence

$$dV_t(\phi) = \phi_t^1 \, dS_t + \phi_t^1 S_t B_t \left(-r\frac{1}{B_t} \, dt \right) + V_t r \, dt$$

strategy (15.68) is substituted and the left member becomes

$$dV_t(\phi) = h_t \, dS_t + (V_t - h_t S_t)r \, dt \tag{15.70}$$

Equation (15.70) is equal to Equation (15.69) and, therefore, one may conclude that strategy ϕ_t is self-financing. $\qquad\square$

Proposition 15.6. *The European call price under measure p* is given by BSM formula, ie,*

$$C_t = S_t N(d_1) - Ke^{-r(T-t)} N(d_2) \tag{15.34}$$

where we have (15.35), (15.36) and

$$N(x) = \frac{1}{\sqrt{2\pi}} \int_{-\infty}^x e^{-u^2/2} \, du \tag{15.71}$$

Proof. Based on the contingent claim pricing formula in a risk-neutral econ-omy, ie, (15.65), and rearranging it with respect to a European call, one has

$$C_t = \pi_t[(S_T - K)^+] = B_t E_{P^*}[B_T^{-1}(S_T - K)^+ \mid \Im_t] \qquad (15.72)$$

Let the index function I_D, be defined as

$$I_D = \begin{cases} 1 & \text{if } S_T > K \\ 0 & \text{if } S_T \leq K \end{cases}$$

where D represents the set of events where $S_T > K$, ie,

$$D = \{\omega : S_T(\omega) > K\}$$

Based on this definition, one may write

$$(S_T - K)^+ = (S_T - K)I_D$$

and then, substituting in Equation (15.72),

$$C_t = B_t E_{P^*}(B_T^{-1}S_T I_D \mid \Im_t) - B_t E_{P^*}(B_T^{-1}KI_D \mid \Im_t)$$

The following quantities are defined:

$$J_1 = B_t E_{P^*}(B_T^{-1}S_T I_D \mid \Im_t) \qquad (15.73)$$
$$J_2 = B_t E_{P^*}(B_T^{-1}KI_D \mid \Im_t) \qquad (15.74)$$

Then the formula in Equation (15.34), becomes

$$C_t \overset{?}{=} J_1 - J_2 \qquad (15.75)$$

In order to rearrange this term explicitly J_2 is analysed:

$$J_2 = B_t E_{P^*}(B_T^{-1}KI_D \mid \Im_t)$$

which, based on the definitions of B_t and B_T, becomes

$$J_2 = Ke^{-r(T-t)}P^*\{D \mid \Im_t\}$$

but to define D and using the definition of $S_T^* = S_T/B_T$, one has

$$J_2 = Ke^{-r(T-t)}P^*\{S_T^* > Ke^{-rT} \mid \Im_t\}$$

it was previously demonstrated that S_T^* has a P^*-martingale and, based on Equation (15.62), one gets

$$J_2 = Ke^{-r(T-t)}P^*\{S_t^*e^{-1/2\sigma^2(T-t)+\sigma(W_T^*-W_t^*)} > Ke^{-rT} \mid \Im_t\}$$

taking the logarithm on both the members, and based on the definition of S_t^* given inside Definition 15.2 and by making some simple algebra, one obtains

$$J_2 = Ke^{-r(T-t)}N\left\{\frac{1}{\sigma\sqrt{T-t}}\left[\ln\frac{S_t}{K} + \left(r - \frac{1}{2}\sigma^2\right)(T-t)\right]\right\}$$

and using the definition of d_1 given by Equation (15.35), one obtains

$$J_2 = Ke^{-r(T-t)}N(d_1) \tag{15.76}$$

Now the term J_1 is analysed:

$$J_1 = B_t E_{P^*}(B_T^{-1}S_T I_D \mid \Im_t)$$

By again using Equation (15.62), one obtains

$$J_1 = B_t S_t^* E_{P^*}(e^{-(\sigma^2/2)(T-t)+\sigma(W_T^*-W_t^*)}I_D \mid \Im_t)$$

The new probability measure $\overline{P}$ is now defined by using the Radon–Nikodym derivative:

$$\eta_T = \left.\frac{\partial\overline{P}}{\partial P^*}\right|_T = e^{-(\sigma^2/2)(T-t)+\sigma(W_T^*-W_t^*)}$$

Under this new probability measure, the stochastic process $\overline{W}_t$, defined as

$$\overline{W}_t = W_t^* - \sigma t$$

is a Brownian motion as it may be easily demonstrated by using the Girsanov theorem (see Theorem 12.16).

Hence, the last expression derived for J_1, ie,

$$J_1 = B_t S_t^* E_{P^*}(e^{-(\sigma^2/2)(T-t)+\sigma(W_T^*-W_t^*)}I_D \mid \Im_t)$$

becomes:

$$J_1 = B_t S_t^* E_{P^*}\left(\left.\frac{\partial\overline{P}}{\partial P^*}\right|_T I_D \;\Im_t\right)$$

based on Bayes' theorem (see Theorem 11.14), one has that

$$E_{P^*}\left(\left.\frac{\partial\overline{P}}{\partial P^*}\right|_T X \;\middle|\; \Im_t\right) = E_{\overline{P}}(X \mid \Im_t)$$

and, then,

$$E_{P^*}\left(\left.\frac{\partial \bar{P}}{\partial P^*}\right|_T X \mid \Im_t\right) = S_t E_{\bar{P}}(I_D \mid \Im_t)$$

recalling that $E_{\bar{P}}(I_D \mid \Im_t) = \bar{P}(D \mid \Im_t)$, one gets

$$E_{P^*}\left(\left.\frac{\partial \bar{P}}{\partial P^*}\right|_T X \mid \Im_t\right) = S_t \bar{P}(S_T^* > Ke^{-rT} \mid \Im_t)$$

substituting in Equation (15.62) the definition of W_t^* expressed in terms of $\overline{W}_t$, ie, $W_t^* = \overline{W}_t + \sigma t$, one obtains the behaviour of S_T^*, under filtration $\Im_t$, described in terms of the new probability measure $\bar{P}$, ie,

$$S_T^* = S_t^* e^{\sigma(\overline{W}_T - \overline{W}_t) + (1/2)\sigma^2(T-t)}$$

and adjoining this evolution of S_T^* to the argument of the new probability measure $\bar{P}$, one has

$$J_1 = S_t \bar{P}(S_t^* e^{\sigma(\overline{W}_T - \overline{W}_t) + (1/2)\sigma^2(T-t)} > Ke^{-rT} \mid \Im_t)$$

considering the logarithm of both members of the above inequality and substituting $S_t^* = S_t e^{-rt}$ based on the definition of S_t^* given in Definition 15.2, one obtains

$$J_1 = S_t N\left\{\frac{1}{\sigma\sqrt{T-t}}\left[\ln\frac{S_t}{K} + \left(r + \frac{1}{2}\sigma^2\right)(T-t)\right]\right\}$$

and using the definition of d_2 given in Equation (15.36), one has

$$J_1 = S_t N(d_2) \tag{15.77}$$

substituting the results from Equations (15.76) and (15.77) in Equation (15.75) one obtains (15.34). □

For all of the above, formula (15.34) provides the *arbitrage price in a risk-neutral economy in continuous time.*

15.2.3.3.   The PDE method
15.2.3.3.1.   *PDE derivation for replication portfolio*   In the following, to simplify notation, $W_t = W$, $S_t = S$. In this model, the option price f to be derived is governed by two variables, ie,

$$f = f(S, t) \tag{15.78}$$

The stochastic differential of f is computed, considering f differentiable to the order required and using Itô's algebra (see Section 12.1.5.1)

$$df = \frac{\partial f}{\partial S} dS + \frac{\partial f}{\partial t} dt + \frac{1}{2} \frac{\partial^2 f}{\partial S^2} (dS)^2 \qquad (15.79)$$

Substituting Equation (15.50), in Equation (15.79) to get

$$df = \frac{\partial f}{\partial S} [\mu S \, dt + \sigma S \, dW] + \frac{\partial f}{\partial t} dt + \frac{1}{2} \frac{\partial^2 f}{\partial S^2} \sigma^2 S^2 \, dt \qquad (15.80)$$

Since the solution of the equation above is a stochastic process, the increment of option price f is a stochastic process dependent on the Wiener process which governs the process of the underlying. Then, the option replication portfolio is built, ie,

$$\pi = f - \Delta S \qquad (15.81)$$

where:

- f is the option price;
- Δ is the quantity of the underlying.

In order to derive the equivalence between df and $d\pi$, the latter is derived. By differentiating Equation (15.81) and using (15.80) and (15.50), one has

$$d\pi = df - \Delta \, dS$$

$$= \frac{\partial f}{\partial S} [\mu S \, dt + \sigma S \, dW] + \frac{\partial f}{\partial t} dt + \frac{1}{2} \frac{\partial^2 f}{\partial S^2} \sigma^2 S^2 \, dt - \Delta [\mu S \, dt + \sigma S \, dW] \quad (15.82)$$

Then the coefficient Δ is determined in order to eliminate the term dW, ie, any random portfolio variation,

$$\Delta = \frac{\partial f}{\partial S} \qquad (15.83)$$

Substituting the expression for coefficient Δ defined in (15.83) in Equation (15.82), by simplifying the identical terms with opposite sign, one has

$$d\pi = \frac{\partial f}{\partial t} dt + \frac{1}{2} \frac{\partial^2 f}{\partial S^2} \sigma^2 S^2 \, dt \qquad (15.84)$$

Equation (15.84) represents a portfolio only composed of the deterministic component. Then it becomes possible to apply the no-arbitrage condition, hence

$$d\pi = r\pi \, dt \qquad (15.85)$$

Then Equation (15.85) is expanded, ie,

$$-rf + \frac{\partial f}{\partial S} rS + \frac{\partial f}{\partial t} + \frac{1}{2} \frac{\partial^2 f}{\partial S^2} \sigma^2 S^2 = 0 \qquad (15.86)$$

which is known as the Black–Scholes PDE.

15.2.3.3.2.   PDE specification for the pricing of a call option: derivation of the Cauchy problem   Given the PDE (15.86), the Cauchy problem, where f describes the price of a call option C among all of the contingent claims, is defined by the PDE (15.86) specified to describe the call price (15.87) and by the boundary conditions, ie, the call payoff value at maturity (15.87a):

$$- rC + \frac{\partial C}{\partial S} rS + \frac{\partial C}{\partial t} + \frac{1}{2}\frac{\partial^2 C}{\partial S^2}\sigma^2 S^2 = 0 \tag{15.87}$$

$$C(S, t = T) = \text{Max}[0, S - K] \tag{15.87a}$$

where $C(S, v, t, T)$ is the call option price at time t.

15.2.3.3.3.   The solution of the Cauchy problem via Feynman–Kac and the call price

Proposition 15.7. *The solution of the Cauchy problem determined by PDE (15.87) and it boundary conditions (15.87a) is known as the BSM model (see Equations (15.34)–(15.36)).*

Proof.   One recalls the SDE which governs process S in its version under measure p^*, ie, (15.63) (see also Sections 15.2.3.2 and 15.2.3.3.5), and the Cauchy problem determined by the PDE (15.87) and by the boundary condition (15.87a). Based on Theorem 12.20 whose expression (12.94) is Equation (15.63), and the Cauchy problem of Theorem 12.20 determined by the PDE (12.96) and by its boundary condition that corresponds to the problem inside (15.87), one may expand relation (12.95), ie,

$$C_t = E[\max(S_T - K, 0)e^{\int_t^T r\, ds}|S_t = s] \tag{15.88}$$

solving the integral

$$C_t = e^{-r(T-t)}E[\max(S_t \cdot e^{(\mu-\sigma^2/2)(T-t)+\sigma(W_T^*-W_t^*)} - K, 0)] \tag{15.89}$$

the expected value is computed and, for a property of the integrals,

$$C_t = \int_K^{+\infty} S_T f(S_T)\, dS_T - K \int_K^{+\infty} f(S_T)\, dS_T$$

To simplify notation $y = S_T$. Then it can be derived that

$$E[\max(S_t \cdot e^{(\mu-\sigma^2/2)(T-t)+\sigma(W_T^*-W_t^*)} - K, 0)]$$

$$= \int_K^{+\infty} y f_Y(y)\, dy - K \int_K^{+\infty} f_Y(y)\, dy \tag{15.90}$$

the value of $f_Y(y)$ is determined; since, based on Corollary 15.1,

$$\ln \frac{S_T}{S_t} \sim N\left(\left(\mu - \frac{\sigma^2}{2}\right), \sigma\sqrt{(T-t)}\right)$$

in terms of y

$$y \sim N\left[\ln S_t + \left(\mu - \frac{\sigma^2}{2}\right)(T-t), \sigma\sqrt{(T-t)}\right]$$

on the basis of the results of Example 11.4 the density of $y = S_T$ is determined, ie,

$$f_Y(y) = \frac{1}{\sigma y \sqrt{2\pi(T-t)}} e^{-[\ln y - \ln S_t - (r-\sigma^2/2)(T-t)]^2/2\sigma^2(T-t)}$$

then, the first integral of (15.90) is computed:

$$\int_K^{+\infty} y f_Y(y)\, dy = \int_K^{+\infty} y \frac{1}{\sigma y \sqrt{2\pi(T-t)}} e^{-[\ln y - \ln S_t - (r-\sigma^2/2)(T-t)]^2/2\sigma^2(T-t)}\, dy$$

by posing $y = e^x$ from which $dy = y\, dx$ or $dy = e^x\, dx$, one has

$$\int_K^{+\infty} y f_Y(y)\, dy = \int_K^{+\infty} \frac{1}{\sigma \sqrt{2\pi(T-t)}} e^{-[x - \ln S_t - (r-\sigma^2/2)(T-t)]^2/2\sigma^2(T-t)} e^x\, dx$$

by posing

$$\frac{[x - \ln S_t - (r - \sigma^2/2)(T-t)]}{\sigma\sqrt{T-t}} = u,$$

one has the following relation:

- $dx = du(\sigma\sqrt{T-t})$;
- $[x - \ln S_t - (r - \sigma^2/2)(T-t)]^2/\sigma^2(T-t) = u^2$;
- $x = u\sigma\sqrt{T-t} + \ln S_t + (r - \sigma^2/2)(T-t)$;

to get

$$\int_K^{+\infty} y f_Y(y)\, dy$$

$$= \int_{(\ln K - \ln S_t - (r-\sigma^2/2)(T-t))/\sigma\sqrt{T-t}}^{+\infty} e^{[u\sigma\sqrt{T-t} + \ln S_t + (r-\sigma^2/2)(T-t)]}$$

$$\times \frac{1}{\sigma\sqrt{2\pi(T-t)}} e^{-u^2/2} (\sigma\sqrt{T-t})\, du$$

$$= S_t \int_{(\ln K - \ln S_t - (r - \sigma^2/2)(T-t))/\sigma\sqrt{T-t}}^{+\infty} \frac{1}{\sqrt{2\pi}} e^{-1/2[u^2 - 2u\sigma\sqrt{T-t} - 2r(T-t) + \sigma^2(T-t)]} \, du$$

(simplifying $\ln S_t$ and $\sigma\sqrt{T-t}$)

$$= S_t \int_{(\ln K - \ln S_t - (r - \sigma^2/2)(T-t))/\sigma\sqrt{T-t}}^{+\infty} \frac{1}{\sqrt{2\pi}} e^{-1/2[u^2 - 2u\sigma\sqrt{T-t} + \sigma^2(T-t)] + r(T-t)} \, du$$

(extracting the term $2r(T-t)$ from the brackets)

$$= S_t e^{r(T-t)} \int_{((\ln K - \ln S_t - (r - \sigma^2/2)(T-t))/\sigma\sqrt{T-t}) - \sigma\sqrt{T-t}}^{+\infty} \frac{1}{\sqrt{2\pi}} e^{-(1/2)z^2} \, dz$$

(posing $(u - \sigma\sqrt{T-t}) = z$ and, then, $du = dz$)

$$= S_t e^{r(T-t)} \int_{(-\ln (S_t/K) + (r + \sigma^2/2)(T-t))/\sigma\sqrt{T-t}}^{+\infty} \frac{1}{\sqrt{2\pi}} e^{-(1/2)z^2} \, dz$$

(simplifying the lower extreme of integration)

defining the lower extreme of integration as

$$d_1 = \frac{\ln (S_t/K) + (r + \sigma^2/2)(T-t)}{\sigma\sqrt{T-t}}$$

one has

$$\int_K^{+\infty} y f_Y(y) \, dy = S_t e^{r(T-t)} \int_{-d_1}^{+\infty} \frac{1}{\sqrt{2\pi}} e^{-(1/2)z^2} \, dz$$

in the integrand, the density function of a standardised normal, and, based on the symmetry property of the normal, the expression above may also be written as

$$\int_K^{+\infty} y f_Y(y) \, dy = S_t e^{r(T-t)} \int_{-\infty}^{d_1} \frac{1}{\sqrt{2\pi}} e^{-(1/2)z^2} \, dz$$

defining N as the CDF of the standardised normal density function, one gets

$$\int_K^{+\infty} y f_Y(y) \, dy = S_t e^{r(T-t)} N(d_1)$$

therefore, the result of the first integral computation is

$$\int_K^{+\infty} y f_Y(y) \, dy = S_t e^{r(T-t)} N(d_1) \tag{15.91}$$

The second integral of Equation (15.90) is then computed:

$$\int_K^{+\infty} f_Y(y) \, dy = \int_K^{+\infty} \frac{1}{\sigma y \sqrt{2\pi(T-t)}} e^{-[\ln y - \ln S_t - (r - \sigma^2/2)(T-t)]^2/2\sigma^2(T-t)} \, dy$$

posing $y = e^x$ where $dy = y\,dx$ or $dy = e^x\,dx$, one gets

$$\int_K^{+\infty} f_Y(y)\,dy = \int_K^{+\infty} \frac{1}{\sigma\sqrt{2\pi(T-t)}} e^{-[x - \ln S_t - (r - \sigma^2/2)(T-t)]^2 / 2\sigma^2(T-t)}\,dx$$

posing, as before,

$$\frac{[x - \ln S_t - (r - \sigma^2/2)(T-t)]}{\sigma\sqrt{T-t}} = u,$$

one has

$$\int_K^{+\infty} f_Y(y)\,dy$$

$$= \int_{(\ln K - \ln S_t - (r - \sigma^2/2)(T-t))/\sigma\sqrt{T-t}}^{+\infty} \frac{1}{\sigma\sqrt{2\pi(T-t)}} e^{-u^2/2} (\sigma\sqrt{T-t})\,du$$

simplifying the lower extreme of integration by using an algorithm property:

$$\int_K^{+\infty} f_Y(y)\,dy = \int_{-(\ln(S_t/K) + (r - \sigma^2/2)(T-t))/\sigma\sqrt{T-t}}^{+\infty} \frac{1}{\sqrt{2\pi}} e^{-(1/2)u^2}\,du$$

defining the lower extreme of integration as

$$d_2 = \frac{\ln(S_t/K) + (r - \sigma^2/2)(T-t)}{\sigma\sqrt{T-t}}$$

one has

$$\int_K^{+\infty} f_Y(y)\,dy = \int_{-d_2}^{+\infty} \frac{1}{\sqrt{2\pi}} e^{-(1/2)u^2}\,du$$

again, in the integrand, one recalls the standardised normal density function, and, then, based on the symmetry properties of the normal, the previous expression may also be written as

$$\int_K^{+\infty} f_Y(y)\,dy = \int_{-\infty}^{d_2} \frac{1}{\sqrt{2\pi}} e^{-(1/2)u^2}\,du$$

defining N, the CDF of the standardised normal density function, one has

$$\int_K^{+\infty} f_Y(y)\,dy = N(d_2)$$

therefore, the second integral computation gives

$$\int_K^{+\infty} f_Y(y)\,dy = N(d_2) \tag{15.92}$$

substituting Equations (15.91) and (15.92) in Equation (15.90), one has

$$E\left[\max(S_t \cdot e^{(\mu-\sigma^2/2)(T-t)+\sigma(W_T^*-W_t^*)} - K, 0)\right] = S_t e^{r(T-t)} N(d_1) - KN(d_2)$$
(15.93)

Substituting in Equation (15.89) the computation of the expected value in Equation (15.93), one has

$$C_t = e^{-r(T-t)}[S_t e^{r(T-t)} N(d_1) - KN(d_2)]$$
$$= S_t N(d_1) - Ke^{-r(T-t)} N(d_2)$$

with

$$d_1 = \frac{\ln s + (r + \sigma^2/2)(T-t) - \ln K}{\sigma\sqrt{T-t}}$$

$$d_2 = \frac{\ln s + (r - \sigma^2/2)(T-t) - \ln K}{\sigma\sqrt{T-t}}$$

□

15.2.3.3.4. *Solution to the Cauchy problem via Fourier Transform* The Cauchy problem identified by Equation (15.87) and the boundary condition (15.87a) is solved by an approach based on the use of the Fourier transforms.

15.2.3.3.4.1. *Transformation of the Cauchy problem into the corresponding logarithm version* Equation (15.87) is specified in its equivalent logarithm version. For this purpose, one defines

$$x = \ln(S)$$
(15.94)

Then

$$S = e^x$$
(15.95)

The new version of Equation (15.87) is derived with respect to x. Recalling that $C = f(S(g(x)))$, the relations between $\partial C/\partial x$ and $\partial C/\partial S$ and between $\partial^2 C/\partial x^2$ and $\partial^2 C/\partial S^2$ are derived:

$$\frac{\partial C}{\partial S} = \frac{\partial C}{\partial x}\frac{1}{S}$$
(15.96)

$\partial^2 C/\partial x^2$ is expanded by using the derivation above of $\partial C/\partial x$:

$$\frac{\partial^2 C}{\partial S^2} = \frac{1}{S^2}\frac{\partial^2 C}{\partial x^2} - \frac{1}{S^2}\frac{\partial C}{\partial x}$$
(15.97)

Then the Cauchy problem (15.87) is written with respect to x, by using Equations (15.96) and (15.97), ie,

$$\frac{\partial C}{\partial t} + \frac{1}{2}\frac{\partial^2 C}{\partial x^2}\sigma^2 - rC + \frac{\partial C}{\partial x}\left(r - \frac{1}{2}\sigma^2\right) = 0$$
(15.98)

Equation (15.98) is the logarithmic version of (15.87). To finalise the definition of the Cauchy problem, the boundary condition corresponding to that of (15.87) has to be determined; for this purpose, simply rearranging this equation in its logarithm version by using Equation (15.95), ie,

$$C(x, t = T) = \text{Max}[0, e^{xT} - K]$$

Then, the new Cauchy problem is then derived, ie,

$$\frac{\partial C}{\partial t} + \frac{1}{2}\frac{\partial^2 C}{\partial x^2}\sigma^2 - rC + \frac{\partial C}{\partial x}\left(r - \frac{1}{2}\sigma^2\right) = 0 \tag{15.98}$$

$$C(x, t = T) = \text{Max}[0, e^{xT} - K] \tag{15.98a}$$

15.2.3.3.4.2. The shift into the à-la BSM pricing context The Cauchy problem as in (15.98) is now specified in the classic à-la BSM form, ie,

$$C(S, t, T) = SP_1(S, t, T) - Ke^{-r(T-t)}P_2(S, t, T) \quad \text{or} \tag{15.99}$$
$$C(x, t) = e^x P_1(x, t) - Ke^{-r(T-t)}P_2(x, t)$$

where P_1, P_2 are probability measures, or P_k for $k = 1, 2$.

Equation (15.99) is used to compute the partial derivatives in order to make Equation (15.98) explicit:

$$\frac{\partial C}{\partial x} = e^x P_1(x, t) + e^x \frac{\partial P_1}{\partial x} - Ke^{-r(T-t)}\frac{\partial P_2}{\partial x} \tag{15.100}$$

$$\frac{\partial^2 C}{\partial x^2} = e^x P_1(x, t) + 2e^x \frac{\partial P_1}{\partial x} + e^x \frac{\partial^2 P_1}{\partial x^2} - Ke^{-r(T-t)}\frac{\partial^2 P_2}{\partial x^2} \tag{15.101}$$

$$\frac{\partial C}{\partial t} = e^x \frac{\partial P_1}{\partial t} - K\left[e^{-r(T-t)}\frac{\partial P_2}{\partial t} + re^{-r(T-t)}P_2(x, t)\right] \tag{15.102}$$

Then Equations (15.100), (15.101) and (15.102) are substituted in (15.98) to obtain

$$e^x \cdot \left\{\frac{\partial P_1}{\partial t} + \frac{1}{2}\sigma^2\frac{\partial P_1}{\partial x} + \frac{1}{2}\sigma^2\frac{\partial^2 P_1}{\partial x^2} + r\frac{\partial P_1}{\partial x}\right\}$$
$$- Ke^{-r(T-t)} \cdot \left\{\frac{\partial P_2}{\partial t} + \frac{1}{2}\sigma^2\left[\frac{\partial^2 P_2}{\partial x^2}\right] + r\frac{\partial P_2}{\partial x} - \lambda\mu\frac{\partial P_2}{\partial x} - \frac{1}{2}\sigma^2\frac{\partial P_2}{\partial x}\right\}$$

Since e^x and $Ke^{-r(T-t)}$ are always greater than or equal to zero, in order to verify the equivalence above, it is enough that

$$\frac{\partial P_1}{\partial t} + \frac{1}{2}\sigma^2\frac{\partial^2 P_1}{\partial x^2} + \left(r + \frac{1}{2}\sigma^2\right)\frac{\partial P_1}{\partial x} = 0 \tag{15.103}$$

$$\frac{\partial P_2}{\partial t} + \frac{1}{2}\sigma^2\left[\frac{\partial^2 P_2}{\partial x^2}\right] + \left(r - \frac{1}{2}\sigma^2\right)\frac{\partial P_2}{\partial x} = 0 \tag{15.104}$$

Equations (15.103) and (15.104) are equivalent forms of the PDE (15.98) in the à-la BSM call pricing context as in (15.99). To identify the Cauchy problems in (15.103), and (15.104), equivalent to problem (15.98), one has to determine the boundary condition corresponding to that under (15.98a); for this purpose, the characteristics of function P_k are specified at time $t = T$:

$$P_k(x, T) = \begin{cases} 1 & \text{if } (e^{x_T} - e^{\ln(K)}) \geq 0 \Rightarrow x_T \geq \ln(K) \\ 0 & \text{if } (e^{x_T} - e^{\ln(K)}) < 0 \Rightarrow x_T < \ln(K) \end{cases}$$

by applying the index function definition (see Definition (6.3) one has

$$P_k(x, T) = 1_{(x_T \geq \ln K)}$$

The following equations are the transformed Cauchy problem in the à-la BSM call pricing environment determined as in (15.98) and its boundary conditions:

$$\frac{\partial P_1}{\partial t} + \frac{1}{2}\sigma^2 \frac{\partial^2 P_1}{\partial x^2} + \left(r + \frac{1}{2}\sigma^2\right)\frac{\partial P_1}{\partial x} = 0 \tag{15.103}$$

$$P_1(x, T) = 1_{(x_T \geq \ln[K])} \tag{15.103a}$$

$$\frac{\partial P_2}{\partial t} + \frac{1}{2}\sigma^2 \left[\frac{\partial^2 P_2}{\partial x^2}\right] + \left(r - \frac{1}{2}\sigma^2\right)\frac{\partial P_2}{\partial x} = 0 \tag{15.104}$$

$$P_2(x, T) = 1_{(x_T \geq \ln[K])} \tag{15.104a}$$

Then the characteristics of the probability measure P_j at time t remain to be determined. For this purpose, Equations (15.103) and (15.104) are interpreted by using the deterministic components of the Feynman–Kac formula (see Theorem 12.20). Actually, the corresponding SDEs (15.103) and (15.104) may be determined, ie,

$$dx_t^{(1)} = \left[r + \tfrac{1}{2}\sigma^2\right]dt + \sigma\, dW_t \quad \text{with } x_t^{(1)} = x \tag{15.105}$$

$$dx_t^{(2)} = \left[r - \tfrac{1}{2}\sigma^2\right]dt + \sigma\, dW_t \text{ with } x_t^{(2)} = x \tag{15.106}$$

Then expression (12.95), becomes (for $k = 1, 2$)

$$P_k(x, t) = E\left[1_{(x_T \geq \ln[K])} \mid x_t = x\right]$$

by simplifying, one has

$$P_k(x, t) = P_k[x_T \geq \ln[K] \mid x_t = x]$$

By denoting with x_t the equivalence $x_t = x$, one gets the characteristics of the probability measure P_k at a generic time t:

$$P_k(x, t) = P_k[x_T \geq \ln[K] \mid x_t] \tag{15.107}$$

15.2.3.3.4.3.   The shift in Fourier space   The Cauchy problem identified in (15.103) and (15.104) is now shifted in the Fourier space, ie, it is rearranged as a function of the conditioned characteristic function. For this purpose, 11.123 in Section 11.9.1 is rearranged (by using Notation 11.34) for $P_k(x, t)$ or more simply $P_k(x_t)$, ie[7],

$$P_k(x_t) = P_k[x_T \geq \ln[K] \mid x_t] = \frac{1}{2\pi} \int_{-\infty}^{\infty} \frac{e^{-i\xi \ln[K]}}{i\xi} \tilde{f}_k(x_T, \xi \mid x_t) \, d\xi \qquad (15.108)$$

or, simplifying notation $\tilde{f}_k(x_T, \xi \mid x_t) \doteq \tilde{f}_k$,

$$P_k(x_t) = \frac{1}{2\pi} \int_{-\infty}^{\infty} \frac{e^{-i\xi \ln[K]}}{i\xi} \tilde{f}_k \, d\xi \qquad (15.108)$$

This expression is used to compute partial derivatives (to simplify notation, $(\partial/\partial y)\tilde{f}_j(x_T, \xi \mid x_t) = \partial \tilde{f}_j/\partial y$ for $y = t, x, x^2$), ie,

$$\frac{\partial P_k}{\partial t} = \frac{1}{2\pi} \int_{-\infty}^{\infty} \frac{e^{-i\xi \ln[K]}}{i\xi} \frac{\partial \tilde{f}_k}{\partial t} \, d\xi \qquad (15.109)$$

$$\frac{\partial P_k}{\partial x} = \frac{1}{2\pi} \int_{-\infty}^{\infty} \frac{e^{-i\xi \ln[K]}}{i\xi} \frac{\partial \tilde{f}_k}{\partial x} \, d\xi \qquad (15.110)$$

$$\frac{\partial^2 P_k}{\partial x^2} = \frac{1}{2\pi} \int_{-\infty}^{\infty} \frac{e^{-i\xi \ln[K]}}{i\xi} \frac{\partial^2 \tilde{f}_k}{\partial x^2} \, d\xi \qquad (15.111)$$

The PDE (15.103) is shifted in the Fourier space by replacing in (15.108), (15.109), (15.110) and (15.111):

$$\frac{1}{2\pi} \int_{-\infty}^{\infty} \frac{e^{-i\xi \ln[K]}}{i\xi} \left[\frac{\partial \tilde{f}_1}{\partial t} + \frac{1}{2}\sigma^2 \frac{\partial^2 \tilde{f}_1}{\partial x^2} + \left[r + \frac{1}{2}\sigma^2 \right] \frac{\partial \tilde{f}_1}{\partial x} \right] d\xi = 0$$

This equation is verified under the condition that the term in square brackets is equal to zero. Then the PDE is given only by this last member, ie,

$$\frac{\partial \tilde{f}_1}{\partial t} + \frac{1}{2}\sigma^2 \frac{\partial^2 \tilde{f}_1}{\partial x^2} + \left[r + \frac{1}{2}\sigma^2 \right] \frac{\partial \tilde{f}_1}{\partial x} = 0 \qquad (15.112)$$

Similarly, the PDE in (15.104) is shifted in the Fourier space by substituting (15.108), (15.109), (15.110) and (15.111) inside that space:

$$\frac{1}{2\pi} \int_{-\infty}^{\infty} \frac{e^{-i\xi \ln[K]}}{i\xi} \left[\frac{\partial \tilde{f}_2}{\partial t} + \frac{1}{2}\sigma^2 \frac{\partial^2 \tilde{f}_2}{\partial x^2} + \left[r - \frac{1}{2}\sigma^2 \right] \frac{\partial \tilde{f}_2}{\partial x} \right] d\xi = 0$$

---

[7]Note that Equation (11.123) shows ">" and not "≥"; in this case, the difference is not relevant, given the call *payoff*.

This equation is verified under the condition that the member in square brackets is equal to zero. Then the PDE is given only by the last member, ie,

$$\frac{\partial \tilde{f}_2}{\partial t} + \frac{1}{2}\sigma^2 \frac{\partial^2 \tilde{f}_2}{\partial x^2} + \left[r - \frac{1}{2}\sigma^2\right]\frac{\partial \tilde{f}_2}{\partial x} = 0 \tag{15.113}$$

To complete the shift of the Cauchy problem, one has to specify the final conditions in (15.103) and (15.104). By using Theorem 6.5 this final condition is rearranged as

$$P_k(x, t, T) = 1_{x_T \geq \ln[K]} = \theta_{\ln[K]}(x_T) \overset{\Delta}{=} \theta[x_T - \ln(K)]$$

where θ is the Heaviside function.

Recalling expression (6.10), one has

$$\theta(x_T - \ln(K)) = \int_{-\infty}^{x_T - \ln(K)} \delta(w)\, dw$$

which, under Theorem 9.4 and under the Fubini theorem (see Theorem 10.22), is equal to one has

$$\theta(x_T - \ln(K)) = \frac{1}{2\pi}\int_{-\infty}^{\infty}\left(\int_{-\infty}^{x_T - \ln(K)} e^{i\xi w}\, dw\right) d\xi$$

$$= \frac{1}{2\pi}\int_{-\infty}^{\infty}\frac{1}{i\xi}e^{i\xi[x_T]}e^{-i\xi \ln(K)}\, d\xi$$

comparing this last expression to Equation (15.108) arranged for $t = T$, one obtains

$$\frac{1}{2\pi}\int_{-\infty}^{\infty}\frac{1}{i\xi}e^{i\xi[x_T]}\, d\xi = \frac{1}{2\pi}\int_{-\infty}^{\infty}\frac{e^{-i\xi \ln[K]}}{i\xi}\tilde{f}_k(x_T, \xi)\, d\xi$$

Simplifying, one gets the final conditions of the Cauchy problem as under (15.103) and (15.104), ie,

$$e^{i\xi[x_T]} = \tilde{f}_k(x_T, \xi)$$

The following equations are the original Cauchy problem identified under (15.103) and (15.104) and under the respective boundary conditions shifted in the Fourier space:

$$\frac{\partial \tilde{f}_1}{\partial t} + \frac{1}{2}\sigma^2 \frac{\partial^2 \tilde{f}_1}{\partial x^2} + \left[r + \frac{1}{2}\sigma^2\right]\frac{\partial \tilde{f}_1}{\partial x} = 0 \tag{15.112}$$

$$\tilde{f}_k(x_T, \xi) = e^{i\xi[x_T]} \tag{15.112a}$$

$$\frac{\partial \tilde{f}_2}{\partial t} + \frac{1}{2}\sigma^2 \frac{\partial^2 \tilde{f}_2}{\partial x^2} + \left[r - \frac{1}{2}\sigma^2\right]\frac{\partial \tilde{f}_2}{\partial x} = 0 \tag{15.113}$$

$$\tilde{f}_k(x_T, \xi) = e^{i\xi[x_T]} \tag{15.113a}$$

15.2.3.3.4.4. The temporal shift of the transformed Cauchy problem In order to obtain an explicit solution of the Cauchy problem, another temporal shift in Fourier space is needed. Then $\tau = T - t$ so that $t = T - \tau$. Since, for any generic function $f(T - t) = f(\tau)$, it is true that

$$\frac{\partial f(T - t)}{\partial t} = -\frac{\partial f(\tau)}{\partial \tau}$$

Then, the Cauchy problem, identified by Equations (15.112) and (15.113) and by their final conditions, becomes

$$-\frac{\partial \tilde{f}_1}{\partial \tau} + \frac{1}{2}\sigma^2 \frac{\partial^2 \tilde{f}_1}{\partial x^2} + \left[r + \frac{1}{2}\sigma^2\right]\frac{\partial \tilde{f}_1}{\partial x} = 0 \tag{15.114}$$

$$\tilde{f}_k(x_{\tau=0}, \xi) = e^{i\xi[x_{\tau=0}]} \tag{15.114a}$$

$$-\frac{\partial \tilde{f}_2}{\partial \tau} + \frac{1}{2}\sigma^2 \frac{\partial^2 \tilde{f}_2}{\partial x^2} + \left[r - \frac{1}{2}\sigma^2\right]\frac{\partial \tilde{f}_2}{\partial x} = 0 \tag{15.115}$$

$$\tilde{f}_k(x_{\tau=0}, \xi) = e^{i\xi[x_{\tau=0}]} \tag{15.115a}$$

15.2.3.3.4.5. Specification of Cauchy problem as an ODE system Let the solution to the Cauchy problem $\tilde{f}_k$ identified in (15.114) and (15.115), be written as (for $k = 1, 2$)

$$\tilde{f}_k(x_{\tau=0}, \xi \mid x_\tau) = e^{C_\tau^{(k)} + i\xi x_\tau} \tag{15.116}$$

in order for it to be compatible with the final conditions of this problem it is necessary for $\tau = 0$ that $C_{\tau=0}^{(k)} = 0$. This expression becomes the corresponding final condition in the form (15.116) of the PDE (15.114) and (15.115). The partial derivatives of (15.114) and (15.115) are determined by using the functional form (15.116). For simplicity, the subscript τ is omitted, then $C_\tau^{(k)} \doteq C_k$:

$$\frac{\partial \tilde{f}_k}{\partial x} = i\xi e^{C_k + i\xi x} \tag{15.117}$$

$$\frac{\partial^2 \tilde{f}_k}{\partial x^2} = -\xi^2 e^{[C_k + i\xi x]} \tag{15.118}$$

$$\frac{\partial \tilde{f}_k}{\partial \tau} = e^{[C_k + i\xi x]}\frac{\partial C_k}{\partial \tau} \tag{15.119}$$

Equations (15.117), (15.118) and (15.119) are substituted in Equation (15.114):

$$e^{C_\tau^{(1)} + i\xi x_\tau}\left\{-\frac{\partial C_\tau^{(1)}}{\partial \tau} + \frac{1}{2}\sigma^2 i\xi(\xi + 1) + ri\xi\right\} = 0$$

The term $e^{C_\tau^{(1)}+i\xi x_\tau}$ is always positive, then (15.114) may also be written as

$$\frac{\partial C_t^{(1)}}{\partial \tau} = \frac{1}{2}\sigma^2 i\xi(\xi+1) + ri\xi \qquad (15.120)$$

Equations (15.117), (15.118) and (15.119) are substituted in Equation (15.115):

$$e^{C_\tau^{(2)}+i\xi x_\tau}\left\{-\frac{\partial C_\tau^{(2)}}{\partial \tau} + \frac{1}{2}\sigma^2 i\xi(i\xi-1) + ri\xi\right\} = 0$$

Obviously, the term $e^{[C_\tau^{(2)}+i\xi x]}$ is always positive, hence (15.115) may also be expressed as

$$\frac{\partial C_\tau^{(2)}}{\partial \tau} = \frac{1}{2}\sigma^2 i\xi(i\xi-1) + ri\xi \qquad (15.121)$$

Then the Cauchy problem identified in (15.114) and (15.115) and their final conditions may also be written as

$$\frac{\partial C_t^{(1)}}{\partial \tau} = \frac{1}{2}\sigma^2 i\xi(\xi+1) + ri\xi \qquad (15.120)$$

$$C_{\tau=0}^{(1)} = 0 \qquad (15.120a)$$

$$\frac{\partial C_\tau^{(2)}}{\partial \tau} = \frac{1}{2}\sigma^2 i\xi(i\xi-1) + ri\xi \qquad (15.121)$$

$$C_{\tau=0}^{(2)} = 0 \qquad (15.121a)$$

15.2.3.3.4.6.   The solution of the Cauchy problem   Equation (15.120) is solved, ie,

$$\frac{\partial C_\tau^{(1)}}{\partial \tau} = \frac{1}{2}\sigma^2 i\xi(\xi+1) + ri\xi \qquad (15.120)$$

This is a first-order constant coefficient ODE to be solved by direct integration:

$$C_\tau^{(1)} = ri\xi\tau + \frac{1}{2}\sigma^2[i\xi(i\xi+1)]\tau \qquad (15.122)$$

If Equation (15.122) also satisfies the final condition of the Cauchy problem identified in (15.120), then it must be considered as a solution. Hence, Equation (15.121) is solved:

$$\frac{\partial C_\tau^{(2)}}{\partial \tau} = \frac{1}{2}\sigma^2 i\xi(i\xi-1) + ri\xi \qquad (15.121)$$

Again, this is a first-order constant coefficient ODE to be solved by direct integration:

$$C_\tau^{(2)} = \frac{1}{2}\sigma^2 i\xi\tau(i\xi-1) + ri\xi\tau \qquad (15.123)$$

If Equation (15.123) also satisfies the final condition of the Cauchy problem identified in (15.121), then it must be considered as a solution.

15.2.3.3.4.7. Solutions computable by using quadrature algorithms The solutions to the Cauchy problem as in Equations (15.122) and (15.123) in the form (15.116), ie,

$$\tilde{f}_k(x_{\tau=0}, \xi \mid x_\tau) = e^{C_\tau^{(k)} + i\xi x_\tau} \tag{15.116}$$

where $C_\tau^{(1)}$, $C_\tau^{(2)}$ are the expressions (15.122) and (15.123), allow one to determine, through the relation (15.108), the analytic expression of the probability measures P_k, ie,

$$P_k[x_{\tau=0} \geq \ln[K] \mid x_\tau] = \frac{1}{2\pi} \int_{-\infty}^{\infty} \frac{e^{-i\xi \ln[K]}}{i\xi} \tilde{f}_k(x_{\tau=0}, \xi \mid x_\tau) \, d\xi \tag{15.108}$$

However, relation (15.108) does not have an immediate numerical solution. However, many equivalent solutions exist which allow one to manipulate analytically this quantity (see expressions (11.125) and (11.126)):

$$P_k[x_{\tau=0} \geq \ln[K] \mid x_\tau] = \frac{1}{2} + \frac{1}{\pi} \int_{0}^{\infty} \Im\left[\frac{e^{-i\xi \ln[K]}}{\xi} \tilde{f}_k(x_{\tau=0}, \xi \mid x_\tau)\right] d\xi \tag{15.124}$$

$$P_k[x_{\tau=0} \geq \ln[K] \mid x_\tau] = \frac{1}{2} + \frac{1}{\pi} \int_{0}^{\infty} \Re\left[\frac{e^{-i\xi \ln[K]}}{i\xi} \tilde{f}_k(x_{\tau=0}, \xi \mid x_\tau)\right] d\xi \tag{15.125}$$

15.2.3.3.4.8. The call price The BSM model gives the call pricing formula expressed in a simplified notation:

$$C_t = S_t P_1 - Ke^{-r(T-t)} P_2 \tag{15.99}$$

where, by using (15.125) (or, alternatively, (15.124)), (15.116), (15.122) and (15.123), for $k = 1, 2$, the function P is defined as

$$P_k = \frac{1}{2} + \frac{1}{\pi} \int_{0}^{\infty} \Re\left[\frac{e^{-i\xi \ln[K]}}{i\xi} e^{C_\tau^{(k)} + i\xi x_\tau}\right] d\xi \tag{15.126}$$

with

$$C_\tau^{(1)} = ri\xi\tau + \tfrac{1}{2}\sigma^2 i\xi(i\xi + 1)\tau \tag{15.122}$$

$$C_\tau^{(2)} = ri\xi\tau + \tfrac{1}{2}\sigma^2 i\xi(i\xi - 1)\tau \tag{15.123}$$

15.2.3.3.4.9. Implementation of the BSM model via Fourier transform for call pricing Actually, the BSM model implemented via Fourier transform requires the use of software to compute the integral in (15.126). *Matlab real* and *quad8* or *quadl* functions may be used for this purpose.

15.2.3.3.5. BSM model under the risk-neutral probability measure The results above clearly show a pricing formula derived under the risk-neutral probability measure. Substantially, the results in Section 15.2.3.3.1 make this change of probability measure from a stochastic viewpoint. In the following, a representation of the impact on the SDE determined by the highlighted change of measure is given.

Proposition 15.8. *The SDE (15.50) under the risk-neutral probability measure can be written as (15.63).*

Proof. One recalls the PDE (15.86), ie, the PDE derived for the contingent claim replication portfolio and then the expression of a risk-neutral pricing context, ie,

$$-rf + \frac{\partial f}{\partial t} + \frac{\partial f}{\partial S}rS + \frac{1}{2}\frac{\partial^2 f}{\partial S^2}\sigma S^2 = 0 \qquad (15.86)$$

Then the Feynman–Kac theorem is applied (see Theorem 12.21) on (15.86) to get the corresponding SDE (15.63). □

15.2.3.3.6. Relationship between P_k and $N(d_k)$
Theorem 15.5. *Probability functions P_k in (15.126), for $k = 1, 2$, are an equivalent representation of the normal distribution functions, ie,*

$$P_k = \frac{1}{\sqrt{2\pi}} \int_{-\infty}^{d_k} e^{-z^2/2}\, dz = N(d_k) \qquad (15.127)$$

where d_1, and d_2 are as given in Equations (15.35) and (15.36).

Proof. Property (15.127) is demonstrated for P_1. Considering, as a starting point, the form equivalent to (15.126) given by (15.108) expanded in τ, ie,

$$P_1(x_\tau) = P_1[x_{\tau=0} \geq \ln[K] \mid x_\tau] = \frac{1}{2\pi} \int_{-\infty}^{\infty} \frac{e^{-i\xi \ln[K]}}{i\xi} \tilde{f}_1(x_{\tau=0}, \xi \mid x_\tau)\, d\xi \quad (15.108)$$

substituting Equations (15.116) and (15.122), one obtains

$$P_1 = \Pr[x_{\tau=0} \geq \ln[K] \mid x_\tau] = \frac{1}{2\pi} \int_{-\infty}^{\infty} \frac{e^{-i\xi \ln[K]}}{i\xi} e^{i\xi(r\tau+(1/2)\sigma^2\tau+x_\tau)-(1/2)\xi^2\sigma^2\tau}\, d\xi \quad$$
$$(15.128)$$

Under Equations (15.128) and (15.108) the characteristic function can be written

$$\tilde{f}_1(x_{\tau=0}, \xi \mid x_\tau) = e^{i\xi(r\tau+(1/2)\sigma^2\tau+x_\tau)-1/2\xi^2\sigma^2\tau} \qquad (15.129)$$

hence, for (11.118), one has

$$x_{\tau=0} \sim N\left(x_\tau + \left(r + \tfrac{1}{2}\sigma^2\right)\tau, \sigma\sqrt{\tau}\right) \tag{15.130}$$

Recalling that $x_{\tau=0} = \ln S_T$ and $\tau = (T - t)$, the left-hand side of (15.128) is rearranged as

$$P_1[\ln S_T \geq \ln[K] \mid \ln S_t] \tag{15.131}$$

and (15.130) can be written as

$$\ln S_T \sim N\left(\ln S_t + \left(r + \tfrac{1}{2}\sigma^2\right)(T - t), \sigma\sqrt{T - t}\right) \tag{15.132}$$

Then, for the distribution $\ln S_T$ in Equation (15.132), the probability in (15.131) is computed. Then, for the argument of P_1, ie,

$$\ln S_T \geq \ln[K]$$

and, after some algebra,

$$\frac{\ln S_T - \ln S_t - (r + (1/2)\sigma^2)(T - t)}{\sigma\sqrt{T - t}} \geq \frac{\ln[K] - \ln S_t - (r + (1/2)\sigma^2)(T - t)}{\sigma\sqrt{T - t}} \tag{15.133}$$

and, using normal distribution properties, Equation (15.131) may be rearranged as

$$P_1\left[\frac{\ln S_T - \ln S_t - (r + (1/2)\sigma^2)(T - t)}{\sigma\sqrt{T - t}} \geq \frac{\ln[K] - \ln S_t - (r + (1/2)\sigma^2)(T - t)}{\sigma\sqrt{T - t}}\right]$$

or, writing $(\ln S_T - \ln S_t - (r + (1/2)\sigma^2)(T - t))/\sigma\sqrt{T - t} = Z$,

$$P_1\left[\frac{\ln S_T - \ln S_t - (r + (1/2)\sigma^2)(T - t)}{\sigma\sqrt{T - t}} \geq \frac{\ln[K] - \ln S_t - (r + (1/2)\sigma^2)(T - t)}{\sigma\sqrt{T - t}}\right]$$

$$= P_1\left[Z \leq \frac{\ln(S_t/K) + (r + \sigma^2/2)(T - t)}{\sigma\sqrt{(T - t)}}\right]$$

one recalls in the right-hand side the value of d_1 given by (15.35), ie,

$$P_1\left[\frac{\ln S_T - \ln S_t - (r + (1/2)\sigma^2)(T - t)}{\sigma\sqrt{T - t}} \geq \frac{\ln[K] - \ln S_t - (r + (1/2)\sigma^2)(T - t)}{\sigma\sqrt{T - t}}\right]$$

$$= P_1[Z \leq d_1]$$

and, since $Z \sim N(0, 1)$, one obtains

$$P_1\left[\frac{\ln S_T - \ln S_t - (r + (1/2)\sigma^2)(T - t)}{\sigma\sqrt{T - t}} \geq \frac{\ln[K] - \ln S_t - (r + (1/2)\sigma^2)(T - t)}{\sigma\sqrt{T - t}}\right]$$

$$= N(d_1)$$

then

$$P_1 \left[\frac{\ln S_T - \ln S_t - (r + (1/2)\sigma^2)(T - t)}{\sigma\sqrt{T - t}} \geq \frac{\ln[K] - \ln S_t - (r + (1/2)\sigma^2)(T - t)}{\sigma\sqrt{T - t}} \right]$$

$$= \frac{1}{\sqrt{2\pi}} \int_{-\infty}^{d_1} e^{-z^2/2} \, dz$$

whence

$$P_1 = \frac{1}{\sqrt{2\pi}} \int_{-\infty}^{d_1} e^{-z^2/2} \, dz \tag{15.134}$$

Similarly, property (15.127) is demonstrated for P_2. Consider the equivalent form of Equation (15.126) given by (15.108) expanded in τ, ie,

$$P_2(x_\tau) = P_2[x_{\tau=0} \geq \ln[K] \mid x_\tau] = \frac{1}{2\pi} \int_{-\infty}^{\infty} \frac{e^{-i\xi \ln[K]}}{i\xi} \tilde{f}_2(x_{\tau=0}, \xi \mid x_\tau) \, d\xi \tag{15.108}$$

substituting (15.116) and (15.123), one obtains

$$P_2 = \Pr[x_{\tau=0} \geq \ln[K] \mid x_\tau] = \frac{1}{2\pi} \int_{-\infty}^{\infty} \frac{e^{-i\xi \ln[K]}}{i\xi} e^{i\xi(r\tau - (1/2)\sigma^2\tau + x_\tau) - (1/2)\xi^2\sigma^2\tau} \, d\xi \tag{15.135}$$

From (15.135) and (15.108), the characteristic function can be written as

$$\tilde{f}_2(x_{\tau=0}, \xi \mid x_\tau) = e^{i\xi(r\tau - (1/2)\sigma^2\tau + x_\tau) - (1/2)\xi^2\sigma^2\tau} \tag{15.136}$$

hence, for (11.118), one obtains

$$x_{\tau=0} \sim N\left(x_\tau + \left(r - \tfrac{1}{2}\sigma^2\right)\tau, \sigma\sqrt{\tau}\right) \tag{15.137}$$

Recalling that $x_{\tau=0} = \ln S_T$ and that $\tau = (T - t)$, the left-hand side of Equation (15.135) is rearranged

$$P_2[\ln S_T \geq \ln[K] \mid \ln S_t] \tag{15.138}$$

and (15.137) can be written as

$$\ln S_T \sim N\left(\ln S_t + \left(r - \tfrac{1}{2}\sigma^2\right)(T - t), \sigma\sqrt{T - t}\right) \tag{15.139}$$

then, considering the distribution of $\ln S_T$ in Equation (15.139), one computes the probability in Equation (15.138). Attention is then focused on the argument of P_2, ie,

$$\ln S_T \geq \ln[K]$$

and, after some algebra,

$$\frac{\ln S_T - \ln S_t - (r - (1/2)\sigma^2)(T - t)}{\sigma\sqrt{T - t}} \geq \frac{\ln[K] - \ln S_t - (r - (1/2)\sigma^2)(T - t)}{\sigma\sqrt{T - t}} \tag{15.140}$$

and using the normal distribution properties, Equation (15.138) may be rearranged as

$$P_2\left[\frac{\ln S_T - \ln S_t - (r - (1/2)\sigma^2)(T - t)}{\sigma\sqrt{T - t}} \geq \frac{\ln[K] - \ln S_t - (r - (1/2)\sigma^2)(T - t)}{\sigma\sqrt{T - t}}\right]$$

or, as $(\ln S_T - \ln S_t - (r + (1/2)\sigma^2)(T - t))/\sigma\sqrt{T - t} = Z$,

$$P_2\left[\frac{\ln S_T - \ln S_t - (r - (1/2)\sigma^2)(T - t)}{\sigma\sqrt{T - t}} \geq \frac{\ln[K] - \ln S_t - (r - (1/2)\sigma^2)(T - t)}{\sigma\sqrt{T - t}}\right]$$

$$= P_2\left[Z \leq \frac{\ln(S_t/K) + (r - (1/2)\sigma^2)(T - t)}{\sigma\sqrt{T - t}}\right]$$

one recalls in the right-hand side the value of d_2 given by (15.36), ie,

$$P_2\left[\frac{\ln S_T - \ln S_t - (r - (1/2)\sigma^2)(T - t)}{\sigma\sqrt{T - t}} \geq \frac{\ln[K] - \ln S_t - (r - (1/2)\sigma^2)(T - t)}{\sigma\sqrt{T - t}}\right]$$

$$= P_2[Z \leq d_2]$$

and, since $Z \sim N(0, 1)$, one has

$$P_2\left[\frac{\ln S_T - \ln S_t - (r - (1/2)\sigma^2)(T - t)}{\sigma\sqrt{T - t}} \geq \frac{\ln[K] - \ln S_t - (r - (1/2)\sigma^2)(T - t)}{\sigma\sqrt{T - t}}\right]$$

$$= N(d_2)$$

$$= \frac{1}{\sqrt{2\pi}} \int_{-\infty}^{d_2} e^{-z^2/2}\, dz$$

that is

$$P_2 = \frac{1}{\sqrt{2\pi}} \int_{-\infty}^{d_2} e^{-z^2/2}\, dz \qquad (15.141)$$

□

Corollary 15.3. *The random variable* $\ln S_t$ *distribution implicit in the computation of* P_2 *or underlying the value of* $N(d_2)$ *is identical to that of* $\ln S_t$ *under the risk-neutral probability measure* p^*.

Proof. The demonstration can be derived directly from the comparison between Corollary 15.2 and expression (15.139) reported in the demonstration of Theorem 15.5. □

15.2.3.4. The Greeks

The study of an option price sensitivity to the parameters which determine its value leads to a BSM pricing context by computing its partial derivatives. However, some preliminary information is required.

Proposition 15.9. *The following relation holds between d_1 and d_2:*

$$d_2 = d_1 - \sigma\sqrt{T-t} \qquad (15.142)$$

Proof. This is proved by computing

$$d_2 \overset{?}{=} d_1 - \sigma\sqrt{T-t}$$

by using (15.35) and simplifying:

$$d_2 = \frac{\ln(S_t/K) + (r - (1/2)\sigma^2)(T-t)}{\sigma\sqrt{T-t}} \qquad \square$$

Proposition 15.10. *Given formula (15.34), the following result holds:*

$$S_t N'(d_1) - Ke^{-r(T-t)}N'(d_2) = 0 \qquad (15.143)$$

where $N'(x) = (1/\sqrt{2\pi})e^{-(1/2)x^2}$

Proof. This is proved by computing

$$S_t N'(d_1) - Ke^{-r(T-t)}N'(d_2) \overset{?}{=} 0$$

$$S_t \cdot \frac{1}{\sqrt{2\pi}}e^{-(1/2)(d_1)^2} - Ke^{-r(T-t)} \cdot \frac{1}{\sqrt{2\pi}}e^{-(1/2)(d_2)^2} \overset{?}{=} 0$$

by using (15.142), one has

$$\frac{1}{\sqrt{2\pi}}e^{-(1/2)(d_1)^2} \cdot \left[S_t - Ke^{-r(T-t)}e^{-(1/2)\sigma^2(T-t)+d_1\sigma\sqrt{T-t}}\right] \overset{?}{=} 0$$

using (15.35), one has

$$\frac{1}{\sqrt{2\pi}}e^{-((\ln(S_t/K)+(r+(1/2)\sigma^2)(T-t))/\sigma\sqrt{T-t})^2/2}\left[S_t - Ke^{\ln S - \ln K}\right] \overset{?}{=} 0$$

simplifying, one has

$$e^{-((\ln(S_t/K)+(r+(1/2)\sigma^2)(T-t))/\sigma\sqrt{T-t})^2/2}\left[S_t - S_t\right] = 0 \qquad \square$$

Proposition 15.11. *Given formula (15.34), the following relations holds:*

$$\frac{\partial d_1}{\partial S} = \frac{\partial d_2}{\partial S} \tag{15.144}$$

$$\frac{\partial d_1}{\partial r} = \frac{\partial d_2}{\partial r} \tag{15.145}$$

$$\frac{\partial d_1}{\partial \sigma} = \frac{\partial d_2}{\partial \sigma} + \sqrt{T - t} \tag{15.146}$$

$$\frac{\partial d_1}{\partial t} = \frac{\partial d_2}{\partial t} - \frac{\sigma}{2\sqrt{T - t}} \tag{15.147}$$

Proof. To derive (15.144):

$$\frac{\partial d_1}{\partial S_t} \stackrel{?}{=} \frac{\partial d_2}{\partial S_t}$$

by using (15.142), one gets

$$\frac{\partial d_2}{\partial S_t} = \frac{\partial d_1}{\partial S_t}$$

To derive (15.145):

$$\frac{\partial d_1}{\partial r} \stackrel{?}{=} \frac{\partial d_2}{\partial r}$$

by using (15.142), one gets

$$\frac{\partial d_2}{\partial r} = \frac{\partial d_1}{\partial r}$$

To derive (15.146):

$$\frac{\partial d_1}{\partial \sigma} \stackrel{?}{=} \frac{\partial d_2}{\partial \sigma} + \sqrt{T - t}$$

by using (15.142), one has

$$\frac{\partial d_1}{\partial \sigma} = \frac{\partial d_1}{\partial \sigma}$$

To derive (15.147):

$$\frac{\partial d_1}{\partial t} \stackrel{?}{=} \frac{\partial d_2}{\partial t} - \frac{\sigma}{2\sqrt{T - t}}$$

by using (15.142), one gets

$$\frac{\partial d_1}{\partial t} = \frac{\partial d_1}{\partial t} \qquad \square$$

Proposition 15.12. *A call option Delta is*

$$\frac{\partial C}{\partial S_t} = \Delta_C = N(d_1) \tag{15.148}$$

Proof. One has

$$\frac{\partial C}{\partial S_t} = \frac{\partial}{\partial S_t}[S_t N(d_1) - Ke^{-r(T-t)}N(d_2)]$$

$$= N(d_1) \quad \text{(using (15.144) and (15.143))} \qquad \square$$

Proposition 15.13. *A call option* Gamma *is*

$$\frac{\partial^2 C}{\partial S_t^2} = \Gamma_C = N'(d_1) \cdot \frac{1}{S_t \sigma \sqrt{T-t}} \qquad (15.149)$$

Proof. One has

$$\frac{\partial^2 C}{\partial S_t^2} = \frac{\partial}{\partial S_t}\left(\frac{\partial C}{\partial S_t}\right)$$

$$= \frac{\partial}{\partial S_t}(\Delta) \quad \text{(using (15.148))}$$

$$= N'(d_1) \cdot \frac{1}{\sigma \sqrt{T-t}}\frac{1}{S_t} \quad \text{(using (15.35))} \qquad \square$$

Proposition 15.14. *A call option* rho *is*

$$\frac{\partial C}{\partial r} = \rho_C = (T-t)Ke^{-r(T-t)}N(d_2) \qquad (15.150)$$

Proof. One has

$$\frac{\partial C}{\partial r} = \frac{\partial}{\partial r}[S_t N(d_1) - Ke^{-r(T-t)}N(d_2)]$$

$$= \frac{\partial d_1}{\partial r}[S_t N'(d_1) - Ke^{-r(T-t)}N'(d_2)] + (T-t)Ke^{-r(T-t)}N(d_2)$$

$$\text{(by using (15.145))}$$

$$= (T-t)Ke^{-r(T-t)}N(d_2) \quad \text{by using (15.143))} \qquad \square$$

Proposition 15.15. *A call option* Vega *is*

$$\frac{\partial C}{\partial \sigma} = V_C = S_t N'(d_1)\sqrt{T-t} \qquad (15.151)$$

Proof. One has

$$\frac{\partial C}{\partial \sigma} = \frac{\partial}{\partial \sigma}[S_t N(d_1) - Ke^{-r(T-t)}N(d_2)]$$

$$= S_t N'(d_1)\sqrt{T-t} + \frac{\partial d_2}{\partial \sigma}[S_t N'(d_1) - Ke^{-r(T-t)}N'(d_2)] \quad \text{(using (15.146))}$$

$$= S_t N'(d_1)\sqrt{T-t} \quad \text{(using (15.143))} \qquad \square$$

Proposition 15.16. *A call option* Theta *is*

$$\frac{\partial C}{\partial t} = \Theta_C = -\left[S_t N'(d_1) \frac{\sigma}{2\sqrt{T-t}} + rKe^{-r(T-t)}N(d_2) \right] \tag{15.152}$$

Proof. One has

$$\frac{\partial C}{\partial t} = \frac{\partial}{\partial t}[S_t N(d_1) - Ke^{-r(T-t)}N(d_2)]$$

$$= -S_t N'(d_1)\frac{\sigma}{2\sqrt{T-t}} - rKe^{-r(T-t)}N(d_2)$$

$$+ \frac{\partial d_2}{\partial t}[S_t N'(d_1) - Ke^{-r(T-t)}N'(d_2)] \quad \text{(using (15.147))}$$

$$= -\left[S_t N'(d_1)\frac{\sigma}{2\sqrt{T-t}} + rKe^{-r(T-t)}N(d_2) \right] \quad \text{(using (15.143))} \qquad \square$$

15.2.4. The Merton model (stochastic interest rate)

15.2.4.1. Introduction

In the narrative, it has been assumed that the interest rate to discount option payoff in order to identify the value at time "zero" is constant. This approximation used to provide simple and straightforward explanations provides accurate results when considering short and medium maturity derivatives (not exceeding 12 months).

Concerning options defined on longer time horizons, if interest rate variability is not considered adequately, there may be pricing errors.

Considering the interest rate as constant, two sources of uncertainty are avoided: the first concerns the asset growth rate in time, which in a risk-neutral economy coincides with the short-term interest rate; and the second concerns the discount factor by which the option payoff is discounted at time "zero".

The need to consider the interest rate variability in option pricing for equity-type underlyings was highlighted by Merton in 1973 in his paper *"Theory of rational option pricing"*.

This model is defined by the following SDEs:

$$dS_t = S_t r_t \, dt + S_t \sigma \, dW_{1,t}^* \tag{15.153}$$

$$dP(t, T, r_t) = P(t, T, r_t)r_t \, dt - P(t, T, r_t)\sigma_p \, dW_{P,t}^* \tag{15.154}$$

where:

- (15.153) is the SDE which governs the price process of the underlying;
- S_t is the spot price of the underlying;
- r_t is the instantaneous spot rate;

- $dW_{1,t}^*$ is a standard Wiener process under the risk-neutral probability measure to risk P^*;
- (15.154) is the SDE which governs the zero coupon bond process $P(t, T, r_t)$;
- σ_p is the SDE diffusion coefficient;
- $dW_{P,t}^*$ is a standard Wiener process under the risk-neutral probability measure to risk P^*;
- ρ is the correlation coefficient between $W_{1,t}^*$ and $W_{P,t}^*$ (see Definition 12.25), ie, $d\langle W_{1,t}^*, W_{P,t}^* \rangle = \rho \, dt$

Remark 15.1. SDE (15.153) is different from SDE (15.63) owing to the stochastic nature of r.

Remark 15.2. SDE (15.154) is different from SDE (16.47) owing to the deterministic nature of σ_p.

Theorem 15.6. *The pair of SDEs (15.153) and (15.154) may also be expressed as*

$$dS_t = S_t r_t \, dt + S_t \sigma \, dW_{1,t}^* \tag{15.153}$$

$$dP(t, T, r_t) = P(t, T, r_t) r_t \, dt - P(t, T, r_t) \sigma_p [\rho \, dW_{1,t}^* + \sqrt{1 - \rho^2} \, dW_{2,t}^*] \tag{15.155}$$

where $W_{1,t}^*$, $W_{2,t}^*$ are two independent Brownian motions under the risk-neutral probability space P^*, ie, $d\langle W_{1,t}^*, W_{2,t}^* \rangle = 0$.

Proof. It is enough to demonstrate that, after defining the quantity

$$W_{P,t}^* = \rho \, dW_{1,t}^* + \sqrt{1 - \rho^2} \, dW_{2,t}^* \tag{15.156}$$

the relation $d\langle W_{1,t}^*, W_{P,t}^* \rangle = \rho \, dt$ is unchanged.

For this purpose, it is enough to recall Theorem 12.9. □

Proposition 15.17. *SDE (15.155) with initial condition $P(0, T, r_0)$ has the following integrated solution:*

$$P(t, T, r_t) = P(0, T, r_0) \cdot e^{\int_0^t r_u \, du - (1/2)\sigma_p^2 \, dt - \rho \sigma_p \, dW_{1,t}^* - \sqrt{1 - \rho^2} \sigma_p \, dW_{2,t}^*} \tag{15.157}$$

Proof. The demonstration is similar to Theorem 13.3. □

15.2.4.2. Forward prices and probability measures

15.2.4.2.1. A derivative forward price

Let X be the value at time T of a *contingent claim* with maturity at time T and let its value at time t be known and equal to $\pi_t(X)$.

Definition 15.3. Given the probability space $(\Omega, \mathcal{F}, P)$, $F_X(t, T, r_t)$ is defined as the forward price from time t to time T of a *contingent claim* X, as the price expected at time T of the *claim* X. This is denoted as

$$F_X(t, T, r_t) = \frac{E_{P^*}(X/B_T \mid \mathcal{F}_t)}{E_{P^*}(1/B_T \mid \mathcal{F}_t)} \tag{15.158}$$

where $B_t = e^{\left(\int_0^t r_s \, ds\right)}$

Proposition 15.18. *The forward price of a contingent claim X is given by the following equivalence:*

$$F_X(t, T, r_t) = \frac{\pi_t(X)}{P(t, T, r_t)} \tag{15.159}$$

Proof. Recalling (15.158), ie,

$$F_X(t, T, r_t) = \frac{E_{P^*}(X/B_T \mid \mathcal{F}_t)}{E_{P^*}(1/B_T \mid \mathcal{F}_t)}$$

since $E_{P^*}(X B_T^{-1} B_t \mid \mathcal{F}_t) = \pi_t(X)$ (see Equation (15.65)), one has

$$\begin{aligned} F_X(t, T, r_t) &= \frac{\pi_t(X)}{E_{P^*}(B_t(1/B_T) \mid \mathcal{F}_t)} \\ &= \frac{\pi_t(X)}{P(t, T, r_t)} \quad \text{(using (16.57))} \end{aligned} \qquad \square$$

Corollary 15.4. *The value of $\pi_t(X)$ in terms of the forward price $F_X(t, T, r_t)$ is given by*

$$\pi_t(X) = F_X(t, T, r_t) P(t, T, r_t)$$

15.2.4.2.2. Derivative pricing under the forward probability measure

15.2.4.2.2.1. The discounted process for $P(t, T, r_t)$

To define the discounted process of $P(t, T, r_t)$, one has to use Definition 16.8, ie,

$$P^*(t, T, r_t) = \frac{P(t, T, r_t)}{B_t}$$

where

$$B_t = e^{\left(\int_0^t r_s \, ds\right)}$$

$$P^*(0, T, r_0) = P(0, T, r_0)$$

$$P^*(T, T, r_T) = P(T, T, r_T)$$

Then SDE (16.54), is expanded to become

$$dP^*(t, T, r_t) = -\sigma_p P^*(t, T, r_t) \, dW^*_{P,t} \tag{15.160}$$

Theorem 15.7. *SDE (15.160) may also be written as*

$$dP^*(t, T, r_t) = -\sigma_p P^*(t, T, r_t)[\rho \, dW^*_{1,t} + \sqrt{1 - \rho^2} \, dW^*_{2,t}] \tag{15.161}$$

where $W^*_{1,t}$, $W^*_{2,t}$ are two independent Brownian motions under the risk-neutral probability measure P^*, ie, $d\langle W^*_{1,t} W^*_{2,t} \rangle = 0$.

Proof. The demonstration is similar to Theorem 15.6. □

Proposition 15.19. *SDE (15.155) with initial condition $P(0, T, r_0)$ shows the following integrated solution:*

$$P^*(t, T, r_t) = P(0, T, r_0) \cdot e^{-(1/2)\sigma_P^2 \, dt - \rho \sigma_P \, dW^*_{1,t} - \sqrt{1-\rho^2}\sigma_P \, dW^*_{2,t}} \tag{15.162}$$

Proof. The demonstration is similar to Theorem 13.3. □

15.2.4.2.2.2.   *The forward probability measure P^T*

Theorem 15.8. *Given the probability space $(\Omega, \mathcal{F}, P^*)$, the following random variable is defined:*

$$Z_t := e^{-(1/2)\sigma_P^2 \, dt - \rho \sigma_P \, dW^*_{1,t} - \sqrt{1-\rho^2}\sigma_P \, dW^*_{2,t}}$$

then Z_t is the Radon–Nikodym derivative of the probability measure P^T with respect to the equivalent probability measure (see Equation (11.3)) P^* on the measurable space $(\Omega, \mathcal{F})$:

$$\left.\frac{dP^T}{dP^*}\right|_{\mathcal{F}_t} \equiv e^{-(1/2)\sigma_P^2 \, dt - \rho \sigma_P \, dW^*_{1,t} - \sqrt{1-\rho^2}\sigma_P \, dW^*_{2,t}}$$

and

$$W^T_{1,t} = W^*_{1,t} + \rho \sigma_P t \tag{15.163}$$

$$W^T_{2,t} = W^*_{2,t} + \sqrt{1 - \rho^2}\sigma_P t \tag{15.164}$$

are standard Brownian motions under the measure P^T.

Proof. The demonstration that Z_t is the Radon–Nikodym derivative of probability measure P^T with respect to the equivalent probability measure P^* can be derived from Corollary 12.14.

The verification that $W_{1,t}^T$ and $W_{2,t}^T$ are two standard Brownian motions under the measure P^T is an immediate consequence of Theorem 12.18. $\quad\square$

Corollary 15.5. *The following relations hold:*

$$W_{1,t}^* = W_{1,t}^T - \rho \sigma_P t \tag{15.165}$$

$$dW_{1,t}^* = dW_{1,t}^T - \rho \sigma_P \, dt \tag{15.166}$$

$$W_{2,t}^* = W_{2,t}^T - \sqrt{1 - \rho^2}\sigma_P t \tag{15.167}$$

$$dW_{2,t}^* = dW_{2,t}^T - \sqrt{1 - \rho^2}\sigma_P \, dt \tag{15.168}$$

Corollary 15.6. *The following relation holds:*

$$\left.\frac{dP^T}{dP^*}\right|_{\mathcal{F}_t} = \frac{P(t, T, r_t)}{B_t P(0, T, r_0)} \tag{15.169}$$

Proof. Recalling relation (15.157), ie,

$$P(t, T, r_t) = P(0, T, r_0) \cdot e^{\int_0^t r_u \, du - (1/2)\sigma_P^2 \, dt - \rho \sigma_P \, dW_{1,t}^* - \sqrt{1-\rho^2}\sigma_P \, dW_{2,t}^*} \tag{15.157}$$

substituting this expression in Equation (15.169), one obtains

$$\left.\frac{dP^T}{dP^*}\right|_{\mathcal{F}_t} \overset{?}{=} \frac{P(0, T, r_0) \cdot e^{\int_0^t r_u \, du - (1/2)\sigma_P^2 \, dt - \rho \sigma_P \, dW_{1,t}^* - \sqrt{1-\rho^2}\sigma_P \, dW_{2,t}^*}}{B_t P(0, T, r_0)}$$

$$= e^{-(1/2)\sigma_P^2 \, dt - \rho \sigma_P \, dW_{1,t}^* - \sqrt{1-\rho^2}\sigma_P \, dW_{2,t}^*} \quad \text{(by simplifying)} \quad \square$$

15.2.4.2.3. Derivative pricing: the relation between the forward price and the forward probability measure

Proposition 15.20. *Given the probability space $(\Omega, \mathcal{F}, P^T)$, let $F_X(t, T, r_t)$ be the forward price of a contingent claim X with value $\pi_t(X)$ at time t, then the following relation holds:*

$$E_{P^T}(X \mid \mathcal{F}_t) = F_X(t, T, r_t)$$

Proof. Recalling the expanded version of Theorem 11.14:

$$E_{P^T}(X \mid \mathcal{F}_t) = E_{P^*}\left(X \left.\frac{dP^T}{dP^*}\right|_{\mathcal{F}_T} \middle| \mathcal{F}_t\right)$$

and recalling (15.169) specified at time T, one obtains

$$E_{P^T}(X \mid \mathcal{F}_t) = E_{P^*}\left(X \frac{P(T, T, r_T)}{B_T P(0, T, r_0)} \Big| \mathcal{F}_t\right)$$

$$= E_{P^*}\left(X \frac{P(T, T, r_T)}{B_T P(0, T, r_0)} \Big| \mathcal{F}_t\right)$$

$$= E_{P^*}\left(X \frac{1}{B_T P(0, T, r_0)} \Big| \mathcal{F}_t\right)$$

(using (16.9))

$$= E_{P^*}\left(\frac{X}{B_T} \frac{B_t}{e^{\int_0^t r_u \, du} \cdot E_{P^*}(e^{-\int_0^T r_u \, du} \mid \mathcal{F}_t)} \Big| \mathcal{F}_t\right)$$

(using (16.57) expanded at time T)

$$= E_{P^*}\left(\frac{X}{B_T} \frac{B_t}{E_{P^*}(e^{-\int_t^T r_u \, du} \mid \mathcal{F}_t)} \Big| \mathcal{F}_t\right)$$

(since $e^{\int_0^t r_u \, du}$ are adapted to $\mathcal{F}_t$)

$$= E_{P^*}\left(\frac{X}{B_T} \frac{B_t}{P(t, T, r_t)} \Big| \mathcal{F}_t\right)$$

(using, again, (16.57) expanded at time t)

$$= B_t E_{P^*}\left(\frac{X}{B_T} \Big| \mathcal{F}_t\right) \frac{1}{P(t, T, r_t)}$$

(since $P(t, T, r_t)$ and B_t are adapted to $\mathcal{F}_t$)

$$= \pi_t(X) \frac{1}{P(t, T, r_t)}$$

(recalling relation (15.65))

$$= F_X(t, T, r_t) \quad \text{(recalling (15.159))} \qquad \square$$

15.2.4.2.3.1. *Call pricing specification*

Proposition 15.21. *A European call price with maturity T under measure P^T has the following functional form:*

$$C_t = P(t, T, r_t) \cdot E_{P^T}((S_T - K)^+ \mid \mathcal{F}_t) \qquad (15.170)$$

Proof. Under Corollary 15.4,

$$\pi_t(X) = F_X(t, T, r_t) P(t, T, r_t)$$

under Proposition 15.20 expanded for the call, one has

$$C_t = E_{P^T}((S_T - K)^+ \mid \mathcal{F}_t) P(t, T, r_t) \qquad \square$$

15.2.4.2.4. The forward process of S

Definition 15.4. The forward price of the security process underlying the derivative S_t is defined as

$$F_S(t, T, r_t) = \frac{S_t}{P(t, T, r_t)}$$

Proposition 15.22. *The following relation holds:*

$$F_S(T, T, r_T) = S_T \tag{15.171}$$

Proof. Under Definition 15.4, specified for $t = T$, ie,

$$F_S(T, T, r_T) = \frac{S_T}{P(T, T, r_T)}$$

using relation (16.9) one obtains

$$F_S(T, T, r_T) = S_T \qquad \qquad \square$$

Proposition 15.23. *Given the probability space* $(\Omega, \mathcal{F}, P^*)$, *process* $1/P(t, T, r_t)$ *is governed by the following SDE:*

$$d\frac{1}{P(t, T, r_t)} = -\frac{1}{P^2(t, T, r_t)} dP(t, T, r_t) + \frac{\sigma_p^2}{P(t, T, r_t)} dt \tag{15.172}$$

Proof. Applying Itô's lemma (see Theorem 12.12 and Example 12.2), one obtains

$$d\frac{1}{P(t, T, r_t)} = -\frac{1}{P^2(t, T, r_t)} dP(t, T, r_t) + \frac{dP^2(t, T, r_t)}{P^3(t, T, r_t)}$$

$$= -\frac{1}{P^2(t, T, r_t)} dP(t, T, r_t) + \frac{\sigma_p^2 \, dt}{P(t, T, r_t)}$$

$$\text{(substituting the SDE (15.154))} \qquad \qquad \square$$

Proposition 15.24. *Given the probability space* $(\Omega, \mathcal{F}, P^*)$, *the process* $F_S(t, T, r_t)$ *is ruled by the following SDE:*

$$dF_S(t, T, r_t) = F_S(t, T, r_t)[\sigma \, dW_{1,t}^* + \sigma_p[\rho \, dW_{1,t}^* + \sqrt{1 - \rho^2} \, dW_{2,t}^*]$$
$$+ [\sigma_p^2 \, dt + \rho \sigma \sigma_p \, dt]] \tag{15.173}$$

Proof. Recalling Definition 15.4, ie,

$$F_S(t, T, r_t) = \frac{S_t}{P(t, T, r_t)}$$

differentiating and applying the Leibniz rule (see Theorem 12.15), one has

$dF_S(t, T, r_t)$

$$= \frac{1}{P(t, T, r_t)} \, dS_t + S_t \, d\frac{1}{P(t, T, r_t)} + dS_t \, d\frac{1}{P(t, T, r_t)}$$

$$= \frac{dS_t}{P(t, T, r_t)} - \frac{S_t}{P^2(t, T, r_t)} \, dP(t, T, r_t) + \frac{\sigma_p^2 S_t}{P(t, T, r_t)} \, dt$$

$$+ \frac{S_t \rho \sigma \sigma_p \, dt}{P(t, T, r_t)} \quad \text{(substituting the SDE (15.172))}$$

$$= \frac{S_t r_t \, dt + S_t \sigma \, dW_{1,t}^*}{P(t, T, r_t)} - \frac{S_t}{P^2(t, T, r_t)} \, dP(t, T, r_t) + \frac{\sigma_p^2 S_t}{P(t, T, r_t)} \, dt$$

$$+ \frac{S_t \rho \sigma \sigma_p \, dt}{P(t, T, r_t)} \quad \text{(substituting the SDE (15.172))}$$

$$= \frac{S_t r_t \, dt + S_t \sigma \, dW_{1,t}^*}{P(t, T, r_t)} - \frac{S_t}{P(t, T, r_t)} [r_t \, dt - \sigma_p [\rho \, dW_{1,t}^* + \sqrt{1 - \rho^2} \, dW_{2,t}^*]]$$

$$+ \frac{\sigma_p^2 S_t}{P(t, T, r_t)} \, dt + \frac{S_t \rho \sigma \sigma_p \, dt}{P(t, T, r_t)} \quad \text{(substituting the SDE (15.155))}$$

$$= F_S(t, T, r_t) \sigma \, dW_{1,t}^* + F_S(t, T, r_t) \sigma_p [[\rho \, dW_{1,t}^* + \sqrt{1 - \rho^2} \, dW_{2,t}^*]]$$

$$+ F_S(t, T, r_t) \sigma_p^2 \, dt + F_S(t, T, r_t) \rho \sigma \sigma_p \, dt \quad \text{(recalling Definition 15.4)}$$

$$= F_S(t, T, r_t) [\sigma \, dW_{1,t}^* + \sigma_p [\rho \, dW_{1,t}^* + \sqrt{1 - \rho^2} \, dW_{2,t}^*]$$

$$+ [\sigma_p^2 \, dt + \rho \sigma \sigma_p \, dt]] \quad \text{(factorising } F_S(t, T, r_t)) \qquad \square$$

Proposition 15.25. *Given the probability space* $(\Omega, \mathcal{F}, P^T)$, *the process* $F_S(t, T, r_t)$ *is ruled by the following SDE:*

$$dF_S(t, T, r_t) = F_S(t, T, r_t) [(\sigma + \rho \sigma_p) \, dW_{1,t}^T + \sigma_p \sqrt{1 - \rho^2} \, dW_{2,t}^T] \qquad (15.174)$$

Proof. Recalling the SDE (15.173), and recalling the measure change under Corollary 15.5, expressions (15.165) and (15.168) are replaced by the previous SDE (15.173), ie,

$$dF_S(t, T, r_t) = F_S(t, T, r_t) [\sigma \, dW_{1,t}^T - \rho \sigma \sigma_p \, dt + \rho \sigma_p \, dW_{1,t}^T - \rho^2 \sigma_p^2 \, dt$$

$$+ \sigma_p \sqrt{1 - \rho^2} \, dW_{2,t}^T - \sigma_p^2 (1 - \rho^2) \, dt + \sigma_p^2 \, dt + \rho \sigma \sigma_p \, dt]$$

factorising, one has

$$dF_S(t, T, r_t) = F_S(t, T, r_t)[(\sigma + \rho\sigma_P)\,dW_{1,t}^T + \sigma_P\sqrt{1 - \rho^2}\,dW_{2,t}^T] \qquad \Box$$

Proposition 15.26. *SDE (15.174) with initial condition $F_S(t, T, r_t)$ has the following integrated solution:*

$$F_S(T, T, r_T) = F_S(t, T, r_t) \cdot e^{-((\sigma_P^2 + \sigma^2 + 2\rho\sigma_P\sigma)/2)\,dt + (\sigma + \rho\sigma_P)\,dW_{1,t}^T + \sigma_P\sqrt{1-\rho^2}\,dW_{2,t}^T}$$

$$(15.175)$$

Proof. Under Theorem 13.3 which, here, can be written as

$$F_S(T, T, r_T)$$
$$= F_S(t, T, r_t) \cdot e^{-(((\sigma + \rho\sigma_P)^2 + (\sigma_P\sqrt{1-\rho^2})^2)/2)\,dt + (\sigma + \rho\sigma_P)\,dW_{1,t}^T + \sigma_P\sqrt{1-\rho^2}\,dW_{2,t}^T}$$

if one computes

$$F_S(t, T, r_T) = F_S(t, T, r_t) \cdot e^{-(\sigma^2 + 2\rho\sigma_P\sigma + \sigma_P^2)/2\,dt + (\sigma + \rho\sigma_P)\,dW_{1,t}^T + \sigma_P\sqrt{1-\rho^2}\,dW_{2,t}^T} \qquad \Box$$

Definition 15.5. To simplify the narrative, let one define

$$\eta_t \doteq (\sigma + \rho\sigma_P)\,dW_{1,t}^T + \sigma_P\sqrt{1 - \rho^2}\,dW_{2,t}^T$$

Theorem 15.9. *Given the probability space $(\Omega, \mathcal{F}, P^T)$, the stochastic process $\eta_t = (\sigma + \rho\sigma_P)\,dW_{1,t}^T + \sigma_P\sqrt{1 - \rho^2}\,dW_{2,t}^T$ is distributed as follows:*

$$\eta_t \sim N[0; (\sigma^2 + 2\rho\sigma_P\sigma + \sigma_P^2)\,dt] \qquad (15.176)$$

Proof. The stochastic process η_t is distributed according to a normal probability law, since it is the summation of two processes distributed as a normal random variable (see Definition 12.23).

Then one verifies whether the expected value is equal to zero, ie,

$$E_{P_T}(\eta_t) \overset{?}{=} 0$$

$$E_{P_T}[(\sigma + \rho\sigma_P)\,dW_{1,t}^T + \sigma_P\sqrt{1 - \rho^2}\,dW_{2,t}^T] \overset{?}{=} 0$$

since $W_{1,t}^T$ and $W_{2,t}^T$ are independent, one obtains

$$(\sigma + \rho\sigma_P)E_{P_T}[dW_{1,t}^T] + \sigma_P\sqrt{1 - \rho^2}E_{P_T}[dW_{2,t}^T] \overset{?}{=} 0$$

recalling Definition 12.23, one obtains

$$0 + 0 = 0$$

To verify the variance value, Proposition 11.27 is recalled, which here becomes

$$\text{VAR}_{P_T}(\eta_t) = E_{P_T}(\eta_t^2) - E_{P_T}^2(\eta_t)$$

Considering that $E_{P_T}(\eta_t) = 0$, one has

$$\text{VAR}_{P_T}(\eta_t) = E_{P_T}(\eta_t^2)$$

then the second moment is determined, ie,

$$E_{P_T}(\eta_t^2) = E_{P_T}[((\sigma + \rho\sigma_p)\, dW_{1,t}^T + \sigma_P\sqrt{1 - \rho^2}\, dW_{2,t}^T)^2]$$

simplifying, one has

$$\text{VAR}_{P_T}(\eta_t) = (\sigma^2 + 2\rho\sigma_P\sigma + \sigma_P^2)\, dt \qquad (15.177)$$

$\square$

Theorem 15.10. *Given the probability space* $(\Omega, \mathcal{F}, P^T)$, *the stochastic process* $F_S(t, T, r_t)$ *is a* P^T-*martingale.*

Proof. There are two possible demonstrations.

First demonstration. The integral is specified from SDE (15.174):

$$F_S(t, T, r_t) = F_S(0, T, r_0) + \int_0^t F_S(u, T, r_u)(\sigma + \rho\sigma_p)\, dW_{1,u}^T$$

$$+ \int_0^t F_S(u, T, r_u)\sigma_p\sqrt{1 - \rho^2}\, dW_{2,u}^T$$

Considering the expected value with respect to the risk-neutral probability measure P^T, and under information available at time zero, one has

$$E_{P^T}(F_S(t, T, r_t)|r_0) = F_S(0, T, r_0) + E_{P^T}\left[\left(\int_0^t F_S(u, T, r_u)(\sigma + \rho\sigma_p)\, dW_{1,u}^T\right.\right.$$

$$\left.\left. + \int_0^t F_S(u, T, r_u)\sigma_p\sqrt{1 - \rho^2}\, dW_{2,u}^T\right)\bigg|\mathcal{F}_0\right]$$

The argument of the expected value of the right-hand side is a stochastic integral, and then a martingale (see property (7) of Proposition 12.9), under which the expected value conditioned to r_0 is zero. It can be derived that

$$E_{P^T}(F_S(t, T, r_t)|\mathcal{F}_0) = F_S(0, T, r_0) \tag{15.178}$$

In (15.178) one recalls the martingale definition (see Definition 12.16). For all of the above, it can be derived that the process $F_S(t, T, r_t)$ is a P^T-martingale.

Second demonstration. Verifying the martingale definition under (15.178), expanded for a generic time t, ie,

$$E_{P^T}(F_S(T, T, r_T)|\mathcal{F}_t) \overset{?}{=} F_S(t, T, r_t) \tag{15.179}$$

substituting expression (15.162), ie,

$$F_S(t, T, r_t) \cdot E_{P^T}\left(e^{-((\sigma_P^2+\sigma^2+2\rho\sigma_P\sigma)/2)\,dt+(\sigma+\rho\sigma_P)\,dW_{1,t}^T+\sigma_P\sqrt{1-\rho^2}\,dW_{2,t}^T}\Big|\mathcal{F}_t\right)$$
$$\overset{?}{=} F_S(t, T, r_t)$$

simplifying, one has

$$e^{-((\sigma_P^2+\sigma^2+2\rho\sigma_P\sigma)/2)\,dt} \cdot E_{P^T}\left(e^{(\sigma+\rho\sigma_P)\,dW_{1,t}^T+\sigma_P\sqrt{1-\rho^2}\,dW_{2,t}^T}\Big|\mathcal{F}_t\right) \overset{?}{=} 1$$

then $e^{(\sigma+\rho\sigma_P)\,dW_{1,t}^T+\sigma_P\sqrt{1-\rho^2}\,dW_{2,t}^T}$ is specified with respect to $\mathcal{F}_t$:

$$E_{P^T}\left(e^{(\sigma+\rho\sigma_P)\,dW_{1,t}^T+\sigma_P\sqrt{1-\rho^2}\,dW_{2,t}^T}\right) \overset{?}{=} e^{((\sigma_P^2+\sigma^2+2\rho\sigma_P\sigma)/2)\,dt}$$

recalling Definition 15.5, one has

$$E_{P^T}(e^{\eta_t}) \overset{?}{=} e^{((\sigma_P^2+\sigma^2+2\rho\sigma_P\sigma)/2)\,dt} \tag{15.180}$$

recalling the distributive properties of η_t (see Equation (15.176)), one recalls in the left-hand side of (15.180) the moment generating function (see Example 11.5) of η_t; hence,

$$E_{P^T}(e^{\eta_t}) = e^{((\sigma_P^2+\sigma^2+2\rho\sigma_P\sigma)/2)\,dt}$$

and, then, (15.179) is verified. $\qquad\square$

15.2.4.2.4.1. Call pricing specification with respect to the forward process of S
Proposition 15.27. *A European call price, with maturity at time T under measure P^T, can be written as*

$$C_t = J_1 - J_2 \tag{15.181}$$

where

$$J_1 = P(t, T, r_t) \cdot E_{PT}(F_S(T, T, r_T) \cdot 1_D | \mathcal{F}_t) \qquad (15.182)$$

$$J_2 = P(t, T, r_t) \cdot K \cdot P^T(D | \mathcal{F}_t) \qquad (15.183)$$

and $D = S_T > K$.

Proof. Recalling expression (15.170) and Proposition 6.5 one obtains

$$C_t = P(t, T, r_t) \cdot E_{PT}((S_T \cdot 1_{\{S_T > K\}}) | \mathcal{F}_t) - P(t, T, r_t) \cdot K \cdot P^T(S_T > K)$$

recalling relation (15.171), one has

$$C_t = P(t, T, r_t) \cdot E_{PT}((F_S(T, T, r_T) \cdot 1_{\{S_T > K\}}) | \mathcal{F}_t) - P(t, T, r_t) \cdot K \cdot P^T(S_T > K)$$

defining J_1 and J_2 as in (15.182) and (15.183). □

15.2.4.3. The call price
Theorem 15.11. *The value of*

$$J_2 = P(t, T, r_t) K P^T(D | \mathcal{F}_t) \qquad (15.183)$$

is equal to

$$J_2 = P(t, T, r_t) \cdot K \cdot N[d_2] \qquad (15.184)$$

where

$$d_2 = \frac{\ln(S_t / K) - \ln P(t, T, r_t) - (1/2)(\sigma^2 + 2\rho\sigma_P\sigma + \sigma_P^2)(T - t)}{\sqrt{(\sigma^2 + 2\rho\sigma_P\sigma + \sigma_P^2)(T - t)}} \qquad (15.185)$$

Proof. Recalling expression (15.183), D is expanded as in Proposition 15.27:

$$J_2 = P(t, T, r_t) K P^T(S_T > K | \mathcal{F}_t)$$

recalling (15.171), one has

$$J_2 = P(t, T, r_t) K P^T(F_S(T, T, r_T) > K | \mathcal{F}_t)$$

substituting expression (15.175), ie,

$$J_2 = P(t, T, r_t) K$$
$$\cdot P^T \left[(F_S(t, T, r_t) \cdot e^{-((\sigma_P^2 + \sigma^2 + 2\rho\sigma_P\sigma)/2)\,dt + (\sigma + \rho\sigma_P)\,dW_{1,t}^T + \sigma_P \sqrt{1 - \rho^2}\,dW_{2,t}^T} > K) \right]$$

with logarithm

$$J_2 = P(t, T, r_t) \cdot K \cdot P^T \left[\ln \frac{F_S(t, T, r_t)}{K} - \frac{\sigma_P^2 + \sigma^2 + 2\rho\sigma_P\sigma}{2} \, dt \right.$$
$$\left. > - \underbrace{\left[(\sigma + \rho\sigma_P) \, dW_{1,t}^T + \sigma_P \sqrt{1 - \rho^2} \, dW_{2,t}^T \right]}_{\eta_t} \right]$$

recalling Definition 15.5, one has

$$J_2 = P(t, T, r_t) K P^T \left[\ln \frac{F_S(t, T, r_t)}{K} - \frac{\sigma_P^2 + \sigma^2 + 2\rho\sigma_P\sigma}{2} \, dt > -\eta_t \right] \qquad (15.186)$$

recalling the distributive properties of η_t (see (15.176)), the two terms of (15.186) are divided by the standard deviation of η_t to get a standard normal random variable, ie,

$$J_2 = P(t, T, r_t) K P^T \left[\frac{\ln F_S(t, T, r_t)/K - ((\sigma_P^2 + \sigma^2 + 2\rho\sigma_P\sigma)/2) \, dt}{\sqrt{(\sigma^2 + 2\rho\sigma_P\sigma + \sigma_P^2) \, dt}} \right.$$
$$\left. > -\frac{\eta_t}{\sqrt{(\sigma^2 + 2\rho\sigma_P\sigma + \sigma_P^2) \, dt}} \right]$$

specifying $dt = T - t$ and recalling definition 15.4, one has

$$J_2 = P(t, T, r_t)$$
$$\cdot K \cdot N \left[\frac{\ln(S_t/K) - \ln P(t, T, r_t) - ((\sigma_P^2 + \sigma^2 + 2\rho\sigma_P\sigma)/2)(T - t)}{\sqrt{(\sigma^2 + 2\rho\sigma_P\sigma + \sigma_P^2)(T - t)}} \right]$$

hence, using relation (15.185) one obtains (15.184). □

Theorem 15.12. *Given the probability space* $(\Omega, \mathcal{F}, P^T)$, *the following random variable below is defined*

$$Z_t := e^{-((\sigma_P^2 + \sigma^2 + 2\rho\sigma_P\sigma)/2) \, dt + (\sigma + \rho\sigma_P) \, dW_{1,t}^T + \sigma_P \sqrt{1-\rho^2} \, dW_{2,t}^T}$$

then Z_t *is the Radon–Nikodym derivative of probability measure* $\widetilde{P^T}$ *with respect to the equivalent probability measure (see Equation (11.3))* P^T *on the measurable space* $(\Omega, \mathcal{F})$:

$$\left. \frac{d\widetilde{P^T}}{dP^T} \right|_{\mathcal{F}_t} \equiv e^{-((\sigma_P^2 + \sigma^2 + 2\rho\sigma_P\sigma)/2) \, dt + (\sigma + \rho\sigma_P) \, dW_{1,t}^T + \sigma_P \sqrt{1-\rho^2} \, dW_{2,t}^T} \qquad (15.187)$$

and

$$\widetilde{W^T_{1,t}} = W^T_{1,t} - (\sigma + \rho\sigma_P)t \tag{15.188}$$

$$\widetilde{W^T_{2,t}} = W^T_{2,t} - \sigma_P\sqrt{1-\rho^2}\,t \tag{15.189}$$

are standard Brownian motions under measure P^T.

Proof. The demonstration that Z_t is the Radon–Nikodym derivative of the probability measure $\widetilde{P^T}$ with respect to the equivalent probability measure P^T can be derived from Corollary 12.14.

The fact that $\widetilde{W^T_{1,t}}$ and $\widetilde{W^T_{2,t}}$ are standard Brownian motions under measure $\widetilde{P^T}$ is an immediate consequence of Theorem 12.18. □

Corollary 15.7. *The following relations hold:*

$$W^T_{1,t} = \widetilde{W^T_{1,t}} + (\sigma + \rho\sigma_P)t \tag{15.190}$$

$$dW^T_{1,t} = d\widetilde{W^T_{1,t}} + (\sigma + \rho\sigma_P)\,dt \tag{15.191}$$

$$W^T_{2,t} = \widetilde{W^T_{2,t}} + \sigma_P\sqrt{1-\rho^2}\,t \tag{15.192}$$

$$dW^T_{2,t} = d\widetilde{W^T_{2,t}} + \sigma_P\sqrt{1-\rho^2}\,dt \tag{15.193}$$

Proposition 15.28. *Given the probability space $(\Omega, \mathcal{F}, \widetilde{P^T})$, the process $F_S(t, T, r_t)$ is governed by the following SDE:*

$$dF_S(t, T, r_t) = F_S(t, T, r_t)\Big[(\sigma + \rho\sigma_P)\,d\widetilde{W^T_{1,t}} + \sigma_P\sqrt{1-\rho^2}\,d\widetilde{W^T_{2,t}}$$
$$+ (\sigma_P^2 + \sigma^2 + 2\rho\sigma_P\sigma)\,dt\Big] \tag{15.194}$$

Proof. Recalling the SDE (15.174) one recalls the measure change under Corollary 15.7, and expressions (15.191) and (15.193) are replaced by SDE (15.174) above, ie,

$$dF_S(t, T, r_t) = F_S(t, T, r_t)\Big[(\sigma + \rho\sigma_P)\,d\widetilde{W^T_{1,t}} + (\sigma + \rho\sigma_P)(\sigma + \rho\sigma_P)\,dt$$
$$+ \sigma_P\sqrt{1-\rho^2}\,d\widetilde{W^T_{2,t}} + \sigma_P\sqrt{1-\rho^2}\sigma_P\sqrt{1-\rho^2}\,dt\Big]$$

simplifying, one obtains (15.194). □

Proposition 15.29. *SDE (15.194) with initial condition $F_S(t, T, r_t)$ has the following integrated solution:*

$$F_S(T, T, r_T) = F_S(t, T, r_t) \cdot e^{((\sigma_P^2 + \sigma^2 + 2\rho\sigma_P\sigma)/2) \, dt + (\sigma + \rho\sigma_P) \, d\widetilde{W}_{1,t}^T + \sigma_P \sqrt{1-\rho^2} \, d\widetilde{W}_{2,t}^T}$$

$$(15.195)$$

Proof. Recalling Theorem 13.3, which here becomes

$$F_S(T, T, r_T) = F_S(t, T, r_t) \cdot e^{(((\sigma + \rho\sigma_P)^2 + (\sigma_P\sqrt{1-\rho^2})^2)/2) \, dt + (\sigma + \rho\sigma_P) \, d\widetilde{W}_{1,t}^T + \sigma_P \sqrt{1-\rho^2} \, d\widetilde{W}_{2,t}^T}$$

computing

$$F_S(t, T, r_t) = F_S(t, T, r_t) \cdot e^{((\sigma^2 + 2\rho\sigma_P\sigma + \sigma_P^2)/2) \, dt + (\sigma + \rho\sigma_P) \, d\widetilde{W}_{1,t}^T + \sigma_P \sqrt{1-\rho^2} \, d\widetilde{W}_{2,t}^T} \qquad \square$$

Theorem 15.13. *The value of Equation (15.182) is equal to*

$$J_1 = S_t \cdot N[d_1] \qquad (15.196)$$

where

$$d_1 = \frac{\ln(S_t/K) - \ln P(t, T, r_t) + (1/2)(\sigma^2 + 2\rho\sigma_P\sigma + \sigma_P^2)(T-t)}{\sqrt{(\sigma^2 + 2\rho\sigma_P\sigma + \sigma_P^2)(T-t)}} \qquad (15.197)$$

Proof. Recalling (15.182), substituting expression (15.175), ie,

$$J_1 = P(t, T, r_t)$$
$$\cdot E_{P^T}\left[\left(F_S(t, T, r_t) \cdot e^{-((\sigma_P^2 + \sigma^2 + 2\rho\sigma_P\sigma)/2) \, dt + (\sigma + \rho\sigma_P) \, d\widetilde{W}_{1,t}^T + \sigma_P \sqrt{1-\rho^2} \, d\widetilde{W}_{2,t}^T} \cdot 1_D\right)\Big|\mathcal{F}_t\right]$$

Recalling the Radon–Nikodym derivative (15.187):

$$J_1 = P(t, T, r_t) \cdot E_{P^T}\left[\left(F_S(t, T, r_t) \cdot \frac{d\widetilde{P^T}}{dP^T} \cdot 1_D\right)\Big|\mathcal{F}_t\right]$$

Recalling the expanded form of Theorem 11.14:

$$E_{\widetilde{P^T}}(F_S(t, T, r_t) \cdot 1_D|\mathcal{F}_t) = E_{P^T}\left(F_S(t, T, r_t)\frac{d\widetilde{P^T}}{dP^T}\Big|_{\mathcal{F}_T} \cdot 1_D\Big|\mathcal{F}_t\right)$$

and, then,

$$E_{\widetilde{P^T}}(F_S(t, T, r_t) \cdot 1_D|\mathcal{F}_t) = P(t, T, r_t) \cdot E_{\widetilde{P^T}}(F_S(t, T, r_t) \cdot 1_D|\mathcal{F}_t)$$

hence,

$$E_{\widetilde{P_T}}(F_S(t,T,r_t) \cdot 1_D | \mathcal{F}_t) = P(t,T,r_t) \cdot F_S(t,T,r_t) \cdot \widetilde{P^T}(D | \mathcal{F}_t)$$

D is expanded as in Proposition 15.27 and recalling relation (15.171) and Definition 15.4, one obtains

$$E_{\widetilde{P_T}}(F_S(t,T,r_t) \cdot 1_D | \mathcal{F}_t) = S_t \cdot \widetilde{P^T}(F_S(T,T,r_T) > K | \mathcal{F}_t)$$

substituting expression (15.195), ie,

$$E_{\widetilde{P_T}}(F_S(t,T,r_t) \cdot 1_D | \mathcal{F}_t)$$
$$= S_t \cdot \widetilde{P^T}(F_S(t,T,r_t) \cdot e^{((\sigma_P^2 + \sigma^2 + 2\rho\sigma_P\sigma)/2)\,dt + (\sigma + \rho\sigma_P)\,d\widetilde{W}_{1,t}^T + \sigma_P \sqrt{1-\rho^2}\,d\widetilde{W}_{2,t}^T} > K)$$

hence,

$$E_{\widetilde{P_T}}(F_S(t,T,r_t) \cdot 1_D | \mathcal{F}_t) = S_t \cdot \widetilde{P^T}\left[\ln \frac{F_S(t,T,r_t)}{K} + \frac{\sigma_P^2 + \sigma^2 + 2\rho\sigma_P\sigma}{2}\,dt\right.$$
$$\left. > -\underbrace{\left[(\sigma + \rho\sigma_P)\,d\widetilde{W}_{1,t}^T + \sigma_P \sqrt{1-\rho^2}\,d\widetilde{W}_{2,t}^T\right]}_{\eta_t}\right]$$

Recalling Definition 15.5, one has

$$J_1 = S_t \cdot \widetilde{P^T}\left[\ln \frac{F_S(t,T,r_t)}{K} + \frac{\sigma_P^2 + \sigma^2 + 2\rho\sigma_P\sigma}{2}\,dt > -\eta_t\right] \qquad (15.198)$$

under the distributive properties of η_t, one has

$$J_1 = S_t \cdot \widetilde{P^T}\left[\frac{\ln(F_S(t,T,r_t)/K) + ((\sigma_P^2 + \sigma^2 + 2\rho\sigma_P\sigma)/2)\,dt}{\sqrt{(\sigma^2 + 2\rho\sigma_P\sigma + \sigma_P^2)\,dt}}\right.$$
$$\left. > -\frac{\eta_t}{\sqrt{(\sigma^2 + 2\rho\sigma_P\sigma + \sigma_P^2)\,dt}}\right]$$

or, specifying $dt = T - t$,

$$J_1 = S_t \cdot N\left[\frac{\ln(F_S(t,T,r_t)/K) + ((\sigma_P^2 + \sigma^2 + 2\rho\sigma_P\sigma)/2)(T-t)}{\sqrt{(\sigma^2 + 2\rho\sigma_P\sigma + \sigma_P^2)(T-t)}}\right]$$

recalling Definition 15.4

$$J_1 = S_t \cdot N\left[\frac{\ln(S_t/P(t,T,r_t))/K + ((\sigma_P^2 + \sigma^2 + 2\rho\sigma_P\sigma)/2)(T-t)}{\sqrt{(\sigma^2 + 2\rho\sigma_P\sigma + \sigma_P^2)(T-t)}}\right]$$

then using relation 15.197, one obtains (15.196). $\qquad\square$

Theorem 15.14. *The Merton model gives the following formula to price a call option:*

$$C_t = S_t \cdot N[d_1] - P(t, T, r_t) \cdot K \cdot N[d_2] \tag{15.199}$$

where

$$d_1 = \frac{\ln(S_t/K) - \ln P(t, T, r_t) + (1/2)(\sigma^2 + 2\rho\sigma_P\sigma + \sigma_P^2)(T - t)}{\sqrt{(\sigma^2 + 2\rho\sigma_P\sigma + \sigma_P^2)(T - t)}} \tag{15.200}$$

$$d_2 = \frac{\ln(S_t/K) - \ln P(t, T, r_t) - (1/2)(\sigma^2 + 2\rho\sigma_P\sigma + \sigma_P^2)(T - t)}{\sqrt{(\sigma^2 + 2\rho\sigma_P\sigma + \sigma_P^2)(T - t)}} \tag{15.201}$$

15.2.4.4. The Greeks

Proposition 15.30. *The following relation holds between d_1 and d_2:*

$$d_2 = d_1 - \sqrt{(\sigma^2 + 2\rho\sigma_P\sigma + \sigma_P^2)(T - t)} \tag{15.202}$$

Proof. Relation (15.200) is substituted in (15.202) to obtain

$$d_2 = \frac{\ln(S_t/K) - \ln P(t, T, r_t) + (1/2)(\sigma^2 + 2\rho\sigma_P\sigma + \sigma_P^2)(T - t)}{\sqrt{(\sigma^2 + 2\rho\sigma_P\sigma + \sigma_P^2)(T - t)}}$$

$$- \sqrt{(\sigma^2 + 2\rho\sigma_P\sigma + \sigma_P^2)(T - t)}$$

and, then,

$$d_2 = \frac{\ln(S_t/K) - \ln P(t, T, r_t) - (1/2)(\sigma^2 + 2\rho\sigma_P\sigma + \sigma_P^2)(T - t)}{\sqrt{(\sigma^2 + 2\rho\sigma_P\sigma + \sigma_P^2)(T - t)}} \qquad \square$$

Proposition 15.31. *Given formula (15.199) the following result holds:*

$$S_t N'(d_1) - P(t, T, r_t) K N'(d_2) = 0 \tag{15.203}$$

where $N'(x) = (1/\sqrt{2\pi})e^{-x^2/2}$.

Proof. Directly computing

$$S_t N'(d_1) - P(t, T, r_t) K N'(d_2) \overset{?}{=} 0$$

$$S_t \cdot \frac{1}{\sqrt{2\pi}} e^{-(d_1)^2/2} - P(t, T, r_t) \cdot K \frac{1}{\sqrt{2\pi}} e^{-(d_2)^2/2} \overset{?}{=} 0$$

using (15.202) one obtains

$$S_t \cdot \frac{1}{\sqrt{2\pi}} e^{-(d_1)^2/2} - P(t, T, r_t) \cdot K \frac{1}{\sqrt{2\pi}} e^{-(d_1 - \sqrt{(\sigma^2 + 2\rho\sigma_P\sigma + \sigma_P^2)(T-t)})^2/2} \overset{?}{=} 0$$

using (15.200), one has

$$
\frac{1}{\sqrt{2\pi}} e^{-\frac{1}{2}\left(\frac{\ln \frac{S_t}{K}-\ln P(t,T,r_t)+\frac{1}{2}(\sigma^2+2\rho\sigma p\sigma+\sigma_p^2)(T-t)}{\sqrt{(\sigma^2+2\rho\sigma p\sigma+\sigma_p^2)(T-t)}}\right)^2} \left[S_t - P(t, T, r_t)\cdot K\cdot \right.
$$

$$
\left. \cdot e^{-\frac{1}{2}(\sigma^2+2\rho\sigma p\sigma+\sigma_p^2)(T-t)+\frac{\ln \frac{S_t}{K}-\ln P(t,T,r_t)+\frac{1}{2}(\sigma^2+2\rho\sigma p\sigma+\sigma_p^2)(T-t)}{\sqrt{(\sigma^2+2\rho\sigma p\sigma+\sigma_p^2)(T-t)}} \sqrt{(\sigma^2+2\rho\sigma p\sigma+\sigma_p^2)(T-t)}} \right] \overset{?}{=} 0
$$

simplifying, one has

$$
\frac{1}{\sqrt{2\pi}} e^{-\frac{1}{2}\left(\frac{\ln \frac{S_t}{K}-\ln P(t,T,r_t)+\frac{1}{2}(\sigma^2+2\rho\sigma p\sigma+\sigma_p^2)(T-t)}{\sqrt{(\sigma^2+2\rho\sigma p\sigma+\sigma_p^2)(T-t)}}\right)^2} \left[S_t - P(t, T, r_t)\cdot K\cdot \right.
$$

$$
\left. \cdot e^{\ln S_t - \ln K\cdot P(t,T,r_t)} \right] \overset{?}{=} 0
$$

and, then,

$$
\frac{1}{\sqrt{2\pi}} e^{-\frac{1}{2}\left(\frac{\ln \frac{S_t}{K}-\ln P(t,T,r_t)+\frac{1}{2}(\sigma^2+2\rho\sigma p\sigma+\sigma_p^2)(T-t)}{\sqrt{(\sigma^2+2\rho\sigma p\sigma+\sigma_p^2)(T-t)}}\right)^2} [S_t - S_t] = 0 \qquad \square
$$

Proposition 15.32. *Given formula (15.199), the following relations hold:*

$$
\frac{\partial d_1}{\partial S} = \frac{\partial d_2}{\partial S} \tag{15.204}
$$

$$
\frac{\partial d_1}{\partial P(t, T, r_t)} = \frac{\partial d_2}{\partial P(t, T, r_t)} \tag{15.205}
$$

$$
\frac{\partial d_1}{\partial \sigma} = \frac{\partial d_2}{\partial \sigma} + \frac{(\rho\sigma_P + \sigma)\sqrt{T-t}}{\sqrt{(\sigma^2 + 2\rho\sigma p\sigma + \sigma_P^2)}} \tag{15.206}
$$

$$
\frac{\partial d_1}{\partial \sigma_P} = \frac{\partial d_2}{\partial \sigma_P} + \frac{(\rho\sigma + \sigma_P)\sqrt{T-t}}{\sqrt{(\sigma^2 + 2\rho\sigma p\sigma + \sigma_P^2)}} \tag{15.207}
$$

$$
\frac{\partial d_1}{\partial t} = \frac{\partial d_2}{\partial t} - \frac{\sqrt{(\sigma^2 + 2\rho\sigma p\sigma + \sigma_P^2)}}{2\sqrt{T-t}} \tag{15.208}
$$

Proof. Equation (15.204) is derived

$$
\frac{\partial d_1}{\partial S_t} \overset{?}{=} \frac{\partial d_2}{\partial S_t}
$$

by using (15.202)

$$
\frac{\partial d_2}{\partial S_t} = \frac{\partial d_1}{\partial S_t}
$$

Equation (15.205) is derived

$$\frac{\partial d_1}{\partial P(t, T, r_t)} \overset{?}{=} \frac{\partial d_2}{\partial P(t, T, r_t)}$$

by using (15.202), one obtains

$$\frac{\partial d_2}{\partial P(t, T, r_t)} = \frac{\partial d_1}{\partial P(t, T, r_t)}$$

Equation (15.206) is derived

$$\frac{\partial d_1}{\partial \sigma} \overset{?}{=} \frac{\partial d_2}{\partial \sigma} + \frac{(\rho \sigma_P + \sigma)\sqrt{T - t}}{\sqrt{(\sigma^2 + 2\rho \sigma_P \sigma + \sigma_P^2)}}$$

by using (15.202) to obtain

$$\frac{\partial d_1}{\partial \sigma} \overset{?}{=} \frac{\partial d_1}{\partial \sigma} - \frac{\partial}{\partial \sigma}\left[\sqrt{(\sigma^2 + 2\rho \sigma_P \sigma + \sigma_P^2)(T - t)}\right] + \frac{(\rho \sigma_P + \sigma)\sqrt{T - t}}{\sqrt{(\sigma^2 + 2\rho \sigma_P \sigma + \sigma_P^2)}}$$

differentiating, one has

$$\frac{\partial d_1}{\partial \sigma} \overset{?}{=} \frac{\partial d_1}{\partial \sigma} - \left[\frac{(\rho \sigma_P + \sigma)\sqrt{(T - t)}}{\sqrt{(\sigma^2 + 2\rho \sigma_P \sigma + \sigma_P^2)(T - t)}}\right] + \frac{(\rho \sigma_P + \sigma)\sqrt{T - t}}{\sqrt{(\sigma^2 + 2\rho \sigma_P \sigma + \sigma_P^2)}}$$

$$\frac{\partial d_1}{\partial \sigma} = \frac{\partial d_1}{\partial \sigma}$$

Equation (15.207) is derived

$$\frac{\partial d_1}{\partial \sigma_P} \overset{?}{=} \frac{\partial d_2}{\partial \sigma_P} + \frac{(\rho \sigma + \sigma_P)\sqrt{T - t}}{\sqrt{(\sigma^2 + 2\rho \sigma_P \sigma + \sigma_P^2)}}$$

by using (15.202) to obtain

$$\frac{\partial d_1}{\partial \sigma_P} \overset{?}{=} \frac{\partial d_1}{\partial \sigma_P} - \frac{\partial}{\partial \sigma_P}\left[\sqrt{(\sigma^2 + 2\rho \sigma_P \sigma + \sigma_P^2)(T - t)}\right] + \frac{(\rho \sigma + \sigma_P)\sqrt{T - t}}{\sqrt{(\sigma^2 + 2\rho \sigma_P \sigma + \sigma_P^2)}}$$

differentiating, one has

$$\frac{\partial d_1}{\partial \sigma_P} \overset{?}{=} \frac{\partial d_1}{\partial \sigma_P} - \left[\frac{(\rho \sigma + \sigma_P)\sqrt{(T - t)}}{\sqrt{(\sigma^2 + 2\rho \sigma_P \sigma + \sigma_P^2)(T - t)}}\right] + \frac{(\rho \sigma + \sigma_P)\sqrt{T - t}}{\sqrt{(\sigma^2 + 2\rho \sigma_P \sigma + \sigma_P^2)}}$$

$$\frac{\partial d_1}{\partial \sigma_P} = \frac{\partial d_1}{\partial \sigma_P}$$

Equation (15.208) is derived

$$\frac{\partial d_1}{\partial t} \stackrel{?}{=} \frac{\partial d_2}{\partial t} - \frac{\sigma}{2\sqrt{T-t}}$$

by using (15.202) to obtain

$$\frac{\partial d_1}{\partial t} \stackrel{?}{=} \frac{\partial}{\partial t} d_1 - \frac{\partial}{\partial t}\sqrt{(\sigma^2 + 2\rho\sigma_P\sigma + \sigma_P^2)(T-t)} - \frac{\sqrt{(\sigma^2 + 2\rho\sigma_P\sigma + \sigma_P^2)}}{2\sqrt{T-t}}$$

differentiating, one has

$$\frac{\partial d_1}{\partial t} = \frac{\partial d_1}{\partial t} \qquad \qquad \square$$

Proposition 15.33. *A call option* Delta *is*

$$\frac{\partial C}{\partial S_t} = \Delta_C = N(d_1) \qquad (15.209)$$

Proof. One has

$$\frac{\partial C}{\partial S_t} = \frac{\partial}{\partial S_t}[S_t \cdot N[d_1] - P(t, T, r_t) \cdot K \cdot N[d_2]]$$

$$= N(d_1) + S_t N'(d_1)\frac{\partial d_1}{\partial S_t} - KP(t, T, r_t)N'(d_2)\frac{\partial d_2}{\partial S_t}$$

$$= N(d_1) + \frac{\partial d_1}{\partial S_t}[S_t N'(d_1) - KP(t, T, r_t)N'(d_2)] \quad \text{(Using (15.204))}$$

$$= N(d_1) \quad \text{(Using (15.203))} \qquad \qquad \square$$

Proposition 15.34. *A call option* Gamma *is*

$$\frac{\partial^2 C}{\partial S_t^2} = \Gamma_C = N'(d_1) \cdot \frac{1}{S_t\sqrt{(\sigma^2 + 2\rho\sigma_P\sigma + \sigma_P^2)(T-t)}} \qquad (15.210)$$

Proof. One has

$$\frac{\partial^2 C}{\partial S_t^2} = \frac{\partial}{\partial S_t}\left(\frac{\partial C}{\partial S_t}\right)$$

$$= \frac{\partial}{\partial S_t}(\Delta) \quad \text{(using (15.209))}$$

$$= N'(d_1) \cdot \frac{\partial}{\partial S_t}\left[\frac{\ln(S_t/K) - \ln P(t, T, r_t) + (1/2)(\sigma^2 + 2\rho\sigma_P\sigma + \sigma_P^2)(T-t)}{\sqrt{(\sigma^2 + 2\rho\sigma_P\sigma + \sigma_P^2)(T-t)}}\right]$$

$$\text{(using (15.200))}$$

$$= N'(d_1) \cdot \frac{1}{\sqrt{(\sigma^2 + 2\rho\sigma_P\sigma + \sigma_P^2)(T-t)}}\frac{1}{S_t} \qquad \qquad \square$$

Proposition 15.35. *A call option* Vega *is*

$$\frac{\partial C}{\partial \sigma} = \mathcal{V}_C = S_t N'(d_1) \frac{(\rho \sigma_P + \sigma)\sqrt{T-t}}{\sqrt{(\sigma^2 + 2\rho \sigma_P \sigma + \sigma_P^2)}} \tag{15.211}$$

Proof. One has

$$\frac{\partial C}{\partial \sigma} = \frac{\partial}{\partial \sigma}[S_t \cdot N[d_1] - P(t, T, r_t) \cdot K \cdot N[d_2]]$$

$$= S_t N'(d_1)\frac{\partial d_1}{\partial \sigma} - KP(t, T, r_t)N'(d_2)\frac{\partial d_2}{\partial \sigma}$$

$$= S_t N'(d_1)\frac{(\rho \sigma_P + \sigma)\sqrt{T-t}}{\sqrt{(\sigma^2 + 2\rho \sigma_P \sigma + \sigma_P^2)}} + \frac{\partial d_2}{\partial \sigma}[S_t N'(d_1) - KP(t, T, r_t)N'(d_2)]$$

$$(\text{using } (15.206))$$

$$= S_t N'(d_1)\frac{(\rho \sigma_P + \sigma)\sqrt{T-t}}{\sqrt{(\sigma^2 + 2\rho \sigma_P \sigma + \sigma_P^2)}} \quad (\text{using } (15.203)) \qquad \square$$

Proposition 15.36. *A call option* VegaP *is*

$$\frac{\partial C}{\partial \sigma_P} = \mathcal{V}_C^P = S_t N'(d_1)\frac{(\rho \sigma + \sigma_P)\sqrt{T-t}}{\sqrt{(\sigma^2 + 2\rho \sigma_P \sigma + \sigma_P^2)}} \tag{15.212}$$

Proof. One has

$$\frac{\partial C}{\partial \sigma} = \frac{\partial}{\partial \sigma}[S_t \cdot N[d_1] - P(t, T, r_t) \cdot K \cdot N[d_2]]$$

$$= S_t N'(d_1)\frac{\partial d_1}{\partial \sigma} - KP(t, T, r_t)N'(d_2)\frac{\partial d_2}{\partial \sigma}$$

$$= S_t N'(d_1)\frac{(\rho \sigma + \sigma_P)\sqrt{T-t}}{\sqrt{(\sigma^2 + 2\rho \sigma_P \sigma + \sigma_P^2)}} + \frac{\partial d_2}{\partial \sigma}[S_t N'(d_1) - KP(t, T, r_t)N'(d_2)]$$

$$(\text{using } (15.207))$$

$$= S_t N'(d_1)\frac{(\rho \sigma + \sigma_P)\sqrt{T-t}}{\sqrt{(\sigma^2 + 2\rho \sigma_P \sigma + \sigma_P^2)}} \quad (\text{using } (15.203)) \qquad \square$$

The computation of *Theta* and *rho* depends on the functional form taken by $P(t, T, r_t)$ which varies with respect to the dynamic chosen for r_t (see Equations (16.102), (16.123), and (16.167)). Expressions (15.205) and (15.208) may be used to determine these quantities.

15.2.5. The Merton model (jump)

15.2.5.1. Introduction

The Merton model preliminarily requires one to split the stochastic process S_t, the spot price level of the underlying at time t, down into its continuous and discrete components, ie,

$$S_t = S_t^C + S_t^D \tag{15.213}$$

In differential terms, the expression above may also be written as

$$dS_t = dS_t^C + dS_t^D \tag{15.214}$$

The discrete component is governed by the following SDE:

$$dS_t^D = S_t J_t \, dq_t \tag{15.215}$$

where:

- dq_t is a diffusive Poisson process (see Notation 12.13) with intensity $\lambda \, dt$, ie, $\Pr(dq_t = 1) = \lambda \, dt$ and $\Pr(dq_t = 0) = 1 - \lambda \, dt$;
- $dq(t)$ is not correlated with J_t and dW_t;
- J_t is the percentage jump size for process S and is distributed as follows:

$$J(t) \sim \text{Log } N(\mu, (1 + \mu)(e^{\sigma^2} - 1)) \tag{15.216}$$

The continuous component is governed by the following SDE:

$$dS_t^C = [r - \lambda\mu]S_t \, dt + \sqrt{v}S_t \, dW_t \tag{15.217}$$

where:

- r is the instantaneous risk-free rate at time t (constant);
- v is process S variance;
- dW is a standard Brownian motion.

Finally, based on the characteristics of the stochastic processes described above, the Merton model may be described by the following equation:

$$dS_t = [r - \lambda\mu]S_t \, dt + \sqrt{v}S_t \, dW_t + S_t J_t \, dq_t \tag{15.218}$$

Notation 15.1. In the following, in order to simplify notation, $W_t = W$, $S_t = S$, $q_t = q$.

15.2.5.2.   PDE derivation for portfolio replication

In this model, the option price f to be determined is governed by two variables, ie,

$$f = f(S, t) \tag{15.219}$$

Considering f differentiable to the order required and using Itô's algebra (see Section 12.1.5.1), the stochastic differential of f is computed with respect to S^C and S^D. Specifically, the computation of df with respect to dS^C is

$$df = \frac{\partial f}{\partial S} dS^C + \frac{\partial f}{\partial t} dt + \frac{1}{2} \left[\frac{\partial^2 f}{\partial S^2} (dS^C)^2 \right] \tag{15.220}$$

and the computation of df with respect to dS^D is

$$df = [f[(J+1)S, t] - f[S, t]] \, dq \tag{15.221}$$

Finally, the following SDE is derived:

$$df = \frac{\partial f}{\partial S} dS^C + \frac{\partial f}{\partial t} dt + \frac{1}{2} \left[\frac{\partial^2 f}{\partial S^2} (dS^C)^2 \right] + [f[(J+1)S, t] - f[S, t]] \, dq \tag{15.222}$$

Substituting (15.217) in (15.222) one obtains

$$df = \frac{\partial f}{\partial S} [[r - \lambda \mu]S \, dt + \sqrt{v}S \, dW] + \frac{\partial f}{\partial t} dt + \frac{1}{2} \left[\frac{\partial^2 f}{\partial S^2} [vS^2] \, dt \right]$$
$$+ [f[(J+1)S, t] - f[S, t]] \, dq \tag{15.223}$$

Based on the solution of the equation above, the increment of option price f is a stochastic process dependent on the Wiener process which governs the process of the underlying and of the volatility and from the Poisson process which governs the jump process. Then, as in the above derivation of the BSM formula, the option replication portfolio is built without hedging the risk of discontinuous jumps of the underlying asset, ie,

$$\pi = f - \Delta S \tag{15.224}$$

where:

- f is the option price;
- Δ is the quantity of the underlying.

In order to derive the equivalence between df and $d\pi$, the latter is derived. By differentiating (15.224) and using (15.223) and (15.218), one has

$$d\pi = df - \Delta dS$$
$$= \frac{\partial f}{\partial S}[[r - \lambda\mu_j]S\,dt + \sqrt{v}S\,dW] + \frac{\partial f}{\partial t}\,dt + \frac{1}{2}\left[\frac{\partial^2 f}{\partial S^2}[vS^2]\,dt\right]$$
$$+ [f[(J+1)S, t] - f[S, t]]\,dq - \Delta[[r - \lambda\mu_j]S\,dt + \sqrt{v}S\,dW + SJ\,dq]$$
$$(15.225)$$

To nullify any random variable of that portfolio, ie, to eliminate terms in dz_i from (15.446), the coefficients Δ_1, Δ_0 are appropriately chosen

Coefficient Δ is determined to eliminate terms in dW, ie, any random variation on that portfolio. The portfolio is hedged against the risk of variation due to the randomness of the continuous component of S by imposing that

$$\Delta = \frac{\partial f}{\partial S} \qquad (15.226)$$

Substituting the expression by the coefficient Δ defined in (15.226) in Equation (15.225), one obtains

$$d\pi = \underbrace{\frac{\partial f}{\partial t}\,dt + \frac{1}{2}\left[\frac{\partial^2 f}{\partial S^2}[vS^2]\,dt\right]}_{\text{Deterministic component}} + \underbrace{[f[(J+1)S, t] - f[S, t]]\,dq - \frac{\partial f}{\partial S}[SJ]\,dq}_{\text{Pure jump component}}$$
$$(15.227)$$

Then (15.227) is a portfolio with a deterministic component and a jump risk sensitive component, ie, pure jump. Hence, the no arbitrage hypothesis which is derived from the above

$$d\pi = r\pi\,dt \qquad (15.228)$$

may not be of immediate use since the pure jump component was not previously nullified. However, the pure jump component may not be mathematically and instantaneously hedged, as for the stochastic component of the continuous part of process S, but the expected value of the "pure jump" component, with an adequate choice of f, may be nullified. Based on the above, after defining $E_{J,q}[h(J, q)]$, the expected value of any function h whose dependent variables are J and q is

$$E_{J,q}(d\pi) \doteq \frac{\partial f}{\partial t}\,dt + \frac{1}{2}\left[\frac{\partial^2 f}{\partial S^2}[vS^2]\,dt\right]$$
$$+ E_{J,q}\left[[f[(J+1)S, t] - f[S, t]]\,dq - \frac{\partial f}{\partial S}(SJ)\,dq\right] \qquad (15.229)$$

In this case, the no arbitrage hypothesis (15.228) takes the form

$$E_{J,q}(d\pi) = r\pi\, dt \tag{15.230}$$

Then, (15.230) is computed, ie,

$$\frac{\partial f}{\partial t}\, dt + \frac{1}{2}\left[\frac{\partial^2 f}{\partial S^2}[vS^2]\, dt\right] + E_{J,q}[[f[(J+1)S, t] - f[S, t]]\, dq]$$
$$- E_{J,q}\left[\frac{\partial f}{\partial S}(SJ)\, dq\right] = r\pi\, dt$$

by using (15.224) and (15.226), one obtains

$$\frac{\partial f}{\partial t}\, dt + \frac{1}{2}\left[\frac{\partial^2 f}{\partial S^2}[vS^2]\, dt\right] + E_{J,q}\left\{dq\left[[f[(J+1)S, t] - f[S, t]] - \frac{\partial f}{\partial S}(SJ)\right]\right\}$$
$$= rf\, dt - \frac{\partial f}{\partial S}S\, dt$$

Based on the characteristics of dq, for distributive properties of J and based on the independence of the various processes (see Section 15.2.5.1), one obtains

$$\underbrace{-rf + \frac{\partial f}{\partial S}rS + \frac{\partial f}{\partial t} + \frac{1}{2}\left[\frac{\partial^2 f}{\partial S^2}[vS^2]\right]}_{\text{Deterministic component}} + \underbrace{\lambda E_J[f[(J+1)S, t] - f[S, t]] - \frac{\partial f}{\partial S}\lambda S\mu}_{\text{Pure jump component}} = 0$$

$$\tag{15.231}$$

By some simple algebra, (15.231) is returned to the form of the original Merton paper where, to simplify notation, the subscript J will be omitted in the expected value formula, ie, $E_J \doteq E$.

$$-rf + \frac{\partial f}{\partial S}S[r - \lambda\mu] + \frac{\partial f}{\partial t} + \frac{1}{2}\left[\frac{\partial^2 f}{\partial S^2}[vS^2]\right] + \lambda E[f[(J+1)S, t] - f[S, t]] = 0$$

$$\tag{15.231}$$

15.2.5.3. PDE specification for a Call option pricing: derivation of the Cauchy problem

Given the PDE (15.231) the Cauchy problem, when f describes a call option C price among all of the contingent claims, is defined by PDE (15.231) specified to describe the call price (15.232) and by boundary conditions, ie, the call (15.232a) payoff value at maturity:

$$\underbrace{-rC + \frac{\partial C}{\partial S}rS + \frac{\partial C}{\partial t} + \frac{1}{2}\left[\frac{\partial^2 C}{\partial S^2}[vS^2]\right]}_{\text{Deterministic component}} + \underbrace{\lambda E_J[C[(J+1)S, t] - C[S, t]] - \frac{\partial C}{\partial S}\lambda S\mu}_{\text{Pure jump component}} = 0$$

$$\tag{15.232}$$

$$C(S, t = T) = \text{Max}[0, S - K] \tag{15.232a}$$

where $C(S, t, T)$ is the call option price at time t.

15.2.5.3.1. Transformation of the Cauchy problem into the corresponding logarithm version Equation (15.232) is specified in its equivalent logarithm version. For this purpose, one defines

$$x = \ln(S) \tag{15.233}$$

then

$$S = e^x \tag{15.234}$$

Then, the new version of (15.232) is derived with respect to x. Recalling that $C = f(S(g(x)))$, the relations between $\partial C / \partial x$ and $\partial C / \partial S$ and between $\partial^2 C / \partial x^2$ and $\partial^2 C / \partial S^2$ are then derived:

$$\frac{\partial C}{\partial S} = \frac{\partial C}{\partial x} \frac{1}{S} \tag{15.235}$$

Then $\partial^2 C / \partial x^2$ is computed by using the differentiation above of $\partial C / \partial x$:

$$\frac{\partial^2 C}{\partial S^2} = \frac{1}{S^2} \frac{\partial^2 C}{\partial x^2} - \frac{1}{S^2} \frac{\partial C}{\partial x} \tag{15.236}$$

Then the expected value of (15.232) with respect to x, is expanded, ie,

$$E[C[(J + 1)S, t] - C[S, t]]$$

which (using (15.234)) is equal to

$$E\{C[x + \ln(J + 1), t] - C[x, t]\} \tag{15.237}$$

Then the Cauchy problem (15.232) is written with respect to x, by using (15.235), (15.236) and (15.237), ie,

$$\frac{\partial C}{\partial t} + \frac{1}{2}\left[\frac{\partial^2 C}{\partial x^2}[v]\right] - rC + \frac{\partial C}{\partial x}\left(r - \lambda\mu - \frac{1}{2}v\right)$$
$$+ \lambda E\{C[x + \ln(J + 1), t] - C[x, t]\} = 0 \tag{15.238}$$

Equation (15.238) is the logarithmic version of (15.232). To finalise the definition of the Cauchy problem, the boundary condition corresponding to that of (15.232a) has to be determined; for this purpose, simply rearrange this equation in its logarithmic version by using (15.234), ie,

$$C(x, t = T) = \text{Max}[0, e^{x_T} - K]$$

The new Cauchy problem is then derived, ie,

$$\underbrace{\frac{\partial C}{\partial t} + \frac{1}{2}\left[\frac{\partial^2 C}{\partial x^2}[v]\right] - rC + \frac{\partial C}{\partial x}\left(r - \frac{1}{2}v\right)}_{\text{Deterministic component}}$$

$$\underbrace{+ \lambda E\{C[x + \ln(J + 1), t] - C[x, t]\} - \frac{\partial C}{\partial x}\lambda\mu}_{\text{Pure jump component}} = 0 \qquad (15.238)$$

$$C(x, t = T) = \text{Max}[0, e^{x_T} - K] \qquad (15.238a)$$

15.2.5.3.2. The shift into the à-la BSM pricing context The Cauchy problem as in (15.238) is now specified in the classic à-la BSM form, ie,

$$C_t(S, t, T) = S_t P_1(S, v, t, T) - Ke^{-r(T-t)}P_2(S, v, t, T) \quad \text{or}$$
$$C(x, t) = e^x P_1(x, t) - Ke^{-r(T-t)}P_2(x, t) \qquad (15.239)$$

where P_1, P_2 are probability measures, or P_k for $k = 1, 2$.

Equation (15.239) is used to compute the partial derivatives in order to make (15.238) explicit:

$$\frac{\partial C}{\partial x} = e^x P_1(x, t) + e^x \frac{\partial P_1}{\partial x} - Ke^{-r(T-t)}\frac{\partial P_2}{\partial x} \qquad (15.240)$$

$$\frac{\partial^2 C}{\partial x^2} = e^x P_1(x, t) + 2e^x \frac{\partial P_1}{\partial x} + e^x \frac{\partial^2 P_1}{\partial x^2} - Ke^{-r(T-t)}\frac{\partial^2 P_2}{\partial x^2} \qquad (15.241)$$

$$\frac{\partial C}{\partial t} = e^x \frac{\partial P_1}{\partial t} - K\left[e^{-r(T-t)}\frac{\partial P_2}{\partial t} + re^{-r(T-t)}P_2(x, t)\right] \qquad (15.242)$$

The expected value of (15.238) based on (15.239) remains to be expanded:

$$E\left\{C\left[\underbrace{x + \ln(J + 1)}_{\text{argument } x \text{ of (15.239)}}, t\right] - C[x, t]\right\}$$

factorising P_1 and P_2, one has:

$$E\{C[x + \ln(J + 1), t] - C[x, t]\} = E\{e^x[[(J + 1)P_1[x + \ln(J + 1), t] - P_1(x, t)]$$
$$- Ke^{-r(T-t)} \cdot [P_2[x + \ln(J + 1), t] - P_2(x, t)]\} \qquad (15.243)$$

Substituting the equivalences (15.240), (15.241), (15.242) and (15.243) in (15.238) to obtain

$$
e^x \cdot \left\{ \frac{\partial P_1}{\partial t} + \frac{1}{2}v\frac{\partial P_1}{\partial x} + \frac{1}{2}v\frac{\partial^2 P_1}{\partial x^2} + r\frac{\partial P_1}{\partial x} - \lambda\mu P_1(x,t) - \lambda\mu\frac{\partial P_1}{\partial x} \right.
$$
$$
\left. + \lambda E[[(J+1)P_1[x + \ln(J+1), t] - P_1(x,t)]] \right\}
$$
$$
- Ke^{-r(T-t)} \cdot \left\{ \frac{\partial P_2}{\partial t} + \frac{1}{2}v\left[\frac{\partial^2 P_2}{\partial x^2}\right] + r\frac{\partial P_2}{\partial x} - \lambda\mu\frac{\partial P_2}{\partial x} - \frac{1}{2}v\frac{\partial P_2}{\partial x} \right.
$$
$$
\left. + \lambda E[[P_2[x + \ln(J+1), t] - P_2(x,t)]] \right\}
$$

Since e^x and the term $Ke^{-r\tau}$ are always greater than or equal to zero, the equation above will be satisfied if and only if

$$
\frac{\partial P_1}{\partial t} + \frac{1}{2}v\frac{\partial^2 P_1}{\partial x^2} + \left(r - \lambda\mu + \frac{1}{2}v\right)\frac{\partial P_1}{\partial x}
$$
$$
- \lambda\mu P_1(x,t)\lambda E[[(J+1)P_1[x + \ln(J+1), t] - P_1(x,t)] = 0 \qquad (15.244)
$$
$$
\frac{\partial P_2}{\partial t} + \frac{1}{2}v\left[\frac{\partial^2 P_2}{\partial x^2}\right] + \left(r - \lambda\mu - \frac{1}{2}v\right)\frac{\partial P_2}{\partial x}
$$
$$
+ \lambda E[[P_2[x + \ln(J+1), t] - P_2(x,t)]] = 0 \qquad (15.245)
$$

Equations (15.244) and (15.245) are equivalent forms of PDE (15.238) in the à-la BSM call pricing context as in (15.239). To identify the Cauchy problems in (15.244) and (15.245), equivalent to problem (15.238), one has to derive the boundary condition; for this purpose, the characteristics of function P_k are specified at time $t = T$:

$$
P_k(x,T) = \begin{cases} 1 & \text{if } (e^{x_T} - e^{\ln(K)}) \geq 0 \Rightarrow x_T \geq \ln(K) \\ 0 & \text{if } (e^{x_T} - e^{\ln(K)}) < 0 \Rightarrow x_T < \ln(K) \end{cases}
$$

and using the index function definition (see Definition 6.3) one obtains

$$
P_k(x,T) = 1_{(x_T \geq \ln K)}
$$

The following equations are the transformed Cauchy problem in the à-la BSM call pricing environment determined as in (15.238) and its boundary conditions with the deterministic and the pure jump components:

$$\underbrace{\frac{\partial P_1}{\partial t} + \frac{1}{2}v\frac{\partial^2 P_1}{\partial x^2} + \left(r + \frac{1}{2}v\right)\frac{\partial P_1}{\partial x}}_{\text{Deterministic component}}$$

$$\underbrace{+ \lambda E[[(J+1)P_1[x + \ln(J+1), t] - P_1(x, t)] - \lambda\mu\frac{\partial P_1}{\partial x} - \lambda\mu P_1(x, t)}_{\text{Pure jump component}} = 0$$

$$\tag{15.244}$$

$$P_1(x, T) = 1_{(x_T \geq \ln[K])} \tag{15.244a}$$

$$\underbrace{\frac{\partial P_2}{\partial t} + \frac{1}{2}v\left[\frac{\partial^2 P_2}{\partial x^2}\right] + \left(r - \frac{1}{2}v\right)\frac{\partial P_2}{\partial x}}_{\text{Deterministic component}}$$

$$\underbrace{+ \lambda E[[P_2[x + \ln(J+1), t] - P_2(x, t)]] - \lambda\mu\frac{\partial P_2}{\partial x}}_{\text{Pure jump component}} = 0 \tag{15.245}$$

$$P_2(x, T) = 1_{(x_T \geq \ln[K])} \tag{15.245a}$$

Then the characteristics of probability measure P_k at time t remain to be determined. For this purpose, (15.244) and (15.245) are interpreted by using the deterministic component of the Feynman–Kac formula (see Theorem 12.20). Actually, the corresponding SDEs of (15.244) and (15.245) may be determined, ie,

$$dx_t^{(1)} = \left[r + \frac{1}{2}v\right]dt + \sqrt{v}\,dW_t \quad \text{with } x_t^{(1)} = x \tag{15.246}$$

$$dx_t^{(2)} = \left[r - \frac{1}{2}v\right]dt + \sqrt{v}\,dW_t \quad \text{with } x_t^{(2)} = x \tag{15.247}$$

The expansion of (12.95) is derived, ie, for $k = 1, 2$,

$$P_k(x, t) = E[1_{(x_T \geq \ln[K])} \mid x_t = x]$$

simplifying, one has

$$P_k(x, t) = P_k[x_T \geq \ln[K] \mid x_t = x]$$

to simplify notation, $x_t = x$ is denoted by x_t. One obtains the characteristics of the probability measure P_k at time t:

$$P_k(x, t) = P_k[x_T \geq \ln[K] \mid x_t] \tag{15.248}$$

15.2.5.3.3. The shift in Fourier space The Cauchy problem identified in (15.244) and (15.245) is now shifted in the Fourier space, ie, it is rearranged as a function of the conditioned characteristic function. For this purpose, (11.123) is rearranged by using Notation 11.34 for $P_j(x_t, v_t, t)$, or more simply $P_k(x_t)$, then[8]

$$P_k(x_t) = P_k[x_T \geq \ln[K] \mid x_t] = \frac{1}{2\pi} \int_{-\infty}^{\infty} \frac{e^{-i\xi \ln[K]}}{i\xi} \tilde{f}_k(x_T, \xi \mid x_t)\, d\xi \qquad (15.249)$$

or, simplifying notation by writing $\tilde{f}_k(x_T, \xi \mid x_t) \doteq \tilde{f}_k$,

$$P_k(x_t) = \frac{1}{2\pi} \int_{-\infty}^{\infty} \frac{e^{-i\xi \ln[K]}}{i\xi} \tilde{f}_k\, d\xi \qquad (15.249)$$

This expression is used to compute partial derivatives (to simplify notation $(\partial / \partial y) \tilde{f}_j(x_T, \xi \mid x_t) = \partial \tilde{f}_j / \partial y$ for $y = t, x, x^2$), ie,

$$\frac{\partial P_k}{\partial t} = \frac{1}{2\pi} \int_{-\infty}^{\infty} \frac{e^{-i\xi \ln[K]}}{i\xi} \frac{\partial \tilde{f}_k}{\partial t}\, d\xi \qquad (15.250)$$

$$\frac{\partial P_k}{\partial x} = \frac{1}{2\pi} \int_{-\infty}^{\infty} \frac{e^{-i\xi \ln[K]}}{i\xi} \frac{\partial \tilde{f}_k}{\partial x}\, d\xi \qquad (15.251)$$

$$\frac{\partial^2 P_k}{\partial x^2} = \frac{1}{2\pi} \int_{-\infty}^{\infty} \frac{e^{-i\xi \ln[K]}}{i\xi} \frac{\partial^2 \tilde{f}_k}{\partial x^2}\, d\xi \qquad (15.252)$$

The other members of (15.244) and of (15.245) remain to be rearranged as a function of the conditioned characteristic function. Specifically, with respect to the argument of the expected value of (15.244), one has

$$E[(1 + J)P_1(\ln(1 + J) + x, t) - P_1(x, t)]$$
$$= \frac{1}{2\pi} \int_{-\infty}^{\infty} \frac{e^{-i\xi \ln[K]}}{i\xi}$$
$$\times E[(1 + J)\tilde{f}_1(x_T + \ln(1 + J), \xi \mid x_t + \ln(1 + J)) - \tilde{f}_1(x_T, \xi \mid x_t)]\, d\xi$$
$$(\text{using } (15.249))$$

simplifying notation by writing $\tilde{f}_1(x_T + \ln(1 + J), \xi \mid x_t + \ln(1 + J)) \doteq \tilde{f}_1^{[J]}$ and again using the simplified notation $\tilde{f}_1(x_T, \xi \mid x_t) \doteq \tilde{f}_1$, one has

$$E[(1 + J)P_1(\ln(1 + J) + x, t) - P_1(x, t)] = \frac{1}{2\pi} \int_{-\infty}^{\infty} \frac{e^{-i\xi \ln[K]}}{i\xi} E\left[(1 + J)\tilde{f}_1^{[J]} - \tilde{f}_1\right] d\xi$$
$$(15.253)$$

---

[8]Equation (11.123) shows ">" and not "≥"; in this case, the difference is not relevant, given the call payoff.

Similarly, with respect to the argument of the expected value of (15.245), one has

$$E[P_2(\ln(1+J)+x,t) - P_2(x,t)]$$
$$= \frac{1}{2\pi} \int_{-\infty}^{\infty} \frac{e^{-i\xi \ln[K]}}{i\xi} E[\tilde{f}_2(x_T + \ln(1+J), \xi \mid x_t + \ln(1+J)) - \tilde{f}_2(x_T, \xi \mid x_t)] \, d\xi$$

(using (15.249))

simplifying notation by writing $\tilde{f}_2(x_T + \ln(1+J), \xi \mid x_t + \ln(1+J)) \doteq \tilde{f}_2^{[J]}$ and again using the simplified notation $\tilde{f}_2(x_T, \xi \mid x_t) \doteq \tilde{f}_2$, one has

$$E[P_2(\ln(1+J)+x,t) - P_2(x,t)] = \frac{1}{2\pi} \int_{-\infty}^{\infty} \frac{e^{-i\xi \ln[K]}}{i\xi} E\left[\tilde{f}_2^{[J]} - \tilde{f}_2\right] d\xi \quad (15.254)$$

PDE (15.244) is shifted in the Fourier space by substituting (15.250), (15.251), (15.252) and (15.253) in (15.249):

$$\frac{1}{2\pi} \int_{-\infty}^{\infty} \frac{e^{-i\xi \ln[K]}}{i\xi} \left\{ -\lambda\mu\tilde{f}_1 + \frac{\partial \tilde{f}_1}{\partial t} + \frac{1}{2}v\frac{\partial^2 \tilde{f}_1}{\partial x^2} + \left[r - \lambda\mu + \frac{1}{2}v\right]\frac{\partial \tilde{f}_1}{\partial x} \right.$$
$$\left. + \lambda E\left[(1+J)\tilde{f}_1^{[J]} - \tilde{f}_1\right] \right\} d\xi = 0$$

This equation is verified under the condition that the member inside square brackets is equal to zero. Then the PDE is given only by this last member, ie,

$$-\lambda\mu\tilde{f}_1 + \frac{\partial \tilde{f}_1}{\partial t} + \frac{1}{2}v\frac{\partial^2 \tilde{f}_1}{\partial x^2} + \left[r - \lambda\mu + \frac{1}{2}v\right]\frac{\partial \tilde{f}_1}{\partial x} + \lambda E\left[(1+J)\tilde{f}_1^{[J]} - \tilde{f}_1\right] = 0$$
$$(15.255)$$

Similarly, the PDE in (15.245) is shifted in the Fourier space by substituting (15.249), (15.250), (15.251), (15.252) and (15.254) inside that space:

$$\frac{1}{2\pi} \int_{-\infty}^{\infty} \frac{e^{-i\xi \ln[K]}}{i\xi} \left[\frac{\partial \tilde{f}_2}{\partial t} + \frac{1}{2}v\frac{\partial^2 \tilde{f}_2}{\partial x^2} + \left[r - \lambda\mu - \frac{1}{2}v\right]\frac{\partial \tilde{f}_2}{\partial x} + \lambda E\left(\tilde{f}_2^{[J]} - \tilde{f}_2\right)\right] d\xi = 0$$

This equation is verified under the condition that the member in square brackets is equal to zero. Then the PDE is given only by the last member, ie,

$$\frac{\partial \tilde{f}_2}{\partial t} + \frac{1}{2}v\frac{\partial^2 \tilde{f}_2}{\partial x^2} + \left[r - \lambda\mu - \frac{1}{2}v\right]\frac{\partial \tilde{f}_2}{\partial x} + \lambda E\left(\tilde{f}_2^{[J]} - \tilde{f}_2\right) = 0 \quad (15.256)$$

To complete the shift of the Cauchy problem one has to specify the final conditions of the Cauchy problem in (15.244) and (15.245). By using Remark 6.5

this final condition is rearranged as:

$$P_k(x, t, T) = 1_{x_T \geq \ln(K)} = \theta_{\ln[K]}(x_T) \triangleq \theta[x_T - \ln(K)]$$

where θ is the Heaviside function.

Recalling Proposition 6.10, one has

$$\theta(x_T - \ln(K)) = \int_{-\infty}^{x_T - \ln(K)} \delta(w)\, dw$$

which, under Theorem 9.4 and under the Fubini theorem (see Theorem 10.22), is equal to

$$\theta(x_T - \ln(K)) = \frac{1}{2\pi} \int_{-\infty}^{\infty} \left(\int_{-\infty}^{x_T - \ln(K)} e^{i\tilde{\zeta}w}\, dw \right) d\tilde{\zeta}$$

$$= \frac{1}{2\pi} \int_{-\infty}^{\infty} \frac{1}{i\tilde{\zeta}} e^{i\tilde{\zeta}[x_T]} e^{-i\tilde{\zeta}\ln(K)}\, d\tilde{\zeta}$$

comparing this last expression to (15.249) arranged for $t = T$ the final conditions of the Cauchy problem determined by (15.244) and (15.245) are then derived, ie,

$$e^{i\tilde{\zeta}[x_T]} = \tilde{f}_k(x_T, \tilde{\zeta})$$

The following equations are the original Cauchy problem identified under (15.244) and (15.245) and under the respective boundary conditions shifted in the Fourier space:

$$-\lambda\mu\tilde{f}_1 + \frac{\partial \tilde{f}_1}{\partial t} + \frac{1}{2}v\frac{\partial^2 \tilde{f}_1}{\partial x^2} + \left[r - \lambda\mu + \frac{1}{2}v \right]\frac{\partial \tilde{f}_1}{\partial x} + \lambda E\left((1 + J)\tilde{f}_1^{[J]} - \tilde{f}_1 \right) = 0$$

$$\tag{15.255}$$

$$\tilde{f}_k(x_T, \tilde{\zeta}) = e^{i\tilde{\zeta}[x_T]} \tag{15.225a}$$

$$\frac{\partial \tilde{f}_2}{\partial t} + \frac{1}{2}v\frac{\partial^2 \tilde{f}_2}{\partial x^2} + \left[r - \lambda\mu - \frac{1}{2}v \right]\frac{\partial \tilde{f}_2}{\partial x} + \lambda E\left(\tilde{f}_2^{[J]} - \tilde{f}_2 \right) = 0 \tag{15.256}$$

$$\tilde{f}_k(x_T, \tilde{\zeta}) = e^{i\tilde{\zeta}[x_T]} \tag{15.256a}$$

15.2.5.3.3.1.   *The temporal shift of the transformed Cauchy problem*   In order to obtain an explicit solution of the Cauchy problem, another temporal shift in Fourier space is needed. Then $\tau = T - t$ so that $t = T - \tau$. Since, for any generic function, $f(T - t) = f(\tau)$, it is true that

$$\frac{\partial f(T - t)}{\partial t} = -\frac{\partial f(\tau)}{\partial \tau}$$

Then, the Cauchy problem, identified by Equations (15.255) and (15.256) and by their final conditions, becomes

$$-\lambda\mu\tilde{f}_1 - \frac{\partial\tilde{f}_1}{\partial\tau} + \frac{1}{2}v\frac{\partial^2\tilde{f}_1}{\partial x^2} + \left[r - \lambda\mu + \frac{1}{2}v\right]\frac{\partial\tilde{f}_1}{\partial x} + \lambda E\left[(1+J)\tilde{f}_1^{[J]} - \tilde{f}_1\right] = 0$$

(15.257)

$$\tilde{f}_k(x_{\tau=0}, \xi) = e^{i\xi[x_{\tau=0}]}$$

(15.257a)

$$-\frac{\partial\tilde{f}_2}{\partial\tau} + \frac{1}{2}v\frac{\partial^2\tilde{f}_2}{\partial x^2} + \left[r - \lambda\mu - \frac{1}{2}v\right]\frac{\partial\tilde{f}_2}{\partial x} + \lambda E\left[\tilde{f}_2^{[J]} - \tilde{f}_2\right] = 0$$

(15.258)

$$\tilde{f}_k(x_{\tau=0}, \xi) = e^{i\xi[x_{\tau=0}]}$$

(15.258a)

15.2.5.4. Specification of the Cauchy problem as an ODE system

Let $\tilde{f}_k$ be the solution to the Cauchy problem, identified in (15.257) and (15.258), for any $k = 1, 2$:

$$\tilde{f}_k(x_{\tau=0}, \xi \mid x_\tau) = e^{C_\tau^{(k)} + i\xi x_\tau}$$

(15.259)

In order for it to be compatible with the final conditions of this problem it is necessary, for $\tau = 0$, that $C_0^{(j)} = 0$. This expression becomes the corresponding final condition in the form (15.259) of the PDEs (15.257) and (15.258). The partial derivatives of (15.257) and (15.258) are determined by using the functional form (15.259). For simplicity, the subscript τ is omitted and the notation $C_\tau^{(k)} \doteq C_k$ is used:

$$\frac{\partial\tilde{f}_k}{\partial x} = i\xi e^{C_k + i\xi x}$$

(15.260)

$$\frac{\partial^2\tilde{f}_k}{\partial x^2} = -\xi^2 e^{[C_k + i\xi x]}$$

(15.261)

$$\frac{\partial\tilde{f}_k}{\partial\tau} = e^{[C_k + i\xi x]}\frac{\partial C_k}{\partial\tau}$$

(15.262)

The member contained in the expected value of (15.257) is expressed as in (15.259):

$$E\left[(1+J)\tilde{f}_1^{[J]} - \tilde{f}_1\right]$$

which, by expanding the simplified notation, is equal to

$$= e^{C_\tau^{(1)} + i\xi x_\tau} E[(J+1)e^{i\xi[\ln(J+1)]} - 1]$$

then $E[e^{(i\xi+1)\ln(J+1)}]$ is computed. Actually, recalling that (15.216), by using the properties of the moments and the relation between normal and lognormal distributions (see Example 11.4), one may compute the distributive properties of the normal random variable $\ln(1 + J)$. By solving the following system, one derives the mean and the variance of this variable, ie,

$$\begin{cases} \mu + 1 = e^{a+b^2/2} \\ (1 + \mu)(e^{\sigma^2} - 1) = e^{a+b^2/2} \cdot (e^{b^2} - 1) \end{cases}$$

then

$$\begin{cases} a = \ln(\mu + 1) - \dfrac{\sigma^2}{2} \\ b^2 = \sigma^2 \end{cases} \tag{15.263}$$

By using (15.263) the distribution properties of the random variable of $\ln(1 + J)$, become

$$\ln[1 + J] \sim N\left(\ln[1 + \mu] - \tfrac{1}{2}\sigma^2, \sigma^2\right) \tag{15.264}$$

In order to compute $E[e^{(i\xi+1)\ln(J+1)}]$, since $\ln[1 + J]$ is a normal random variable, one may use the moment generating function for this type of variable (see Equation (11.115)), ie,

$$E[e^{(i\xi+1)\ln(J+1)}] = e^{(i\xi\sigma^2/2)(i\xi+1)}(1 + \mu)^{(i\xi+1)} \tag{15.265}$$

by using (15.265); it can be derived that the expected value of (15.257) rearranged as in (15.259) becomes

$$E\left[(1 + J)\tilde{f}_1^{[J]} - \tilde{f}_1\right] = e^{C_\tau^{(1)}+i\xi x_\tau}\left[e^{(i\xi\sigma^2/2)(i\xi+1)}(1 + \mu)^{(i\xi+1)} - 1\right] \tag{15.266}$$

Equations (15.260), (15.261), (15.262) and (15.266) are substituted in (15.257):

$$e^{C_\tau^{(1)}+i\xi x_\tau}\left\{-\lambda\mu(i\xi + 1) - \frac{\partial C_\tau^{(1)}}{\partial \tau} + \frac{1}{2}vi\xi(\xi + 1) + ri\xi\right.$$

$$\left. + \lambda[e^{(i\xi\sigma^2/2)(i\xi+1)}(1 + \mu)^{(i\xi+1)} - 1]\right\} = 0$$

The term $e^{C_\tau^{(1)}+i\xi x_\tau}$ is always positive, then (15.257) may be rearranged as

$$\frac{\partial C_t^{(1)}}{\partial \tau} = -\lambda\mu(i\xi + 1) + \frac{1}{2}vi\xi(\xi + 1) + ri\xi + \lambda[e^{(i\xi\sigma^2/2)(i\xi+1)}(1 + \mu)^{(i\xi+1)} - 1] \tag{15.267}$$

The term inside the expected value of (15.258) is rearranged as in (15.259):

$$E\left[\tilde{f}_2^{[J]} - \tilde{f}_2\right] = e^{C_\tau^{(2)}+i\xi x_\tau}\{E[e^{i\xi\ln(J+1)}] - 1\}$$

(by expanding the simplified notations)

to compute $E[e^{i\xi \ln(J+1)}]$. By recalling the random variable distributive properties $\ln(1+J)$ (see (15.264)) to again compute $E[e^{i\xi \ln(J+1)}]$, since $\ln[1+J]$ is a normal random variable, the moment generating function for random variable is used (see Equation (11.115)), ie,

$$E[e^{i\xi \ln(J+1)}] = e^{(\sigma^2/2)i\xi(i\xi-1)}(1+\mu)^{i\xi} \tag{15.268}$$

By using (15.268) it can be derived that the term in (15.257) rearranged as in (15.259) becomes

$$E\left[(1+J)\tilde{f}_2^{[J]} - \tilde{f}_2\right] = e^{C_\tau^{(2)}+i\xi x_\tau}\left[e^{(\sigma^2/2)i\xi(i\xi-1)}(1+\mu)^{i\xi} - 1\right] \tag{15.269}$$

Then (15.260), (15.261), (15.262) and (15.269) are replaced in (15.258):

$$e^{C_\tau^{(2)}+i\xi x_\tau}\left\{ -\frac{\partial C_\tau^{(2)}}{\partial \tau} + \frac{1}{2}v i\xi(i\xi - 1) + r i\xi - \lambda\mu i\xi \right.$$

$$\left. + \lambda\left[e^{(\sigma^2/2)i\xi(i\xi-1)}(1+\mu)^{i\xi} - 1\right]\right\} = 0$$

Obviously, the term $e^{[C_\tau^{(2)}+i\xi x]}$ is always positive, hence (15.258) may be rearranged as

$$\frac{\partial C_\tau^{(2)}}{\partial \tau} = \frac{1}{2}v i\xi(i\xi - 1) + r i\xi - \lambda\mu i\xi + \lambda\left[e^{(\sigma^2/2)i\xi(i\xi-1)}(1+\mu)^{i\xi} - 1\right] \tag{15.270}$$

The Cauchy problem identified in (15.257), and (15.258) and by the relative final conditions may be rearranged as follows:

$$\frac{\partial C_t^{(1)}}{\partial \tau} = -\lambda\mu(i\xi + 1) + \frac{1}{2}v i\xi(\xi + 1) + r i\xi + \lambda\left[e^{(i\xi\sigma^2/2)(i\xi+1)}(1+\mu)^{(i\xi+1)} - 1\right] \tag{15.267}$$

$$C_{\tau=0}^{(1)} = 0 \tag{15.267a}$$

$$\frac{\partial C_\tau^{(2)}}{\partial \tau} = \frac{1}{2}v i\xi(i\xi - 1) + r i\xi - \lambda\mu i\xi + \lambda\left[e^{(\sigma^2/2)i\xi(i\xi-1)}(1+\mu)^{i\xi} - 1\right] \tag{15.270}$$

$$C_{\tau=0}^{(2)} = 0 \tag{15.270a}$$

15.2.5.5. The solution of the Cauchy problem

Equation (15.267) is solved as follows. It is a first-order constant coefficient ODE to be solved by direct integration:

$$C_\tau^{(1)} = r i\xi\tau - \lambda\mu[i\xi + 1]\tau + \frac{1}{2}v[i\xi(i\xi + 1)]\tau + \lambda\tau e^{(i\xi\sigma^2/2)(i\xi+1)}(1+\mu)^{(i\xi+1)} - \lambda\tau \tag{15.271}$$

If Equation (15.271) also satisfies the final condition of the Cauchy problem identified in (15.267), then it must be considered as a solution to the Cauchy problem.

Equation (15.270) is solved as follows. Here, again, this is a constant coefficient first-order ODE to be solved by direct integration:

$$C_\tau^{(2)} = \tfrac{1}{2}v i \xi \tau (i \xi - 1) + r i \xi \tau - \lambda \mu i \xi \tau + \lambda \tau e^{(\sigma^2/2) i \xi (i \xi - 1)} (1 + \mu)^{i \xi} - \lambda \tau \quad (15.272)$$

If Equation (15.272) also satisfies the final condition of the Cauchy problem identified in (15.270), then it must be considered as a solution to the Cauchy problem.

By construction, these solutions nullify the pure jump component determined in the previous section to make the model risk-neutral also with respect to this second component according to a no-arbitrage scheme.

15.2.5.5.1. Solutions computable by using quadrature algorithms The solutions to the Cauchy problem as in (15.271) and (15.272) in the form (15.259) where $C_\tau^{(1)}, C_\tau^{(2)}$ are given by the expressions (15.271) and (15.272) allows, through the relation (15.249), the analytic expression of probability measures P_k to be determined, ie,

$$P_k[x_{\tau=0} \geq \ln[K] \mid x_\tau] = \frac{1}{2\pi} \int_{-\infty}^{\infty} \frac{e^{-i \xi \ln[K]}}{i \xi} \tilde{f}_k(x_{\tau=0}, \xi \mid x_\tau) \, d\xi \quad (15.249)$$

However, the relation (15.249) does not have an immediate numerical solution. However, many equivalent solutions exist which allow this quantity to be manipulated analytically (see expressions (11.125) and (11.126)):

$$P_k[x_{\tau=0} \geq \ln[K] \mid x_\tau] = \frac{1}{2} + \frac{1}{\pi} \int_0^{\infty} \Im \left[\frac{e^{-i \xi \ln[K]}}{\xi} \tilde{f}_k(x_{\tau=0}, \xi \mid x_\tau) \right] d\xi \quad (15.273)$$

$$P_k[x_{\tau=0} \geq \ln[K] \mid x_\tau] = \frac{1}{2} + \frac{1}{\pi} \int_0^{\infty} \Re \left[\frac{e^{-i \xi \ln[K]}}{i \xi} \tilde{f}_k(x_{\tau=0}, \xi \mid x_\tau) \right] d\xi \quad (15.274)$$

15.2.5.6. The call price
The Merton model gives the following call pricing simplified notation formula:

$$C_t = S_t P_1 - K e^{-r(T-t)} P_2 \quad (15.239)$$

where, by using (15.274) (or, instead, (15.273)), (15.259), (15.271) and (15.272), for $k = 1, 2$, the function P is defined as

$$P_k = \frac{1}{2} + \frac{1}{\pi} \int_0^{\infty} \Re \left[\frac{e^{-i \xi \ln[K]}}{i \xi} e^{C_\tau^{(k)} + i \xi x_\tau} \right] d\xi \quad (15.275)$$

with Equations (15.271) and (15.272).

15.2.5.7. Pricing a call with the Merton model: implementation

Actually, the Merton model requires the use of some software to compute the integral in (15.275). Matlab *real and quad8* or *quadl* functions may be used for this purpose.

15.2.5.8. The Greeks

Theorem 15.15. *If $C(S_t, K): \mathbb{R}^2 \to \mathbb{R}$ is differentiable to the second order and is homogeneous of first degree and written as in Equation (15.239) then, the following equivalences hold:*

$$S_t \frac{\partial P_1}{\partial S_t} + K \frac{\partial P_1}{\partial K} = 0 \tag{15.276}$$

$$S_t \frac{\partial P_2}{\partial S_t} + K \frac{\partial P_2}{\partial K} = 0 \tag{15.277}$$

$$\frac{\partial^2 P_1}{\partial S_t \partial K} = \frac{\partial^2 P_1}{\partial K \partial S_t} \tag{15.278}$$

$$\frac{\partial^2 P_2}{\partial S_t \partial K} = \frac{\partial^2 P_2}{\partial K \partial S_t} \tag{15.279}$$

$$S_t \frac{\partial P_1}{\partial S_t} - e^{-r(T-t)} K \frac{\partial P_2}{\partial S_t} = 0 \tag{15.280}$$

$$P_1 = \frac{\partial C_t}{\partial S_t}$$
$$\frac{\partial C_t}{\partial K} = -e^{-r(T-t)} P_2 \tag{15.281}$$

Notation 15.2. The notation may be simplified as follows:

$$\tilde{f}_j \doteq \tilde{f}_j(x_T, \tau = 0, \xi | x_T) \tag{15.282}$$

Proof. The demonstration is in four parts.

Demonstration for (15.276) and (15.277). Since the function in (15.239) is a first-degree homogeneous function, one has

$$C_t(S, K) = \frac{\partial C_t}{\partial S_t} S_t + \frac{\partial C_t}{\partial K} K \tag{15.283}$$

Then $\partial C_t / \partial S_t$ and $\partial C_t / \partial K$ are computed with respect to (15.354), ie,

$$\frac{\partial C_t}{\partial S_t} = S_t \frac{\partial P_1}{\partial S_t} + P_1 - K e^{-r(T-t)} \frac{\partial P_2}{\partial S_t} \tag{15.284}$$

$$\frac{\partial C_t}{\partial K} = S_t \frac{\partial P_1}{\partial K} - e^{-r(T-t)} P_2 - K e^{-r(T-t)} \frac{\partial P_2}{\partial K} \tag{15.285}$$

Replacing the partial derivatives (15.284) and (15.285) in (15.283):

$$C_t(S, K) = S_t P_1 - Ke^{-r(T-t)} P_2 + S_t\left[S_t\frac{\partial P_1}{\partial S_t} + K\frac{\partial P_1}{\partial K}\right]$$

$$- Ke^{-r(T-t)}\left[S_t\frac{\partial P_2}{\partial S_t} + K\frac{\partial P_2}{\partial K}\right]$$

Since $S_t, K, e^{-r(T-t)} > 0$, and considering the equivalence in (15.239) then we have (15.276) and (15.277). □

Demonstration for (15.278) and (15.279). The crossed derivatives inside (15.239) are computed as follows:

$$\frac{\partial^2 C_t}{\partial S_t \partial K} = S_t\frac{\partial^2 P_1}{\partial S_t \partial K} + \frac{\partial P_1}{\partial K} - e^{-r(T-t)}\frac{\partial P_2}{\partial S_t} - Ke^{-r(T-t)}\frac{\partial^2 P_2}{\partial S_t \partial K} \qquad (15.286)$$

$$\frac{\partial^2 C_t}{\partial K \partial S_t} = \frac{\partial P_1}{\partial K} + S_t\frac{\partial^2 P_1}{\partial K \partial S_t} - e^{-r(T-t)}\frac{\partial P_2}{\partial S_t} - Ke^{-r(T-t)}\frac{\partial^2 P_2}{\partial K \partial S_t} \qquad (15.287)$$

By using the homogeneous function property,

$$\frac{\partial^2 C_t}{\partial S_t \partial K} - \frac{\partial^2 C_t}{\partial K \partial S_t} = S_t\left[\frac{\partial^2 P_1}{\partial S_t \partial K} - \frac{\partial^2 P_1}{\partial K \partial S_t}\right] - Ke^{-r(T-t)}\left[\frac{\partial^2 P_2}{\partial S_t \partial K} - \frac{\partial^2 P_2}{\partial K \partial S_t}\right] = 0$$

Since $S_t, Ke^{-r(T-t)} > 0$, this equivalence is satisfied if and only if

$$\frac{\partial^2 P_j}{\partial S_t \partial K} = \frac{\partial^2 P_j}{\partial K \partial S_t} \qquad (15.288)$$

for $j = 1, 2$.

Demonstration for (15.280). Since the function in (15.239) is a first-degree homogeneous function,

$$S_t^2\left[\frac{\partial^2 C_t}{\partial S_t^2}\right] = K^2\left[\frac{\partial^2 C_t}{\partial K^2}\right] \qquad (15.289)$$

Then $\partial^2 C_t/\partial S_t^2$ and $\partial^2 C_t/\partial K^2$ are computed with respect to (15.239), and by using quantities (15.284) and (15.285), ie,

$$\frac{\partial^2 C_t}{\partial S_t^2} = S_t\frac{\partial^2 P_1}{\partial S_t^2} + 2\frac{\partial P_1}{\partial S_t} - Ke^{-r(T-t)}\frac{\partial^2 P_2}{\partial S_t^2} \qquad (15.290)$$

$$\frac{\partial^2 C_t}{\partial K^2} = S_t\frac{\partial^2 P_1}{\partial K^2} - 2e^{-r(T-t)}\frac{\partial P_2}{\partial K} - Ke^{-r(T-t)}\frac{\partial^2 P_2}{\partial K^2} \qquad (15.291)$$

Replacing the partial derivatives (15.290) and (15.291), in Equation (15.289) one obtains

$$
S_t^3 \frac{\partial^2 P_1}{\partial S_t^2} + 2S_t^2 \frac{\partial P_1}{\partial S_t} - S_t^2 K e^{-r(T-t)} \frac{\partial^2 P_2}{\partial S_t^2}
$$
$$
= S_t K^2 \frac{\partial^2 P_1}{\partial K^2} - 2K^2 e^{-r(T-t)} \frac{\partial P_2}{\partial K} - K^3 e^{-r(T-t)} \frac{\partial^2 P_2}{\partial K^2} \tag{15.292}
$$

then the following can be derived:

$$
S_t^2 \frac{\partial^2 C_t}{\partial S_t^2} = S_t^3 \frac{\partial^2 P_1}{\partial S_t^2} + 2S_t^2 \frac{\partial P_1}{\partial S_t} - S_t^2 K e^{-r(T-t)} \frac{\partial^2 P_2}{\partial S_t^2}
$$
$$
= K^2 \frac{\partial^2 C_t}{\partial K^2} = S_t K^2 \frac{\partial^2 P_1}{\partial K^2} - 2K^2 e^{-r(T-t)} \frac{\partial P_2}{\partial K} - K^3 e^{-r(T-t)} \frac{\partial^2 P_2}{\partial K^2} \tag{15.293}
$$

Now, from relations (15.276) and (15.277), it is clear how

$$
\frac{\partial^2 P_j}{\partial S_t^2} = \frac{K}{S_t^2} \frac{\partial P_j}{\partial K} - \frac{K}{S_t} \frac{\partial^2 P_j}{\partial K \partial S_t} \tag{15.294}
$$

$$
\frac{\partial^2 P_j}{\partial K^2} = \frac{S_t}{K^2} \frac{\partial P_j}{\partial S_t} - \frac{S_t}{K} \frac{\partial^2 P_j}{\partial S_t \partial K} \tag{15.295}
$$

The following relations are derived from (15.294) and (15.295):

$$
\frac{\partial^2 P_j}{\partial K \partial S_t} = \frac{1}{S_t} \frac{\partial P_j}{\partial K} - \frac{S_t}{K} \frac{\partial^2 P_j}{\partial S_t^2} \tag{15.296}
$$

$$
\frac{\partial^2 P_j}{\partial S_t \partial K} = \frac{1}{K} \frac{\partial P_j}{\partial S_t} - \frac{K}{S_t} \frac{\partial^2 P_j}{\partial K^2} \tag{15.297}
$$

Under (15.278) and (15.279),

$$
\frac{\partial^2 P_j}{\partial K \partial S_t} = \frac{\partial^2 P_j}{\partial S_t \partial K},
$$

then

$$
\frac{1}{S_t} \frac{\partial P_j}{\partial K} - \frac{1}{K} \frac{\partial P_j}{\partial S_t} = \frac{S_t}{K} \frac{\partial^2 P_j}{\partial S_t^2} - \frac{K}{S_t} \frac{\partial^2 P_j}{\partial K^2} \tag{15.298}
$$

Property (15.298) is substituted in (15.293), after rearranging the terms of the equation

$$
S_t^2 \frac{\partial^2 C_t}{\partial S_t^2} - K^2 \frac{\partial^2 C_t}{\partial K^2} = KS_t \frac{\partial P_1}{\partial K} + S_t^2 \frac{\partial P_1}{\partial S_t} + K^2 e^{-r(T-t)} \frac{\partial P_2}{\partial K} + S_t K e^{-r(T-t)} \frac{\partial P_2}{\partial S_t} = 0
$$

Since

$$KS_t \frac{\partial P_1}{\partial K} + S_t^2 \frac{\partial P_1}{\partial S_t} = 0$$

under (15.276), and

$$K^2 e^{-r(T-t)} \frac{\partial P_2}{\partial K} + S_t K e^{-r(T-t)} \frac{\partial P_2}{\partial S_t} = 0$$

under (15.277), the following equivalences hold:

$$KS_t \frac{\partial P_1}{\partial K} + S_t K^2 e^{-r(T-t)} \frac{\partial P_2}{\partial S_t} = 0 \qquad (15.299)$$

$$S_t^2 \frac{\partial P_1}{\partial S_t} + K^2 e^{-r(T-t)} \frac{\partial P_2}{\partial K} = 0 \qquad (15.300)$$

By using (15.277), rearranged as

$$\frac{\partial P_2}{\partial K} = -\frac{S_t}{K} \frac{\partial P_2}{\partial S_t}$$

one has Equation (15.280). □

Demonstration for (15.281). Applying property (15.280) to expressions (15.284) and (15.285), one can derive (15.281). □

Proposition 15.37. *The following equivalences hold:*

$$\frac{\partial}{\partial S_t} \tilde{f}_j(.x_\tau, \tau = 0, \xi | x_\tau) = \tilde{f}_j(x_\tau, \tau = 0, \xi | x_\tau) \cdot i\xi \frac{1}{S_t} \qquad (15.301)$$

$$\frac{\partial^2}{\partial S_t^2} (\tilde{f}_j(x_\tau, \tau = 0, \xi | x_\tau)) = \frac{1}{S_t^2} i\xi(i\xi - 1) \tilde{f}_j(x_\tau, \tau = 0, \xi | x_\tau) \qquad (15.302)$$

Proof. The following partial derivatives below are computed:

- For $j = 1, 2$

$$\frac{\partial}{\partial S_t} \tilde{f}_j(x_\tau, \tau = 0, \xi | x_\tau)$$

One has

$$\frac{\partial}{\partial S_t} (\tilde{f}_j(x_\tau, \tau = 0, \xi | x_\tau)) = \frac{\partial}{\partial S_t} e^{(C_\tau^{(j)} + i\xi x_\tau)}$$

so one obtains (15.301).
- For $j = 1, 2$

$$\frac{\partial^2}{\partial S_t^2} \tilde{f}_j(x_\tau, \tau = 0, \xi | x_\tau)$$

by using (15.301), one obtains (15.302). □

Proposition 15.38. *The following equivalences hold:*

$$\frac{\partial}{\partial K}\left[\frac{e^{-i\xi \ln K}}{i\xi}\right] = -\frac{1}{K}e^{-i\xi \ln K} \tag{15.303}$$

$$\frac{\partial^2}{\partial K^2}\left[\frac{e^{-i\xi \ln K}}{i\xi}\right] = \frac{1}{K^2}e^{-i\xi \ln K}(i\xi + 1) \tag{15.304}$$

Proof. The following partial derivatives are computed.

- $(\partial/\partial K)[e^{-i\xi \ln K}/i\xi]$ is given by

$$\frac{\partial}{\partial K}\left(\frac{e^{-i\xi \ln K}}{i\xi}\right) = \frac{\partial}{\partial K}\left(\frac{e^{-\ln(K)i\xi}}{i\xi}\right)$$

  so one obtains (15.303).
- $(\partial^2/\partial K^2)[e^{-i\xi \ln K}/i\xi]$ is given by the above, and by using (15.303) one obtains (15.304). □

Proposition 15.39. *The following equivalences hold:*

$$\frac{\partial P_j}{\partial S_t} = \frac{1}{\pi S_t}\int_0^\infty \Re[e^{-i\xi \ln K}(\tilde{f}_j(x_\tau, \tau = 0, \xi|x_\tau))]\,d\xi \tag{15.305}$$

$$\frac{\partial^2 P_j}{\partial S_t^2} = \frac{1}{\pi S_t^2}\int_0^\infty \Re[e^{-i\xi \ln K}((i\xi - 1)\tilde{f}_j(x_\tau, \tau = 0, \xi|x_\tau))]\,d\xi \tag{15.306}$$

$$\frac{\partial P_j}{\partial K} = -\frac{1}{\pi K}\int_0^\infty \Re[(e^{-i\xi \ln K}\tilde{f}_j(x_\tau, \tau = 0, \xi|x_\tau))\,d\xi] \tag{15.307}$$

$$\frac{\partial^2 P_j}{\partial K^2} = \frac{1}{\pi K^2}\int_0^\infty \Re[e^{-i\xi \ln K}(i\xi + 1)\,\tilde{f}_j(x_\tau, \tau = 0, \xi|x_\tau)\,d\xi] \tag{15.308}$$

Proof. On the basis of (15.273) and (15.274), $\partial P_j/\partial S_t$ is given by

$$\frac{\partial P_j}{\partial S_t} = \frac{\partial}{\partial S_t}\left(\frac{1}{2} + \frac{1}{\pi}\int_0^\infty \Re\left[\frac{e^{-i\xi \ln K}}{i\xi}\tilde{f}_j(x_\tau, \tau = 0, \xi|x_\tau)\,d\xi\right]\right)$$

By using (15.301), one obtains (15.305). By expansion, (15.305) gives the expanded form of $\partial^2 P_j/\partial S_t^2$:

$$\frac{\partial^2 P_j}{\partial S_t^2} = \frac{\partial^2}{\partial S_t^2}\left(\frac{1}{2} + \frac{1}{\pi}\int_0^\infty \Re\left[\frac{e^{-i\xi \ln K}}{i\xi}\tilde{f}_j(x_\tau, \tau = 0, \xi|x_\tau)\,d\xi\right]\right)$$

By using (15.302) one has (15.306). One now computes $\partial P_j/\partial K$. Recalling (15.276) or (15.277) one has

$$\frac{\partial P_j}{\partial K} = -\frac{S_t}{K}\frac{\partial P_j}{\partial S_t}$$

and by using (15.305), one obtains (15.307). By expansion, (15.305) gives the expanded form of $\partial^2 P_j / \partial K^2$:

$$\frac{\partial^2 P_j}{\partial K^2} = \frac{\partial^2}{\partial K^2} \left(\frac{1}{2} + \frac{1}{\pi} \int_0^\infty \Re \left[\frac{e^{-i\xi \ln K}}{i\xi} \tilde{f}_j(x_\tau, \tau = 0, \xi | x_\tau) \, d\xi \right] \right)$$

By using (15.304), one has (15.308). □

Proposition 15.40. *The following relations hold:*

$$\frac{\partial P_1}{\partial v_t} = \frac{1}{\pi} \int_0^\infty \Re \left[\frac{e^{-i\xi \ln K}}{i\xi} \left(e^{C_\tau^{(1)} + i\xi x_\tau} \cdot \frac{1}{2} i\xi(i\xi + 1)\tau \right) \right] d\xi \qquad (15.309)$$

$$\frac{\partial P_2}{\partial v_t} = \frac{1}{\pi} \int_0^\infty \Re \left[\frac{e^{-i\xi \ln K}}{i\xi} \left(e^{C_\tau^{(2)} + i\xi x_\tau} \cdot \frac{1}{2} i\xi(i\xi - 1)\tau \right) \right] d\xi \qquad (15.310)$$

Proof. The partial derivatives are computed by using (15.273) and (15.274), ie,

$$\frac{\partial P_1}{\partial v_t} = \frac{\partial}{\partial v_t} \left(\frac{1}{2} + \frac{1}{\pi} \int_0^\infty \Re \left[\frac{e^{-i\xi \ln K}}{i\xi} \tilde{f}_1(x_\tau, \tau = 0, \xi | x_\tau) \right] d\xi \right)$$

$$= \frac{1}{\pi} \int_0^\infty \Re \left[\frac{e^{-i\xi \ln K}}{i\xi} \left(e^{C_\tau^{(1)} + i\xi x_\tau} \cdot \frac{1}{2} i\xi(i\xi + 1)\tau \right) \right] d\xi \quad \text{(recalling (15.271))}$$

Specularly,

$$\frac{\partial P_2}{\partial v_t} = \frac{\partial}{\partial v_t} \left(\frac{1}{2} + \frac{1}{\pi} \int_0^\infty \Re \left[\frac{e^{-i\xi \ln K}}{i\xi} \tilde{f}_2(x_\tau, \tau = 0, \xi | x_\tau) \right] d\xi \right)$$

$$= \frac{1}{\pi} \int_0^\infty \Re \left[\frac{e^{-i\xi \ln K}}{i\xi} \left(e^{C_\tau^{(2)} + i\xi x_\tau} \cdot \frac{1}{2} i\xi(i\xi - 1)\tau \right) \right] d\xi \quad \text{(recalling (15.272))}$$

□

Proposition 15.41. *The following relations hold:*

$$\frac{\partial P_1}{\partial t} = \frac{1}{\pi} \int_0^\infty \Re \left[\frac{e^{-i\xi \ln K}}{i\xi} e^{C_\tau^{(1)} + i\xi x_\tau} \left(-ri\xi + \lambda\mu[i\xi + 1] - \frac{1}{2} v[i\xi(i\xi + 1)] \right. \right.$$
$$\left. \left. - \lambda e^{(\sigma^2/2)(i\xi+1)}(1 + \mu)^{(i\xi+1)} + \lambda \right) \right] d\xi \qquad (15.311)$$

$$\frac{\partial P_2}{\partial t} = \frac{1}{\pi} \int_0^\infty \Re \left[\frac{e^{-i\xi \ln K}}{i\xi} e^{C_\tau^{(2)} + i\xi x_\tau} \left(-\frac{1}{2} vi\xi(i\xi - 1) - ri\xi \right. \right.$$
$$\left. \left. + \lambda\mu i\xi - \lambda e^{(\sigma^2/2)i\xi(i\xi-1)}(1 + \mu)^{i\xi} + \lambda \right) \right] d\xi \qquad (15.312)$$

Proof. Considering the substitution $\tau = T - t$, (15.273) and (15.274) are rearranged as in (15.275) with

$$
\begin{aligned}
C_t^{(1)} &= ri\xi(T - t) - \lambda\mu[i\xi + 1](T - t) + \tfrac{1}{2}v[i\xi(i\xi + 1)](T - t) \\
&\quad + \lambda(T - t)e^{(\sigma^2/2)(i\xi+1)}(1 + \mu)^{(i\xi+1)} - \lambda(T - t) \quad\quad (15.313) \\
C_t^{(2)} &= \tfrac{1}{2}vi\xi(T - t)(i\xi - 1) + ri\xi(T - t) - \lambda\mu i\xi(T - t) \\
&\quad + \lambda(T - t)e^{(\sigma^2/2)i\xi(i\xi-1)}(1 + \mu)^{i\xi} - \lambda(T - t) \quad\quad (15.314)
\end{aligned}
$$

for $k = 1, 2$.

Then, the partial derivatives are computed by using (15.313) and (15.314), ie,

$$
\begin{aligned}
\frac{\partial P_1}{\partial t} &= \frac{\partial}{\partial t}\left(\frac{1}{2} + \frac{1}{\pi}\int_0^\infty \Re\left[\frac{e^{-i\xi \ln K}}{i\xi}\tilde{f}_1(x_t, t = T, \xi|x_t)\right]d\xi\right) \\
&= \frac{1}{\pi}\int_0^\infty \Re\left[\frac{e^{-i\xi \ln K}}{i\xi}e^{C_T^{(1)}+i\xi x_\tau}\left(-ri\xi + \lambda\mu[i\xi + 1] - \frac{1}{2}v[i\xi(i\xi + 1)]\right.\right. \\
&\quad \left.\left.- \lambda e^{(\sigma^2/2)(i\xi+1)}(1 + \mu)^{(i\xi+1)} + \lambda\right)\right]d\xi
\end{aligned}
$$

Specularly,

$$
\begin{aligned}
\frac{\partial P_2}{\partial t} &= \frac{\partial}{\partial t}\left(\frac{1}{2} + \frac{1}{\pi}\int_0^\infty \Re\left[\frac{e^{-i\xi \ln K}}{i\xi}\tilde{f}_2(x_t, t = T, \xi|x_t)\right]d\xi\right) \\
&= \frac{1}{\pi}\int_0^\infty \Re\left[\frac{e^{-i\xi \ln K}}{i\xi}\left(-\frac{1}{2}vi\xi(i\xi - 1) - ri\xi + \lambda\mu i\xi\right.\right. \\
&\quad \left.\left.- \lambda e^{(\sigma^2/2)i\xi(i\xi-1)}(1 + \mu)^{i\xi} + \lambda\right)\right]d\xi \qquad \square
\end{aligned}
$$

Proposition 15.42. *A call option* Delta *is*

$$
\Delta_C = P_1 \qquad\qquad (15.315)
$$

Proof. To define a call option Delta at time t, one has

$$
\Delta_C = \frac{\partial C_t}{\partial S_t}
$$
$$
= P_1 \quad \text{(under (15.280))} \qquad\qquad \square
$$

Proposition 15.43. *A call option* Gamma *is*

$$
\Gamma_C = \frac{\partial P_1}{\partial S_t} \qquad\qquad (15.316)
$$

(for the expression $\partial P_1/\partial S_t$, see expression (15.305)).

Proof. To define a call option Gamma at time t, one has

$$\Gamma_C = \frac{\partial^2 C_t}{\partial S_t^2}$$

$$= \frac{\partial \Delta_t}{\partial S_t} \quad \text{(under (15.315))}$$

$$= \frac{\partial P_1}{\partial S_t} \qquad \qquad \square$$

Proposition 15.44. *A call option* Vega *is*

$$\mathcal{V}_C = S_t \frac{\partial P_1}{\partial v_t} - K e^{-r\tau} \frac{\partial P_2}{\partial v_t} \tag{15.317}$$

(for the expression $\partial P_j / \partial v_t$, see expression (15.309)).

Proof. To define a call option Vega at time t, one has

$$\mathcal{V}_C = \frac{\partial C_t}{\partial v_t}$$

$$= S_t \frac{\partial P_1}{\partial v_t} - K e^{-r\tau} \frac{\partial P_2}{\partial v_t} \qquad \square$$

Corollary 15.8. *The second-order crossed derivative with respect to v_t and S_t is*

$$\frac{\partial^2 C_t}{\partial S_t \partial v_t} = \frac{\partial P_1}{\partial v_t} \tag{15.318}$$

Proof. This is proved by differentiating (15.315) with respect to v_t. $\qquad \square$

Proposition 15.45. *A call option* Theta *is*

$$\Theta_C = S_t \frac{\partial P_1}{\partial t} - K \left(r e^{-r(T-t)} P_2 + e^{-r(T-t)} \frac{\partial P_2}{\partial t} \right) \tag{15.319}$$

(for the expression $\partial P_j / \partial t$, see expressions (15.311) and (15.312)).

Proof. To prove this, it is enough to differentiate (15.239) with respect to t. $\qquad \square$

Proposition 15.46. *A call option* Rho *is*

$$\mathcal{C}_C = K \tau e^{-r\tau} P_2 \tag{15.320}$$

Proof. Under the definition of a call option rho at time t, one has

$$\frac{\partial C_t}{\partial r} = \frac{\partial}{\partial r}[S_t P_1 - Ke^{-r\tau}P_2]$$

and, then,

$$\rho_C = \left[S_t \frac{\partial P_1}{\partial r} - K\left(-\tau e^{-r\tau}P_2 + e^{-r\tau}\frac{\partial P_2}{\partial r}\right)\right] \tag{15.321}$$

where $\partial P_1/\partial r$ and $\partial P_2/\partial r$ become

$$\frac{\partial P_j}{\partial r} = \frac{\partial}{\partial r}\left(\frac{1}{2} + \frac{1}{\pi}\int_0^\infty \Re\left[\frac{e^{-i\xi \ln K}}{i\xi}\tilde{f}_j(.x_\tau, \tau = 0, \xi| x_\tau)\right]d\xi\right)$$

$$= \frac{1}{\pi}\int_0^\infty \Re\left[\frac{e^{-i\xi \ln K}}{i\xi}\left(e^{(C_\tau^{(j)}+i\xi x_\tau)} \cdot \frac{\partial C_\tau^{(j)}}{\partial r}\right)\right]d\xi$$

$$= \frac{\tau}{\pi}\frac{S_t}{S_t}\int_0^\infty \Re\left[e^{-i\xi \ln K}\left(e^{(C_\tau^{(j)}+i\xi x_\tau)}\right)\right]d\xi \quad \text{(recalling (15.271) and (15.272))}$$

recalling (15.305), one has

$$\frac{\partial P_j}{\partial r} = \tau S_t \frac{\partial P_j}{\partial S_t} \tag{15.322}$$

Replacing (15.322) for $j = 1, 2$ in (15.321), one obtains

$$\frac{\partial C_t}{\partial r} = 2\tau S_t^2 \frac{\partial P_1}{\partial S_t} + K\tau e^{-r\tau}P_2 - 2\tau S_t Ke^{-r\tau}\frac{\partial P_2}{\partial S_t}$$

$$= K\tau e^{-r\tau}P_2 \quad \text{(using (15.281))} \qquad \square$$

15.2.6. The Heston model
15.2.6.1. Introduction
The Heston model was the first stochastic volatility model in the literature to provide a closed formula for European option pricing.

This model is defined by the following SDE system:

$$dS_t = \mu S_t \, dt + \sqrt{v_t}S_t \, dz_t^{(1)} \tag{15.323}$$

$$dv_t = \kappa[\theta - v_t] \, dt + \sigma\sqrt{v_t} \, dz_t^{(2)} \tag{15.324}$$

where:

- (15.323) is the SDE which governs the price process of the underlying;
- S_t is the spot price of the underlying;
- μ is the logarithm yield of the underlying;
- v_t is the variance of the process;

- $dz_t^{(1)}$ is a standard Wiener process;
- (15.324) is the SDE which governs the variance process of the underlying v_t;
- κ, θ, σ are the SDE parameters;
- $dz_t^{(2)}$ is a standard Wiener process;
- $\rho_{1,2}$ is the correlation coefficient between $z_t^{(1)}$ and $z_t^{(2)}$, ie, $dz_t^{(1)} \cdot dz_t^{(2)} = \rho_{1,2}\, dt$.

Notation 15.3. In the following, in order to simplify notation, the subscript t in the SDE is omitted to have the notation $dz_t^{(i)} = dz_i$.

15.2.6.2.   PDE derivation for portfolio replication

In this model, the option price f to be determined is governed by the behaviour of the underlying, by time and by the variance evolution trends, ie,

$$f = f(S, v, t) \tag{15.325}$$

Considering f differentiable to the order required and considering that the members of order $dt^2, dt\, dv, dt\, dS$, are equal to zero based on some fundamental stochastic calculus rules, ie, Itô's algebra (see Proposition 12.7), the computation of the stochastic differential of f gives the following equation:

$$df = \frac{\partial f}{\partial S}dS + \frac{\partial f}{\partial t}dt + \frac{\partial f}{\partial v}dv + \frac{1}{2}\left[\frac{\partial^2 f}{\partial S^2}dS^2 + \frac{\partial^2 f}{\partial v^2}dv^2\right] + \frac{\partial^2 f}{\partial S\partial v}dS\,dv \tag{15.326}$$

Replacing the expressions which describe the processes of S and v inside 15.326, one has

$$\begin{aligned}
df = {} & \frac{\partial f}{\partial S}(\mu S\,dt + \sqrt{v}S\,dz_1) + \frac{\partial f}{\partial t}dt + \frac{\partial f}{\partial v}[\kappa(\theta - v)\,dt + \sigma\sqrt{v}\,dz_2] \\
& + \frac{1}{2}\frac{\partial^2 f}{\partial S^2}(vS^2\,dt) + \frac{1}{2}\frac{\partial^2 f}{\partial v^2}(\sigma^2 v\,dt) + \frac{\partial^2 f}{\partial S\partial v}(S\sigma\rho_{1,2}v)\,dt
\end{aligned} \tag{15.327}$$

Then, as above for the BSM formula derivation, the option replication portfolio is built, ie,

$$\pi = f_1 - \Delta_1 f_0 - \Delta_0 S \tag{15.328}$$

where:

- f_i for $i = 0, 1$ are the prices of the two options;
- Δ_i for $i = 0, 1$ are the quantities of the underlying S.

In order to derive the equivalence between df and $d\pi$, the latter is derived:

$$d\pi = \left[\sqrt{v}S\left(\frac{\partial f_1}{\partial S} - \Delta_1 \frac{\partial f_0}{\partial S} - \Delta_0\right)\right] dz_1 + \left[\sigma\sqrt{v}\left(\frac{\partial f_1}{\partial v} - \Delta_1 \frac{\partial f_0}{\partial v}\right)\right] dz_2$$

$$+ \frac{\partial f_1}{\partial S}(\mu S\, dt) + \frac{\partial f_1}{\partial t} dt + \frac{\partial f_1}{\partial v}[\kappa(\theta - v)\, dt] + \frac{1}{2}\frac{\partial^2 f_1}{\partial S^2}(vS^2\, dt) + \frac{1}{2}\frac{\partial^2 f_1}{\partial v^2}(\sigma^2 v\, dt)$$

$$+ \frac{\partial^2 f_1}{\partial S \partial v}(S\sigma\rho_{1,2}v)\, dt - \Delta_1\left[\frac{\partial f_0}{\partial S}(\mu S\, dt) + \frac{\partial f_0}{\partial t} dt + \frac{\partial f_0}{\partial v}[\kappa(\theta - v)\, dt]\right.$$

$$\left. + \frac{1}{2}\frac{\partial^2 f_0}{\partial S^2}(vS^2\, dt) + \frac{1}{2}\frac{\partial^2 f_0}{\partial v^2}(\sigma^2 v\, dt) + \frac{\partial^2 f_0}{\partial S \partial v}(S\sigma\rho_{1,2}v)\, dt\right] - \Delta_0(\mu S\, dt)$$

$$(15.329)$$

To nullify any random variable of that portfolio, ie, to eliminate terms in dz_i from Equation (15.329), the coefficients Δ_1, Δ_0, are appropriately chosen, ie,

$$\begin{cases} \left(\frac{\partial f_1}{\partial S} - \Delta_1 \frac{\partial f_0}{\partial S} - \Delta_0\right) = 0 \\ \left(\frac{\partial f_1}{\partial v} - \Delta_1 \frac{\partial f_0}{\partial v}\right) = 0 \end{cases}$$

$$(15.330)$$

Then, the system is solved:

$$\begin{cases} \Delta_0 = \frac{\partial f_1}{\partial S} - \frac{\partial f_1/\partial v}{\partial f_0/\partial v}\frac{\partial f_0}{\partial S} \\ \Delta_1 = \frac{\partial f_1/\partial v}{\partial f_0/\partial v} \end{cases}$$

$$(15.331)$$

Substituting the expressions by coefficients Δ_1, Δ_0 defined in (15.331) in Equation (15.329), one obtains

$$d\pi = \frac{\partial f_1}{\partial t} dt + \frac{1}{2}\frac{\partial^2 f_1}{\partial S^2}(vS^2\, dt) + \frac{\partial f_1}{\partial v}[\kappa(\theta - v)\, dt] + \frac{1}{2}\frac{\partial^2 f_1}{\partial v^2}(\sigma^2 v\, dt)$$

$$+ \frac{\partial^2 f_1}{\partial S \partial v}(S\sigma\rho_{1,2}v)\, dt - \frac{\partial f_1/\partial v}{\partial f_0/\partial v}\frac{\partial f_0}{\partial t} dt - \frac{\partial f_1/\partial v}{\partial f_0/\partial v}\frac{\partial f_0}{\partial v}[\kappa(\theta - v)\, dt]$$

$$- \frac{\partial f_1/\partial v}{\partial f_0/\partial v}\frac{1}{2}\frac{\partial^2 f_0}{\partial S^2}(vS^2\, dt) - \frac{\partial f_1/\partial v}{\partial f_0/\partial v}\frac{1}{2}\frac{\partial^2 f_0}{\partial v^2}(\sigma^2 v\, dt) - \frac{\partial f_1/\partial v}{\partial f_0/\partial v}\frac{\partial^2 f_0}{\partial S \partial v}(S\sigma\rho_{1,2}v)\, dt$$

$$(15.332)$$

In the case of the no-arbitrage hypothesis, defining r the risk-free yield, the following equivalence must hold for the replication portfolio π:

$$\frac{d\pi}{dt} = r\pi, \quad \text{that is } d\pi = r\pi\, dt$$

$$(15.333)$$

To apply equivalence (15.333), expressions (15.328), (15.332) and (15.331) have to be used. It can be derived that

$$\frac{\partial f_1}{\partial t} dt + \frac{1}{2}\frac{\partial^2 f_1}{\partial S^2}(vS^2\,dt) + \frac{\partial f_1}{\partial v}[\kappa(\theta - v)\,dt] + \frac{1}{2}\frac{\partial^2 f_1}{\partial v^2}(\sigma^2 v\,dt)$$

$$+ \frac{\partial^2 f_1}{\partial S\partial v}(S\sigma\rho_{1,2}v)\,dt - \frac{\partial f_1/\partial v}{\partial f_0/\partial v}\frac{\partial f_0}{\partial t}\,dt - \frac{\partial f_1/\partial v}{\partial f_0/\partial v}\frac{\partial f_0}{\partial v}[\kappa(\theta - v)\,dt]$$

$$- \frac{\partial f_1/\partial v}{\partial f_0/\partial v}\frac{1}{2}\frac{\partial^2 f_0}{\partial S^2}(vS^2\,dt) - \frac{\partial f_1/\partial v}{\partial f_0/\partial v}\frac{1}{2}\frac{\partial^2 f_0}{\partial v^2}(\sigma^2 v\,dt) - \frac{\partial f_1/\partial v}{\partial f_0/\partial v}\frac{\partial^2 f_0}{\partial S\partial v}(S\sigma\rho_{1,2}v)\,dt$$

$$= r\left(f_1 - \frac{\partial f_1/\partial v}{\partial f_0/\partial v}f_0 - \frac{\partial f_1}{\partial S}S + \frac{\partial f_1/\partial v}{\partial f_0/\partial v}\frac{\partial f_0}{\partial S}S\right)dt$$

It now becomes possible to isolate all of the members f_1 in the right member of the equation and all of the members in f_0 in the left member to get to the following equivalence:

$$\frac{-rf_0 + \frac{\partial f_0}{\partial t} + \frac{\partial f_0}{\partial S}rS + \frac{1}{2}\frac{\partial^2 f_0}{\partial S^2}vS^2 + \frac{1}{2}\frac{\partial^2 f_0}{\partial v^2}\sigma^2 v + \frac{\partial^2 f_0}{\partial S\partial v}S\sigma\rho_{1,2}v - [\kappa(\theta - v)]\partial f_0/\partial v}{\partial f_0/\partial v}$$

$$= \frac{-rf_1 + \frac{\partial f_1}{\partial t} + \frac{\partial f_1}{\partial S}rS + \frac{1}{2}\frac{\partial^2 f_1}{\partial S^2}vS^2 + \frac{1}{2}\frac{\partial^2 f_1}{\partial v^2}\sigma^2 v + \frac{\partial^2 f_1}{\partial S\partial v}S\sigma\rho_{1,2}v - [\kappa(\theta - v)]\partial f_1/\partial v}{\partial f_1/\partial v}$$

(15.334)

Equation (15.334) represents the no-arbitrage hypothesis (15.333) applied to portfolio (15.328). Since the elements in both the left and right members of the equation are identical except for the subscript of function f, ie, the price of a generic *contingent claim*, the choice of f_0 and of f_1 (ie, the maturity date or the strike price of the two options) has no influence on the replication portfolio buildup. This observation allows to consider only one of the quantities, and ignore subscripts so that it can be defined as

$$\frac{-rf + \frac{\partial f}{\partial t} + \frac{\partial f}{\partial S}rS + \frac{1}{2}\frac{\partial^2 f}{\partial S^2}vS^2 + \frac{1}{2}\frac{\partial^2 f}{\partial v^2}\sigma^2 v + \frac{\partial^2 f}{\partial S\partial v}S\sigma\rho_{1,2}v - [\kappa(\theta - v)]\partial f/\partial v}{\partial f/\partial v}$$

$$= \lambda^*(S, v, t) \quad (15.335)$$

or

$$- rf + \frac{\partial f}{\partial t} + \frac{\partial f}{\partial S}rS + \frac{1}{2}\frac{\partial^2 f}{\partial S^2}vS^2 + \frac{1}{2}\frac{\partial^2 f}{\partial v^2}\sigma^2 v$$

$$+ \frac{\partial^2 f}{\partial S\partial v}S\sigma\rho_{1,2}v + \frac{\partial f}{\partial v}[\kappa(\theta - v) - \lambda^*(S, v, t)] = 0 \quad (15.335)$$

where $\lambda^*(S, v, t)$, defined in the literature as the volatility risk premium, is any function which takes values other than zero.

15.2.6.3. PDE specification for the pricing of a call option: derivation of the Cauchy problem

Given the PDE (15.335) the Cauchy problem, where f describes the price of a call option C among all of the contingent claims, is defined by the PDE (15.335) specified to describe the call price and by its boundary conditions, ie, the call payoff value at maturity:

$$- rC + \frac{\partial C}{\partial t} + \frac{\partial C}{\partial S} rS + \frac{1}{2} \frac{\partial^2 C}{\partial S^2} vS^2 + \frac{1}{2} \frac{\partial^2 C}{\partial v^2} \sigma^2 v$$
$$+ \frac{\partial C}{\partial S \partial v} S\sigma\rho_{1,2}v + \frac{\partial C}{\partial v}[\kappa(\theta - v) - \lambda^*(S, v, t)] = 0 \qquad (15.336)$$
$$C(S, v, t = T) = \max(0, S_T - K) \qquad (15.336a)$$

where $C(S, v, t, T)$ is the call option price at time t.

15.2.6.3.1. Transformation of the Cauchy problem into the corresponding forward version

Equation (15.335) is specified in its equivalent *forward* price version.

For this purpose, one defines the following.

- At the place of S the forward price $F_{t,T} \doteq e^{r(T-t)}S_t$, ie,
  - posing $\tau \doteq (T - t)$;
  - defining $x_{t,T} \doteq x_\tau$;
  - defining $F_{t,T} \doteq F_\tau$;
  - defining $x_{t,T} \doteq \ln F_{t,T}$ or $x_\tau \doteq \ln F_\tau$;

  the following equivalences are derived:

  $$F_\tau = e^{x_\tau} = e^{r\tau}S_t \qquad (15.337)$$
  $$S_t = e^{x_\tau - r\tau} \qquad (15.338)$$
  $$\ln S_t = x_\tau - r\tau \qquad (15.339)$$
  $$x_\tau = \ln S_t + r\tau \qquad (15.340)$$

- At the place of the call option price $C(S, v, t, T) \doteq C(x, v, \tau)$, its corresponding *forward* version, ie,

  $$\tilde{C}(x, v, \tau) = e^{r\tau}C(x, v, \tau) = e^{r(t-t)}C(S, v, t, T) \qquad (15.341)$$

Then the new version of (15.335) is derived, first as a function of x, and after of $\tilde{C}$.

Recalling that $C = f(S(g(x))$, the relations between $\partial C/\partial x$ and $\partial C/\partial S$ and between $\partial^2 C/\partial x^2$ and $\partial^2 C/\partial S^2$ are then derived:

$$\frac{\partial C}{\partial S} = \frac{\partial C}{\partial x}\frac{1}{S} \tag{15.342}$$

$$\frac{\partial^2 C}{\partial S^2} = \frac{\partial^2 C}{\partial x^2}\frac{1}{S^2} - \frac{\partial C}{\partial x}\frac{1}{S^2} \tag{15.343}$$

The Cauchy problem (15.336) is rearranged for x, by using (15.342) and (15.343) by simplifying and defining

$$\lambda^*(S, v, t) = \tilde{\lambda}v \tag{15.344}$$

$$\frac{\partial C}{\partial t} + r\left[\frac{\partial C}{\partial x} - C\right] + \frac{1}{2}\frac{\partial^2 C}{\partial v^2}(\sigma^2 v) + \frac{\partial^2 C}{\partial x \partial v}(v\sigma\rho_{1,2})$$

$$+ \frac{1}{2}\left[\frac{\partial^2 C}{\partial x^2} - \frac{\partial C}{\partial x}\right]v + \frac{\partial C}{\partial v}[\kappa(\theta - v) - \tilde{\lambda}v] = 0 \tag{15.345}$$

Equation (15.345) is shifted into the corresponding forward version of (15.336). The PDE is expressed on the base of a call option forward price as in (15.341). To this end, the partial derivatives of $\tilde{C}$ are computed and the relation with the partial derivatives with respect to C are derived:

$$\frac{\partial C}{\partial t} = -e^{-r\tau}\frac{\partial \tilde{C}}{\partial \tau} + rC \tag{15.346}$$

$$\frac{\partial C}{\partial x} = e^{-r\tau}\frac{\partial \tilde{C}}{\partial x} \tag{15.347}$$

$$\frac{\partial^2 C}{\partial x^2} = e^{-r\tau}\frac{\partial^2 \tilde{C}}{\partial x^2} \tag{15.348}$$

$$\frac{\partial C}{\partial v} = e^{-r\tau}\frac{\partial \tilde{C}}{\partial v} \tag{15.349}$$

$$\frac{\partial^2 C}{\partial v^2} = e^{-r\tau}\frac{\partial^2 \tilde{C}}{\partial v^2} \tag{15.350}$$

$$\frac{\partial^2 C}{\partial x \partial v} = e^{-r\tau}\frac{\partial^2 \tilde{C}}{\partial x \partial v} \tag{15.351}$$

By replacing (15.346), (15.347), (15.348), (15.349), (15.350) and (15.351) in (15.345), one obtains

$$e^{-r\tau}\left[-\frac{\partial \tilde{C}}{\partial \tau} + r\frac{\partial \tilde{C}}{\partial x} + \frac{1}{2}\frac{\partial^2 \tilde{C}}{\partial v^2}(\sigma^2 v) + \frac{\partial^2 \tilde{C}}{\partial x \partial v}(v\sigma\rho_{1,2})\right.$$

$$\left.+ \frac{1}{2}\left(\frac{\partial^2 \tilde{C}}{\partial x^2} - \frac{\partial \tilde{C}}{\partial x}\right)v + \frac{\partial \tilde{C}}{\partial v}[\kappa(\theta - v) - \tilde{\lambda}v]\right] = 0 \tag{15.352}$$

Considering that $e^{-r\tau} > 0$, Equation (15.352) may also be written as

$$-\frac{\partial \tilde{C}}{\partial \tau} + r\frac{\partial \tilde{C}}{\partial x} + \frac{1}{2}\frac{\partial^2 \tilde{C}}{\partial v^2}(\sigma^2 v) + \frac{\partial^2 \tilde{C}}{\partial x \partial v}(v\sigma\rho_{1,2})$$
$$+ \frac{1}{2}\left(\frac{\partial^2 \tilde{C}}{\partial x^2} - \frac{\partial \tilde{C}}{\partial x}\right)v + \frac{\partial \tilde{C}}{\partial v}[\kappa(\theta - v) - \tilde{\lambda}v] = 0 \qquad (15.353)$$

Equation (15.353) is the forward version of (15.336). To finalise the definition of the Cauchy problem, the boundary condition corresponding to that of (15.336a) has to be determined; for this purpose, simply rearrange this equation in its logarithmic version by using (15.339), ie,

$$C(S_t, v_t, t = T) = \max(0, S_T - K)$$
$$e^{-r\cdot 0}\tilde{C}(x_\tau, v_\tau, \tau = 0) = \max(0, e^{x_\tau - r\cdot 0} - K)$$

and, finally,

$$\tilde{C}(x_\tau, v_\tau, \tau = 0) = \max(0, e^{x_\tau} - K)$$

The new Cauchy problem is then derived, ie,

$$-\frac{\partial \tilde{C}}{\partial \tau} + r\frac{\partial \tilde{C}}{\partial x} + \frac{1}{2}\frac{\partial^2 \tilde{C}}{\partial v^2}(\sigma^2 v) + \frac{\partial^2 \tilde{C}}{\partial x \partial v}(v\sigma\rho_{1,2})$$
$$+ \frac{1}{2}\left(\frac{\partial^2 \tilde{C}}{\partial x^2} - \frac{\partial \tilde{C}}{\partial x}\right)v + \frac{\partial \tilde{C}}{\partial v}[\kappa(\theta - v) - \tilde{\lambda}v] = 0 \qquad (15.353)$$
$$\tilde{C}(x_\tau, v_\tau, \tau = 0) = \max(0, e^{x_{\tau=0}} - K) \qquad (15.353a)$$

15.2.6.3.2. The shift into the à-la BSM pricing context The Cauchy problem as in (15.353) is now specified in the classic à-la BSM form, ie,

$$C_t(S, v, t, T) = S_t P_1(S, v, t, T) - Ke^{-r(T-t)}P_2(S, v, t, T) \quad \text{or}$$
$$C_t(x, v, \tau) = S_t P_1(x, v, \tau) - Ke^{-r\tau}P_2(x, v, \tau) \qquad (15.354)$$

where P_1, P_2 are probability measures.

Considering that (15.353) is the forward version of (15.336), the forward version of (15.354) is derived similarly. Equation (15.354), rearranged by using $x_{t,T} = x_\tau$ and (15.339), can be written as

$$C_t(x, v, \tau) = e^{x_\tau - r\tau}P_1(x, v, \tau) - Ke^{-r\tau}P_2(x, v, \tau) \qquad (15.355)$$

Equation (15.355), rearranged in the terms of $\tilde{C}$ using (15.341), can be written as

$$\tilde{C}_t(x, v, \tau) = e^{x_\tau}P_1(x, v, \tau) - KP_2(x, v, \tau) \qquad (15.356)$$

Notation 15.4. In the following, $x = x_\tau$ is used to simplify notation.

Then the derivatives are computed to expand (15.353) by using (15.356):

$$\frac{\partial \tilde{C}}{\partial x} = e^x P_1(x, v, \tau) + e^x \frac{\partial P_1}{\partial x} - K \frac{\partial P_2}{\partial x} \tag{15.357}$$

$$\frac{\partial^2 \tilde{C}}{\partial x^2} = e^x P_1(x, v, \tau) + 2e^x \frac{\partial P_1}{\partial x} + e^x \frac{\partial^2 P_1}{\partial x^2} - K \frac{\partial^2 P_2}{\partial x^2} \tag{15.358}$$

$$\frac{\partial \tilde{C}}{\partial v} = e^x \frac{\partial P_1}{\partial v} - K \frac{\partial P_2}{\partial v} \tag{15.359}$$

$$\frac{\partial^2 \tilde{C}}{\partial v^2} = e^x \frac{\partial^2 P_1}{\partial v^2} - K \frac{\partial^2 P_2}{\partial v^2} \tag{15.360}$$

$$\frac{\partial^2 \tilde{C}}{\partial x \partial v} = e^x \frac{\partial P_1}{\partial v} + e^x \frac{\partial^2 P_1}{\partial x \partial v} - K \frac{\partial^2 P_2}{\partial x \partial v} \tag{15.361}$$

$$\frac{\partial \tilde{C}}{\partial \tau} = e^x \left[\frac{\partial P_1}{\partial \tau} + r P_1(x, v, \tau) \right] - K \frac{\partial P_2}{\partial \tau} \tag{15.362}$$

Then (15.357), (15.358), (15.359), (15.360), (15.361) and (15.362) are replaced in (15.353) to obtain

$$e^x \left[-\frac{\partial P_1}{\partial \tau} + \frac{\partial P_1}{\partial x} \left(r + \frac{1}{2} v \right) + \frac{1}{2} \left(\frac{\partial^2 P_1}{\partial v^2} (\sigma^2 v) \right) + \frac{\partial^2 P_1}{\partial x \partial v} (v \sigma \rho_{1,2}) + \frac{1}{2} \left(\frac{\partial^2 P_1}{\partial x^2} v \right) \right.$$

$$\left. + \frac{\partial P_1}{\partial v} [\kappa \theta - \kappa v - \tilde{\lambda} v + v \sigma \rho_{1,2}] \right] - K \left[-\frac{\partial P_2}{\partial \tau} + \frac{\partial P_2}{\partial x} \left(r - \frac{1}{2} v \right) + \frac{\partial^2 P_2}{\partial v^2} (\sigma^2 v) \right.$$

$$\left. - \frac{\partial^2 P_2}{\partial x \partial v} (v \sigma \rho_{1,2}) + \frac{1}{2} v \left(\frac{\partial^2 P_2}{\partial x^2} \right) + \frac{\partial P_2}{\partial v} [\kappa \theta - \kappa v - \tilde{\lambda} v] \right] = 0$$

Since $e^x > 0$ and also $K > 0$, in order to verify the equivalence above, it is enough that

$$\begin{cases} -\dfrac{\partial P_1}{\partial \tau} + r \dfrac{\partial P_1}{\partial x} + \dfrac{1}{2} v \dfrac{\partial P_1}{\partial x} + \dfrac{1}{2} \dfrac{\partial^2 P_1}{\partial v^2} (\sigma^2 v) + \dfrac{\partial^2 P_1}{\partial x \partial v} (v \sigma \rho_{1,2}) \\ + \dfrac{1}{2} \dfrac{\partial^2 P_1}{\partial x^2} v + \dfrac{\partial P_1}{\partial v} [\kappa \theta - v(\kappa + \tilde{\lambda} - \sigma \rho_{1,2})] = 0 \\[2mm] -\dfrac{\partial P_2}{\partial \tau} + r \dfrac{\partial P_2}{\partial x} - \dfrac{1}{2} v \dfrac{\partial P_2}{\partial x} + \dfrac{1}{2} \dfrac{\partial^2 P_2}{\partial v^2} (\sigma^2 v) + \dfrac{\partial^2 P_2}{\partial x \partial v} (v \sigma \rho_{1,2}) \\ + \dfrac{1}{2} \dfrac{\partial^2 P_2}{\partial x^2} v + \dfrac{\partial P_2}{\partial v} [\kappa \theta - v(\kappa + \tilde{\lambda})] = 0 \end{cases} \tag{15.363}$$

By substituting, for $j = 1, 2$,

$$c_1 = \frac{1}{2}, \quad c_2 = -\frac{1}{2}, \quad a = \kappa \theta, \quad b_1 = \kappa + \tilde{\lambda} - \rho_{1,2} \sigma, \quad b_2 = \kappa + \tilde{\lambda} \tag{15.364}$$

Equation (15.363) may also be written as one PDE, ie,

$$-\frac{\partial P_j}{\partial \tau} + \frac{\partial P_j}{\partial x}(r + c_j v) + \frac{1}{2}\frac{\partial^2 P_j}{\partial v^2}(\sigma^2 v) + \frac{\partial^2 P_j}{\partial x \partial v}(v\sigma \rho_{1,2})$$
$$+ \frac{1}{2}\frac{\partial^2 P_j}{\partial x^2}v + \frac{\partial P_j}{\partial v}(a - b_j v) = 0 \qquad (15.365)$$

Equation (15.365) is the PDE (15.353), the forward version of (15.336), rearranged in the à-la BSM call pricing context as in (15.356). To identify the Cauchy problems in (15.365), equivalent to the problem in (15.353) and then to (15.456), one has to derive the boundary condition which corresponds to that inside (15.353a); for this purpose, the characteristics of function P_j are specified at time $\tau = 0$, ie,

$$P_j(x_\tau, v_\tau, \tau = 0) = \begin{cases} 1 & \text{if } (e^{x_\tau} - K) \geq 0 \\ 0 & \text{if } (e^{x_\tau} - K) < 0 \end{cases} \quad \text{for } j = 1, 2$$

applying the logarithm

$$P_j(x_\tau, v_\tau, \tau = 0) = \begin{cases} 1 & \text{if } x_\tau \geq \ln K \\ 0 & \text{if } x_\tau < \ln K \end{cases} \quad \text{for } j = 1, 2$$

and using the definition of the index function (see Definition 6.3), this gives

$$P_j(x_\tau, v_\tau, \tau = 0) = 1_{(x_\tau \geq \ln K)}$$

The following equations are the transformed Cauchy problem in the à-la BSM call pricing environment, determined as in (15.353), and its boundary conditions:

$$-\frac{\partial P_j}{\partial \tau} + \frac{\partial P_j}{\partial x}(r + c_j v) + \frac{1}{2}\frac{\partial^2 P_j}{\partial v^2}(\sigma^2 v) + \frac{\partial^2 P_j}{\partial x \partial v}(v\sigma \rho_{1,2})$$
$$+ \frac{1}{2}\frac{\partial^2 P_j}{\partial x^2}v + \frac{\partial P_j}{\partial v}(a - b_j v) = 0 \qquad (15.365)$$

$$P_j(x_\tau, v_\tau, \tau = 0) = 1_{(x_\tau \geq \ln K)} \qquad (15.365a)$$

Then the characteristics of the probability measure P_j at the generic time τ remain to be determined. For this purpose (15.365) is rearranged by using the Feynman–Kac formula (see Theorem 12.21). Actually, the corresponding SDE of (15.365) may be determined, ie,

$$dx_\tau^{(j)} = (r + c^{(j)}v_\tau)\, d\tau + \sqrt{v_\tau}\, dz_\tau^{(1)} \quad \text{with } x_\tau = x \qquad (15.366)$$

$$dv_\tau^{(j)} = (a - b^{(j)}v_\tau)\, d\tau + \sigma\sqrt{v_\tau}\, dz_\tau^{(2)} \quad \text{with } v_\tau = v \qquad (15.367)$$

respectively, for $j = 1$ and $j = 2$, with $dz_\tau^{(1)} \cdot dz_\tau^{(2)} = \rho_{1,2}\, d\tau$.

The specification of (12.99) can be derived from the theorem above, ie,

$$P_j(x_\tau, v_\tau, \tau) = E_j[1_{(x_{\tau=0} \geq \ln K)} | x_\tau = x, v_\tau = v]$$

simplifying, one has

$$P_j(x_\tau, v_\tau, \tau) = P_j[x_{\tau=0} \geq \ln K | x_\tau = x, v_\tau = v]$$

By denoting the equivalence $x_t = x$ by x_t and the equivalence $v_t = v$ by v_t, one obtains the characteristics of the probability measure P_j at a generic time τ:

$$P_j(x_\tau, v_\tau, \tau) = P_j(.x_{\tau=0} \geq \ln K | x_\tau, v_\tau) \qquad (15.368)$$

15.2.6.3.3. *The shift in Fourier space* The Cauchy problem identified in (15.365) is now shifted in the Fourier space, ie, it is rearranged as a function of the conditioned characteristic function. For this purpose, (11.123) is rearranged, by using Notation 11.34, for $P_j(x_\tau, v_\tau, \tau)$, ie[9],

$$P_j(x_{\tau=0} \geq \ln K | x_\tau, v_\tau) = \frac{1}{2\pi} \int_{-\infty}^{\infty} \frac{e^{-i\xi \ln K}}{i\xi} \tilde{f}_j(x_\tau, v_\tau, \tau = 0, \xi | x_\tau, v_\tau) \, d\xi \quad (15.369)$$

This expression, by denoting for simplicity $\tilde{f}_j(x_\tau, v_\tau, \tau = 0, \xi | x_\tau, v_\tau) \doteq \tilde{f}_j$, is used to compute partial derivatives (to simplify notation $\tilde{f}_j(x_T, v_T, \xi | x_t, v_t) = f_j(\xi)$), ie,

$$\frac{\partial P_j}{\partial \tau} = \frac{\partial}{\partial \tau} \left[\frac{1}{2\pi} \int_{-\infty}^{\infty} \frac{e^{-i\xi \ln K}}{i\xi} \tilde{f}_j(\xi) \, d\xi \right] = \frac{1}{2\pi} \int_{-\infty}^{\infty} \frac{e^{-i\xi \ln K}}{i\xi} \frac{\partial \tilde{f}_j}{\partial \tau} \, d\xi \qquad (15.370)$$

$$\frac{\partial P_j}{\partial x} = \frac{\partial}{\partial x} \left[\frac{1}{2\pi} \int_{-\infty}^{\infty} \frac{e^{-i\xi \ln K}}{i\xi} \tilde{f}_j(\xi) \, d\xi \right] = \frac{1}{2\pi} \int_{-\infty}^{\infty} \frac{e^{-i\xi \ln K}}{i\xi} \frac{\partial \tilde{f}_j}{\partial x} \, d\xi \qquad (15.371)$$

$$\frac{\partial P_j}{\partial v} = \frac{\partial}{\partial v} \left[\frac{1}{2\pi} \int_{-\infty}^{\infty} \frac{e^{-i\xi \ln K}}{i\xi} \tilde{f}_j(\xi) \, d\xi \right] = \frac{1}{2\pi} \int_{-\infty}^{\infty} \frac{e^{-i\xi \ln K}}{i\xi} \frac{\partial \tilde{f}_j}{\partial v} \, d\xi \qquad (15.372)$$

The second-order derivative in x is computed based on (15.371):

$$\frac{\partial^2 P_j}{\partial x^2} = \frac{\partial}{\partial x} \left[\frac{1}{2\pi} \int_{-\infty}^{\infty} \frac{e^{-i\xi \ln K}}{i\xi} \frac{\partial \tilde{f}_j}{\partial x} \, d\xi \right] = \frac{1}{2\pi} \int_{-\infty}^{\infty} \frac{e^{-i\xi \ln K}}{i\xi} \frac{\partial^2 \tilde{f}_j}{\partial x^2} \, d\xi \qquad (15.373)$$

The second-order derivative in v is computed based on (15.372):

$$\frac{\partial^2 P_j}{\partial v^2} = \frac{\partial}{\partial v} \left[\frac{1}{2\pi} \int_{-\infty}^{\infty} \frac{e^{-i\xi \ln K}}{i\xi} \frac{\partial \tilde{f}_j}{\partial v} \, d\xi \right] = \frac{1}{2\pi} \int_{-\infty}^{\infty} \frac{e^{-i\xi \ln K}}{i\xi} \frac{\partial^2 \tilde{f}_j}{\partial v^2} \, d\xi \qquad (15.374)$$

[9] Equation (11.123) shows ">" and not "≥"; in this case, the difference is not relevant, given the call *payoff*.

The second-order crossed derivative is computed either from (15.371) or from (15.372):

$$\frac{\partial^2 P_j}{\partial x \partial v} = \frac{\partial}{\partial v}\left[\frac{1}{2\pi}\int_{-\infty}^{\infty}\frac{e^{-i\xi \ln K}}{i\xi}\frac{\partial \tilde{f}_j}{\partial x}d\xi\right] = \frac{1}{2\pi}\int_{-\infty}^{\infty}\frac{e^{-i\xi \ln K}}{i\xi}\frac{\partial^2 \tilde{f}_j}{\partial v \partial x}d\xi \qquad (15.375)$$

Then (15.370), (15.371), (15.372), (15.373), (15.374) and (15.375) are substituted in (15.365) to obtain

$$\frac{1}{2\pi}\int_{-\infty}^{\infty}\frac{e^{-i\xi \ln K}}{i\xi}\left[\frac{\partial \tilde{f}_j}{\partial \tau} + \frac{\partial \tilde{f}_j}{\partial x}(r + c_j v) + \frac{1}{2}\frac{\partial^2 \tilde{f}_j}{\partial v^2}(\sigma^2 v) + \frac{\partial^2 \tilde{f}_j}{\partial v \partial x}(v \sigma \rho_{1,2})\right.$$
$$\left. + \frac{\partial^2 \tilde{f}_j}{\partial x^2}v + \frac{\partial \tilde{f}_j}{\partial v}(a - b_j v)\right]d\xi = 0$$

This equation is verified under the condition that the member inside square brackets is equal to zero. Then the PDE is given only by this last member, ie,

$$-\frac{\partial \tilde{f}_j}{\partial \tau} + \frac{\partial \tilde{f}_j}{\partial x}(r + c_j v) + \frac{1}{2}\frac{\partial^2 \tilde{f}_j}{\partial v^2}(\sigma^2 v) + \frac{\partial^2 \tilde{f}_j}{\partial v \partial x}(v \sigma \rho_{1,2}) + \frac{\partial^2 \tilde{f}_j}{\partial x^2}v + \frac{\partial \tilde{f}_j}{\partial v}[a - b_j v]$$
$$(15.376)$$

To complete the shift of the Cauchy problem as in (15.365) one has to specify the final conditions inside (15.365a). By using Theorem 6.5, this final condition is rearranged as

$$P_j(x_\tau, v_\tau, \tau = 0) = 1_{(x_\tau = 0 \geq \ln K)} = \theta_{\ln K}(x_\tau = 0) \triangleq \theta(x_\tau = 0 - \ln K)$$

where θ is the Heaviside function.

Recalling Proposition 6.10 one has

$$\theta(x_\tau = 0 - \ln K) = \int_{-\infty}^{x_\tau = 0 - \ln K}\delta(w)\,dw$$

which, under Theorem 9.4 and under the Fubini theorem (see Theorem 10.22), is equal to

$$\theta(x_\tau = 0 - \ln K) = \frac{1}{2\pi}\int_{-\infty}^{+\infty}\left(\int_{-\infty}^{x_\tau = 0 - \ln K}e^{i\xi w}\,dw\right)d\xi$$
$$= \frac{1}{2\pi}\int_{-\infty}^{+\infty}\frac{1}{i\xi}e^{-i\xi \ln K}e^{i\xi x_\tau = 0}\,d\xi$$

comparing this last expression to (15.482), arranged for $\tau = 0$ and simplifying, one obtains the final conditions of the Cauchy problem as under 15.376, ie,

$$e^{i\xi x_\tau = 0} = \tilde{f}_j(x_\tau = 0, v_\tau = 0, \tau = 0, \xi)$$

The following equations are the original Cauchy problem identified under (15.365) and under the respective boundary conditions shifted in the Fourier space:

$$-\frac{\partial \tilde{f}_j}{\partial \tau} + \frac{\partial \tilde{f}_j}{\partial x}(r + c_j v) + \frac{1}{2}\frac{\partial^2 \tilde{f}_j}{\partial v^2}(\sigma^2 v) + \frac{\partial^2 \tilde{f}_j}{\partial v \partial x}(v\sigma \rho_{1,2}) + \frac{\partial^2 \tilde{f}_j}{\partial x^2}v + \frac{\partial \tilde{f}_j}{\partial v}[a - b_j v]$$

(15.376)

$$\tilde{f}_j(x_\tau, v_\tau, \tau = 0, \xi) = e^{i\xi x_{\tau}=0}$$

(15.376a)

15.2.6.4. Specification of Cauchy problem as an ODE system

Let $\tilde{f}_j$ be the solution to the Cauchy problem, identified by (15.376), and written as

$$\tilde{f}_j(x_\tau, v_\tau, \tau = 0, \xi | x_\tau, v_\tau) = e^{(C_\tau^{(j)} + D_\tau^{(j)} v_t + i\xi x_\tau)}$$

(15.377)

In order for it to be compatible with the final conditions (15.376a) it is necessary, for $\tau = 0$, that $C_0^{(j)} = 0$ and $D_0^{(j)} = 0$. Then these final conditions in the form (15.377) are equivalent to those determined by the Cauchy problem identified by PDE (15.376). The partial derivatives of (15.376) are computed by using the functional form (15.377). For simplicity, the subscripts τ and t on v are omitted:

$$\frac{\partial \tilde{f}_j}{\partial \tau} = e^{(C_j + D_j v + i\xi x)}\left(\frac{\partial C_j}{\partial \tau} + \frac{\partial D_j}{\partial \tau}v\right)$$

(15.378)

$$\frac{\partial \tilde{f}_j}{\partial x} = e^{(C_j + D_j v + i\xi x)}\, i\xi$$

(15.379)

$$\frac{\partial^2 \tilde{f}_j}{\partial x^2} = -\xi^2 e^{(C_j + D_j v + i\xi x)}$$

(15.380)

$$\frac{\partial \tilde{f}_j}{\partial v} = e^{(C_j + D_j v + i\xi x)}\, D_j$$

(15.381)

$$\frac{\partial^2 \tilde{f}_j}{\partial v^2} = e^{(C_j + D_j v + i\xi x)}\, D_j^2$$

(15.382)

$$\frac{\partial^2 \tilde{f}_j}{\partial x \partial v} = i\xi D_j e^{(C_j + D_j v + i\xi x)}$$

(15.383)

Then (15.378), (15.379), (15.380), (15.381), (15.382) and (15.383) are substituted in (15.376), to obtain

$$e^{(C_j + D_j v + i\xi x)}\left(-\frac{\partial C_j}{\partial \tau} + ri\xi + aD_j\right) + ve^{(C_j + D_j v + i\xi x)}$$

$$\times \left(-\frac{\partial D_j}{\partial \tau} + c_j i\xi + \frac{1}{2}D_j^2\sigma^2 + i\xi D_j\sigma\rho_{1,2} - \frac{1}{2}\xi^2 - b_j D_j\right) = 0$$

since the term $e^{(C_j + D_j v + i\xi x)}$ is always positive, the equivalence above becomes

$$\underbrace{-\frac{\partial C_j}{\partial \tau} + ri\xi + aD_j}_{1^a} + v \underbrace{\left(-\frac{\partial D_j}{\partial \tau} + c_j i\xi + \frac{1}{2}D_j^2 \sigma^2 + i\xi D_j \sigma \rho_{1,2} - \frac{1}{2}\xi^2 - b_j D_j \right)}_{2^a} = 0$$

the equivalence above is verified even if the two expressions have a trivial solution; the v of the second expression may be neglected since it is positive. Then, the Cauchy problem inside (15.376) and inside the final condition (15.376a) may be rearranged as

$$\frac{\partial C_j}{\partial \tau} = ri\xi + aD_j \tag{15.384}$$

$$C_0^{(j)} = 0 \tag{15.384a}$$

$$\frac{\partial D_j}{\partial \tau} = c_j i\xi + \frac{1}{2}D_j^2 \sigma^2 + i\xi D_j \sigma \rho_{1,2} - \frac{1}{2}\xi^2 - b_j D_j \tag{15.385}$$

$$D_0^{(j)} = 0 \tag{15.385a}$$

This is an ODE system and the corresponding boundary conditions.

15.2.6.5. The solution of the Cauchy problem
15.2.6.5.1. *The equation in D* The first ODE (15.385) is solved by recalling the à-la Riccati structure (see Section 8.1.1.2).

Then substitution (8.7) is made in order to derive a second-order ODE (8.8) (by D_j we mean $D_\tau^{(j)}$, while by E we mean E_τ):

$$D_j = -\frac{E'}{(\sigma^2/2)E} \tag{15.386}$$

The first-order derivative of (15.386) is computed (useful for below), ie,

$$D_j' = \frac{(-E''E + (E')^2)}{(\sigma^2/2)E^2} \tag{15.387}$$

Now (15.386) and (15.387) are substituted in (15.385) to obtain

$$E'' - (\rho_{1,2}\sigma\xi i - b_j)E' + \frac{\sigma^2}{2}\left(-\frac{1}{2}\xi^2 + c_j\xi i \right)E = 0 \tag{15.388}$$

Actually, (15.388), which is result of a substitution à-la Equation (8.7), is a constant coefficient homogenous second-order linear ODE.

The general solution to Equation (15.388), (see Theorem 8.5) can be written as

$$E_\tau = Ae^{\alpha_1 \tau} + Be^{\alpha_2 \tau} \tag{15.389}$$

Solutions of the kind $E(\tau) = e^{\alpha \tau}$ are necessary to identify this general solution. Then $E'(\tau) = \alpha e^{\alpha \tau}$ and $E''(\tau) = \alpha^2 e^{\alpha \tau}$ are computed. The terms E_τ, E'_τ and E''_τ are substituted in Equation (15.388), ie,

$$e^{\alpha \tau} \left[\alpha^2 - (\rho_{1,2}\sigma \xi i - b_j)\alpha + \frac{\sigma^2}{2}\left(-\frac{1}{2}\xi^2 + c_j \xi i \right) \right] = 0 \qquad (15.390)$$

Equation (15.390) is only satisfied if the second degree equation in α in brackets has a trivial solution. The roots of this equation in α are computed by writing

$$d = \sqrt{(\rho_{1,2}\sigma \xi i - b_j)^2 - \sigma^2(2c_j \xi i - \xi^2)} \qquad (15.391)$$

to obtain the two roots:

$$\alpha_1 = \frac{\rho_{1,2}\sigma \xi i - b_j + d}{2}, \qquad \alpha_2 = \frac{\rho_{1,2}\sigma \xi i - b_j - d}{2} \qquad (15.392)$$

Knowing the roots α_1 and α_2, the general solution to (15.388) is based on (15.389):

$$E_\tau = A e^{\rho_{1,2}\sigma \xi i - b_j + d/2\tau} + B e^{\rho_{1,2}\sigma \xi i - b_j - d/2\tau} \qquad (15.393)$$

Then (15.393) is specified under the initial condition (15.386). This is rearranged in light of substitution (15.386), ie,

$$D_0^{(j)} = -\frac{E'_0}{((\sigma^2/2)E_0)} = 0 \qquad (15.394)$$

To verify (15.394), the first derivative of the general solution (15.389) is computed:

$$E'_\tau = A e^{\alpha_1 \tau}\alpha_1 + B e^{\alpha_2 \tau}\alpha_2 \qquad (15.395)$$

Then (15.389) and (15.395) are specified for $\tau = 0$, ie,

$$E_0 = A + B \qquad (15.396)$$
$$E'_0 = A\alpha_1 + B\alpha_2 \qquad (15.397)$$

Equations (15.396) and (15.397) are substituted in (15.394), ie,

$$D_0^{(j)} = -\frac{A\alpha_1 + B\alpha_2}{(\sigma^2/2)(A + B)} = 0 \qquad (15.398)$$

Equation (15.398) implies the function system below to identify A and B which allow the solution (15.393) to be specified, ie,

$$\begin{cases} A\alpha_1 + B\alpha_2 = 0 \\ E_0 = A + B \end{cases}$$

One denotes $\alpha_1/\alpha_2 = 1/g$ to obtain, with a little algebra,

$$\begin{cases} A = \dfrac{gE_0}{g-1} \\ B = -\dfrac{E_0}{1-g} \end{cases}$$

(15.399)

Substituting expressions in (15.399) in the general solution (15.389),

$$E_\tau = \frac{E_0}{g-1}(ge^{\alpha_1\tau} - e^{\alpha_2\tau})$$

(15.400)

and, in its first-order derivative (15.395),

$$E'_\tau = \frac{E_0}{g-1}(g\alpha_1 e^{\alpha_1\tau} - \alpha_2 e^{\alpha_2\tau})$$

(15.401)

Knowing (15.400) and (15.401), one may recall (15.386) and then derive the solution of (15.385), ie,

$$D_\tau^{(j)} = -\frac{2\alpha_2}{\sigma^2}\frac{1-e^{d\tau}}{1-ge^{d\tau}}$$

(15.402)

where[10]

$$d = \sqrt{(\rho_{1,2}\sigma\xi i - b_j)^2 - \sigma^2(2c_j\xi i - \xi^2)}$$

$$\alpha_1 = \frac{\rho_{1,2}\sigma\xi i - b_j + d}{2},$$

$$\alpha_2 = \frac{\rho_{1,2}\sigma\xi i - b_j - d}{2}$$

$$g = \frac{\alpha_2}{\alpha_1}$$

---

[10]Specifically, in the Heston paper, the value of D_j is expressed as

$$D_j = \frac{b_j + d - \rho_{1,2}\sigma\xi i}{\sigma^2}\frac{1-e^{d\tau}}{1-ge^{d\tau}}$$

This value is derived by the algebraic steps

$$D_\tau^{(j)} = -\frac{2\alpha_2}{\sigma^2}\frac{1-e^{d\tau}}{1-ge^{d\tau}}$$

using the value of α_2 inside (15.392), one obtains

$$D_\tau^{(j)} = -\frac{2(\rho_{1,2}\sigma\xi i - b_j - d/2)}{\sigma^2}\frac{1-e^{d\tau}}{1-ge^{d\tau}}$$

$$= -\frac{\rho_{1,2}\sigma\xi i - b_j - d}{\sigma^2}\frac{1-e^{d\tau}}{1-ge^{d\tau}}$$

$$= \frac{b_j + d - \rho_{1,2}\sigma\xi i}{\sigma^2}\frac{1-e^{d\tau}}{1-ge^{d\tau}}$$

15.2.6.5.2. The equation in C Equation in (15.384) is a constant coefficient first-order linear ODE. It may be solved by a simple integration (by C_j we mean $C_\tau^{(j)}$):

$$C_\tau^{(j)} = ri\tilde{\zeta}\tau - \frac{2a}{\sigma^2}\ln\frac{E_0}{g-1}(ge^{\alpha_1\tau} - e^{\alpha_2\tau}) - F \tag{15.403}$$

by using the initial condition (15.386), the value of F is specified, ie,

$$C_\tau^{(j)} = ri\tilde{\zeta}\tau - \frac{2a}{\sigma^2}\left(\alpha_2\tau + \ln\frac{ge^{d\tau}-1}{g-1}\right) \tag{15.404}$$

where[11]

$$d = \sqrt{(\rho_{1,2}\sigma\tilde{\zeta}i - b_j)^2 - \sigma^2(2c_j\tilde{\zeta}i - \tilde{\zeta}^2)}$$

$$\alpha_1 = \frac{\rho_{1,2}\sigma\tilde{\zeta}i - b_j + d}{2},$$

$$\alpha_2 = \frac{\rho_{1,2}\sigma\tilde{\zeta}i - b_j - d}{2}$$

$$g = \frac{\alpha_2}{\alpha_1}$$

15.2.6.5.3. Solutions computable by using quadrature algorithms The solutions to the Cauchy problem (15.365) in the form (15.377), where $C_\tau^{(j)}$ is given by expression (15.402) and $D_\tau^{(j)}$ is expression (15.404), allow the analytic expression of the probability measures P_j to be determined by using the relation (15.369).

However, the relation (15.369) does not have an immediate numerical solution. Nonetheless, many equivalent solutions exist which allow this quantity to

---

[11]Specifically, in the Heston paper, the value of C_j is expressed as

$$C_j = ri\tilde{\zeta}\tau + \frac{a}{\sigma^2}\left[(b_j + d - \rho_{1,2}\sigma\tilde{\zeta}i)\tau - 2\ln\frac{1-ge^{d\tau}}{1-g}\right]$$

This value is derived after the following algebra

$$C_\tau^{(j)} = ri\tilde{\zeta}\tau - \frac{2a}{\sigma^2}\left(\alpha_2\tau + \ln\frac{ge^{d\tau}-1}{g-1}\right)$$

by using the value of α_2 as in (15.392) to obtain

$$C_\tau^{(j)} = ri\tilde{\zeta}\tau - \frac{a}{\sigma^2}(\rho_{1,2}\sigma\tilde{\zeta}i - b_j - d)\tau - \frac{2a}{\sigma^2}\left[\ln\frac{ge^{d\tau}-1}{g-1}\right]$$

$$= ri\tilde{\zeta}\tau + \frac{a}{\sigma^2}(b_j + d - \rho_{1,2}\sigma\tilde{\zeta}i)\tau - \frac{2a}{\sigma^2}\left[\ln\frac{1-ge^{d\tau}}{1-g}\right]$$

$$= ri\tilde{\zeta}\tau + \frac{a}{\sigma^2}\left[(b_j + d - \rho_{1,2}\sigma\tilde{\zeta}i)\tau - 2\ln\frac{1-ge^{d\tau}}{1-g}\right]$$

be manipulated analytically (see expressions (11.125) and (11.126)):

$$P_j(x_{\tau=0} \geq \ln K \mid x_\tau, v_\tau) = \frac{1}{2} + \frac{1}{\pi} \int_0^\infty \Im \left[\frac{e^{-i\check\zeta \ln K} \tilde f_j(x_\tau, v_\tau, \tau = 0, \check\zeta \mid x_\tau, v_\tau)}{\check\zeta} \right] d\check\zeta$$

(15.405)

$$P_j(x_{\tau=0} \geq \ln K \mid x_\tau, v_\tau) = \frac{1}{2} + \frac{1}{\pi} \int_0^\infty \Re \left[\frac{e^{-i\check\zeta \ln K} \tilde f_j(x_\tau, v_\tau, \tau = 0, \check\zeta \mid x_\tau, v_\tau)}{i\check\zeta} \right] d\check\zeta$$

(15.406)

15.2.6.6. The call price

The Heston model gives the following formulae of call option pricing expressed in a simplified notation:

$$C_t = S_t P_1 - K e^{-r(T-t)} P_2$$

(15.354)

where, by using (15.405) (or, alternatively, (15.406)), (15.377) and (15.339), for $j = 1, 2$, the function P is defined as

$$P_j = \frac{1}{2} + \frac{1}{\pi} \int_0^\infty \Re \left\{ \frac{e^{-i\check\zeta \ln K}}{i\check\zeta} e^{[C_\tau^{(j)} + D_\tau^{(j)} v_t + i\check\zeta[\ln S_t + r(T-t)]]} \right\} d\check\zeta$$

(15.407)

with (15.391), (15.392) and

$$C_j = r i \check\zeta (T - t) - \frac{2a}{\sigma^2} \left(\alpha_2 (T - t) + \ln \frac{(\alpha_2 / \alpha_1) e^{d(T-t)} - 1}{\alpha_2 / \alpha_1 - 1} \right)$$

(15.404)

$$D_j = -\frac{2\alpha_2}{\sigma^2} \frac{1 - e^{d(T-t)}}{1 - (\alpha_2 / \alpha_1) e^{d(T-t)}}$$

(15.402)

$$c_{1/2} = \pm \frac{1}{2}, \quad a = \kappa\theta, \quad b_1 = \kappa + \tilde\lambda - \rho_{1,2}\sigma, \quad b_2 = \kappa + \tilde\lambda$$

(15.364)

15.2.6.7. The Heston model under the Risk-neutral probability measure

The formulas above represent a pricing formula derived under a risk-neutral probability measure. Substantially, the formulae in the previous section describe the change of probability measure implemented under a stochastic viewpoint. In the following, a description from the diffusion viewpoint of the implications of the measure change above is given.

Proposition 15.47. *The SDEs (15.323) and (15.324) under the risk-neutral measure take the form*

$$dS_t = r S_t \, dt + \sqrt{v_t} S_t \, dz_t^{*(1)}$$

(15.408)

$$dv_t = \kappa^* [\theta^* - v_t] \, dt + \sigma \sqrt{v_t} \, dz_t^{*(2)}$$

(15.409)

Proof. One recalls the PDE (15.335), ie, the PDE derived for the *contingent claim* replication portfolio, and then the expression of a risk-neutral pricing environment. By using definition (15.344), (15.335) becomes

$$
-rf + \frac{\partial f}{\partial t} + \frac{\partial f}{\partial S}rS + \frac{1}{2}\frac{\partial^2 f}{\partial S^2}vS^2 + \frac{1}{2}\frac{\partial^2 f}{\partial v^2}\sigma^2 v
$$
$$
+ \frac{\partial^2 f}{\partial S\partial v}S\sigma\rho_{1,2}v + \frac{\partial f}{\partial v}[\kappa(\theta - v) - \tilde{\lambda}v] = 0
$$

Defining

$$
\kappa^* = \kappa + \tilde{\lambda} \tag{15.410}
$$

$$
\theta^* = \frac{\kappa\theta}{\kappa + \tilde{\lambda}} \tag{15.411}
$$

one obtains

$$
-rf + \frac{\partial f}{\partial t} + \frac{\partial f}{\partial S}rS + \frac{1}{2}\frac{\partial^2 f}{\partial S^2}vS^2 + \frac{1}{2}\frac{\partial^2 f}{\partial v^2}\sigma^2 v + \frac{\partial^2 f}{\partial S\partial v}S\sigma\rho_{1,2}v + \frac{\partial f}{\partial v}[\kappa^*(\theta^* - v)] = 0
$$

Applying the Feynman–Kac theorem (see Theorem 12.21), one derives the SDEs (15.408) and (15.409), which represent the diffusion process at the base of the Heston pricing model as derived in this section. □

Corollary 15.9. *The call pricing expressed in terms of κ^* and θ^*, ie, $C_t(S, K, v, \tau, r, \theta^*, \kappa^*, \sigma, \rho_{1,2})$ shows the same formula as in Section 15.2.6.6 except for the following parametric specification*

$$
c_{1/2} = \pm\tfrac{1}{2}, \quad a = \kappa^*\theta^*, \quad b_1 = \kappa^* - \rho_{1,2}\sigma, \quad b_2 = \kappa^* \tag{15.412}
$$

Proof. One recalls the pair of PDEs (15.363), then the coefficient of $\partial f/\partial v$ is manipulated, definitions (15.410) and (15.411) are replaced to obtain the following:

$$
\begin{cases}
-\dfrac{\partial P_1}{\partial \tau} + r\dfrac{\partial P_1}{\partial x} + \dfrac{1}{2}v\dfrac{\partial P_1}{\partial x} + \dfrac{1}{2}\dfrac{\partial^2 P_1}{\partial v^2}(\sigma^2 v) + \dfrac{\partial^2 P_1}{\partial x\partial v}(v\sigma\rho_{1,2}) \\
+ \dfrac{1}{2}\dfrac{\partial^2 P_1}{\partial x^2}v + \dfrac{\partial P_1}{\partial v}[\kappa^*\theta^* - v\kappa^* + v\sigma\rho_{1,2}] = 0 \\[2ex]
-\dfrac{\partial P_2}{\partial \tau} + r\dfrac{\partial P_2}{\partial x} - \dfrac{1}{2}v\dfrac{\partial P_2}{\partial x} + \dfrac{1}{2}\dfrac{\partial^2 P_2}{\partial v^2}(\sigma^2 v) + \dfrac{\partial^2 P_2}{\partial x\partial v}(v\sigma\rho_{1,2}) \\
+ \dfrac{1}{2}\dfrac{\partial^2 P_2}{\partial x^2}v + \dfrac{\partial P_2}{\partial v}[\kappa^*\theta^* - v\kappa^*] = 0
\end{cases} \tag{15.413}
$$

By substituting, for $j = 1, 2$,

$$
c_1 = \tfrac{1}{2}, \quad c_2 = -\tfrac{1}{2}, \quad a = \kappa^*\theta^*, \quad b_1 = \kappa^* - \rho_{1,2}\sigma, \quad b_2 = \kappa^* \tag{15.412}
$$

Equation (15.413) may be expressed as a single PDE analogous to (15.365) except for the parametric specification (15.412). The equivalence of the PDE implies that the mathematical procedure which leads to pricing formulation remains unchanged until the formula of Section 15.2.6.6 is derived, leaving the different and simplified parametric formulation unchanged. □

15.2.6.8. Pricing a call with the Heston model: implementation

Actually, the Heston model requires the use of some software to compute the integral in (15.407), derived from (15.405) or from (15.406). Matlab *real and quad8* or *quadl* functions may be used for this purpose.

In addition, to reduce the number of parameters in this model which is estimated empirically, the formula of Corollary 15.9 may be used.

Proposition 15.48. *Empirical verifications proved that the following expression for $C_\tau^{(j)}$ makes computation faster:*

$$C_j = ri\zeta\tau - \frac{a}{\sigma^2}(\rho_{1,2}\sigma\zeta i - b_j + d)\tau - \frac{a}{\sigma^2}2\ln\left(1 - \frac{(1 - e^{-d\tau})(\rho_{1,2}\sigma\zeta i - b_j + d)}{2d}\right)$$

(15.414)

Proof. Starting from (15.404) the definition of $g = \alpha_2/\alpha_1$ is substituted, ie,

$$C_\tau^{(j)} = ri\zeta\tau - \frac{2a}{\sigma^2}\left(\alpha_2\tau + \ln\frac{(\alpha_2/\alpha_1)e^{d\tau} - 1}{\alpha_2/\alpha_1 - 1}\right)$$

which, by multiplying, simplifying, substituting the definition of α_1 and α_2 and recalling that $\alpha_1 - \alpha_2 = d$, one has

$$C_\tau^{(j)} = ri\zeta\tau - \frac{a}{\sigma^2}(\rho_{1,2}\sigma\zeta i - b_j + d)\tau - \frac{a}{\sigma^2}2\ln\left(1 - \frac{(1 - e^{-d\tau})(\rho_{1,2}\sigma\zeta i - b_j + d)}{2d}\right)$$

□

Proposition 15.49. *Empirical verifications proved that the following expression for $D_\tau^{(j)}$ makes computation faster:*

$$D_j = \frac{(2c_j\zeta i - \zeta^2)(1 - e^{-d\tau})}{2d - (\rho_{1,2}\sigma\zeta i - b_j + d)(1 - e^{-d\tau})}$$

(15.415)

Proof. Starting from (15.402) replacing the definition of $g = \alpha_2/\alpha_1$, ie,

$$D_j = -\frac{2\alpha_2}{\sigma^2}\frac{1 - e^{d\tau}}{1 - (\alpha_2/\alpha_1)e^{d\tau}}$$

which, by substituting the definitions of α_1 and α_2, simplifying and substituting the definition of d, is equal to

$$D_j = \frac{(2c_j\xi i - \xi^2)(1 - e^{-d\tau})}{2d - (\rho_{1,2}\sigma\xi i - b_j + d)(1 - e^{-d\tau})} \qquad \Box$$

15.2.6.9. The Greeks

Theorem 15.16. *If $C(S_t, K) : \mathbb{R}^2 \rightarrow \mathbb{R}$ is differentiable to the second-order and is homogeneous of degree one by (15.354), then the equivalences (15.276)–(15.281) hold.*

Notation 15.5. The following simplified notation will be used:

$$\tilde{f}_j \doteq \tilde{f}_j(x_\tau, v_\tau, \tau = 0, \xi | x_\tau, v_\tau) \qquad (15.416)$$

Proof. Under the equivalence between (15.354) and (15.239) (see Section 15.2.5.3.2), see Theorem 15.15, for the demonstration of the above equivalence. $\qquad \Box$

Proposition 15.50. *The following equivalences hold:*

$$\frac{\partial}{\partial S_t} \tilde{f}_j(x_\tau, v_\tau, \tau = 0, \xi | x_\tau, v_\tau) = \tilde{f}_j(x_\tau, v_\tau, \tau = 0, \xi | x_\tau, v_\tau) \cdot i\xi \frac{1}{S_t} \qquad (15.417)$$

$$\frac{\partial^2}{\partial S_t^2} (\tilde{f}_j(x_\tau, v_\tau, \tau = 0, \xi | x_\tau, v_\tau)) = \frac{1}{S_t^2} i\xi(i\xi - 1) \tilde{f}_j(x_\tau, v_\tau, \tau = 0, \xi | x_\tau, v_\tau) \qquad (15.418)$$

Proof. It is necessary to compute the following partial derivative

$$\frac{\partial}{\partial S_t} \tilde{f}_j(x_\tau, v_\tau, \tau = 0, \xi | x_\tau, v_\tau) \quad \text{for } j = 1, 2$$

$$\frac{\partial}{\partial S_t} (\tilde{f}_j(x_\tau, v_\tau, \tau = 0, \xi | x_\tau, v_\tau)) = \frac{\partial}{\partial S_t} e^{(C_\tau^{(j)} + D_\tau^{(j)} v_t + i\xi x_\tau)}$$

and after some algebra, one obtains (15.417).

One has

$$\frac{\partial^2}{\partial S_t^2} \tilde{f}_j(x_\tau, v_\tau, \tau = 0, \xi | x_\tau, v_\tau) \quad \text{for } j = 1, 2$$

By using (15.417) one obtains (15.418). $\qquad \Box$

Proposition 15.51. *The following equivalences hold:*

$$\frac{\partial P_j}{\partial S_t} = \frac{1}{\pi S_t} \int_0^\infty \Re[e^{-i\xi \ln K}(\tilde{f}_j(x_\tau, v_\tau, \tau = 0, \xi | x_\tau, v_\tau))] \, d\xi \qquad (15.419)$$

$$\frac{\partial^2 P_j}{\partial S_t^2} = \frac{1}{\pi S_t^2} \int_0^\infty \Re[e^{-i\xi \ln K}((i\xi - 1)\tilde{f}_j(x_\tau, v_\tau, \tau = 0, \xi | x_\tau, v_\tau))] \, d\xi \qquad (15.420)$$

$$\frac{\partial P_j}{\partial K} = -\frac{1}{\pi K} \int_0^\infty \Re[(e^{-i\xi \ln K}\tilde{f}_j(.x_\tau, v_\tau, \tau = 0, \xi | \, x_\tau, v_\tau)) \, d\xi] \qquad (15.421)$$

$$\frac{\partial^2 P_j}{\partial K^2} = \frac{1}{\pi K^2} \int_0^\infty \Re[e^{-i\xi \ln K}(i\xi + 1) \, \tilde{f}_j(.x_\tau, v_\tau, \tau = 0, \xi | \, x_\tau, v_\tau) \, d\xi] \qquad (15.422)$$

Proof. Since the particular form of the characteristic function has no influence on the differentiation with respect to parameters S_t, K, the computation of these quantities is analogous to the Merton model. Therefore, $\partial P_j/\partial S_t$, computed on the basis of (15.407), are given by expression (15.305). Expression (15.419) gives an explicit expression for $\partial^2 P_j/\partial S_t^2$ (see expression (15.306)).

One computes $\partial P_j/\partial K$ (see expression (15.307)). Expression (15.419) gives an explicit expression for $\partial^2 P_j/\partial K^2$ (see expression (15.308)). □

Proposition 15.52. *The following relation holds:*

$$\frac{\partial P_j}{\partial v_t} = \frac{1}{\pi} \int_0^\infty \Re\left[\frac{e^{-i\xi \ln K}}{i\xi} (e^{(C_\tau^{(j)} + D_\tau^{(j)} v_t + i\xi x_\tau)} D_\tau^{(j)}) \right] d\xi \qquad (15.423)$$

Proof. The partial derivative is computed on the basis of (15.407) ie,

$$\frac{\partial P_j}{\partial v_t} = \frac{\partial}{\partial v_t} \left(\frac{1}{2} + \frac{1}{\pi} \int_0^\infty \Re\left[\frac{e^{-i\xi \ln K}}{i\xi} \tilde{f}_j(x_\tau, v_\tau, \tau = 0, \xi | x_\tau, v_\tau) \right] d\xi \right)$$

$$= \frac{1}{\pi} \int_0^\infty \Re\left[\frac{e^{-i\xi \ln K}}{i\xi} (e^{(C_\tau^{(j)} + D_\tau^{(j)} v_t + i\xi x_\tau)} D_\tau^{(j)}) \right] d\xi \qquad □$$

Proposition 15.53. *The following relation holds:*

$$\frac{\partial^2 P_j}{\partial v_t^2} = \frac{1}{\pi} \int_0^\infty \Re\left[\frac{e^{-i\xi \ln K}}{i\xi} (e^{(C_\tau^{(j)} + D_\tau^{(j)} v_t + i\xi x_\tau)} (D_\tau^{(j)})^2) \right] d\xi \qquad (15.424)$$

Proof. The partial derivative is computed on the basis of (15.406) and by using the result (15.423), ie,

$$\frac{\partial^2 P_j}{\partial v_t^2} = \frac{\partial}{\partial v_t} \left[\frac{1}{\pi} \int_0^\infty \Re\left[\frac{e^{-i\xi \ln K}}{i\xi} (e^{(C_\tau^{(j)} + D_\tau^{(j)} v_t + i\xi x_\tau)} D_\tau^{(j)}) \right] d\xi \right]$$

$$= \frac{1}{\pi} \int_0^\infty \Re\left[\frac{e^{-i\xi \ln K}}{i\xi} (e^{(C_\tau^{(j)} + D_\tau^{(j)} v_t + i\xi x_\tau)} (D_\tau^{(j)})^2) \right] d\xi \qquad □$$

Proposition 15.54. *A call option* Delta *is*

$$\Delta_C = P_1 \tag{15.425}$$

Proof. To define a call option Delta at time t, one has

$$\Delta_C = \frac{\partial C_t}{\partial S_t}$$
$$= P_1 \quad \text{(using (15.280))} \qquad \square$$

Proposition 15.55. *A call option* Gamma *is*

$$\Gamma_C = \frac{\partial P_1}{\partial S_t} \tag{15.426}$$

(under $\partial P_1 / \partial S_t$, see Expression (15.419)).

Proof. To define a call option Gamma at time t, one has

$$\Gamma_C = \frac{\partial^2 C_t}{\partial S_t^2}$$
$$= \frac{\partial P_1}{\partial S_t} \quad \text{(using (15.425))} \qquad \square$$

Proposition 15.56. *A call option* Vega *is*

$$\mathcal{V}_C = S_t \frac{\partial P_1}{\partial v_t} - Ke^{-r\tau} \frac{\partial P_2}{\partial v_t} \tag{15.427}$$

(for the expression $\partial P_j / \partial v_t$, see expression (15.423)).

Proof. To define a call option Vega at time t, one has

$$\mathcal{V}_C = \frac{\partial C_t}{\partial v_t}$$
$$= S_t \frac{\partial P_1}{\partial v_t} - Ke^{-r\tau} \frac{\partial P_2}{\partial v_t} \qquad \square$$

Proposition 15.57. *A call option* Volga *is*

$$\mathfrak{V}_C = S_t \frac{\partial^2 P_1}{\partial v_t^2} - Ke^{-r\tau} \frac{\partial^2 P_2}{\partial v_t^2} \tag{15.428}$$

(for the expression $\partial^2 P_j / \partial v_t^2$, see expression (15.424)).

Proof. To define a call option Volga at time t, one has

$$\mathfrak{V}_C = \frac{\partial^2 C_t}{\partial v_t^2}$$

$$= S_t \frac{\partial^2 P_1}{\partial v_t^2} - K e^{-r\tau} \frac{\partial^2 P_2}{\partial v_t^2} \qquad \square$$

Corollary 15.10. *The second-order crossed derivative with respect to v_t and S_t is*

$$\frac{\partial^2 C_t}{\partial S_t \partial v_t} = \frac{\partial P_1}{\partial v_t} \qquad (15.429)$$

Proof. The corollary is demonstrated by differentiating (15.425) with respect to v_t. $\qquad \square$

Proposition 15.58. *A call option* Theta *is*

$$\Theta_C = -\frac{\partial P_1}{\partial S}\left(\frac{1}{2}vS^2\right) - \frac{\partial P_1}{\partial v}S[\sigma\rho_{1,2}v + [\kappa(\theta - v) - \lambda v]] - \frac{\partial^2 P_1}{\partial v^2}\left(\frac{1}{2}S\sigma^2 v\right)$$

$$- Ke^{-r\tau}\left[rP_2 - \frac{1}{2}\sigma^2 v\frac{\partial^2 P_2}{\partial v^2} - \frac{\partial P_2}{\partial v}[\kappa(\theta - v) - \lambda v]\right] \qquad (15.430)$$

Proof. Recalling (15.336), replacing (15.423), (15.429), (15.425) and (15.419), one obtains

$$= -\frac{\partial P_1}{\partial S}\left(\frac{1}{2}vS^2\right) - \frac{\partial P_1}{\partial v}S[\sigma\rho_{1,2}v + [\kappa(\theta - v) - \lambda v]] - \frac{\partial^2 P_1}{\partial v^2}\left(\frac{1}{2}S\sigma^2 v\right)$$

$$- Ke^{-r\tau}\left[rP_2 - \frac{1}{2}\sigma^2 v\frac{\partial^2 P_2}{\partial v^2} - \frac{\partial P_2}{\partial v}[\kappa(\theta - v) - \lambda v]\right] \qquad \square$$

Proposition 15.59. *A call option* Rho *is*

$$\rho_C = K\tau e^{-r\tau}P_2 \qquad (15.431)$$

Proof. To define a call option rho at time t, one has

$$\frac{\partial C_t}{\partial r} = \frac{\partial}{\partial r}[S_t P_1 - Ke^{-r\tau}P_2]$$

$$= \left[S_t\frac{\partial P_1}{\partial r} - K\left(-\tau e^{-r\tau}P_2 + e^{-r\tau}\frac{\partial P_2}{\partial r}\right)\right]$$

then

$$\rho_C = \left[S_t\frac{\partial P_1}{\partial r} - K\left(-\tau e^{-r\tau}P_2 + e^{-r\tau}\frac{\partial P_2}{\partial r}\right)\right] \qquad (15.432)$$

where $\partial P_1/\partial r$ and $\partial P_2/\partial r$ become

$$
\begin{aligned}
\frac{\partial P_j}{\partial r} &= \frac{\partial}{\partial r}\left(\frac{1}{2} + \frac{1}{\pi}\int_0^\infty \Re\left[\frac{e^{-i\xi\ln K}}{i\xi}\tilde{f}_j(x_\tau, v_\tau, \tau = 0, \xi \mid x_\tau, v_\tau)\right]d\xi\right) \\
&= \frac{1}{\pi}\int_0^\infty \Re\left[\frac{e^{-i\xi\ln K}}{i\xi}\left(e^{(C_\tau^{(j)}+D_\tau^{(j)}v_t+i\xi x_\tau)}\cdot\left(\frac{\partial C_\tau^{(j)}}{\partial r}+i\xi\frac{\partial x_\tau}{\partial r}\right)\right)\right]d\xi \\
&= \frac{2\tau}{\pi}\frac{S_t}{S_t}\int_0^\infty \Re\left[e^{-i\xi\ln K}\left(e^{(C_\tau^{(j)}+D_\tau^{(j)}v_t+i\xi x_\tau)}\right)\right]d\xi
\end{aligned}
$$

(recalling expressions (15.404) and (15.340))

Recalling (15.419), one has

$$
\frac{\partial P_j}{\partial r} = 2\tau S_t\frac{\partial P_j}{\partial S_t} \tag{15.433}
$$

Substituting (15.433) for $j = 1, 2$ in (15.432) to obtain

$$
\begin{aligned}
\frac{\partial C_t}{\partial r} &= 2\tau S_t^2\frac{\partial P_1}{\partial S_t} + K\tau e^{-r\tau}P_2 - 2\tau S_t Ke^{-r\tau}\frac{\partial P_2}{\partial S_t} \\
&= K\tau e^{-r\tau}P_2 \quad \text{(using (15.281))} \qquad \qquad \square
\end{aligned}
$$

15.2.7. The Bates model

15.2.7.1. Introduction

The Bates model first requires the stochastic process S_t, the spot price level of the underlying at time t, to be split into its continuous and the discrete component, ie,

$$
S_t = S_t^C + S_t^D \tag{15.434}
$$

In differential terms the expression above may also be written as

$$
dS_t = dS_t^C + dS_t^D \tag{15.435}
$$

The discrete component is governed by the following SDE:

$$
dS_t^D = S_t J_t\, dq_t \tag{15.436}
$$

where:

- dq_t is a diffusive Poisson process (see Notation 12.13) with intensity $\lambda\, dt$, ie, $\Pr(dq_t = 1) = \lambda\, dt$ and $\Pr(dq_t = 0) = 1 - \lambda\, dt$;
- $dq(t)$ is not correlated with J_t and dW_t;
- J_t is the percentage jump size for the process S and is distributed as follows

$$
J(t) \sim \text{Log } N(\mu, (1 + \mu)(e^{\sigma^2} - 1)) \tag{15.437}
$$

The continuous component is governed by the following SDE:

$$dS_t^C = [r - \lambda\mu]S_t\,dt + \sqrt{v_t}S_t\,dz_t^{(1)} \tag{15.438}$$

where:

- r is the current risk-free rate at time t (constant);
- v_t is the variance of process S at time t;
- $dz_t^{(1)}$ is a standard Wiener process.

Finally, based on all of the above assumptions, the Bates model may be described by the following system of SDEs:

$$dS_t = [r - \lambda\mu]S_t\,dt + \sqrt{v_t}S_t\,dz_t^{(1)} + S_t J_t\,dq_t \tag{15.439}$$

$$dv_t = \kappa[\theta - v_t]dt + \sigma\sqrt{v_t}\,dz_t^{(2)} \tag{15.440}$$

where:

- (15.439) is the SDE which governs the pricing process of the underlying;
- (15.440) is the SDE which governs the variance process of the underlying v_t;
- κ, θ, σ are the SDE parameters;
- $dz_t^{(2)}$ is a standard Wiener process;
- $\rho_{1,2}$ is the correlation coefficient between $z_t^{(1)}$ and $z_t^{(2)}$, ie, $dz_t^{(1)} \cdot dz_t^{(2)} = \rho_{1,2}\,dt$.

Notation 15.6. In the following, in order to simplify notation, the subscript t in the SDE is omitted to have the notation $dz_t^{(i)} = dz_i$ and $\rho_{1,2}$ will be denoted by ρ.

15.2.7.2. PDE derivation for portfolio replication

In this model, the option price f to be determined is governed by the behaviour of the underlying, by time and by variance behaviour, ie,

$$f = f(S, v, t) \tag{15.441}$$

Considering f differentiable to the order required and considering that the members of order dt^2, $dt\,dv$, $dt\,dS$ are equal to zero based on some fundamental stochastic calculus rules, ie, Itô's algebra (see Section 12.1.5.1), then the stochastic differential of f may be computed with respect to S^C and S^D:

- df computation with respect to dS^D is

$$df = [f[(J+1)S, v, t] - f[S, v, t]]\,dq \tag{15.442}$$

- df computation with respect to dS^C is

$$\frac{\partial f}{\partial S} dS^C + \frac{\partial f}{\partial t} dt + \frac{\partial f}{\partial v} dv + \frac{1}{2}\left[\frac{\partial^2 f}{\partial S^2}(dS^C)^2 + \frac{\partial^2 f}{\partial v^2} dv^2\right] + \frac{\partial^2 f}{\partial S \partial v} dS^C dv$$

(15.443)

Then the stochastic differential computation of f brings one to the equation

$$df = \frac{\partial f}{\partial S}([r - \lambda\mu]S\, dt + \sqrt{v}S\, dz_1) + \frac{\partial f}{\partial t} dt + \frac{\partial f}{\partial v}[\kappa(\theta - v)\, dt + \sigma\sqrt{v}\, dz_2]$$
$$+ \frac{1}{2}\frac{\partial^2 f}{\partial S^2}(vS^2\, dt) + \frac{1}{2}\frac{\partial^2 f}{\partial v^2}(\sigma^2 v\, dt) + \frac{\partial^2 f}{\partial S \partial v}(S\sigma\rho v)\, dt$$
$$+ [f[(J+1)S, v, t] - f[S, v, t]]\, dq$$

(15.444)

Based on the solution of the above equation, the increment of option price f is a stochastic process dependent from the Wiener process which governs the process of the underlying and of the volatility. It is also dependent on the Poisson process which governs the jump process. Then, as made above for the BSM formula derivation, the option replication portfolio is built without hedging the risk of discontinuous jumps of the underlying asset, ie,

$$\pi = f_1 - \Delta_1 f_0 - \Delta_0 S$$

(15.445)

where:

- f_i for $i = 0, 1$ are the prices of the two options;
- Δ_i for $i = 0, 1$ are the quantities of the underlying S.

In order to derive the equivalence between df and $d\pi$, the latter is derived. By differentiating (15.445) and using (15.444) and (15.439), one has

$$d\pi = \left[\sqrt{v}S\left(\frac{\partial f_1}{\partial S} - \Delta_1\frac{\partial f_0}{\partial S} - \Delta_0\right)\right] dz_1 + \left[\sigma\sqrt{v}\left(\frac{\partial f_1}{\partial v} - \Delta_1\frac{\partial f_0}{\partial v}\right)\right] dz_2$$
$$+ \frac{\partial f_1}{\partial S}([r - \lambda\mu]S\, dt) + \frac{\partial f_1}{\partial t} dt + \frac{\partial f_1}{\partial v}[\kappa(\theta - v)\, dt] + \frac{1}{2}\frac{\partial^2 f_1}{\partial S^2}(vS^2\, dt)$$
$$+ \frac{1}{2}\frac{\partial^2 f_1}{\partial v^2}(\sigma^2 v\, dt) + \frac{\partial^2 f_1}{\partial S \partial v}(S\sigma\rho v)\, dt + [f_1[(J+1)S, v, t]$$
$$- f_1[S, v, t]]\, dq - \Delta_1\left[\frac{\partial f_0}{\partial S}([r - \lambda\mu]S\, dt) + \frac{\partial f_0}{\partial t} dt + \frac{\partial f_0}{\partial v}[\kappa(\theta - v)\, dt]\right.$$
$$+ \frac{1}{2}\frac{\partial^2 f_0}{\partial S^2}(vS^2\, dt) + \frac{1}{2}\frac{\partial^2 f_0}{\partial v^2}(\sigma^2 v\, dt) + \frac{\partial^2 f_0}{\partial S \partial v}(S\sigma\rho v)\, dt$$
$$\left. + [f_0[(J+1)S, v, t] - f_0[S, v, t]]\, dq\right] - \Delta_0([r - \lambda\mu]S\, dt + SJ\, dq)$$

(15.446)

To nullify any random variable of that portfolio, ie, to eliminate terms in dz_i from (15.446), the coefficients Δ_1, Δ_0, are appropriately chosen, ie,

$$
\begin{cases}
\left(\dfrac{\partial f_1}{\partial S} - \Delta_1 \dfrac{\partial f_0}{\partial S} - \Delta_0 \right) = 0 \\[3mm]
\left(\dfrac{\partial f_1}{\partial v} - \Delta_1 \dfrac{\partial f_0}{\partial v} \right) = 0
\end{cases}
\tag{15.447}
$$

Then, the system is solved

$$
\begin{cases}
\Delta_0 = \dfrac{\partial f_1}{\partial S} - \dfrac{\partial f_1/\partial v}{\partial f_0/\partial v} \dfrac{\partial f_0}{\partial S} \\[4mm]
\Delta_1 = \dfrac{\partial f_1/\partial v}{\partial f_0/\partial v}
\end{cases}
\tag{15.448}
$$

Substituting the expressions by the coefficients Δ_1, Δ_0 defined in (15.448) in Equation (15.446), one obtains

$$
d\pi = \underbrace{\frac{\partial f_1}{\partial t}\, dt + \frac{\partial f_1}{\partial v}\left[\kappa(\theta - v)\, dt\right] + \frac{1}{2}\frac{\partial^2 f_1}{\partial S^2}(vS^2\, dt) + \frac{1}{2}\frac{\partial^2 f_1}{\partial v^2}(\sigma^2 v\, dt)}_{\text{Deterministic component}}
$$

$$
\underbrace{+ \frac{\partial^2 f_1}{\partial S \partial v}(S\sigma\rho v)\, dt - \frac{\partial f_1/\partial v}{\partial f_0/\partial v}\frac{\partial f_0}{\partial t}\, dt - \frac{\partial f_1/\partial v}{\partial f_0/\partial v}\frac{\partial f_0}{\partial v}\left[\kappa(\theta - v)\, dt\right]}_{\text{Deterministic component}}
$$

$$
\underbrace{- \frac{\partial f_1/\partial v}{\partial f_0/\partial v}\frac{1}{2}\frac{\partial^2 f_0}{\partial S^2}(vS^2\, dt) - \frac{\partial f_1/\partial v}{\partial f_0/\partial v}\frac{1}{2}\frac{\partial^2 f_0}{\partial v^2}(\sigma^2 v\, dt) - \frac{\partial f_1/\partial v}{\partial f_0/\partial v}\frac{\partial^2 f_0}{\partial S \partial v}(S\sigma\rho v)\, dt}_{\text{Deterministic component}}
$$

$$
\underbrace{+ \left[f_1[(J+1)S, v, t] - f_1[S, v, t] \right] dq}_{\text{Pure jump component}}
$$

$$
\underbrace{- \frac{\partial f_1/\partial v}{\partial f_0/\partial v}\left[f_0[(J+1)S, v, t] - f_0[S, v, t] \right] dq - \left(\frac{\partial f_1}{\partial S} - \frac{\partial f_1/\partial v}{\partial f_0/\partial v}\frac{\partial f_0}{\partial S} \right) SJ\, dq}_{\text{Pure jump component}}
$$

$$\tag{15.449}$$

Equation (15.449) is a portfolio with a deterministic component and jump risk-sensitive component, ie, pure jump. Hence, the no-arbitrage hypothesis which is derived from the above,

$$
d\pi = r\pi\, dt
\tag{15.450}
$$

may not be of immediate use since the pure jump component was not previously nullified. However, the pure jump component may not be mathematically hedged, as it was for the stochastic component of the continuous part of process S, but the expected value of the "pure jump" component, with an adequate choice of f may be nullified. Based on the above, after defining $E_{J,q}[h(J, q)]$, the expected value of any function h whose dependent variables are J and q, as

$$
\begin{aligned}
E_{J,q}(d\pi) = {} & \frac{\partial f_1}{\partial t} dt + \frac{1}{2}\frac{\partial^2 f_1}{\partial S^2}(vS^2\, dt) + \frac{\partial f_1}{\partial v}[\kappa(\theta - v)\, dt] + \frac{1}{2}\frac{\partial^2 f_1}{\partial v^2}(\sigma^2 v\, dt) \\
& + \frac{\partial^2 f_1}{\partial S \partial v}(S\sigma\rho v)\, dt - \frac{\partial f_1/\partial v}{\partial f_0/\partial v}\frac{\partial f_0}{\partial t}\, dt - \frac{\partial f_1/\partial v}{\partial f_0/\partial v}\frac{\partial f_0}{\partial v}[\kappa(\theta - v)\, dt] \\
& - \frac{\partial f_1/\partial v}{\partial f_0/\partial v}\frac{1}{2}\frac{\partial^2 f_0}{\partial S^2}(vS^2\, dt) - \frac{\partial f_1/\partial v}{\partial f_0/\partial v}\frac{1}{2}\frac{\partial^2 f_0}{\partial v^2}(\sigma^2 v\, dt) \\
& - \frac{\partial f_1/\partial v}{\partial f_0/\partial v}\frac{\partial^2 f_0}{\partial S \partial v}(S\sigma\rho v)\, dt + E_{J,q}\Big[[f_1[(J+1)S, v, t] - f_1[S, v, t]]\, dq \\
& - \frac{\partial f_1/\partial v}{\partial f_0/\partial v}[f_0[(J+1)S, v, t] - f_0[S, v, t]]\, dq - \Big(\frac{\partial f_1}{\partial S} - \frac{\partial f_1/\partial v}{\partial f_0/\partial v}\frac{\partial f_0}{\partial S}\Big)SJ\, dq\Big]
\end{aligned}
$$

$$(15.451)$$

In this case, the no-arbitrage hypothesis (15.450) takes the form

$$E_{J,q}(d\pi) = r\pi\, dt \tag{15.452}$$

Then, (15.452) is computed by using (15.451), (15.445) and (15.448). This gives

$$
\begin{aligned}
& \frac{\partial f_1/\partial t}{\partial f_1/\partial v} + \frac{\frac{1}{2}\partial^2 f_1/\partial S^2}{\partial f_1/\partial v}vS^2 + \frac{\partial f_1/\partial v}{\partial f_1/\partial v}[\kappa(\theta - v)] + \frac{\frac{1}{2}\partial^2 f_1/\partial v^2}{\partial f_1/\partial v}\sigma^2 v \\
& + \frac{\partial^2 f_1/\partial S \partial v}{\partial f_1/\partial v}S\sigma\rho v - \frac{1}{\partial f_0/\partial v}\frac{\partial f_0}{\partial t} - \frac{\partial f_0/\partial v}{\partial f_0/\partial v}[\kappa(\theta - v)\, dt] \\
& - \frac{1}{\partial f_0/\partial v}\frac{1}{2}\frac{\partial^2 f_0}{\partial S^2}vS^2 - \frac{1}{\partial f_0/\partial v}\frac{1}{2}\frac{\partial^2 f_0}{\partial v^2}\sigma^2 v - \frac{1}{\partial f_0/\partial v}\frac{\partial^2 f_0}{\partial S \partial v}S\sigma\rho v \\
& + \frac{1}{\partial f_1/\partial v}\lambda E_{J,q}[[f_1[(J+1)S, v, t] - f_1[S, v, t]]] \\
& - \frac{1}{\partial f_0/\partial v}\lambda E_{J,q}[[f_0[(J+1)S, v, t] - f_0[S, v, t]]] \\
= {} & -\lambda\frac{\partial f_1/\partial S}{\partial f_1/\partial v}S\mu + \lambda\frac{1}{\partial f_0/\partial v}\frac{\partial f_0}{\partial S}S\mu = \frac{rf_1}{\partial f_1/\partial v} - \frac{1}{\partial f_0/\partial v}rf_0 \\
& - \frac{\partial f_1/\partial S}{\partial f_1/\partial v}rS + \frac{1}{\partial f_0/\partial v}\frac{\partial f_0}{\partial S}rS
\end{aligned}
$$

It now becomes possible to isolate all of the members in f_0 in the left member of the equation and all of the members in f_1 in the right member, to obtain the following equivalence:

$$\frac{1}{\partial f_1/\partial v} \cdot \left[-rf_1 + \frac{\partial f_1}{\partial t} + \frac{\partial f_1}{\partial S}rS + \frac{1}{2}\frac{\partial^2 f_1}{\partial S^2}vS^2 + \frac{1}{2}\frac{\partial^2 f_1}{\partial v^2}\sigma^2 v + \frac{\partial^2 f_1}{\partial S\partial v}S\sigma\rho v \right.$$
$$\left. + [\kappa(\theta - v)]\frac{\partial f_0}{\partial v} + \lambda E_{J,q}[f_1[(J+1)S, v, t] - f_1[S, v, t]] - \lambda\frac{\partial f_1}{\partial S}S\mu \right]$$
$$= \frac{1}{\partial f_0/\partial v} \left[-rf_0 + \frac{\partial f_0}{\partial t} + \frac{\partial f_0}{\partial S}rS + \frac{1}{2}\frac{\partial^2 f_0}{\partial S^2}vS^2 + \frac{1}{2}\frac{\partial^2 f_0}{\partial v^2}\sigma^2 v + \frac{\partial^2 f_0}{\partial S\partial v}S\sigma\rho v \right.$$
$$\left. + [\kappa(\theta - v)]\frac{\partial f_0}{\partial v} + \lambda E_{J,q}[f_0[(J+1)S, v, t] - f_0[S, v, t]] - \lambda\frac{\partial f_0}{\partial S}S\mu \right]$$

$$(15.453)$$

Since the elements in both the right and left members of the equation are identical except for the subscript of the function f, ie, the price of a generic *contingent claim*, the choice of f_0 and of f_1 (ie, the maturity date or the strike price of the two options) has no influence on the replication portfolio buildup. This observation allows one to consider only one of the two quantities, ignoring the subscripts so that it is defined as

$$\frac{1}{\partial f/\partial v} \cdot \left[-rf + \frac{\partial f}{\partial t} + \frac{\partial f}{\partial S}rS + \frac{1}{2}\frac{\partial^2 f}{\partial S^2}vS^2 + \frac{1}{2}\frac{\partial^2 f}{\partial v^2}\sigma^2 v + \frac{\partial^2 f}{\partial S\partial v}S\sigma\rho v \right.$$
$$\left. + [\kappa(\theta - v)]\frac{\partial f}{\partial v} + \lambda E_{J,q}[f[(J+1)S, v, t] - f[S, v, t]] - \lambda\frac{\partial f}{\partial S}S\mu \right] = \chi^*(S, v, t)$$

$$(15.454)$$

or

$$-rf + \frac{\partial f}{\partial t} + \frac{\partial f}{\partial S}S[r - \lambda\mu] + \frac{1}{2}\frac{\partial^2 f}{\partial S^2}vS^2 + \frac{1}{2}\frac{\partial^2 f}{\partial v^2}\sigma^2 v + \frac{\partial^2 f}{\partial S\partial v}S\sigma\rho v$$
$$+ \frac{\partial f}{\partial v}[\kappa(\theta - v) - \chi^*(S, v, t)] + \lambda E_{J,q}[f[(J+1)S, v, t] - f[S, v, t]] = 0$$

$$(15.455)$$

where $\chi^*(S, v, t)$, defined in the literature as the volatility risk premium, is any function which takes values other than zero.

15.2.7.3. PDE specification for the pricing of a call option: derivation of the Cauchy problem

Given the PDE (15.455), the Cauchy problem, where f describes the price of a call option C among all of the contingent claims, is defined by the PDE (15.455) specified to describe the call price and by boundary conditions, ie, the call payoff value at maturity:

$$- rC + \frac{\partial C}{\partial t} + \frac{\partial C}{\partial S}S[r - \lambda\mu] + \frac{1}{2}\frac{\partial^2 C}{\partial S^2}vS^2 + \frac{1}{2}\frac{\partial^2 C}{\partial v^2}\sigma^2 v + \frac{\partial^2 C}{\partial S\partial v}S\sigma\rho v$$
$$+ \frac{\partial C}{\partial v}[\kappa(\theta - v) - \chi^*(S, v, t)] + \lambda E_{J,q}[f[(J + 1)S, v, t] - f[S, v, t]] = 0$$

$$(15.456)$$

$$C(S, v, t = T) = \max(0, S_T - K) \qquad (15.456a)$$

where $C(S, v, t, T)$ is the call option price at time t.

15.2.7.3.1. Transformation of the Cauchy problem into the corresponding log-arithmic version Equation (15.456) is specified in its equivalent logarithmic version. For this purpose, one can define

$$x = \ln(S) \qquad (15.457)$$

Then

$$S = e^x \qquad (15.458)$$

Then, the new version of (15.456) is derived with respect to x. Recalling that $C = f(S(g(x)))$, the relations between $\partial C/\partial x$ and $\partial C/\partial S$ and between $\partial^2 C/\partial x^2$ and $\partial^2 C/\partial S^2$ are then derived as

$$\frac{\partial C}{\partial S} = \frac{\partial C}{\partial x}\frac{1}{S} \qquad (15.459)$$

$$\frac{\partial^2 C}{\partial S^2} = \frac{\partial^2 C}{\partial x^2}\frac{1}{S^2} - \frac{\partial C}{\partial x}\frac{1}{S^2} \qquad (15.460)$$

The content of the expected value of (15.456) with respect to x, is now expanded, ie,

$$E[C[(J + 1)S, v, t] - C[S, v, t]] = E\{C[x + \ln(J + 1), v, t] - C[x, v, t]\}$$
$$\text{(using (15.458))} \qquad (15.461)$$

Then the Cauchy problem (15.456) is written with respect to x, by using (15.459), (15.460) and (15.461), by simplifying and defining

$$\chi^*(S, v, t) = \tilde{\chi}v \qquad (15.462)$$

one obtains

$$- rC + \frac{\partial C}{\partial t} + [r - \lambda\mu]\left[\frac{\partial C}{\partial x}\right] + \frac{1}{2}\frac{\partial^2 C}{\partial v^2}(\sigma^2 v) + \frac{\partial^2 C}{\partial x\partial v}(v\sigma\rho) + \frac{1}{2}\left[\frac{\partial^2 C}{\partial x^2} - \frac{\partial C}{\partial x}\right]v$$
$$+ \frac{\partial C}{\partial v}[\kappa(\theta - v) - \tilde{\chi}v] + \lambda E\{C[x + \ln(J + 1), v, t] - C[x, v, t]\} = 0 \quad (15.463)$$

Equation (15.463) is the logarithmic version of (15.456). To finalise the definition of the Cauchy problem, the boundary condition corresponding to that of (15.456a) has to be determined; for this purpose, simply rearrange this equation in its logarithmic version by using (15.458), ie,

$$C(x, t = T) = \text{Max}[0, e^{x_T} - K]$$

The new Cauchy problem is then derived, ie,

$$\underbrace{-rC + \frac{\partial C}{\partial t} + r\left[\frac{\partial C}{\partial x}\right] + \frac{1}{2}\frac{\partial^2 C}{\partial v^2}(\sigma^2 v) + \frac{\partial^2 C}{\partial x \partial v}(v \sigma \rho) + \frac{1}{2}\left[\frac{\partial^2 C}{\partial x^2} - \frac{\partial C}{\partial x}\right]v}_{\text{Deterministic component}}$$

$$+ \underbrace{\frac{\partial C}{\partial v}\left[\kappa(\theta - v) - \tilde{\chi}v\right]}_{\text{Deterministic component}} + \underbrace{\left[\lambda E\{C[x + \ln(J + 1), v, t] - C[x, v, t]\} - \lambda \mu \frac{\partial C}{\partial x}\right]}_{\text{Pure jump component}} = 0$$

(15.463)

$$C(x_t, v_t, t = T) = \max(0, e^{x_T} - K) \tag{15.463a}$$

15.2.7.3.2. The shift into the à-la BSM pricing context The Cauchy problem as in (15.463) is now specified in the classic à-la BSM form, ie,

$$C_t(S, v, t, T) = S_t P_1(S, v, t, T) - Ke^{-r(T-t)}P_2(S, v, t, T) \quad \text{or}$$
$$C_t(x, v, t) = e^{x_t}P_1(x, v, \tau) - Ke^{-r(T-t)}P_2(x, v, t)$$

(15.464)

where P_1, P_2 are probability measures, or P_j for $k = 1, 2$.

Equation (15.464) is used to compute the partial derivatives in order to make (15.463) explicit:

$$\frac{\partial C}{\partial x} = e^x P_1(x, v, t) + e^x \frac{\partial P_1}{\partial x} - Ke^{-r(T-t)}\frac{\partial P_2}{\partial x} \tag{15.465}$$

$$\frac{\partial^2 C}{\partial x^2} = e^x P_1(x, v, t) + 2e^x \frac{\partial P_1}{\partial x} + e^x \frac{\partial^2 P_1}{\partial x^2} - Ke^{-r(T-t)}\frac{\partial^2 P_2}{\partial x^2} \tag{15.466}$$

$$\frac{\partial C}{\partial t} = e^x \frac{\partial P_1}{\partial t} - K\left[e^{-r(T-t)}\frac{\partial P_2}{\partial t} + re^{-r(T-t)}P_2(x, v, t)\right] \tag{15.467}$$

$$\frac{\partial C}{\partial v} = e^x \frac{\partial P_1}{\partial v} - Ke^{-r(T-t)}\frac{\partial P_2}{\partial v} \tag{15.468}$$

$$\frac{\partial^2 C}{\partial v^2} = e^x \frac{\partial^2 P_1}{\partial v^2} - Ke^{-r(T-t)}\frac{\partial^2 P_2}{\partial v^2} \tag{15.469}$$

$$\frac{\partial^2 C}{\partial x \partial v} = e^x \frac{\partial P_1}{\partial v} + e^x \frac{\partial^2 P_1}{\partial x \partial v} - Ke^{-r(T-t)}\frac{\partial^2 P_2}{\partial x \partial v} \tag{15.470}$$

The expected value of (15.461) based on (15.464) remains to be expanded:

$$E\left\{C\left[\underbrace{x + \ln(J+1)}_{\text{argument } x \text{ of (15.464)}}, v, t\right] - C[x, v, t]\right\}$$

factorising P_1 and P_2, one obtains

$$
\begin{aligned}
E\{C[x + \ln(J+1), t] &- C[x, t]\} \\
&= E\{e^x[[(J+1)P_1[x + \ln(J+1), v, t] - P_1(x, v, t)] \\
&\quad - Ke^{-r(T-t)}[P_2[x + \ln(J+1), v, t] - P_2(x, v, t)]\}
\end{aligned}
\tag{15.471}
$$

Then (15.466), (15.467), (15.468), (15.469), (15.470) and (15.471) are substituted in (15.463), to obtain

$$
\begin{aligned}
e^x\bigg[&-\lambda\mu P_1(x, v, t) + \frac{\partial P_1}{\partial t} + \frac{\partial P_1}{\partial x}\left(r - \lambda\mu + \frac{1}{2}v\right) + \frac{1}{2}\left(\frac{\partial^2 P_1}{\partial v^2}(\sigma^2 v)\right) + \frac{\partial^2 P_1}{\partial x \partial v}(v\sigma\rho) \\
&+ \frac{1}{2}\left(\frac{\partial^2 P_1}{\partial x^2}v\right) + \frac{\partial P_1}{\partial v}[\kappa(\theta - v) - \tilde{\chi}v + v\sigma\rho] \\
&+ \lambda E[(J+1)P_1[x + \ln(J+1), v, t] - P_1(x, v, t)]\bigg] \\
- Ke^{-r(T-t)}\bigg[&\frac{\partial P_2}{\partial t} + \frac{\partial P_2}{\partial x}\left(r - \lambda\mu - \frac{1}{2}v\right) + \frac{1}{2}\frac{\partial^2 P_2}{\partial v^2}(\sigma^2 v) + \frac{\partial^2 P_2}{\partial x \partial v}(v\sigma\rho) \\
&+ \frac{1}{2}v(\frac{\partial^2 P_2}{\partial x^2}) + \frac{\partial P_2}{\partial v}[\kappa(\theta - v) - \tilde{\chi}v] + \lambda E[P_2[x + \ln(J+1), v, t] \\
&- P_2(x, v, t)]\bigg] = 0
\end{aligned}
$$

Since $e^x > 0$ and $K > 0$, in order to verify the equivalence above, it is enough that

$$
\begin{cases}
-\lambda\mu P_1(x, v, t) + \dfrac{\partial P_1}{\partial t} + [r - \lambda\mu]\dfrac{\partial P_1}{\partial x} + \dfrac{1}{2}v\dfrac{\partial P_1}{\partial x} + \dfrac{1}{2}\dfrac{\partial^2 P_1}{\partial v^2}(\sigma^2 v) \\
\quad + \dfrac{\partial^2 P_1}{\partial x \partial v}(v\sigma\rho) + \dfrac{1}{2}\dfrac{\partial^2 P_1}{\partial x^2}v + \dfrac{\partial P_1}{\partial v}[\kappa\theta - v(\kappa + \tilde{\chi} - \sigma\rho)] \\
\quad + \lambda E[(J+1)P_1[x + \ln(J+1), v, t] - P_1(x, v, t)] = 0 \\[2mm]
\dfrac{\partial P_2}{\partial t} + [r - \lambda\mu]\dfrac{\partial P_2}{\partial x} - \dfrac{1}{2}v\dfrac{\partial P_2}{\partial x} + \dfrac{1}{2}\dfrac{\partial^2 P_2}{\partial v^2}(\sigma^2 v) + \dfrac{\partial^2 P_2}{\partial x \partial v}(v\sigma\rho) + \dfrac{1}{2}\dfrac{\partial^2 P_2}{\partial x^2}v \\
\quad + \dfrac{\partial P_2}{\partial v}[\kappa\theta - v(\kappa + \tilde{\chi})] + \lambda E[P_2[x + \ln(J+1), v, t] - P_2(x, v, t)] = 0
\end{cases}
\tag{15.472}
$$

Equations (15.472) are equivalent forms of PDE (15.463) in the à-la BSM call pricing context as in (15.464). To identify the Cauchy problems in (15.472), equivalent to problem (15.463) and then to (15.456), one has to derive the boundary condition; for this purpose, the characteristics of function P_j are specified at time $t = T$ in order to determine, based on (15.472), the boundary condition under (15.463a) of the PDE (15.463), ie,

$$P_j(x_T, v_T, T) = \begin{cases} 1 & \text{if } (e^{x_T} - K) \geq 0 \\ 0 & \text{if } (e^{x_T} - K) < 0 \end{cases} \quad \text{for } j = 1, 2$$

by applying the logarithm

$$P_j(x_T, v_T, T) = \begin{cases} 1 & \text{if } x_T \geq \ln K \\ 0 & \text{if } xT < \ln K \end{cases} \quad \text{for } j = 1, 2$$

and using the definition of the index function (see Definition 6.3), one obtains

$$P_j(x_T, v_T, T) = 1_{(x_T \geq \ln K)}$$

The following equations are the transformed Cauchy problem in the à-la BSM call pricing environment determined as in (15.463) and its boundary conditions:

$$\underbrace{\frac{\partial P_1}{\partial t} + \left[r + \frac{1}{2} v \right] \frac{\partial P_1}{\partial x} + \frac{1}{2} \frac{\partial^2 P_1}{\partial v^2} (\sigma^2 v) + \frac{\partial^2 P_1}{\partial x \partial v} (v \sigma \rho) + \frac{1}{2} \frac{\partial^2 P_1}{\partial x^2} v}_{\text{Deterministic component}}$$

$$+ \underbrace{\frac{\partial P_1}{\partial v} [\kappa \theta - v(\kappa + \tilde{\chi} - \sigma \rho)]}_{\text{Deterministic component}}$$

$$\underbrace{- \lambda \mu P_1(x, v, t) + \lambda E[(J + 1)P_1[x + \ln(J + 1), v, t] - P_1(x, v, t)] - \lambda \mu \frac{\partial P_1}{\partial x}}_{\text{Pure jump component}} = 0$$

$$(15.473)$$

$$P_1(x_T, v_T, T) = 1_{(x_T \geq \ln K)} \tag{15.474}$$

$$\frac{\partial P_2}{\partial t} + \left[r - \frac{1}{2}v\right]\frac{\partial P_2}{\partial x} + \frac{1}{2}\frac{\partial^2 P_2}{\partial v^2}(\sigma^2 v) + \frac{\partial^2 P_2}{\partial x \partial v}(v\sigma\rho) + \frac{1}{2}\frac{\partial^2 P_2}{\partial x^2}v$$

Deterministic component

$$+ \frac{\partial P_2}{\partial v}[\kappa\theta - v(\kappa + \tilde{\chi})]$$

Deterministic component

$$+ \lambda[P_2[x + \ln(J+1), v, t] - P_2(x, v, t)] - \lambda\mu\frac{\partial P_2}{\partial x} = 0 \qquad (15.475)$$

Pure jump component

$$P_2(x_T, v_T, T) = 1_{(x_T \geq \ln K)} \qquad (15.476)$$

Then the characteristics of the probability measure P_j at time t remain to be determined. For this purpose, (15.473) and (15.475) are interpreted by using the deterministic components of the Feynman–Kac formula (see Theorem 12.21). Actually, the corresponding SDEs of (15.473) and (15.475) may be determined, ie,

$$dx_t^{(1)} = (r + \tfrac{1}{2}v_t)\,dt + \sigma\sqrt{v_t}\,dz_t^{(1)} \quad \text{with } x_t = x \qquad (15.477)$$

$$dv_t^{(1)} = (\kappa\theta - (\kappa + \tilde{\chi} - \rho\sigma)v_t)\,dt + \sigma\sqrt{v_t}\,dz_t^{(2)} \quad \text{with } v_t = v \qquad (15.478)$$

$$dx_t^{(2)} = (r - \tfrac{1}{2}v_t)\,dt + \sigma\sqrt{v_t}\,dz_t^{(1)} \quad \text{with } x_t = x \qquad (15.479)$$

$$dv_t^{(2)} = (\kappa\theta - (\kappa + \tilde{\chi})v_t)\,dt + \sigma\sqrt{v_t}\,dz_t^{(2)} \quad \text{with } v_t = v \qquad (15.480)$$

with $dz_t^{(1)} \cdot dz_t^{(2)} = \rho\,dt$. Then (12.103) is rearranged, ie,

$$P_j(x_t, v_t, t) = E_j[1_{(x_T \geq \ln K)}|x_t = x, v_t = v]$$

by simplifying, one has

$$P_j(x_t, v_t, t) = P_j[x_T \geq \ln K | x_t = x, v_t = v]$$

for $j = 1$ and 2, respectively.

By denoting the equivalence $x_t = x$ by x_t and the equivalence $v_t = v$ by v_t, one obtains the characteristics of the probability measure P_j at a generic time t:

$$P_j(x_t, v_t, t) = P_j(x_T \geq \ln K \mid x_t, v_t) \qquad (15.481)$$

15.2.7.3.3. The shift in Fourier space The Cauchy problem identified in (15.473) and (15.475) is now shifted in the Fourier space, ie, it is rearranged as a function of the conditioned characteristic function. For this purpose, (11.123) is rearranged, by using notation 11.34, for $P_j(x_t, v_t, t)$, ie[12],

$$P_j(x_T \geq \ln K \mid x_t, v_t) = \frac{1}{2\pi} \int_{-\infty}^{\infty} \frac{e^{-i\xi \ln K}}{i\xi} \tilde{f}_j(x_t, v_t, t = T, \xi \mid x_t, v_t) \, d\xi \quad (15.482)$$

This expression, by denoting for simplicity $\tilde{f}_j(x_t, v_t, t = T, \xi \mid x_t, v_t) \doteq \tilde{f}_j$, is used to compute partial derivatives (to simplify notation $\tilde{f}_j(x_T, v_T, \xi \mid x_t, v_t) = \tilde{f}_j(\xi)$), ie,

$$\frac{\partial P_j}{\partial t} = \frac{\partial}{\partial t} \left[\frac{1}{2\pi} \int_{-\infty}^{\infty} \frac{e^{-i\xi \ln K}}{i\xi} \tilde{f}_j(\xi) \, d\xi \right] = \frac{1}{2\pi} \int_{-\infty}^{\infty} \frac{e^{-i\xi \ln K}}{i\xi} \frac{\partial \tilde{f}_j}{\partial t} \, d\xi \quad (15.483)$$

$$\frac{\partial P_j}{\partial x} = \frac{\partial}{\partial x} \left[\frac{1}{2\pi} \int_{-\infty}^{\infty} \frac{e^{-i\xi \ln K}}{i\xi} \tilde{f}_j(\xi) \, d\xi \right] = \frac{1}{2\pi} \int_{-\infty}^{\infty} \frac{e^{-i\xi \ln K}}{i\xi} \frac{\partial \tilde{f}_j}{\partial x} \, d\xi \quad (15.484)$$

$$\frac{\partial P_j}{\partial v} = \frac{\partial}{\partial v} \left[\frac{1}{2\pi} \int_{-\infty}^{\infty} \frac{e^{-i\xi \ln K}}{i\xi} \tilde{f}_j(\xi) \, d\xi \right] = \frac{1}{2\pi} \int_{-\infty}^{\infty} \frac{e^{-i\xi \ln K}}{i\xi} \frac{\partial \tilde{f}_j}{\partial v} \, d\xi \quad (15.485)$$

The second-order derivative in x is computed based on (15.484), ie,

$$\frac{\partial^2 P_j}{\partial x^2} = \frac{\partial}{\partial x} \left[\frac{1}{2\pi} \int_{-\infty}^{\infty} \frac{e^{-i\xi \ln K}}{i\xi} \frac{\partial \tilde{f}_j}{\partial x} \, d\xi \right] = \frac{1}{2\pi} \int_{-\infty}^{\infty} \frac{e^{-i\xi \ln K}}{i\xi} \frac{\partial^2 \tilde{f}_j}{\partial x^2} \, d\xi \quad (15.486)$$

The second-order derivative in v is computed based on (15.485), ie,

$$\frac{\partial^2 P_j}{\partial v^2} = \frac{\partial}{\partial v} \left[\frac{1}{2\pi} \int_{-\infty}^{\infty} \frac{e^{-i\xi \ln K}}{i\xi} \frac{\partial \tilde{f}_j}{\partial v} \, d\xi \right] = \frac{1}{2\pi} \int_{-\infty}^{\infty} \frac{e^{-i\xi \ln K}}{i\xi} \frac{\partial^2 \tilde{f}_j}{\partial v^2} \, d\xi \quad (15.487)$$

The second-order shifted derivative is computed either from (15.484), or from (15.485):

$$\frac{\partial^2 P_j}{\partial x \partial v} = \frac{\partial}{\partial v} \left[\frac{1}{2\pi} \int_{-\infty}^{\infty} \frac{e^{-i\xi \ln K}}{i\xi} \frac{\partial \tilde{f}_j}{\partial x} \, d\xi \right] = \frac{1}{2\pi} \int_{-\infty}^{\infty} \frac{e^{-i\xi \ln K}}{i\xi} \frac{\partial^2 \tilde{f}_j}{\partial v \partial x} \, d\xi \quad (15.488)$$

The other members of (15.473) and of (15.475) remain to be rearranged as a function of the conditioned characteristic function. Specifically, with respect to the argument of the expected value of (15.473), one has

$$E[(1 + J)P_1(\ln(1 + J) + x, v, t) - P_1(x, v, t)] \quad (15.489)$$

Notation 15.7. In the following, the notation is simplified by writing

$$P_1(\ln(1 + J) + x, v, t) \doteq P_1^{[J]} \quad \text{and} \quad P_1(x, v, t) = P_1.$$

---

[12] Equation (11.123) shows neither ">" nor "≥"; in this case, the difference is not relevant, given the call *payoff*.

Equation (15.489) becomes

$$E[(1+J)P_1^{[J]} - P_1] = \frac{1}{2\pi} \int_{-\infty}^{\infty} \frac{e^{-i\xi \ln[K]}}{i\xi} E[(1+J)\tilde{f}_1(x_T + \ln(1+J), \xi \mid x_t$$
$$+ \ln(1+J)) - \tilde{f}_1(x_T, \xi \mid x_t)] \, d\xi \quad \text{(using (15.482))}$$
$$\text{(15.490)}$$

Notation 15.8. In the following, the notation is simplified by writing

$$\tilde{f}_1(x_T + \ln(1+J), \xi \mid x_t + \ln(1+J)) \doteq \tilde{f}_1^{[J]}$$
$$\tilde{f}_1(x_T, \xi \mid x_t) \doteq \tilde{f}_1$$

Equation (15.490) becomes

$$E[(1+J)P_1^{[J]} - P_1] = \frac{1}{2\pi} \int_{-\infty}^{\infty} \frac{e^{-i\xi \ln[K]}}{i\xi} E[(1+J)\tilde{f}_1^{[J]} - \tilde{f}_1] \, d\xi \qquad \text{(15.491)}$$

Similarly, with respect to the argument of the expected value of (15.475), one has

$$E[P_2(\ln(1+J) + x, v, t) - P_2(x, v, t)] \qquad \text{(15.492)}$$

Notation 15.9. In the following, the notation is simplified by writing

$$P_2(\ln(1+J) + x, v, t) \doteq P_2^{[J]} \quad \text{and} \quad P_2(x, v, t) = P_2.$$

Equation (15.492) becomes

$$E[P_2^{[J]} - P_2] = \frac{1}{2\pi} \int_{-\infty}^{\infty} \frac{e^{-i\xi \ln[K]}}{i\xi} E[\tilde{f}_2(x_T + \ln(1+J), \xi \mid x_t$$
$$+ \ln(1+J)) - \tilde{f}_2(x_T, \xi \mid x_t)] \, d\xi \quad \text{(using (15.482))} \qquad \text{(15.493)}$$

Notation 15.10. In the following, the notation is simplified by writing

$$\tilde{f}_2(x_T + \ln(1+J), \xi \mid x_t + \ln(1+J)) \doteq \tilde{f}_2^{[J]}$$
$$\tilde{f}_2(x_T, \xi \mid x_t) \doteq \tilde{f}_2$$

Equation (15.493) becomes

$$E[P_2^{[J]} - P_2(x_t)] = \frac{1}{2\pi} \int_{-\infty}^{\infty} \frac{e^{-i\xi \ln[K]}}{i\xi} E[\tilde{f}_2^{[J]} - \tilde{f}_2] \, d\xi \qquad \text{(15.494)}$$

Then (15.482), (15.483), (15.484), (15.485), (15.486), (15.487), (15.488) and (15.491) are substituted in Equation (15.473), to obtain

$$
\frac{1}{2\pi} \int_{-\infty}^{\infty} \frac{e^{-i\xi \ln K}}{i\xi} \left[\frac{\partial \tilde{f}_1}{\partial t} + \frac{\partial \tilde{f}_1}{\partial x} \left[r - \lambda\mu + \frac{1}{2}v \right] + \frac{1}{2} \frac{\partial^2 \tilde{f}_1}{\partial v^2}(\sigma^2 v) + \frac{\partial^2 \tilde{f}_1}{\partial v \partial x}(v\sigma\rho) \right.
$$
$$
\left. + \frac{1}{2} \frac{\partial^2 \tilde{f}_1}{\partial x^2}v + \frac{\partial \tilde{f}_1}{\partial v}[\kappa\theta - v(\kappa + \tilde{\chi} - \sigma\rho)] - \lambda\mu\tilde{f}_1 + \lambda E\left[(1+J)\tilde{f}_1^{[J]} - \tilde{f}_1 \right] \right] d\xi = 0
$$

This equation is verified under the condition that the member inside square brackets is equal to zero. Then the PDE is given only by this last member, ie,

$$
-\lambda\mu\tilde{f}_1 + \frac{\partial \tilde{f}_1}{\partial t} + \frac{\partial \tilde{f}_1}{\partial x}\left[r - \lambda\mu + \frac{1}{2}v \right] + \frac{1}{2}\frac{\partial^2 \tilde{f}_1}{\partial v^2}(\sigma^2 v) + \frac{\partial^2 \tilde{f}_1}{\partial v \partial x}(v\sigma\rho) + \frac{1}{2}\frac{\partial^2 \tilde{f}_1}{\partial x^2}v
$$
$$
+ \frac{\partial \tilde{f}_1}{\partial v}[\kappa\theta - v(\kappa + \tilde{\chi} - \sigma\rho)] + \lambda E\left[(1+J)\tilde{f}_1^{[J]} - \tilde{f}_1 \right] = 0 \tag{15.495}
$$

Similarly, the PDE in (15.475) is shifted in the Fourier space by substituting (15.483), (15.484), (15.485), (15.486), (15.487), (15.488) and (15.494) in that space

$$
\frac{1}{2\pi} \int_{-\infty}^{\infty} \frac{e^{-i\xi \ln K}}{i\xi} \left[\frac{\partial \tilde{f}_2}{\partial t} + \frac{\partial \tilde{f}_2}{\partial x} \left[r - \lambda\mu - \frac{1}{2}v \right] + \frac{1}{2} \frac{\partial^2 \tilde{f}_2}{\partial v^2}(\sigma^2 v) + \frac{\partial^2 \tilde{f}_2}{\partial v \partial x}(v\sigma\rho) \right.
$$
$$
\left. + \frac{1}{2} \frac{\partial^2 \tilde{f}_2}{\partial x^2}v + \frac{\partial \tilde{f}_2}{\partial v}[\kappa\theta - v(\kappa + \tilde{\chi})] + \lambda E\left[\tilde{f}_2^{[J]} - \tilde{f}_2 \right] \right] d\xi = 0
$$

This equation is verified under condition that the member in square brackets is equal to zero. Then the PDE is given only by the last member, ie,

$$
\frac{\partial \tilde{f}_2}{\partial t} + \frac{\partial \tilde{f}_2}{\partial x}\left[r - \lambda\mu - \frac{1}{2}v \right] + \frac{1}{2}\frac{\partial^2 \tilde{f}_2}{\partial v^2}(\sigma^2 v) + \frac{\partial^2 \tilde{f}_2}{\partial v \partial x}(v\sigma\rho) + \frac{1}{2}\frac{\partial^2 \tilde{f}_2}{\partial x^2}v
$$
$$
+ \frac{\partial \tilde{f}_2}{\partial v}[\kappa\theta - v(\kappa + \tilde{\chi})] + \lambda E\left[\tilde{f}_2^{[J]} - \tilde{f}_2 \right] = 0 \tag{15.496}
$$

To complete the shift of the Cauchy problem as in (15.473) and (15.475), one has to specify the final conditions in (15.474) and (15.476). By using Remark 6.5 this final condition is rearranged as

$$
P_j(x_t, v_t, t = T) = 1_{(x_T \geq \ln K)} = \theta_{\ln K}(x_T) \triangleq \theta(x_T - \ln K)
$$

where θ is the Heaviside function.
Recalling Proposition 6.10 one has

$$
\theta(x_T - \ln K) = \int_{-\infty}^{x_T - \ln K} \delta(w)\, dw
$$

which, under Theorem 9.4 and under the Fubini theorem (see Theorem 10.22), is equal to

$$\theta(x_T - \ln K) = \frac{1}{2\pi} \int_{-\infty}^{+\infty} \left(\int_{-\infty}^{x_T - \ln K} e^{i\xi w} \, dw \right) d\xi$$

$$= \frac{1}{2\pi} \int_{-\infty}^{+\infty} \frac{1}{i\xi} e^{-i\xi \ln K} e^{i\xi x_T} d\xi$$

comparing this last expression to (15.482), arranged for T, one obtains

$$\frac{1}{2\pi} \int_{-\infty}^{+\infty} \frac{e^{-i\xi \ln K}}{i\xi} e^{i\xi x_T} \, d\xi = \frac{1}{2\pi} \int_{-\infty}^{\infty} \frac{e^{-i\xi \ln K}}{i\xi} \tilde{f}_j(x_T, v_T, T, \xi) \, d\xi$$

simplifying, one obtains the final conditions of the Cauchy problem as under (15.495) and (15.496), ie,

$$e^{i\xi x_T} = \tilde{f}_j(x_T, v_T, T, \xi).$$

The following equations are the original Cauchy problem identified under (15.473) and (15.475) and under the respective boundary conditions shifted in the Fourier space:

$$\frac{\partial \tilde{f}_1}{\partial t} + \frac{\partial \tilde{f}_1}{\partial x}\left[r - \lambda\mu + \frac{1}{2}v\right] + \frac{1}{2}\frac{\partial^2 \tilde{f}_1}{\partial v^2}(\sigma^2 v) + \frac{\partial^2 \tilde{f}_1}{\partial v \partial x}(v\sigma\rho)$$

$$+ \frac{1}{2}\frac{\partial^2 \tilde{f}_1}{\partial x^2}v + \frac{\partial \tilde{f}_1}{\partial v}[\kappa\theta - v(\kappa + \tilde{\chi} - \sigma\rho)] - \lambda\mu\tilde{f}_1 + \lambda E[(1+J)\tilde{f}_1^{[J]} - \tilde{f}_1] = 0$$

$$\hspace{10cm} (15.495)$$

$$\tilde{f}_1(x_T, v_T, T, \xi) = e^{i\xi x_T} \hspace{4cm} (15.495a)$$

$$\frac{\partial \tilde{f}_2}{\partial t} + \frac{\partial \tilde{f}_2}{\partial x}\left[r - \lambda\mu - \frac{1}{2}v\right] + \frac{1}{2}\frac{\partial^2 \tilde{f}_2}{\partial v^2}(\sigma^2 v) + \frac{\partial^2 \tilde{f}_2}{\partial v \partial x}(v\sigma\rho)$$

$$+ \frac{1}{2}\frac{\partial^2 \tilde{f}_2}{\partial x^2}v + \frac{\partial \tilde{f}_2}{\partial v}[\kappa\theta - v(\kappa + \tilde{\chi})] + \lambda E[\tilde{f}_2^{[J]} - \tilde{f}_2] = 0 \hspace{2cm} (15.496)$$

$$\tilde{f}_2(x_T, v_T, T, \xi) = e^{i\xi x_T} \hspace{4cm} (15.496a)$$

15.2.7.3.3.1.   *The temporal shift of the transformed Cauchy problem*   In order to obtain an explicit solution of the Cauchy problem, another temporal shift in Fourier space is needed. Then $\tau = T - t$ so that $t = T - \tau$. Since, for any generic function $f(T - t) = f(\tau)$, it is true that

$$\frac{\partial f(T - t)}{\partial t} = -\frac{\partial f(\tau)}{\partial \tau}$$

Then, the Cauchy problem, identified by Equations (15.495) and (15.496) and by their final conditions, becomes

$$-\frac{\partial \tilde{f_1}}{\partial \tau} + \frac{1}{2}\frac{\partial^2 \tilde{f_1}}{\partial x^2}v + \left[r - \lambda\mu + \frac{1}{2}v\right]\frac{\partial \tilde{f_1}}{\partial x} + \frac{1}{2}\frac{\partial^2 \tilde{f_1}}{\partial v^2}(\sigma^2 v) + \frac{\partial^2 \tilde{f_1}}{\partial v \partial x}(v\sigma\rho)$$

$$+ \frac{\partial \tilde{f_1}}{\partial v}[\kappa\theta - v(\kappa + \tilde{\chi} - \sigma\rho)] - \lambda\mu\tilde{f_1} + \lambda E[(1 + J)\tilde{f_1}^{[J]} - \tilde{f_1}] = 0 \qquad (15.497)$$

$$\tilde{f_j}(x_{\tau=0}, \xi) = e^{i\xi[x_{\tau=0}]} \qquad (15.497a)$$

$$-\frac{\partial \tilde{f_2}}{\partial \tau} + \frac{1}{2}v\frac{\partial^2 \tilde{f_2}}{\partial x^2} + \left[r - \lambda\mu - \frac{1}{2}v\right]\frac{\partial \tilde{f_2}}{\partial x} + \frac{1}{2}\frac{\partial^2 \tilde{f_2}}{\partial v^2}(\sigma^2 v) + \frac{\partial^2 \tilde{f_2}}{\partial v \partial x}(v\sigma\rho)$$

$$+ \frac{\partial \tilde{f_2}}{\partial v}[\kappa\theta - v(\kappa + \tilde{\chi})] + \lambda E[\tilde{f_2}^{[J]} - \tilde{f_2}] = 0 \qquad (15.498)$$

$$\tilde{f_j}(x_{\tau=0}, \xi) = e^{i\xi[x_{\tau=0}]} \qquad (15.498a)$$

15.2.7.4. Specification of Cauchy problem as an ODE system

Let $\tilde{f_j}$ be the solution to the Cauchy problem, identified in (15.495) and (15.496), and written as

$$\tilde{f_j}(x_\tau, v_\tau, \tau = 0, \xi | x_\tau, v_\tau) = e^{(C_\tau^{(j)} + D_\tau^{(j)}v_t + i\xi x_\tau)} \qquad (15.499)$$

in order for it to be compatible with the final conditions (15.497a) and (15.498a) it is necessary, for $\tau = 0$, that $C_0^{(j)} = 0$ and $D_0^{(j)} = 0$. Then these final conditions in the form (15.499) are equivalent to those determined by (15.495a) and (15.496a) in the Cauchy problem identified by (15.495). The partial derivatives of (15.495) and (15.496) are computed by using the functional form (15.499). For simplicity, the subscripts τ and t below v are omitted:

$$\frac{\partial \tilde{f_j}}{\partial \tau} = e^{(C_j + D_j v + i\xi x)}\left(\frac{\partial C_j}{\partial \tau} + \frac{\partial D_j}{\partial \tau}v\right) \qquad (15.500)$$

$$\frac{\partial \tilde{f_j}}{\partial x} = e^{(C_j + D_j v + i\xi x)} i\xi \qquad (15.501)$$

$$\frac{\partial^2 \tilde{f_j}}{\partial x^2} = -\xi^2 e^{(C_j + D_j v + i\xi x)} \qquad (15.502)$$

$$\frac{\partial \tilde{f_j}}{\partial v} = e^{(C_j + D_j v + i\xi x)} D_j \qquad (15.503)$$

$$\frac{\partial^2 \tilde{f_j}}{\partial v^2} = e^{(C_j + D_j v + i\xi x)} D_j^2 \qquad (15.504)$$

$$\frac{\partial^2 \tilde{f_j}}{\partial x \partial v} = i\xi D_j\, e^{(C_j + D_j v + i\xi x)} \qquad (15.505)$$

The member contained in the expected value of (15.497) as in (15.499) can be written as

$$E[(1 + J)\tilde{f}_1^{[J]} - \tilde{f}_1]$$

by expanding the simplified notation:

$$E[(1 + J)\tilde{f}_1^{[J]} - \tilde{f}_1] = e^{C_1 + D_1 v + i\tilde{\zeta}x}\{E[e^{(i\tilde{\zeta}+1)\ln(J+1)}] - 1\} \qquad (15.506)$$

then $E[e^{(i\tilde{\zeta}+1)\ln(J+1)}]$ is computed. Actually, recalling that

$$J + 1 \sim \text{Log } N(\mu + 1, (1 + \mu)(e^{\sigma^2} - 1))$$

one may compute the distributive properties of the normal random variable $\ln(1 + J)$. By solving the following system, one derives the mean and the variance of this variable, ie,

$$\begin{cases} \mu + 1 = e^{a + b^2/2} \\ (1 + \mu)(e^{\sigma^2} - 1) = e^{a + b^2/2} \cdot (e^{b^2} - 1) \end{cases}$$

that is

$$\begin{cases} a = \ln(\mu + 1) - \dfrac{\sigma^2}{2} \\ b^2 = \sigma^2 \end{cases} \qquad (15.507)$$

by using (15.507), the distributional properties of the random variable of $\ln(1 + J)$ become

$$\ln[1 + J] \sim N\left(\ln[1 + \mu] - \tfrac{1}{2}\sigma^2, \sigma^2\right) \qquad (15.508)$$

in order to compute $E[e^{(i\tilde{\zeta}+1)\ln(J+1)}]$ since $\ln[1 + J]$ is a normal random variable, one may use the moment generating function for this type of variable (see expression (11.115)), ie,

$$E[e^{(i\tilde{\zeta}+1)\ln(J+1)}] = e^{(i\tilde{\zeta}\sigma^2/2)(i\tilde{\zeta}+1)}(1 + \mu)^{(i\tilde{\zeta}+1)} \qquad (15.509)$$

by using (15.509) it can be derived that (15.506) may also be written as

$$E[(1 + J)\tilde{f}_1^{[J]} - \tilde{f}_1] = e^{C_1 + D_1 v + i\tilde{\zeta}x}[e^{(i\tilde{\zeta}\sigma^2/2)(i\tilde{\zeta}+1)}(1 + \mu)^{(i\tilde{\zeta}+1)} - 1] \qquad (15.510)$$

Equation (15.510) rearranges the member inside the expected value of (15.497) as in (15.499).

Then (15.500), (15.501), (15.502), (15.503), (15.504), (15.505) and (15.510) are substituted in (15.497), to obtain

$$e^{(C_1+D_1v+i\xi x)}\left(-\frac{\partial C_1}{\partial \tau} + ri\xi + \kappa\theta D_1 - \lambda\mu i\xi - \lambda\mu\right.$$

$$\left. + \lambda\left[e^{(i\xi\sigma^2/2)(i\xi+1)}(1+\mu)^{(i\xi+1)} - 1\right]\right) + ve^{(C_1+D_1v+i\xi x)}$$

$$\times \left[-\frac{\partial D_1}{\partial \tau} + \frac{1}{2}i\xi + \frac{1}{2}D_1^2\sigma^2 + i\xi D_1\sigma\rho - \frac{1}{2}\xi^2 - (\kappa + \tilde{\chi} - \sigma\rho)D_1\right] = 0$$

Since the term $e^{(C_1+D_1v+i\xi x)}$ is always positive, the above equivalence becomes

$$\underbrace{-\frac{\partial C_1}{\partial \tau} + ri\xi + \kappa\theta D_1 - \lambda\mu i\xi - \lambda\mu + \lambda\left[e^{(i\xi\sigma^2/2)(i\xi+1)}(1+\mu)^{(i\xi+1)} - 1\right]}_{1^a}$$

$$\underbrace{+ v\left(-\frac{\partial D_1}{\partial \tau} + \frac{1}{2}i\xi + \frac{1}{2}D_1^2\sigma^2 + i\xi D_1\sigma\rho - \frac{1}{2}\xi^2 - (\kappa + \tilde{\chi} - \sigma\rho)D_1\right)}_{2^a} = 0$$

the equivalence above is verified even if the two expressions have a trivial solution; the v of the second expression may be neglected since it is positive. Then, the Cauchy problem in (15.497) and in the final condition (15.497a) may be rearranged as

$$\frac{\partial C_1}{\partial \tau} = ri\xi + \kappa\theta D_1 + \lambda[-\mu(i\xi+1) + [e^{(i\xi\sigma^2/2)(i\xi+1)}(1+\mu)^{(i\xi+1)} - 1]] \quad (15.511)$$

$$C_0^{(1)} = 0 \quad (15.511a)$$

$$\frac{\partial D_1}{\partial \tau} = \frac{1}{2}i\xi + \frac{1}{2}D_1^2\sigma^2 + i\xi D_1\sigma\rho - \frac{1}{2}\xi^2 - (\kappa + \tilde{\chi} - \sigma\rho)D_1 \quad (15.512)$$

$$D_0^{(1)} = 0 \quad (15.512a)$$

Then, Equation (15.499) is used to rearrange the expected value in (15.498):

$$E[\tilde{f}_2^{[J]} - \tilde{f}_2]$$

expanding the simplified notation and with a little algebra, one has

$$E[\tilde{f}_2^{[J]} - \tilde{f}_2] = e^{C_2+D_2v+i\xi x}\{E[e^{i\xi \ln(J+1)}] - 1\} \quad (15.513)$$

then $E[e^{i\xi \ln(J+1)}]$ is computed. Actually, since $\ln[1+J]$ is a normal random variable, by using the moment generating function for normal random variables (see Expression (11.115)), one may write

$$E[e^{i\xi \ln(J+1)}] = e^{(\sigma^2/2)i\xi(i\xi-1)}(1+\mu)^{i\xi} \tag{15.514}$$

then using (15.514), Equation (15.513) can be written as

$$E[(1+J)\tilde{f}_2^{[J]} - \tilde{f}_2] = e^{C_2+D_2 v+i\xi x}[e^{(\sigma^2/2)i\xi(i\xi-1)}(1+\mu)^{i\xi} - 1] \tag{15.515}$$

Equation (15.515) is used to rearrange the term contained in the expected value in (15.498) as in the form (15.499).

Then (15.500), (15.501), (15.502), (15.503), (15.504) and (15.505) are substituted in (15.498), to obtain

$$e^{(C_2+D_2 v+i\xi x)}\left(-\frac{\partial C_2}{\partial \tau} + ri\xi + \kappa\theta D_2 - \lambda\mu i\xi + \lambda[e^{(\sigma^2/2)i\xi(i\xi-1)}(1+\mu)^{i\xi} - 1]\right)$$

$$+ ve^{(C_2+D_j v+i\xi x)}\left(-\frac{\partial D_2}{\partial \tau} - \frac{1}{2}i\xi + i\xi D_2 + \frac{1}{2}D_2^2\sigma^2 - \frac{1}{2}\xi^2 - (\kappa + \tilde{\chi})D_2\right)$$

since the term $e^{(C_2+D_2 v+i\xi x)}$ is always positive, the above equivalence becomes

$$\underbrace{-\frac{\partial C_2}{\partial \tau} + ri\xi + \kappa\theta D_2 - \lambda\mu i\xi + \lambda[e^{(\sigma^2/2)i\xi(i\xi-1)}(1+\mu)^{i\xi} - 1]}_{1^a}$$

$$+ v\underbrace{\left(-\frac{\partial D_2}{\partial \tau} - \frac{1}{2}i\xi + \frac{1}{2}D_2^2\sigma^2 + i\xi D_2\sigma\rho - \frac{1}{2}\xi^2 - (\kappa + \tilde{\chi})D_2\right)}_{2^a} = 0$$

the equivalence above is also verified if the two expressions have a trivial solution; the factor v of the second expression may be neglected because it is positive. It can be derived that the Cauchy problem as in (15.498) and in the final condition (15.498a) may be rearranged as

$$\frac{\partial C_2}{\partial \tau} = ri\xi + \kappa\theta D_2 - \lambda\mu i\xi + \lambda[e^{(\sigma^2/2)i\xi(i\xi-1)}(1+\mu)^{i\xi} - 1] \tag{15.516}$$

$$C_0^{(2)} = 0 \tag{15.516a}$$

$$\frac{\partial D_2}{\partial \tau} = -\frac{1}{2}i\xi + \frac{1}{2}D_2^2\sigma^2 + i\xi D_2\sigma\rho - \frac{1}{2}\xi^2 - (\kappa + \tilde{\chi})D_2 \tag{15.517}$$

$$D_0^{(2)} = 0 \tag{15.517a}$$

ie, by the ODE system and by the final corresponding final conditions.

15.2.7.5. The solution of the Cauchy problem
15.2.7.5.1. The first system of differential equations
15.2.7.5.1.1. *The equation in D_1* The first ODE (15.512) is solved by recalling the à-la Riccati structure (see Section 8.1.1.2).

Then substitution (8.7) is made, as under Section 8.1.1.2, in order to derive a second-order ODE (by E we mean E_τ):

$$D_1 = -\frac{E'}{((\sigma^2/2)E)} \tag{15.518}$$

The first-order derivative of (15.518) is computed (useful in the following), ie,

$$D_1' = \frac{(-E''E + (E')^2)}{(\sigma^2/2)E^2} \tag{15.519}$$

Now, (15.518) and (15.519) are substituted in (15.512) to obtain

$$E'' - (\rho\sigma\xi i - (\kappa + \tilde{\chi} - \sigma\rho))E' + \frac{\sigma^2}{2}\left(-\frac{1}{2}\xi^2 + \frac{1}{2}\xi i\right)E = 0 \tag{15.520}$$

Actually, (15.520), which results from substitution (8.7), as under Section 8.1.1.2, is a constant coefficient homogenous second-order linear ODE. The general solution to Equation (15.520) can be written as

$$E_\tau = Ae^{\alpha_1\tau} + Be^{\alpha_2\tau} \tag{15.521}$$

Solutions of the kind $E(\tau) = e^{\alpha\tau}$ are necessary to identify this general solution. Then $E'(\tau) = \alpha e^{\alpha\tau}$ and $E''(\tau) = \alpha^2 e^{\alpha\tau}$ are computed. The terms E_τ, E_τ' and E_τ'' are substituted in Equation (15.520), ie,

$$e^{\alpha\tau}\left[\alpha^2 - (\rho\sigma\xi i - (\kappa + \tilde{\chi} - \sigma\rho))\alpha + \frac{\sigma^2}{2}\left(-\frac{1}{2}\xi^2 + \frac{1}{2}\xi i\right)\right] = 0 \tag{15.522}$$

Equation (15.522) is only satisfied if the second degree equation in α in brackets has a trivial solution. The roots of this equation in α are computed by writing

$$d_1 = \sqrt{[\rho\sigma(i\xi + 1) - \kappa - \tilde{\chi}]^2 - \sigma^2 i\xi(i\xi + 1)} \tag{15.523}$$

One obtains the two roots:

$$\begin{aligned}
\alpha_1 &= \frac{\sigma\rho(i\xi + 1) - \kappa - \tilde{\chi} + d_1}{2} \\
\alpha_2 &= \frac{\sigma\rho(i\xi + 1) - \kappa - \tilde{\chi} - d_1}{2}
\end{aligned} \tag{15.524}$$

Hence, it can be derived that

$$d_1 = \alpha_1 - \alpha_2 \tag{15.525}$$

With the roots α_1 and α_2 known, the general solution to (15.520) is based on (15.521):

$$E_\tau = Ae^{(\sigma\rho(i\xi+1)-\kappa-\tilde{\chi}+d_1)/2\tau} + Be^{(\sigma\rho(i\xi+1)-\kappa-\tilde{\chi}-d_1)/2\tau} \tag{15.526}$$

Then (15.526) is specified under the initial condition (15.517a). This is rearranged in light of substitution (15.518), ie,

$$D_1(0) = -\frac{E_0'}{((\sigma^2/2)E_0)} = 0 \tag{15.527}$$

To verify (15.527), the first derivative of the general solution (15.521) is computed:

$$E_\tau' = Ae^{\alpha_1\tau}\alpha_1 + Be^{\alpha_2\tau}\alpha_2 \tag{15.528}$$

Then (15.521) and (15.528) are specified for $t = T$, $\tau = 0$, ie,

$$E_0 = A + B \tag{15.529}$$
$$E_0' = A\alpha_1 + B\alpha_2 \tag{15.530}$$

Equations (15.529) and (15.530) are substituted in (15.527), ie,

$$D_1(0) = -\frac{A\alpha_1 + B\alpha_2}{(\sigma^2/2)(A + B)} = 0 \tag{15.531}$$

Equation (15.531) implies the following function system below to identify A and B, which allow one to specify the solution (15.526), ie,

$$\begin{cases} A\alpha_1 + B\alpha_2 = 0 \\ E_0 = A + B \end{cases} \tag{15.532}$$

whose solution is

$$\begin{cases} A = \dfrac{\alpha_2 E_0}{\alpha_2 - \alpha_1} \\ B = -\dfrac{\alpha_1 E_0}{\alpha_2 - \alpha_1} \end{cases} \tag{15.533}$$

Substituting the expressions of (15.533) in the general solution (15.521), one has

$$E_\tau = \frac{E_0}{\alpha_2 - \alpha_1}(\alpha_2 e^{\alpha_1\tau} - \alpha_1 e^{\alpha_2\tau}) \tag{15.534}$$

and in its first-order derivative (15.528):

$$E'_\tau = \frac{E_0}{\alpha_2 - \alpha_1}(\alpha_2\alpha_1 e^{\alpha_1\tau} - \alpha_1\alpha_2 e^{\alpha_2\tau}) \tag{15.535}$$

Knowing (15.534) and (15.535), one may recall (15.518), then derive the solution of (15.512):

$$D_1 = \frac{i\tilde{\zeta}(i\tilde{\zeta}+1)(1 - e^{-d_1\tau})}{2d_1 - (d_1 + \rho\sigma(i\tilde{\zeta}+1) - \kappa - \tilde{\chi})(1 - e^{-d_1\tau})} \tag{15.536}$$

15.2.7.5.1.2. The equation in C_1 Equation (15.511) is a constant coefficient first-order linear ODE. It may be solved by a simple integration (by C_1 we mean $C_\tau^{(1)}$)

$$\int \frac{\partial C_1}{\partial\tau}\, d\tau = \int \left(ri\tilde{\zeta} - \lambda\mu[i\tilde{\zeta}+1] + \kappa\theta D_1 + \lambda[e^{(\sigma^2/2)i\tilde{\zeta}(i\tilde{\zeta}+1)}(1+\mu)^{(i\tilde{\zeta}+1)} - 1] \right) d\tau$$

Then

$$C_1 = ri\tilde{\zeta}\tau - \lambda\mu[i\tilde{\zeta}+1]\tau - \frac{2\kappa\theta}{\sigma^2} \ln\left[\frac{E_0}{\alpha_2 - \alpha_1}(\alpha_2 e^{\alpha_1\tau} - \alpha_1 e^{\alpha_2\tau})\right]$$
$$+ \lambda\tau[e^{(\sigma^2/2)i\tilde{\zeta}(i\tilde{\zeta}+1)}(1+\mu)^{(i\tilde{\zeta}+1)} - 1] - F \tag{15.537}$$

by using the initial condition (15.517a), the value of F is specified, ie,

$$C_1 = ri\tilde{\zeta}\tau - \lambda\mu[i\tilde{\zeta}+1]\tau - \frac{\kappa\theta}{\sigma^2}[[\rho\sigma(i\tilde{\zeta}+1) - \kappa - \tilde{\chi}] + d_1]\tau$$
$$- \frac{2\kappa\theta}{\sigma^2} \ln\left[1 - \frac{[\rho\sigma(i\tilde{\zeta}+1) - \kappa - \tilde{\chi} + d_1](1 - e^{-d_1\tau})}{2d_1}\right]$$
$$+ \lambda\tau[e^{\frac{\sigma^2}{2}i\tilde{\zeta}(i\tilde{\zeta}+1)}(1+\mu)^{(i\tilde{\zeta}+1)} - 1] \tag{15.538}$$

recalling that

$$d_1 = \sqrt{[\rho\sigma(i\tilde{\zeta}+1) - \kappa - \tilde{\chi}]^2 - \sigma^2 i\tilde{\zeta}(i\tilde{\zeta}+1)}$$

15.2.7.5.2. The second system of differential equations
15.2.7.5.2.1. The equation in D_2 The first-order ODE (15.517) is solved by recalling the à-la Riccati structure (see Section 8.1.1.2).

Then the substitution (8.7) is made in order to obtain a second-order ODE (by E we mean E_τ):

$$D_2 = -\frac{E'}{(\sigma^2/2)E} \tag{15.539}$$

The first-order derivative of (15.539) is derived since it will be useful below, ie,

$$D_2' = \frac{(-E''E + (E')^2)}{(\sigma^2/2)E^2} \tag{15.540}$$

Then (15.539) and (15.540) are substituted in (15.517)

$$E'' - (\rho\sigma\xi i - (\kappa + \tilde{\chi}))E' + \frac{\sigma^2}{2}\left(-\frac{1}{2}\xi^2 - \frac{1}{2}\xi i\right)E = 0 \tag{15.541}$$

Actually, (15.541) which results from a substitution (8.7) is a constant coefficient homogeneous linear ODE. The general solution to Equation (15.541) is

$$E_\tau = Ae^{\alpha_1\tau} + Be^{\alpha_2\tau} \tag{15.542}$$

To determine this general solution, solutions of the kind $E(\tau) = e^{\alpha\tau}$ are necessary. Then $E'(\tau) = \alpha e^{\alpha\tau}$ and $E''(\tau) = \alpha^2 e^{\alpha\tau}$ are computed. The terms E_τ, E_τ' and E_τ'' are substituted in Equation (15.541), ie,

$$e^{\alpha\tau}\left[\alpha^2 - (\rho\sigma\xi i - (\kappa + \tilde{\chi}))\alpha + \frac{\sigma^2}{2}\left(-\frac{1}{2}\xi^2 - \frac{1}{2}\xi i\right)\right] = 0 \tag{15.543}$$

Equation (15.543) is only satisfied if the second-order equation in α inside the brackets has a trivial solution. Then the roots of this equation in α are computed by writing

$$d_2 = \sqrt{[\rho\sigma i\xi - \kappa - \tilde{\chi}]^2 - \sigma^2 i\xi(i\xi - 1)} \tag{15.544}$$

One obtains the roots

$$\alpha_1 = \frac{\sigma\rho i\xi - \kappa - \tilde{\chi} + d_2}{2}$$
$$\alpha_2 = \frac{\sigma\rho i\xi - \kappa - \tilde{\chi} - d_2}{2} \tag{15.545}$$

Hence, it can be derived that

$$d_2 = \alpha_1 - \alpha_2 \tag{15.546}$$

Knowing the roots α_1 and α_2 the general solution to (15.541) is, based on (15.542),

$$E_\tau = Ae^{(\sigma\rho i\xi - \kappa - \tilde{\chi} + d_2)/2\tau} + Be^{(\sigma\rho i\xi - \kappa - \tilde{\chi} - d_2)/2\tau} \tag{15.547}$$

Equation (15.547) is then expanded under the initial condition (15.517a). This must be rearranged in light of substitution (15.539), ie,

$$D_2(0) = -\frac{E_0'}{((\sigma^2/2)E_0)} = 0 \tag{15.548}$$

To verify (15.548), the first-order derivative of the general solution (15.542) is computed:

$$E'_\tau = A e^{\alpha_1 \tau} \alpha_1 + B e^{\alpha_2 \tau} \alpha_2 \tag{15.549}$$

Then (15.542) and (15.549) are rearranged for $t = T$, ie,

$$E_0 = A + B \tag{15.550}$$

$$E'_0 = A \alpha_1 + B \alpha_2 \tag{15.551}$$

Equations (15.550) and (15.551) are substituted in (15.548), ie,

$$D_2(0) = -\frac{A \alpha_1 + B \alpha_2}{(\sigma^2/2)(A + B)} = 0 \tag{15.552}$$

Equation (15.552) again implies the equation system (15.532):

$$\begin{cases} A \alpha_1 + B \alpha_2 = 0 \\ E_0 = A + B \end{cases} \tag{15.532}$$

This system, whose solution above is

$$\begin{cases} A = \dfrac{\alpha_2 E_0}{\alpha_2 - \alpha_1} \\ B = -\dfrac{\alpha_1 E_0}{\alpha_2 - \alpha_1} \end{cases} \tag{15.533}$$

identifies quantities A and B which allow one to specify the solution (15.547).

Then the expressions in (15.533) are substituted in the general solution (15.542), ie,

$$E_\tau = \frac{E_0}{\alpha_2 - \alpha_1} (\alpha_2 e^{\alpha_1 \tau} - \alpha_1 e^{\alpha_2 \tau}) \tag{15.553}$$

and in the first-order derivative, ie, (15.549),

$$E'_\tau = \frac{E_0}{\alpha_2 - \alpha_1} (\alpha_2 \alpha_1 e^{\alpha_1 \tau} - \alpha_1 \alpha_2 e^{\alpha_2 \tau}) \tag{15.554}$$

Knowing (15.553) and (15.554), one recalls the relation (15.539) and derives the solution of (15.517):

$$D_2 = \frac{i\xi(i\xi - 1)(1 - e^{-d_2 \tau})}{2 d_2 - (d_2 + \rho \sigma i \xi - \kappa - \tilde{\chi})(1 - e^{-d_2 \tau})} \tag{15.555}$$

15.2.7.5.2.2. The equation in C_2 Equation (15.516) is a constant coefficient first-order ODE. It may be solved by the simple integration (by C_1 we mean $C_\tau^{(2)}$):

$$\int \frac{\partial C_2}{\partial \tau} d\tau = \int \left(ri\xi - \lambda\mu i\xi + \kappa\theta D_2 + \lambda[e^{(\sigma^2/2)i\xi(i\xi-1)}(1+\mu)^{i\xi} - 1] \right) d\tau$$

Then

$$C_2 = ri\xi\tau - \lambda\mu i\xi\tau - \frac{2\kappa\theta}{\sigma^2} \ln\left[\frac{E_0}{\alpha_2 - \alpha_1}(\alpha_2 e^{\alpha_1\tau} - \alpha_1 e^{\alpha_2\tau})\right]$$
$$+ \lambda\tau\left[e^{(\sigma^2/2)i\xi(i\xi-1)}(1+\mu)^{i\xi} - 1\right] - F \tag{15.556}$$

by using the initial condition (15.517a), one specifies the value of F, ie,

$$C_2 = ri\xi\tau - \lambda\mu i\xi\tau - \frac{\kappa\theta}{\sigma^2}[[\rho\sigma i\xi - \kappa - \tilde{\chi}] + d_2]\tau$$
$$- \frac{2\kappa\theta}{\sigma^2} \ln\left[1 - \frac{[\rho\sigma i\xi - \kappa - \tilde{\chi} + d_2](1 - e^{-d_2\tau})}{2d_2}\right]$$
$$+ \lambda\tau[e^{\frac{\sigma^2}{2}i\xi(i\xi-1)}(1+\mu)^{i\xi} - 1] \tag{15.557}$$

where

$$d_2 = \sqrt{[\rho\sigma i\xi - \kappa - \tilde{\chi}]^2 - \sigma^2 i\xi(i\xi - 1)}$$

15.2.7.5.3. Solutions computable by using quadrature algorithms The solutions to the Cauchy problem as in (15.511) and (15.512) in the form (15.499), where $C_\tau^{(j)}$ is given by expressions (15.538) and (15.557) and $D_\tau^{(j)}$ by expressions (15.536) and (15.555) allow one to determine, through the relation (15.482), the analytic expression of the probability measures P_j, ie,

$$P_j(x_{\tau=0} \geq \ln K \mid x_\tau, v_\tau) = \frac{1}{2\pi} \int_{-\infty}^{\infty} \frac{e^{-i\xi \ln K}}{i\xi} \tilde{f}_j(x_\tau, v_\tau, \tau = 0, \xi \mid x_\tau, v_\tau) \, d\xi$$
$$\tag{15.482}$$

However, the relation (15.482) does not have an immediate numerical solution, but many equivalent solutions exist which allow this quantity to be manipulated analytically (see expressions (11.125) and (11.126)):

$$P_j(x_{\tau=0} \geq \ln K \mid x_\tau, v_\tau) = \frac{1}{2} + \frac{1}{\pi} \int_0^{\infty} \Im\left[\frac{e^{-i\xi \ln K} \tilde{f}_j(x_\tau, v_\tau, \tau = 0, \xi \mid x_\tau, v_\tau)}{\xi}\right] d\xi$$
$$\tag{15.558}$$

$$P_j(x_{\tau=0} \geq \ln K \mid x_\tau, v_\tau) = \frac{1}{2} + \frac{1}{\pi} \int_0^{\infty} \Re\left[\frac{e^{-i\xi \ln K} \tilde{f}_j(x_\tau, v_\tau, \tau = 0, \xi \mid x_\tau, v_\tau)}{i\xi}\right] d\xi$$
$$\tag{15.559}$$

15.2.7.6. The call price

The Bates model gives the following formula of call pricing expressed in a simplified notation:

$$C_t = S_t P_1 - K e^{-r(T-t)} P_2 \tag{15.464}$$

where, by using (15.558) (or, alternatively, (15.559)), (15.499) and (15.457), for $j = 1, 2$, the function P is defined as

$$P_j = \frac{1}{2} + \frac{1}{\pi} \int_0^\infty \Re \left\{ \frac{e^{-i\xi \ln K}}{i\xi} e^{[C_\tau^{(j)} + D_\tau^{(j)} v_t + i\xi[\ln S_t]]} \right\} d\xi \tag{15.560}$$

with (15.253), (15.544) and

$$
\begin{aligned}
C_\tau^{(1)} &= ri\xi\tau - \lambda\mu[i\xi + 1]\tau - \frac{\kappa\theta}{\sigma^2}[[\rho\sigma(i\xi + 1) - \kappa - \tilde{\chi}] + d_1]\tau \\
&\quad - \frac{2\kappa\theta}{\sigma^2} \ln\left[1 - \frac{[\rho\sigma(i\xi + 1) - \kappa - \tilde{\chi} + d_1](1 - e^{-d_1\tau})}{2d_1}\right] \\
&\quad - \lambda\tau[e^{\frac{\sigma^2}{2}i\xi(i\xi+1)}(1 + \mu)^{(i\xi+1)} - 1]
\end{aligned}
\tag{15.538}
$$

$$D_\tau^{(1)} = \frac{i\xi(i\xi + 1)(1 - e^{-d_1\tau})}{2d_1 - (d_1 + \rho\sigma(i\xi + 1) - \kappa - \tilde{\chi})(1 - e^{-d_1\tau})} \tag{15.536}$$

$$
\begin{aligned}
C_\tau^{(2)} &= ri\xi\tau - \lambda\mu i\xi\tau - \frac{\kappa\theta}{\sigma^2}[[\rho\sigma i\xi - \kappa - \tilde{\chi}] + d_2]\tau \\
&\quad - \frac{2\kappa\theta}{\sigma^2} \ln\left[1 - \frac{[\rho\sigma i\xi - \kappa - \tilde{\chi} + d_2](1 - e^{-d_2\tau})}{2d_2}\right] \\
&\quad - \lambda\tau[e^{\frac{\sigma^2}{2}i\xi(i\xi-1)}(1 + \mu)^{i\xi} - 1]
\end{aligned}
\tag{15.557}
$$

$$D_\tau^{(2)} = \frac{i\xi(i\xi - 1)(1 - e^{-d_2\tau})}{2d_2 - (d_2 + \rho\sigma i\xi - \kappa - \tilde{\chi})(1 - e^{-d_2\tau})} \tag{15.555}$$

15.2.7.7. Pricing a call with the Bates model: implementation

Actually, the Bates model requires the use of some software to compute the integral in (15.560), derived from (15.558) or from (15.559). Matlab *real and quad8* or *quadl* functions may be used for this purpose.

15.2.7.8. The Greeks

Theorem 15.17. *If $C_t(S_t, K) : \mathbb{R}^2 \to \mathbb{R}$ is differentiable to the second order and is homogeneous of first degree by writing*

$$C_t(S_t, K) = S_t P_1(S, K) - K e^{-r(T-t)} P_2(S, K)$$

then the equivalences (15.276)–(15.281) hold.

Proof. Under the equivalence between (15.464) and (15.239), see Theorem 15.15, for the demonstration. $\square$

Proposition 15.60. *The following equivalences hold for $j = 1, 2$:*

$$\frac{\partial}{\partial S_t}\tilde{f}_j(.x_\tau, v_\tau, \tau = 0, \xi | x_\tau, v_\tau) = \tilde{f}_j(x_\tau, v_\tau, \tau = 0, \xi | x_\tau, v_\tau) \cdot i\xi \frac{1}{S_t} \qquad (15.561)$$

$$\frac{\partial^2}{\partial S_t^2}(\tilde{f}_j(x_\tau, v_\tau, \tau = 0, \xi | x_\tau, v_\tau)) = \frac{1}{S_t^2}i\xi(i\xi - 1)\tilde{f}_j(x_\tau, v_\tau, \tau = 0, \xi | x_\tau, v_\tau) \qquad (15.562)$$

Proof. Under the equivalence between (15.499) and (15.377), see Proposition 15.50 for the demonstration. $\square$

Proposition 15.61. *The following equivalences hold:*

$$\frac{\partial P_j}{\partial S_t} = \frac{1}{\pi S_t}\int_0^\infty \Re[e^{-i\xi \ln K}(\tilde{f}_j(x_\tau, v_\tau, \tau = 0, \xi | x_\tau, v_\tau))]\,d\xi \qquad (15.563)$$

$$\frac{\partial^2 P_j}{\partial S_t^2} = \frac{1}{\pi S_t^2}\int_0^\infty \Re[e^{-i\xi \ln K}((i\xi - 1)\tilde{f}_j(x_\tau, v_\tau, \tau = 0, \xi | x_\tau, v_\tau))]\,d\xi \qquad (15.564)$$

$$\frac{\partial P_j}{\partial K} = -\frac{1}{\pi K}\int_0^\infty \Re[(e^{-i\xi \ln K}\tilde{f}_j(.x_\tau, v_\tau, \tau = 0, \xi \,|\, x_\tau, v_\tau))\,d\xi] \qquad (15.565)$$

$$\frac{\partial^2 P_j}{\partial K^2} = \frac{1}{\pi K^2}\int_0^\infty \Re[e^{-i\xi \ln K}(i\xi + 1)\,\tilde{f}_j(x_\tau, v_\tau, \tau = 0, \xi \,|\, x_\tau, v_\tau)\,d\xi] \qquad (15.566)$$

Proof. For the proof, see Proposition 15.51. $\square$

Proposition 15.62. *The following equivalence holds:*

$$\frac{\partial P_j}{\partial v_t} = \frac{1}{\pi}\int_0^\infty \Re\left[\frac{e^{-i\xi \ln K}}{i\xi}\left(e^{(C_\tau^{(j)}+D_\tau^{(j)}v_t+i\xi x_\tau)}D_\tau^{(j)}\right)\right]d\xi \qquad (15.567)$$

Proof. Under the equivalence between (15.499) and (15.377) see Proposition 15.52 for the demonstration. $\square$

Proposition 15.63. *The following equivalence holds:*

$$\frac{\partial^2 P_j}{\partial v_t^2} = \frac{1}{\pi}\int_0^\infty \Re\left[\frac{e^{-i\xi \ln K}}{i\xi}(e^{(C_\tau^{(j)}+D_\tau^{(j)}v_t+i\xi x_\tau)}(D_\tau^{(j)})^2)\right]d\xi \qquad (15.568)$$

Proof. Under the equivalence between (15.499) and (15.377), see Proposition 15.53 for the demonstration. $\square$

Proposition 15.64. *The following equivalence holds:*

$$\lambda E_{J,q}[C[(J+1)S, v, t] - C[S, v, t]]$$

$$= \lambda e^x \left[\frac{1}{2\pi} \int_{-\infty}^{\infty} \frac{e^{-i\xi \ln[K]}}{i\xi} \cdot e^{C_1 + D_1 v + i\xi x} [e^{(\sigma^2/2)(i\xi+1)} (1+\mu)^{(i\xi+1)} - 1] \, d\xi \right]$$

$$+ \lambda K e^{-r\tau} \left[\frac{1}{2\pi} \int_{-\infty}^{\infty} \frac{e^{-i\xi \ln[K]}}{i\xi} e^{C_2 + D_2 v + i\xi x} [e^{(\sigma^2/2)i\xi(i\xi-1)} (1+\mu)^{i\xi} - 1] \, d\xi \right]$$

$$\tag{15.569}$$

Proof. The following relation $\lambda E_{J,q}[C[(J+1)S, v, t] - C[S, v, t]]$ is expanded as

$$\lambda E_{J,q}[C[(J+1)S, v, t] - C[S, v, t]]$$

$$= \lambda e^x \frac{1}{2\pi} \int_{-\infty}^{\infty} \frac{e^{-i\xi \ln[K]}}{i\xi} E[(1+J)\tilde{f}_1^{[J]} - \tilde{f}_1] \, d\xi$$

$$+ \lambda K e^{-r\tau} \frac{1}{2\pi} \int_{-\infty}^{\infty} \frac{e^{-i\xi \ln[K]}}{i\xi} E[\tilde{f}_2^{[J]} - \tilde{f}_2] \, d\xi \quad \text{(using (15.491) and (15.494))}$$

Finally, under (15.510) and (15.515), one obtains (15.569). □

Proposition 15.65. *A call option* Delta *is*

$$\Delta_C = P_1 \tag{15.570}$$

Proof. To define a call option Delta at time t, one has

$$\Delta_C = \frac{\partial C_t}{\partial S_t}$$

$$= P_1 \quad \text{(under (15.281))} \qquad □$$

Proposition 15.66. *A call option* Gamma *is*

$$\Gamma_C = \frac{\partial P_1}{\partial S_t} \tag{15.571}$$

(for the expression $\partial P_1 / \partial S_t$, see expression (15.563)).

Proof. To define a call option Gamma at time t, one has

$$\Gamma_C = \frac{\partial^2 C_t}{\partial S_t^2}$$

$$= \frac{\partial P_1}{\partial S_t} \quad \text{(under (15.570))} \qquad □$$

Proposition 15.67. *A call option* Vega *is*

$$\mathcal{V}_C = S_t \frac{\partial P_1}{\partial v_t} - Ke^{-r\tau} \frac{\partial P_2}{\partial v_t} \tag{15.572}$$

(for the expression $\partial P_j / \partial v_t$, see expression (15.567)).

Proof. To define a call option Vega at time t, one has

$$\mathcal{V}_C = \frac{\partial C_t}{\partial v_t}$$
$$= S_t \frac{\partial P_1}{\partial v_t} - Ke^{-r\tau} \frac{\partial P_2}{\partial v_t} \qquad\qquad \square$$

Proposition 15.68. *A call option* Volga *is*

$$\mathfrak{V}_C = S_t \frac{\partial^2 P_1}{\partial v_t^2} - Ke^{-r\tau} \frac{\partial^2 P_2}{\partial v_t^2} \tag{15.573}$$

(for the expression $\partial^2 P_j / \partial v_t^2$, see expression (15.568)).

Proof. To define a call option Volga at time t, one has

$$\mathfrak{V}_C = \frac{\partial^2 C_t}{\partial v_t^2}$$
$$= S_t \frac{\partial^2 P_1}{\partial v_t^2} - Ke^{-r\tau} \frac{\partial^2 P_2}{\partial v_t^2} \qquad\qquad \square$$

Corollary 15.11. *The cross second-order derivative with respect to v_t and S_t is*

$$\frac{\partial^2 C_t}{\partial S_t \partial v_t} = \frac{\partial P_1}{\partial v_t} \tag{15.574}$$

Proof. The proposition is demonstrated by differentiating (15.570) with respect to v_t. $\qquad\qquad \square$

Proposition 15.69. *A call option theta is*

$$\Theta_C = -\frac{\partial P_1}{\partial S}\left(\frac{1}{2}vS^2\right) - \frac{\partial^2 P_1}{\partial v^2}\left(\frac{1}{2}S\sigma^2 v\right) - \frac{\partial P_1}{\partial v}S[\sigma\rho v + [\kappa(\theta - v) - \chi v]]$$
$$- Ke^{-r\tau}\left[rP_2 - \frac{1}{2}\sigma^2 v\frac{\partial^2 P_2}{\partial v^2} - \frac{\partial P_2}{\partial v}[\kappa(\theta - v) - \chi v]\right]$$
$$- \lambda E_{J,q}[C[(J+1)S, v, t] - C[S, v, t]] + \lambda\mu SP_1 \tag{15.575}$$

where the expression $\lambda E_{J,q}[C[(J+1)S, v, t] - C[S, v, t]]$ is determined by (15.569).

Proof. Recall (15.456) determined by (15.462). Replacing (15.464), (15.570), (15.571) and (15.572), one obtains

$$\frac{\partial C}{\partial t} = -\frac{\partial P_1}{\partial S}\left(\frac{1}{2}vS^2\right) - \frac{\partial^2 P_1}{\partial v^2}\left(\frac{1}{2}S\sigma^2 v\right) - \frac{\partial P_1}{\partial v}S[\sigma\rho v + [\kappa(\theta - v) - \chi v]]$$

$$- Ke^{-r\tau}\left[rP_2 - \frac{1}{2}\sigma^2 v\frac{\partial^2 P_2}{\partial v^2} - \frac{\partial P_2}{\partial v}[\kappa(\theta - v) - \chi v]\right]$$

$$- \lambda E_{J,q}[C[(J+1)S, v, t] - C[S, v, t]] + \lambda\mu SP_1 \qquad (15.575)$$

$\square$

Proposition 15.70. *A call option* rho *is*

$$\rho_C = K\tau e^{-r\tau}P_2 \qquad (15.576)$$

Proof. Under the equivalence between (15.499) and (15.377), see Proposition 15.59, for the demonstration. $\square$

Term-structure models

16.1. INTRODUCTION

This section will focus on continuously compounded interest rates (see Section 14.2).

Definition 16.1. A *risk-free pure discount bond*, also called a "risk-free zero-coupon bond", is a contract which pays a currency unit at maturity. Its value is denoted by $P(t, T)$, with $t \leq T$, where t is the current date and T the maturity date.

Corollary 16.1. *By construction, the following equivalence holds:*

$$P(T, T) = 1 \tag{16.1}$$

Remark 16.1. In the following, the narrative will refer to continuously compounded interest rates.

Definition 16.2. *Yield to maturity*, denoted by $r(t, T)$, is the interest rate available at time t for an investment or a loan which begins at time t and will terminate in time T, where $t \leq T$.

Lemma 16.1. *By construction, the following equivalence holds:*

$$\frac{P(T, T)}{P(t, T)} = e^{r(t,T)(T-t)}$$

or

$$P(t, T) = e^{-r(t,T) \cdot (T-t)} \tag{16.2}$$

Proposition 16.1. *The following relation holds between $P(t, T)$ and $r(t, T)$:*

$$r(t, T) = -\frac{\ln(P(t, T))}{T - t} \tag{16.3}$$

or

$$r(t, T)(T - t) = -\ln(P(t, T)) \tag{16.4}$$

Proof. Under Equation (16.4) the following holds:

$$r(t, T)(T - t) = - \ln(P(t, T))$$

considering the exponential

$$\frac{1}{P(t, T)} = e^{r(t,T) \cdot [T-t]}$$

which returns expression (16.2). □

Definition 16.3. The *interest rate term structure* is the set of the spot yield-to-maturity $r(t, T)$, $\forall t < T$.

Definition 16.4. The instantaneous spot interest rate, also called the *short rate*, denoted by r_t is the interest rate applied to instantaneous spot investments or loans:

$$r_t = \lim_{T \to t} r(t, T) \tag{16.5}$$

Proposition 16.2. *The following relation between r_t and $P(t, t)$ holds:*

$$r_t = - \frac{\partial \ln P(t, t)}{\partial t} \tag{16.6}$$

Proof. Under Equation (16.5) the following holds:

$$r(t) = \lim_{T \to t} r(t, T)$$

$$= \lim_{T \to t} - \frac{\ln(P(t, T))}{T - t} \quad \text{(by using (16.3))}$$

Since this is an indeterminate form $\frac{0}{0}$, by using the De l'Hospital rule, one has

$$r(t) = \lim_{T \to t} \left(\frac{-(P(t, T))^{-1}(\partial \ln P(t, T)/\partial T)}{1} \right)$$

$$= - \frac{\partial \ln P(t, t)}{\partial t} \qquad □$$

Definition 16.5. The price of a risk-free pure discount bond at maturity is defined as

$$P(t, T_1, T_2) = \frac{P(t, T_2)}{P(t, T_1)} \tag{16.7}$$

then, under Equation (16.2),

$$P(t, T_1, T_2) = \frac{e^{-(r(t,T_2) \cdot [T_2-t])}}{e^{-(r(t,T_1) \cdot [T_1-t])}} \tag{16.8}$$

Corollary 16.2. *By construction, the following equivalence holds:*

$$P(T, T, T) = P(T, T) = 1 \tag{16.9}$$

Definition 16.6. The forward rate, denoted by $f(t, T_1, T_2)$ where $t \leq T_1 \leq T_2$, is the interest rate at time t for an investment or a loan beginning at time T_1 and ending at time T_2.

Lemma 16.2. *By construction, the following equivalence holds:*

$$\frac{P(T, T, T)}{P(t, T_1, T_2)} = e^{f(t, T_1, T_2)(T_2 - T_1)}$$

or

$$P(t, T_1, T_2) = e^{-f(t, T_1, T_2)(T_2 - T_1)} \tag{16.10}$$

Proposition 16.3. *The following relation holds between $P(t, T_1, T_2)$ and $f(t, T_1, T_2)$:*

$$f(t, T_1, T_2) = -\frac{\ln(P(t, T_1, T_2))}{T_2 - T_1} \tag{16.11}$$

or

$$f(t, T_1, T_2)(T_2 - T_1) = -\ln[P(t, T_1, T_2)] \tag{16.12}$$

Proof. Under (16.12) one has

$$f(t, T_1, T_2)(T_2 - T_1) = -\ln[P(t, T_1, T_2)]$$

The exponential gives

$$e^{f(t, T_1, T_2)(T_2 - T_1)} = \frac{1}{P(t, T_1, T_2)}$$

which returns expression (16.10). ☐

Theorem 16.1. *In arbitrage-free conditions, the following relation holds between the spot rates and the forward rates:*

$$e^{\{r(t, T_2) \cdot (T_2 - t)\}} = e^{\{r(t, T_1) \cdot (T_1 - t)\}} \cdot e^{\{f(t, T_1, T_2) \cdot (T_2 - T_1)\}} \tag{16.13}$$

Proof. Under (16.7), the forward price of a risk-free zero-coupon bond is

$$P(t, T_1, T_2) = \frac{P(t, T_2)}{P(t, T_1)}$$

ie, by using (16.8),

$$P(t, T_1, T_2) = \frac{e^{-(r(t,T_2)\cdot[T_2-t])}}{e^{-(r(t,T_1)\cdot[T_1-t])}}$$

Equivalence (16.10) represents the forward price of a risk-free zero-coupon bond by

$$P(t, T_1, T_2) = e^{-(f(t,T_1,T_2)\cdot[T_2-T_1])}$$

In order to prevent any arbitrage, the two expressions above for the forward price of a risk-free zero-coupon bond must be equivalent:

$$\frac{e^{-(r(t,T_2)\cdot[T_2-t])}}{e^{-(r(t,T_1)\cdot[T_1-t])}} = e^{-(f(t,T_1,T_2)\cdot[T_2-T_1])}$$

ie,

$$e^{(f(t,T_1,T_2)\cdot[T_2-T_1])} = \frac{e^{(r(t,T_2)\cdot[T_2-t])}}{e^{(r(t,T_1)\cdot[T_1-t])}}$$

and then

$$e^{(f(t,T_1,T_2)\cdot[T_2-T_1])} = e^{\{r(t,T_2)\cdot[T_2-t]\}} \cdot e^{-\{r(t,T_1)\cdot[T_1-t]\}}$$

Hence, solving by $e^{\{r(t,T_2)\cdot[T_2-t]\}}$, one has

$$e^{(r(t,T_2)\cdot[T_2-t])} = e^{(r(t,T_1)\cdot[T_1-t])} \cdot e^{(f(t,T_1,T_2)\cdot[T_2-T_1])} \qquad \square$$

Definition 16.7. The instantaneous forward rate, like the instantaneous spot rate, is the interest rate applied to instantaneous forward investments or loans:

$$f(t, T_1) = f(t, T_1, T_1) = \lim_{T_2 \longrightarrow T_1} f(t, T_1, T_2) \qquad (16.14)$$

Proposition 16.4. *The following relation holds between* $f(t, T_1)$ *and* $P(t, T_1, T_1)$:

$$f(t, T_1, T_1) = -\frac{\partial \ln P(t, T_1, T_1)}{\partial T_1} \qquad (16.15)$$

or

$$f(t, T_1) = -\frac{\partial \ln P(t, T_1)}{\partial T_1} \qquad (16.15)$$

Proof. Under (16.14), the following holds:

$$f(t, T_1) = \lim_{T_2 \longrightarrow T_1} f(t, T_1, T_2)$$

$$= \lim_{T_2 \longrightarrow T_1} -\frac{\ln(P(t, T_1, T_2))}{T_2 - T_1} \quad \text{(by using (16.11))}$$

Since this is an indeterminate form $\frac{0}{0}$, by using the De l'Hospital rule, one has:

$$f(t, T_1) = \lim_{T_2 \longrightarrow T_1} \left(\frac{-(P(t, T_1, T_2))^{-1} (\partial \ln P(t, T_1, T_2)/T_2)}{1} \right)$$
$$= -\frac{\partial \ln P(t, T_1, T_1)}{\partial T_1} \qquad \qquad \square$$

Theorem 16.2. *A pure discount bond price may be expressed with respect to $f(t, s)$, as the instantaneous forward rate valued in t for an instantaneous investment at time s, as follows:*

$$P(t, T) = e^{-\int_t^T f(t,s)\, ds} \qquad (16.16)$$

or as

$$\ln P(t, T) = -\int_t^T f(t, s)\, ds \qquad (16.17)$$

Proof. Under Theorem 16.1, one has that

$$e^{\{r(t,T_1) \cdot (T_1 - t)\}} = e^{\{r(t,T) \cdot (T - t)\}} \cdot e^{\{f(t,T,T_1) \cdot (T_1 - T)\}}$$

Applying the logarithm, one has

$$r(t, T_1) \cdot (T_1 - t) = r(t, T) \cdot (T - t) + f(t, T, T_1) \cdot (T_1 - T)$$

hence

$$f(t, T, T_1) = \frac{1}{(T_1 - T)} [r(t, T_1) \cdot (T_1 - t) - r(t, T) \cdot (T - t)]$$

Then, under (16.4), one has

$$f(t, T, T_1) = -\frac{1}{(T_1 - T)} \ln \frac{P(t, T_1)}{P(t, T)}$$

The limit is applied for $T_1 \longrightarrow T$, ie,

$$\lim_{T_1 \longrightarrow T} f(t, T, T_1) = \lim_{T_1 \longrightarrow T} -\frac{1}{(T_1 - T)} \ln \frac{P(t, T_1)}{P(t, T)}$$

Recalling Definition 16.7, ie, the instantaneous forward rate, one has

$$f(t, T) = \lim_{T_1 \longrightarrow T} -\frac{1}{(T_1 - T)} \ln \frac{P(t, T_1)}{P(t, T)}$$
$$= \lim_{T_1 \longrightarrow T} -\frac{(\ln P(t, T_1) - \ln P(t, T))}{(T_1 - T)}$$

specifying $T_1 - T = h$ and then also $T_1 = T + h$, the limit is rearranged as follows:

$$f(t, T) = \lim_{h \to 0} -\frac{(\ln P(t, T + h) - \ln P(t, T))}{h}$$

where recalling the definition of the first derivative (see expression (4.2)) of function $P(t, T)$ with respect to variable T, one has

$$f(t, T) = -\frac{\partial}{\partial T}(\ln P(t, T))$$

By integrating one has

$$\int_t^T f(t, s)\, ds = -\ln P(t, T)$$

and then one has Equation (16.16). □

Corollary 16.3. *The instantaneous forward rate for investments or loans which begin at the short term, ie, at date t, corresponds to the instantaneous spot rate:*

$$f(t, t) = r_t \qquad (16.18)$$

16.2. SHORT-RATE DIFFUSIVE PROCESSES

It is assumed that the instantaneous spot rate evolves following the Markovian diffusive process

$$dr_t = \phi(r_t, t)\, dt + \sigma(r_t, t)\, dW_t \qquad (16.19)$$

where $\{W_t; 0 \le t \le T\}$ is a standard Brownian motion with respect to a given probability space $(\Omega, \Im, P)$.

Notation 16.1. Given the hypothesis of the interest rate Markovian evolution, the price $P(t, T)$ will be a function of the instantaneous spot rate at the starting period, ie,

$$P(t, T) = P(t, T, r_t) \qquad (16.20)$$

16.2.1. Price of a risk-free zero-coupon bond

Given (16.20), Itô's Lemma (see Theorem 12.12) is applied to derive the SDE which describes the behaviour of $P(t, T, r_t)$:

$$dP(t, T, r_t) = \frac{\partial}{\partial t}P(t, T, r_t)\, dt + \frac{\partial}{\partial r}P(t, T, r_t)\, dr_t + \frac{1}{2}\frac{\partial^2}{\partial r^2}P(t, T, r_t)[dr_t]^2$$

substituting (16.19), one has

$$dP(t, T, r_t) = \frac{\partial}{\partial t} P(t, T, r_t)\, dt + \frac{\partial}{\partial r} P(t, T, r_t)[\phi(r_t, t)\, dt + \sigma(r_t, t)\, dW_t]$$

$$+ \frac{1}{2}\frac{\partial^2}{\partial r^2} P(t, T, r_t) \cdot [\phi(r_t, t)\, dt + \sigma(r_t, t)\, dW_t]^2$$

By using Itô's algebra (see Proposition 12.7), one has

$$dP(t, T, r_t) = \frac{\partial}{\partial t} P(t, T, r_t)\, dt + \frac{\partial}{\partial r} P(t, T, r_t)[\phi(r_t, t)\, dt + \sigma(r_t, t)\, dW_t]$$

$$+ \frac{1}{2}\frac{\partial^2}{\partial r^2} P(t, T, r_t)\sigma^2(r_t, t)\, dt$$

specifying in dt one has

$$dP(t, T, r_t) = \left(\frac{\partial}{\partial t} P(t, T, r_t) + \frac{\partial}{\partial r} P(t, T, r_t)\phi(r_t, t) + \frac{\sigma^2(r_t, t)}{2}\frac{\partial^2}{\partial r^2} P(t, T, r_t) \right) dt$$

$$+ \sigma(r_t, t)\frac{\partial}{\partial r} P(t, T, r_t)\, dW_t \tag{16.21}$$

solving for a given initial condition, ie, $P(0, T, r_T) = p$, Equation (16.21) may be specified in its integral form as in the following equation:

$$P(t, T, r_t)$$

$$= p + \int_0^t \left(\frac{\partial}{\partial s} P(s, T, r_s) + \frac{\partial}{\partial r} P(s, T, r_s)\phi(r_s, s) + \frac{\sigma^2(r_t, s)}{2}\frac{\partial^2}{\partial r^2} P(s, T, r_s) \right) ds$$

$$+ \int_0^t \sigma(r_s, s)\frac{\partial}{\partial r} P(s, T, r_s)\, dW_s \tag{16.22}$$

16.2.1.1.   The process $P(t, T, r_t)$ in arbitrage-free conditions
The arbitrage-free condition drift and diffusion found in Equation (16.21) may be specified as

$$\mu(t, T, r_t)P(t, T, r_t) = \frac{\partial}{\partial t} P(t, T, r_t) + \frac{\partial}{\partial r} P(t, T, r_t)\phi(r_t, t)$$

$$+ \frac{\sigma^2(r_t, t)}{2}\frac{\partial^2}{\partial r^2} P(t, T, r_t) \tag{16.23}$$

$$-\hat{\sigma}(t, T, r_t)P(t, T, r_t) = \sigma(r_t, t)\frac{\partial}{\partial r} P(t, T, r_t)$$

Consequently, the price process of the risk-free pure discount bond $P(t, T, r_t)$ described by (16.21) may also be specified as a geometric Brownian motion (see Section 13.1.2), ie,

$$dP(t, T, r_t) = P(t, T, r_t)\mu(t, T, r_t)\, dt - P(t, T, r_t)\hat{\sigma}(t, T, r_t)\, dW_t \tag{16.24}$$

16.2.1.1.1. PDE derivation Consider now two zero-coupon bonds with different maturity, $P(t, T_1, r_t)$ and $P(t, T_2, r_t)$, used to create a self-financing portfolio, denoted as V, whose value at time t is

$$V_t = u_1 P(t, T_1, r_t) + u_2 P(t, T_2, r_t) \tag{16.25}$$

where u_1 and u_2 are the respective weights of the bond priced $P(t, T_1, r_t)$ and $P(t, T_2, r_t)$ in this portfolio.

The yield of this portfolio may be described as a weighted mean of the two underlying bond yields, ie,

$$\frac{dV_t}{V_t} = u_1 \frac{dP(t, T_1, r_t)}{P(t, T_1, r_t)} + u_2 \frac{dP(t, T_2, r_t)}{P(t, T_2, r_t)} \tag{16.26}$$

Substituting Equation (16.24) in the addends in (16.26), one obtains

$$\frac{dV_t}{V_t} = u_1 \left[\frac{P(t, T_1, r_t)\mu(t, T, r_t)\, dt - P(t, T_1, r_t)\widehat{\sigma}(t, T, r_t)\, dW_t}{P(t, T_1, r_t)} \right]$$
$$+ u_2 \left[\frac{P(t, T_2, r_t)\mu(t, T, r_t)\, dt - P(t, T_2, r_t)\widehat{\sigma}(t, T, r_t)\, dW_t}{P(t, T_2, r_t)} \right]$$

by simplifying, one obtains

$$\frac{dV_t}{V_t} = u_1[\mu(t, T_1, r_t)\, dt - \widehat{\sigma}(t, T_1, r_t)\, dW_t] + u_2[\mu(t, T_2, r_t)\, dt - \widehat{\sigma}(t, T_2, r_t)\, dW_t]$$

factorising in dt and dW_t, one has

$$\frac{dV_t}{V_t} = [u_1\mu(t, T_1, r_t) + u_2\mu(t, T_2, r_t)]\, dt - [u_1\widehat{\sigma}(t, T_1, r_t) + u_2\widehat{\sigma}(t, T_2, r_t)]\, dW_t \tag{16.27}$$

Weights u_1 and u_2 are chosen in order to set the coefficient of dW_t to zero, ie, to eliminate the random component in the portfolio yield. Consequently, the values of u_1 and u_2 which satisfy the following equations have to be determined:

$$\begin{cases} u_1 + u_2 = 1 \\ u_1 \widehat{\sigma}(t, T_1, r_t) + u_2 \widehat{\sigma}(t, T_2, r_t) = 0 \end{cases} \Rightarrow$$

$$\begin{cases} u_1 = 1 - u_2 \\ u_1 = -\dfrac{u_2 \widehat{\sigma}(t, T_2, r_t)}{\widehat{\sigma}(t, T_1, r_t)} \end{cases} \Rightarrow$$

$$\begin{cases} -\dfrac{u_2 \widehat{\sigma}(t, T_2, r_t)}{\widehat{\sigma}(t, T_1, r_t)} + u_2 = 1 \\ / \end{cases} \Rightarrow$$

$$\begin{cases} \dfrac{-u_2 \widehat{\sigma}(t, T_2, r_t) + u_2 \widehat{\sigma}(t, T_1, r_t)}{\widehat{\sigma}(t, T_1, r_t)} = 1 \\ / \end{cases} \Rightarrow$$

$$\begin{cases} -u_2 \widehat{\sigma}(t, T_2, r_t) + u_2 \widehat{\sigma}(t, T_1, r_t) = \widehat{\sigma}(t, T_1, r_t) \\ / \end{cases} \Rightarrow$$

$$\begin{cases} u_2 = \dfrac{\widehat{\sigma}(t, T_1, r_t)}{\widehat{\sigma}(t, T_1, r_t) - \widehat{\sigma}(t, T_2, r_t)} \\ / \end{cases} \Rightarrow$$

$$\begin{cases} u_2 = \dfrac{\widehat{\sigma}(t, T_1, r_t)}{\widehat{\sigma}(t, T_1, r_t) - \widehat{\sigma}(t, T_2, r_t)} \\ u_1 = -\dfrac{\frac{\widehat{\sigma}(t, T_1, r_t)}{\widehat{\sigma}(t, T_1, r_t) - \widehat{\sigma}(t, T_2, r_t)} \widehat{\sigma}(t, T_2, r_t)}{\widehat{\sigma}(t, T_1, r_t)} \end{cases} \Rightarrow$$

$$\begin{cases} u_2 = \dfrac{\widehat{\sigma}(t, T_1, r_t)}{\widehat{\sigma}(t, T_1, r_t) - \widehat{\sigma}(t, T_2, r_t)} \\ u_1 = -\dfrac{\widehat{\sigma}(t, T_2, r_t)}{\widehat{\sigma}(t, T_1, r_t) - \widehat{\sigma}(t, T_2, r_t)} \end{cases}$$

then the weights which eliminate the diffusive component of (16.27) are

$$u_1 = \frac{-\widehat{\sigma}(t, T_2, r_t)}{\widehat{\sigma}(t, T_1, r_t) - \widehat{\sigma}(t, T_2, r_t)} \tag{16.28}$$

and

$$u_2 = \frac{\widehat{\sigma}(t, T_1, r_t)}{\widehat{\sigma}(t, T_1, r_t) - \widehat{\sigma}(t, T_2, r_t)} \tag{16.29}$$

Substituting these values in (16.27), one obtains

$$
\begin{aligned}
\frac{dV_t}{V_t} = &\left(\frac{-\widehat{\sigma}(t, T_2, r_t)}{\widehat{\sigma}(t, T_1, r_t) - \widehat{\sigma}(t, T_2, r_t)} \mu(t, T_1, r_t) \right. \\
&+ \left. \frac{\widehat{\sigma}(t, T_1, r_t)}{\widehat{\sigma}(t, T_1, r_t) - \widehat{\sigma}(t, T_2, r_t)} \mu(t, T_2, r_t) \right) dt \\
&- \left(\frac{-\widehat{\sigma}(t, T_2, r_t)}{\widehat{\sigma}(t, T_1, r_t) - \widehat{\sigma}(t, T_2, r_t)} \widehat{\sigma}(t, T_1, r_t) \right. \\
&+ \left. \frac{\widehat{\sigma}(t, T_1, r_t)}{\widehat{\sigma}(t, T_1, r_t) - \widehat{\sigma}(t, T_2, r_t)} \widehat{\sigma}(t, T_2, r_t) \right) dW_t
\end{aligned}
$$

and, simplifying, one has

$$
\frac{dV_t}{V_t} = \left(\frac{-\widehat{\sigma}(t, T_2, r_t)\mu(t, T_1, r_t)}{\widehat{\sigma}(t, T_1, r_t) - \widehat{\sigma}(t, T_2, r_t)} + \frac{\widehat{\sigma}(t, T_1, r_t)\mu(t, T_2, r_t)}{\widehat{\sigma}(t, T_1, r_t) - \widehat{\sigma}(t, T_2, r_t)} \right) dt \qquad (16.30)
$$

Then, the stochastic component has been eliminated from the equation which describes the dynamics of the yield inside portfolio V. This portfolio is now risk-free in the time interval dt. Consequently, on such a time interval, the portfolio must yield the risk-free rate r_t to avoid any arbitrage, ie,

$$
\frac{dV_t}{V_t} = r_t \, dt \qquad (16.31)
$$

Hence, substituting the left-hand side term by the expression (16.30), one obtains

$$
\left(\frac{-\widehat{\sigma}(t, T_2, r_t)\mu(t, T_1, r_t)}{\widehat{\sigma}(t, T_1, r_t) - \widehat{\sigma}(t, T_2, r_t)} + \frac{\widehat{\sigma}(t, T_1, r_t)\mu(t, T_2, r_t)}{\widehat{\sigma}(t, T_1, r_t) - \widehat{\sigma}(t, T_2, r_t)} \right) dt = r_t \, dt
$$

and then

$$
\frac{\widehat{\sigma}(t, T_1, r_t)\mu(t, T_2, r_t) - \widehat{\sigma}(t, T_2, r_t)\mu(t, T_1, r_t)}{\widehat{\sigma}(t, T_1, r_t) - \widehat{\sigma}(t, T_2, r_t)} = r_t
$$

by simplifying, one has

$$
\widehat{\sigma}(t, T_1, r_t)\mu(t, T_2, r_t) - \widehat{\sigma}(t, T_2, r_t)\mu(t, T_1, r_t) = r_t[\widehat{\sigma}(t, T_1, r_t) - r_t\widehat{\sigma}(t, T_2, r_t)]
$$

and factorising, one obtains

$$
\widehat{\sigma}(t, T_1, r_t)[\mu(t, T_2, r_t) - r_t] = \widehat{\sigma}(t, T_2, r_t)[\mu(t, T_1, r_t) - r_t]
$$

and then

$$
\frac{\mu(t, T_2, r_t) - r_t}{\widehat{\sigma}(t, T_2, r_t)} = \frac{\mu(t, T_1, r_t) - r_t}{\widehat{\sigma}(t, T_1, r_t)}
$$

The following equivalence is obtained:

$$\frac{\mu(t, T_2, r_t) - r_t}{\hat{\sigma}(t, T_2, r_t)} = \frac{\mu(t, T_1, r_t) - r_t}{\hat{\sigma}(t, T_1, r_t)} = \lambda(r_t, t) \tag{16.32}$$

Generalising, for any maturity T, (16.32) may be respecified as follows:

$$\mu(t, T, r_t) - r_t = \lambda(r_t, t)\hat{\sigma}(t, T, r_t) \tag{16.33}$$

and then, using (16.23), one arrives at

$$\left(\frac{\partial}{\partial t} P(t, T, r_t) + \frac{\partial}{\partial r} P(t, T, r_t)\phi(r_t, t) + \frac{\sigma^2(r_t, t)}{2}\frac{\partial^2}{\partial r^2} P(t, T, r_t)\right) P(t, T, r_t)^{-1} - r_t$$

$$= \lambda(r_t, t)\left[-\frac{\sigma(r_t, t)(\partial/\partial r)P(t, T, r_t)}{P(t, T, r_t)}\right]$$

simplifying, one has

$$\frac{\partial}{\partial t} P(t, T, r_t) + \frac{\partial}{\partial r} P(t, T, r_t)\phi(r_t, t) + \frac{\sigma^2(r_t, t)}{2}\frac{\partial^2}{\partial r^2} P(t, T, r_t) - r_t P(t, T, r_t)$$

$$= -\lambda(r_t, t) \cdot \sigma(r_t, t) \cdot \frac{\partial}{\partial r} P(t, T, r_t)$$

factorising, one obtains

$$\frac{\partial}{\partial t} P(t, T, r_t) + [\phi(r_t, t) + \lambda(r_t, t)\sigma(r_t, t)]\frac{\partial}{\partial r} P(t, T, r_t)$$

$$+ \frac{\sigma^2(r_t, t)}{2}\frac{\partial^2}{\partial r^2} P(t, T, r_t) - r_t P(t, T, r_t) = 0$$

This PDE describes the dynamics of any risk-free zero-coupon bond as a function of a short-rate stochastic process as indicated in (16.19) under no-arbitrage conditions and in the presence of the boundary condition, ie, pool-to-par condition (see expression (16.1)).

The Cauchy problem may be described as follows:

$$\frac{\partial}{\partial t} P(t, T, r_t) + [\phi(r_t, t) + \lambda(r_t, t)\sigma(r_t, t)]\frac{\partial}{\partial r} P(t, T, r_t)$$

$$+ \frac{\sigma^2(r_t, t)}{2}\frac{\partial^2}{\partial r^2} P(t, T, r_t) - r_t P(t, T, r_t) = 0 \tag{16.34}$$

$$P(T, T, r_T) = 1 \tag{16.34a}$$

or, defining $\bar{\phi}(r_t, t) = \phi(r_t, t) + \lambda(t, r_t)\sigma(r_t, t)$, ie,

$$\frac{\partial}{\partial t} P(t, T, r_t) + \bar{\phi}(r_t, t)\frac{\partial}{\partial r} P(t, T, r_t) + \frac{\sigma^2(r_t, t)}{2}\frac{\partial^2}{\partial r^2} P(t, T, r_t) - r_t P(t, T, r_t) = 0 \tag{16.35}$$

$$P(T, T, r_T) = 1 \tag{16.35a}$$

16.2.1.1.2. $P(t, T, r_t)$ SDE derivation   Equation (16.33) is rearranged as follows:

$$\mu(t, T, r_t) = r_t + \lambda(r_t, t)\widehat{\sigma}(t, T, r_t) \tag{16.36}$$

Substituting (16.36) inside (16.24), one has

$$dP(t, T, r_t) = P(t, T, r_t)[r_t + \lambda(r_t, t)\widehat{\sigma}(t, T, r_t)] \, dt - P(t, T, r_t)\widehat{\sigma}(t, T, r_t) \, dW_t \tag{16.37}$$

which is then the SDE that rules the process $P(t, T, r_t)$ in arbitrage-free conditions.

Theorem 16.3. *The solution of (16.37) gives a pure discount bond price under the empirical probability measure P:*

$$P(t, T, r_t) = e^{\int_t^T [r_s + \lambda(r_s, s)\widehat{\sigma}(s,T,r_s) - \widehat{\sigma}^2(s,T,r_s)/2] \, ds - \int_t^T \widehat{\sigma}(s,T,r_s) \, dW_s} \tag{16.38}$$

Proof. The application of Theorem 13.3 to SDE (16.37) gives the solution to this equation, ie,

$$P(t, T, r_t) = e^{\int_t^T [r_s + \lambda(r_s, s)\widehat{\sigma}(s,T,r_s) - \widehat{\sigma}^2(s,T,r_s)/2] \, ds - \int_t^T \widehat{\sigma}(s,T,r_s) \, dW_s} \qquad \square$$

16.2.1.1.3.   The price $P(t, T, r_t)$ as conditional expected value under the empirical measure

Theorem 16.4. *The solution to the Cauchy problem determined in Equation (16.34) is given by the following expression:*

$$P(t, T, r_t) = E^P\left(e^{\{-\int_t^T r_s \, ds - (1/2)\int_t^T \lambda^2(s,r_s) \, ds + \int_t^T \lambda(s,r_s) \, dW_s\}}\Big|r_t\right) \tag{16.39}$$

Proof. Consider the geometric Brownian motion

$$dX_u = -X_u r_u \, du + X_u \lambda(u, r_u) \, dW_u, \quad u \geqslant t \tag{16.40}$$

whose initial condition is, by hypothesis,

$$X_t = 1 \tag{16.41}$$

the integrated solution is (see Theorem 13.3)

$$X_u = X_t \cdot e^{\{-\int_t^u r_s \, ds - (1/2)\int_t^u \lambda^2(s,r_s) \, ds + \int_t^u \lambda(s,r_s) \, dW_s\}} \tag{16.42}$$

Consider now the process

$$g(P(u, T, r_u), X_u) = P(u, T, r_u) \cdot X_u$$

dg is derived by applying the Leibniz rule (see Theorem 12.15). Then one gets

$$d(P(u, T, r_u) \cdot X_u) = P(u, T, r_u)\, dX_u + X_u\, dP(u, T, r_u) + dP(u, T, r_u)\, dX_u$$
(16.43)

Substituting (16.21) and (16.40) in (16.43), one has

$$
\begin{aligned}
d(P(u, T, r_u) \cdot X_u) &= P(u, T, r_u)[-X_u r_u\, du + X_u \lambda(u, r_u)\, dW_u] \\
&\quad + X_u \left\{ \left[\frac{\partial}{\partial u} P(u, T, r_u) + \frac{\partial}{\partial r} P(u, T, r_u)\phi(r_u, u) + \frac{\sigma^2(r_u, u)}{2} \right. \right. \\
&\qquad \left. \cdot \frac{\partial^2}{\partial r^2} P(u, T, r_u) \right] du + \sigma(r_u, u)\frac{\partial}{\partial r} P(u, T, r_u)\, dW_u \left. \right\} \\
&\quad + \left\{ \left[\frac{\partial}{\partial u} P(u, T, r_u) + \frac{\partial}{\partial r} P(u, T, r_u)\phi(r_u, u) + \frac{\sigma^2(r_u, u)}{2} \right. \right. \\
&\qquad \left. \cdot \frac{\partial^2}{\partial r^2} P(u, T, r_u) \right] du + \sigma(r_u, u)\frac{\partial}{\partial r} P(u, T, r_u)\, dW_u \left. \right\} \\
&\qquad \cdot [-X_u r_u\, du + X_u \lambda(u, r_u)\, dW_u]
\end{aligned}
$$

Simplifying by using the Itô algebra, one obtains

$$
\begin{aligned}
&d(P(u, T, r_u) \cdot X_u) \\
&= P(u, T, r_u)[-X_u r_u\, du + X_u \lambda(u, r_u)\, dW_u] \\
&\quad + X_u \left\{ \left[\frac{\partial}{\partial u} P(u, T, r_u) + \frac{\partial}{\partial r} P(u, T, r_u)\phi(r_u, u) \right. \right. \\
&\quad + \left. \frac{\sigma^2(r_u, u)}{2}\frac{\partial^2}{\partial r^2} P(u, T, r_u) \right] du + \sigma(r_u, u)\frac{\partial}{\partial r} P(u, T, r_u)\, dW_u \left. \right\} \\
&\quad + \sigma(r_u, u)\frac{\partial}{\partial r} P(u, T, r_u) X_u \lambda(u, r_u)\, du
\end{aligned}
$$

factorising, one has

$$
\begin{aligned}
d(P(u, T, r_u) \cdot X_u) &= \left[-X_u P(u, T, r_u) r_u + X_u \frac{\partial}{\partial u} P(u, T, r_u) \right. \\
&\quad + X_u \frac{\partial}{\partial r} P(u, T, r_u)\phi(r_u, u) + X_u \frac{\sigma^2(r_u, u)}{2}\frac{\partial^2}{\partial r^2} P(u, T, r_u) \\
&\quad + \left. \sigma(r_u, u)\frac{\partial}{\partial r} P(u, T, r_u) X_u \lambda(u, r_u) \right] du \\
&\quad + \left[X_u P(u, T, r_u)\lambda(u, r_u) + X_u \sigma(r_u, u)\frac{\partial}{\partial r} P(u, T, r_u) \right] dW_u
\end{aligned}
$$

factorising again, one has

$$d(P(u, T, r_u) \cdot X_u) = X_u\left[-P(u, T, r_u)r_u + \frac{\partial}{\partial u}P(u, T, r_u)\right.$$

$$+ \frac{\partial}{\partial r}P(u, T, r_u)[\phi(r_u, u) + \sigma(r_u, u)\lambda(u, r_u)]$$

$$\left.+ \frac{\sigma^2(r_u, u)}{2}\frac{\partial^2}{\partial r^2}P(u, T, r_u)\right] du$$

$$+ X_u\left[P(u, T, r_u)\lambda(u, r_u) + \sigma(r_u, u)\frac{\partial}{\partial r}P(u, T, r_u)\right] dW_u$$

One recalls (16.34) in the term inside the square brackets which is equal to zero. It can be derived that

$$d(P(u, T, r_u) \cdot X_u) = X_u[P(u, T, r_u)\lambda(u, r_u) + \sigma(r_u, u)\frac{\partial}{\partial r}P(u, T, r_u)] dW_u$$

which, in its integral form, becomes

$$P(u, T, r_u) \cdot X_u = P(t, T, r_t) \cdot X_t + \int_t^u X_s\sigma(s, r_s)\frac{\partial}{\partial r}P\, dW_s$$

$$+ \int_t^u X_s P(s, T, r_s)\lambda(s, r_s)\, dW_s$$

and then, for $u = T$,

$$P(T, T, r_T) \cdot X_T = P(t, T, r_t) \cdot X_t + \int_t^T X_s\sigma(s, r_s)\frac{\partial}{\partial r}P\, dW_s$$

$$+ \int_t^T X_s P(s, T, r_s)\lambda(s, r_s)\, dW_s$$

Substituting the values of $P(T, T, r_T)$ and of X_t identified, respectively, by the final condition of the Cauchy problem (16.34) and by (16.41), one obtains

$$X_T = P(t, T, r_t) + \int_t^T X_s\sigma(s, r_s)\frac{\partial}{\partial r}P\, dW_s + \int_t^T X_s P(s, T, r_s)\lambda(s, r_s)\, dW_s$$

One computes the expected value of both terms conditioned to r_t:

$$E^P[X_T|r_t] = E^P\left[\left(P(t, T, r_t) + \int_t^T X_s\sigma(s, r_s)\frac{\partial}{\partial r}P\, dW_s\right.\right.$$

$$\left.\left.+ \int_t^T X_s P(s, T, r_s)\lambda(s, r_s)\, dW_s\right)\Big|r_t\right]$$

Actually, $P(t, T, r_t)$ is rearranged with respect to r_t and therefore it may be taken out from the conditioned expected value:

$$
E^P[X_T|r_t] = P(t, T, r_t) + E^P\left[\left(\int_t^T X_s\sigma(s, r_s)\frac{\partial}{\partial r}P(s, T, r_s)\, dW_s\right.\right.
$$
$$
\left.\left. + \int_t^T X_s P(s, T, r_s)\lambda(s, r_s)dW_s\right)\bigg|r_t\right]
$$

The second and the third addends of the right-hand side are two stochastic integrals, and then two martingales (see property (7) in proposition 12.9), then their expected value conditioned to r_t is zero. It can be derived that

$$
E^P[X_T|r_t] = P(t, T, r_t)
$$

substituting the value of $X(T)$ which is derived from (16.42) the demonstration is derived, ie, one has (16.39) □

16.2.1.2. The process $P(t, T, r_t)$ in arbitrage-free conditions and under the risk-neutral probability measure

16.2.1.2.1. Shift to the risk-neutral probability measure

Theorem 16.5. *Given the probability space $(\Omega, \mathcal{F}, P)$, the following random variable is defined:*

$$
Z_t := e^{\int_0^t \lambda(s,r_s)\, dW_s - (1/2)\int_0^t \lambda^2(s,r_s)\, ds}, \quad 0 \le t \le T
$$

then Z_t is the Radon–Nikodym derivative of probability measure $\widetilde{P}$ with respect to the equivalent probability measure (see Equation (11.3)) P on the measurable space $(\Omega, \mathcal{F})$:

$$
\frac{d\widetilde{P}}{dP} \equiv e^{\int_0^t \lambda(s,r_s)\, dW_s - (1/2)\int_0^t \lambda^2(s,r_s)\, ds} \quad on\ (\Omega, \mathcal{F})
$$

and

$$
\widetilde{W}_t = W_t - \int_0^t \lambda(s, r_s)\, ds \tag{16.44}
$$

is a standard Brownian motion under measure $\widetilde{P}$.

Proof. The demonstration that Z_t is the Radon–Nikodym derivative of probability measure $\widetilde{P}$ with respect to the equivalent probability measure P derived from the application of Corollary 12.14.

The verification that $\widetilde{W}_t$ is a standard Brownian motion under measure $\widetilde{P}$ is an immediate consequence of Theorem 12.18. □

Corollary 16.4. *The following relations hold:*

$$W_t = \widetilde{W}_t + \int_0^t \lambda(s, r_s)\, ds \tag{16.45}$$

$$dW_t = d\widetilde{W}_t + \lambda(t, r_t)\, dt \tag{16.46}$$

16.2.1.2.1.1. $P(t, T, r_t)$ SDE derivation

Proposition 16.5. *The SDE which describes $P(t, T, r_t)$ in arbitrage-free conditions and under the risk-neutral probability measure $\widetilde{P}$ is given by*

$$dP(t, T, r_t) = r_t P(t, T, r_t)\, dt - \widehat{\sigma}(t, T, r_t) P(t, T, r_t)\, d\widetilde{W}_t \tag{16.47}$$

Proof. Expression (16.46) in (16.37) is substituted to obtain

$$dP(t, T, r_t) = P(t, T, r_t)[r_t + \lambda(r_t, t)\widehat{\sigma}(t, T, r_t)]\, dt$$
$$- P(t, T, r_t)\widehat{\sigma}(t, T, r_t)[d\widetilde{W}_t + \lambda(t, r_t)\, dt]$$

hence

$$dP(t, T, r_t) = P(t, T, r_t)r_t + P(t, T, r_t)\lambda(r_t, t)\widehat{\sigma}(t, T, r_t)\, dt$$
$$- P(t, T, r_t)\widehat{\sigma}(t, T, r_t)\, d\widetilde{W}_t - P(t, T, r_t)\widehat{\sigma}(t, T, r_t)\lambda(t, r_t)\, dt$$

whence

$$dP(t, T, r_t) = P(t, T, r_t)r_t - P(t, T, r_t)\widehat{\sigma}(t, T, r_t)\, d\widetilde{W}_t \qquad \square$$

Theorem 16.6. *The solution of (16.47) is*

$$P(t, T, r_t) = e^{\int_t^T [r_s - \widehat{\sigma}^2(s, T, r_s)/2]\, ds - \int_t^T \widehat{\sigma}(s, T, r_s)\, d\widetilde{W}_s} \tag{16.48}$$

Proof. The application of Theorem 13.3 to SDE (16.47) gives the solution to this equation, ie,

$$P(t, T, r_t) = e^{\int_t^T [r_s - \widehat{\sigma}^2(s, T, r_s)/2]\, ds - \int_t^T \widehat{\sigma}(s, T, r_s)\, dW_s} \qquad \square$$

16.2.1.2.1.2. r_t SDE derivation

Proposition 16.6. *The SDE which describes the instantaneous spot rate r_t under the risk-neutral probability measure $\widetilde{P}$ is given by*

$$dr_t = \bar{\phi}(r_t, t)\, dt + \sigma(r_t, t)\, d\widetilde{W}_t \tag{16.49}$$

where $\bar{\phi}(r_t, t) = \phi(r_t, t) + \lambda(t, r_t)\sigma(r_t, t)$.

Proof. Expression (16.46) is substituted in (16.19) to obtain

$$dr_t = \phi(r_t, t)\, dt + \sigma(r_t, t)(d\widetilde{W}_t + \lambda(t, r_t)\, dt)$$

simplifying, one has

$$dr_t = [\phi(r_t, t) + \lambda(t, r_t)\sigma(r_t, t)]\, dt + \sigma(r_t, t)\, d\widetilde{W}_t$$

and defining $\bar{\phi}(r_t, t) = \phi(r_t, t) + \lambda(t, r_t)\sigma(r_t, t)$ one obtains

$$dr_t = \bar{\phi}(r_t, t)\, dt + \sigma(r_t, t)\, d\widetilde{W}_t \qquad \square$$

Remark 16.2. However, $\bar{\phi}(r_t, t)$, ie, the drift of the diffusive process (16.49), is equal to the drift defined under the original probability measure P, $\phi(r_t, t)$, added to the product of the risk premium, $\lambda(t, r_t)$, by the diffusion defined under the original probability measure P, $\sigma(r_t, t)$.

16.2.1.2.1.3. The process $P^*(t, T, r_t)$ The discounted process of $P(t, T, r_t)$ is defined. Specifically, assuming that the following ODE represents money capitalisation through a continuously compounded interest rate, for all $t \in [0, T]$ (see Theorem 8.1 and Proposition 14.5):

$$dK_t = r_t K_t\, dt$$

whose solution is

$$K_t = e^{\left(\int_0^t r_s\, ds\right)} \qquad (16.50)$$

to obtain the relation with discount factor $e^{\left(-\int_0^t r_s\, ds\right)}$ as follows (see Proposition 14.5):

$$\frac{1}{K_t} = e^{\left(-\int_0^t r_s\, ds\right)} \qquad (16.51)$$

In addition

$$d\frac{1}{K_t} = -r_t \frac{1}{K_t}\, dt \qquad (16.52)$$

Definition 16.8. One can define $P^*(t, T, r_t)$ to be the discounted process of $P(t, T, r_t)$, ie,

$$P^*(t, T, r_t) = \frac{P(t, T, r_t)}{K_t} \qquad (16.53)$$

where

- $K_t = e^{\left(\int_0^t r_s\, ds\right)}$;
- $P^*(0, T, r_0) = P(0, T, r_0)$;
- $P^*(T, T, r_T) = P(T, T, r_T)$.

Proposition 16.7. *The SDE which governs process $P^*(t, T, r_t)$ under measure $\widetilde{P}$ is*

$$dP^*(t, T, r_t) = -\widehat{\sigma}(s, T, r_s)P^*(t, T, r_t)\, d\widetilde{W}_t \qquad (16.54)$$

Proof. The stochastic differential of process $P^*(t, T, r_t)$ is derived by applying the Leibniz rule (see Theorem 12.15), ie,

$$dP^*(t, T, r_t) = P(t, T, r_t)\, d\frac{1}{K_t} + \frac{1}{K_t}\, dP(t, T, r_t) + d\frac{1}{K_t}\, dP(t, T, r_t)$$

substituting (16.52) and (16.47), one obtains

$$
\begin{aligned}
dP^*(t, T, r_t) = {}& P(t, T, r_t)\left[-r_t\frac{1}{K_t}dt\right] + \frac{1}{K_t}[r_t P(t, T, r_t)\, dt \\
& - \widehat{\sigma}(t, T, r_t)P(t, T, r_t)\, d\widetilde{W}_t] + \left[-r_t\frac{1}{K_t}\, dt\right][r_t P(t, T, r_t)\, dt \\
& - \widehat{\sigma}(t, T, r_t)P(t, T, r_t)\, d\widetilde{W}_t]
\end{aligned}
$$

simplifying by using Itô's algebra (see Proposition 12.7), one obtains

$$
\begin{aligned}
dP^*(t, T, r_t) = {}& -r_t P(t, T, r_t)\frac{1}{K_t}\, dt \\
& + \frac{1}{K_t}[r_t P(t, T, r_t)\, dt - \widehat{\sigma}(t, T, r_t)P(t, T, r_t)\, d\widetilde{W}_t]
\end{aligned}
$$

simplifying, one has

$$dP^*(t, T, r_t) = -\widehat{\sigma}(s, T, r_s)P^*(t, T, r_t)\, d\widetilde{W}_t \qquad \square$$

Theorem 16.7. *The solution of (16.54) is*

$$P^*(t, T, r_t) = e^{\int_t^T -(\widehat{\sigma}^2(s,T,r_s)/2)\, ds - \int_t^T \widehat{\sigma}(s,T,r_s)\, d\widetilde{W}_s} \qquad (16.55)$$

Proof. The application of Theorem 13.3 to SDE (16.47) gives the solution to this equation, ie,

$$P^*(t, T, r_t) = e^{\int_t^T -(\widehat{\sigma}^2(s,T,r_s)/2)\, ds - \int_t^T \widehat{\sigma}(s,T,r_s)\, d\widetilde{W}_s} \qquad \square$$

Corollary 16.5. *The discounted process of the risk-free zero-coupon bond price, ie, $P^*(t, T, r_t) = P(t, T, r_t)/K_t$, is a $\widetilde{P}$-martingale.*

Proof. From (16.54), one arrives at the relative integral from

$$P^*(t, T, r_t) = P^*(0, T, r_0) - \int_0^t \hat{\sigma}(s, T, r_s) P^*(s, T, r_s)\, d\tilde{W}_s$$

Considering the expected value with respect to the risk-neutral probability measure $\tilde{P}$, and under the condition of the information available at time zero, one has

$$E^{\tilde{P}}(P^*(t, T, r_t)|r_0) = E^{\tilde{P}}\left[\left(P^*(0, T, r_0) - \int_0^t \hat{\sigma}(s, T, r_s) P^*(s, T, r_s)\, d\tilde{W}_s\right)\Big| r_0\right]$$

However, $P^*(0, T, r_0)$ is adapted with respect to r_0 and then it may be taken out from the conditioned expected value:

$$E^{\tilde{P}}(P^*(t, T)|r_0) = P^*(0, T, r_0) - E^{\tilde{P}}\left[\left(\int_0^t \hat{\sigma}(s, T, r_s) P^*(s, T, r_s)\, d\tilde{W}_s\right)\Big| r_0\right]$$

The argument of the expected value of the right-hand side is a stochastic integral. Then, it is a martingale (see property (7) of Proposition 12.9), whose expected value conditioned to r_0 is zero. It can be derived that

$$E^{\tilde{P}}(P^*(t, T, r_t)|r_0) = P^*(0, T, r_0) \tag{16.56}$$

One recalls in (16.56) the definition of the martingale (see Definition 12.16). This implies that the discounted process of the risk-free zero-coupon bond price, ie, $P^*(t, T, r_t)$, is a $\tilde{P}$-martingale. □

16.2.1.2.1.4. The price $P(t, T, r_t)$ as a conditional expected value under the risk-neutral measure

Theorem 16.8. *The price of a pure discount bond which was given by (16.39) under the empirical probability measure P, is given by*

$$P(t, T, r_t) = E^{\tilde{P}}\left(e^{\{-\int_t^T r_s\, ds\}}\Big| r_t\right) \tag{16.57}$$

under the risk-neutral probability measure $\tilde{P}$.

Proof. In the following we give two possible demonstrations.

First demonstration. Recalling (16.56), generalising it at time T and conditioning in t, ie,

$$E^{\tilde{P}}[P^*(T, T, r_T) \mid r_t] = P^*(t, T, r_t)$$

Recalling (16.53) one has

$$E^{\widetilde{P}}\left(\frac{P(T, T, r_T)}{K_T} \,\middle|\, r_t\right) = \frac{P(t, T, r_t)}{K_t}$$

Multiplying by $1/K_t$, one obtains

$$K_t E^{\widetilde{P}}\left(\frac{P(T, T, r_T)}{K_T} \,\middle|\, r_t\right) = K_t \frac{P(t, T, r_t)}{K_t}$$

Recalling the boundary condition of the Cauchy problem (16.34) and putting K_t inside the expected conditioned value, one obtains

$$E^{\widetilde{P}}\left(\frac{K_t}{K_T} \,\middle|\, r_t\right) = P(t, T, r_t)$$

using (16.50), one has

$$E^{\widetilde{P}}\left(\frac{e^{\int_0^t r_s\, ds}}{e^{\int_0^T r_s\, ds}} \,\middle|\, r_t\right) = P(t, T, r_t)$$

and, then,

$$E^{\widetilde{P}}\left(e^{\int_0^t r_s\, ds} e^{-\int_0^T r_s\, ds} \,\middle|\, r_t\right) = P(t, T, r_t)$$

Finally,

$$E^{\widetilde{P}}\left(e^{\{-\int_t^T r_s\, ds\}} \,\middle|\, r_t\right) = P(t, T, r_t)$$

or

$$P(t, T, r_t) = E^{\widetilde{P}}\left(e^{\{-\int_t^T r_s\, ds\}} \,\middle|\, r_t\right) \tag{16.57}$$

Second demonstration. Equation (16.49) is specified by amending, to simplify notation, the index of the stochastic process from t to s and giving as initial condition $r_t = r$, ie,

$$dr_s = [\phi(s, r_s) + \lambda(s, r_s)\sigma(r_s, s)]\, ds + \sigma(s, r_s)\, d\widetilde{W}_s \tag{16.58}$$

$$r_t = r$$

Then one recalls the Cauchy problem identified in Equations (16.34) and (16.34a). Equations (16.58) and (16.34) allow one to apply the Feynman–Kac formula of Theorem 12.20. Then, referring to the theorem above and defining

$$dX_s = dr_s$$
$$f(X_T) = f(r_T)$$
$$g(s, r_s) = -r_s$$
$$v(t, r_t) = P(t, T, r_t)$$

Equation (16.58) represents the equivalent to (12.94), while (16.34) represents the equivalent to (12.96). Then the equation

$$P(t, T, r_t) = E^{\tilde{P}}[f(r_T)e^{\int_t^T -r_s \, ds} \mid r_t = r] \tag{16.59}$$

corresponds to (12.95).

Considering

$$\lim_{t \to T} P(t, T, r_t) = P(T, T, r_T)$$

and under the final condition of the Cauchy problem identified in (16.34) one has that $P(T, T, r_T) = 1$, then

$$\lim_{t \to T} P(t, T, r_t) = 1 \tag{16.60}$$

Under Theorem 12.20, the following equivalence holds:

$$\lim_{t \to T} P(t, T, r_t) = f(r_T) \tag{16.61}$$

and then equating the right-hand side in (16.60) to right-hand side in (16.61), one obtains

$$f(r_T) = 1 \tag{16.62}$$

Substituting the value of $f(r_T)$ in (16.62) in (16.59), one obtains

$$P(t, T, r_t) = E^{\tilde{P}}\left[e^{\int_t^T -r_s \, ds} \mid r_t = r\right] \tag{16.57}$$

$\square$

16.3.   THE AFFINE TERM-STRUCTURE MODELS
16.3.1.   Introduction

The affine term-structure models are specified by assuming that the future dynamic of the interest rates depends on the evolution of any observed or non-observed factor. Such a factor, also defined as a state variable, is a random process linked to the assumption of arbitrage-free conditions in the underlying financial market. The arbitrage-free condition allows one to derive a deterministic relation between the term structure of the interest rate and these state variables. Some affine term-structure models allow one to obtain an analytical solution for the function which represents the zero-coupon bond price.

In the following, a sub-class of the one-factorial affine term-structure models is considered, ie, the class where the state variable is the instantaneous sport interest r_t.

In the affine term-structure models considered in the following, the risk-free zero-coupon bond price is

$$P(t, T, r_t) = e^{[A(t,T) - D(t,T)r_t]} \tag{16.63}$$

where

$$A(T, T) = A(t, T) + \int_t^T A(s, T) \, ds \tag{16.64}$$

$$D(T, T) = D(0, t) + \int_t^T D(s, T) \, ds \tag{16.65}$$

These models are defined as "affine" because the yield to maturity $r(t, T)$ is expressed as an affine transformation of the instantaneous spot rate r_t. Specifically, as seen above, a risk-free zero-coupon bond price must satisfy the following equation:

$$P(t, T, r_t) = e^{[-r(t,T) \cdot (T-t)]} \tag{16.2}$$

Considering (16.63) and (16.2) together, one observes that the yield to maturity is defined as an affine transformation of the instantaneous short-term rate:

$$r(t, T) = \frac{-A(t, T) + D(t, T)r(t)}{(T - t)}$$

16.3.2. The PDE that describes the process $P(t, T, r_t)$ in affine models

It was demonstrated that (see Section 16.2.1.2) the price of a risk-free pure discount bond, $P(t, T, r_t)$, in an arbitrage-free condition under the risk-neutral probability measure P, is given by Equation (16.57) and it has also been shown that in arbitrage-free and risk-neutral conditions, the short rate r_t process is governed by the SDE (16.49) and that the price $P(t, T, r_t)$ is given by the solution of the Cauchy problem (16.35) and (16.35a). It was also demonstrated that $P(t, T, r_t) = e^{\{-\int_t^T f(t,s) \, ds\}}$ (see Equation (16.16)).

The arbitrage-free condition for this model class may then be derived by setting (16.63) equal to (16.16):

$$e^{[A(t,T) - D(t,T)r_t]} = e^{\{-\int_t^T f(t,s) \, ds\}}$$

Specifying for $t = 0$,

$$e^{[A(0,T) - D(0,T)r_0]} = e^{\{-\int_0^T f(0,s) \, ds\}}$$

Considering the logarithm,

$$A(0, T) - D(0, T)r_0 = -\int_0^T f(0, s) \, ds$$

and deriving with respect to T

$$\frac{\partial}{\partial T}A(0, T) - \frac{\partial}{\partial T}D(0, T)r_0 = \frac{\partial}{\partial T}\left[-\int_0^T f(0, s)\, ds\right]$$

$$\frac{\partial}{\partial T}A(0, T) - \frac{\partial}{\partial T}D(0, T)r_0 = -f(0, T)$$

so

$$f(0, T) = \frac{\partial}{\partial T}D(0, T)r_0 - \frac{\partial}{\partial T}A(0, T) \quad \text{(arbitrage-free condition)} \qquad (16.66)$$

While the Cauchy problem for this class of models is obtained by computing the partial derivatives of $P(t, T, r_t)$ in (16.63), ie,

$$\frac{\partial P(t, T, r_t)}{\partial t} = \frac{\partial(e^{[A(t,T)-D(t,T)r_t]})}{\partial t}$$

$$= e^{[A(t,T)-D(t,T)r_t]} \cdot \left[\frac{\partial}{\partial t}A(t, T) - r\frac{\partial}{\partial t}D(t, T)\right]$$

$$= P(t, T, r_t)\left[\frac{\partial}{\partial t}A(t, T) - r\frac{\partial}{\partial t}D(t, T)\right] \qquad (16.67)$$

$$\frac{\partial P(t, T, r_t)}{\partial r} = \frac{\partial(e^{[A(t,T)-D(t,T)r_t]})}{\partial r}$$

$$= e^{[A(t,T)-D(t,T)r_t]} \cdot [-D(t, T)]$$

$$= -P(t, T, r_t)D(t, T) \qquad (16.68)$$

$$\frac{\partial^2 P(t, T, r_t)}{\partial r^2} = \frac{\partial^2(e^{[A(t,T)-D(t,T)r_t]})}{\partial r^2}$$

$$= e^{[A(t,T)-D(t,T)r_t]} \cdot D^2(t, T)$$

$$= P(t, T, r_t)D^2(t, T) \qquad (16.69)$$

Substituting the partial derivatives from (16.68), (16.69) and (16.67) in (16.35), one has

$$\left[\frac{\partial}{\partial t}A(t, T) - \frac{\partial}{\partial t}D(t, T)r_t\right]P(t, T, r_t) - \bar{\phi}(r, t)D(t, T)P(t, T, r_t)$$

$$+ \frac{\sigma(r_t, t)^2}{2}D^2(t, T)P(t, T, r_t) - r_t P(t, T, r_t) = 0 \qquad (16.70)$$

A boundary condition has to be added to (16.70). For this purpose, relation (16.1) is specified in the context of affine models, ie,

$$P(T, T, r_T) = e^{(A(T,T)-D(T,T)r(T))} = 1 \qquad (16.71)$$

To verify, (16.71) requires that

$$A(T, T) = 0 \tag{16.72}$$
$$D(T, T) = 0 \tag{16.73}$$

Then the Cauchy problem in this model class becomes (16.70), (16.72) and (16.73), whose solution gives the price $P(t, T, r_t)$ of a risk-free zero-coupon bond in arbitrage-free conditions, with a short-rate risk-neutral process as described in (16.49), and with an affine term-structure model as described in (16.63).

16.3.2.1. Vasicek model

16.3.2.1.1. Introduction In the Vasicek model, the parameters $\phi(r_t, t)$ and $\sigma(r_t, t)$ from SDE (16.19), which gives a generic description of the instantaneous spot rate r_t under the original probability measure Q, are specified as follows:

$$dr_t = (\eta - \gamma r_t)\, dt + \sigma\, dW_t \tag{16.74}$$

Consequently, SDE (16.49) which describes the instantaneous spot rate r_t under the risk-neutral probability measure $\widetilde{P}$ is specified as

$$dr_t = (\bar{\eta} - \gamma r_t)\, dt + \sigma\, d\widetilde{W}_t \tag{16.75}$$

where $\bar{\eta} = \eta - \lambda\sigma$.

Recalling relation (16.63), one defines

$$C(t, T) = e^{A(t,T)} \tag{16.76}$$

Then, relation (16.63) becomes

$$P(t, T, r_t) = C(t, T)e^{-D(t,T)r_t} \tag{16.77}$$

The Cauchy problem is derived with respect to this model. To this end, the partial derivatives of $P(t, T, r_t)$ are computed from (16.77), ie,

$$\frac{\partial}{\partial t}P(t, T, r_t) = \left[\frac{\partial}{\partial t}C(t, T) - C(t, T)\frac{\partial}{\partial t}D(t, T)r_t\right]e^{-D(t,T)r_t} \tag{16.78}$$

so

$$\frac{\partial}{\partial r}P(t, T, r_t) = -D(t, T)P(t, T, r_t)$$

hence

$$\frac{\partial}{\partial r}P(t, T, r_t) = -D(t, T)C(t, T)e^{-D(t,T)r_t} \tag{16.79}$$

so

$$\frac{\partial^2}{\partial r^2} P(t, T, r_t) = D^2(t, T) P(t, T, r_t)$$

whence

$$\frac{\partial^2}{\partial r^2} P(t, T, r_t) = D^2(t, T) C(t, T) e^{-D(t,T)r_t} \tag{16.80}$$

Recalling (16.35), and specifying it by the partial derivatives computed in (16.78), (16.79) and (16.80), and by the corresponding values of $\bar{\phi}$ and σ of the SDE (16.49) in (16.75), one has

$$\left[\frac{\partial}{\partial t} C(t, T) - C(t, T) \frac{\partial}{\partial t} D(t, T) r_t \right] e^{-D(t,T)r_t} - [\bar{\eta} - \gamma r_t] C(t, T) D(t, T)$$

$$\cdot e^{-D(t,T)r_t} + \frac{\sigma^2}{2} C(t, T) D^2(t, T) e^{-D(t,T)r_t} - r_t C(t, T) e^{-D(t,T)r_t} = 0$$

dividing by $e^{-D(t,T)r_t}$ and making appropriate factorisation, one obtains

$$\left[\frac{\partial}{\partial t} C(t, T) - C(t, T) D(t, T) \bar{\eta} + \frac{\sigma^2}{2} C(t, T) D^2(t, T) \right]$$

$$- \left[\frac{\partial}{\partial t} D(t, T) - \gamma D(t, T) + 1 \right] \cdot r_t \cdot C(t, T) = 0 \tag{16.81}$$

Equation (16.81) is equivalent to the summation of the two addends that both have to be equal to zero, ie,

$$\frac{\partial}{\partial t} C(t, T) - C(t, T) D(t, T) \bar{\eta} + \frac{\sigma^2}{2} C(t, T) D^2(t, T) = 0 \tag{16.82}$$

$$1 - \gamma D(t, T) + \frac{\partial}{\partial t} D(t, T) = 0 \tag{16.83}$$

The correspondent final conditions to (16.72) and to (16.73) are given by

$$C(T, T) = 1 \tag{16.84}$$

$$D(T, T) = 0 \tag{16.73}$$

Summarising, the Cauchy problem for the Vasicek model becomes

$$\frac{\partial}{\partial t} C(t, T) - C(t, T) D(t, T) \bar{\eta} + \frac{\sigma^2}{2} C(t, T) D^2(t, T) = 0 \tag{16.82}$$

$$1 - \gamma D(t, T) + \frac{\partial}{\partial t} D(t, T) = 0 \tag{16.83}$$

with (16.84) and (16.73).

16.3.2.1.2. Arbitrage-free condition The different functional form for $P(t, T, r_t)$, given by (16.77), requires a new specification of the arbitrage-free condition. For this purpose, (16.66) is recovered, and the logarithm of (16.76) gives

$$\ln C(t, T) = A(t, T)$$

Deriving with respect to T, one has

$$\frac{\partial}{\partial T} \ln C(t, T) = \frac{\partial}{\partial T} A(t, T) \tag{16.85}$$

substituting expression (16.82) in (16.66), one obtains the arbitrage-free condition for the Vasicek model, ie,

$$f(0, T) = \frac{\partial}{\partial T} D(0, T) r_0 - \frac{\partial}{\partial T} \ln C(0, T) \quad \text{(arbitrage-free condition)} \tag{16.86}$$

Quantities $(\partial/\partial T)D(t, T)$ and $(\partial/\partial T) \ln C(t, T)$ are now computed.

Concerning $(\partial/\partial T)D(t, T)$, the following Cauchy problem is given by Equation (16.83) and by the final condition in (16.73).

Since, after defining any function $h(t, T)$, where $T > t$, it is true that

$$\frac{\partial h(t, T)}{\partial T} = -\frac{\partial h(t, T)}{\partial t}$$

one may rearrange the Cauchy problem given by Equation (16.83) as follows and with the final condition as in (16.73):

$$\frac{\partial}{\partial T} D(t, T) + \gamma D(t, T) = 1 \tag{16.87}$$

Since function $D(t, T)$ is of the type $D(T - t)$, defining $(T - t) = \tau$, it is true that

$$\frac{\partial h(T - t)}{\partial T} = \frac{\partial h_\tau}{\partial \tau}$$

it can then be derived that the Cauchy problem given by Equation (16.87) and by the final condition in (16.73) may also be written as

$$\frac{\partial}{\partial \tau} D_\tau + \gamma D_\tau = 1 \tag{16.88}$$

$$D_0 = 0 \tag{16.89}$$

In order to solve the problem, the Laplace transform is used (see Example 9.14 and Section 9.1.3.3) to obtain

$$D_\tau = \frac{1}{\gamma} - \frac{1}{\gamma} e^{-\gamma \tau}$$

Substituting τ by the value $(T - t)$, one obtains

$$D(t, T) = \frac{1}{\gamma}(1 - e^{-\gamma(T-t)}) \qquad (16.90)$$

Substituting (16.90) inside (16.87), one obtains

$$\frac{\partial}{\partial T}D(t, T) + \gamma\frac{1}{\gamma}(1 - e^{-\gamma(T-t)}) = 1$$

$$\frac{\partial}{\partial T}D(t, T) + 1 - e^{-\gamma(T-t)} = 1$$

$$\frac{\partial}{\partial T}D(t, T) = e^{-\gamma(T-t)}$$

hence,

$$\frac{\partial}{\partial T}D(t, T) = e^{-\gamma(T-t)} \qquad (16.91)$$

As for $(\partial/\partial T)\ln C(t, T)$, recalling the Cauchy problem given by Equation (16.82) and by the respective final condition (16.84), by using (16.90 in the last term, (16.82) becomes

$$\frac{\partial}{\partial t}C(t, T) - C(t, T)D(t, T)\bar{\eta} + \frac{\sigma^2}{2}C(t, T)\frac{(1 - e^{-\gamma(T-t)})^2}{\gamma^2} = 0$$

hence

$$\frac{\partial}{\partial t}C(t, T) = C(t, T)D(t, T)\bar{\eta} - \frac{\sigma^2}{2}C(t, T)\frac{(1 - e^{-\gamma(T-t)})^2}{\gamma^2}$$

Dividing by $C(t, T)$, one has

$$\frac{\frac{\partial}{\partial t}C(t, T)}{C(t, T)} = D(t, T)\bar{\eta} - \frac{\sigma^2}{2}\frac{(1 - e^{-\gamma(T-t)})^2}{\gamma^2}$$

ie,

$$\frac{dC(t, T)}{C(t, T)} = \left(D(t, T)\bar{\eta} - \frac{\sigma^2}{2}\frac{(1 - e^{-\gamma(T-t)})^2}{\gamma^2}\right)dt$$

By integrating both members, one obtains

$$\int_t^T \frac{dC(s, T)}{C(s, T)} = \int_t^T \left(D(t, T)\bar{\eta} - \frac{\sigma^2}{2}\frac{(1 - e^{-\gamma(T-s)})^2}{\gamma^2}\right)ds$$

$$\ln C(T, T) - \ln C(t, T) = \int_t^T \bar{\eta}D(t, T)\,ds - \frac{\sigma^2}{2}\int_t^T \frac{(1 - 2e^{-\gamma(T-s)} + e^{-2\gamma(T-s)})}{\gamma^2}ds$$

Using the final condition (16.84), one obtains

$$\ln 1 - \ln C(t, T) = \int_t^T \bar{\eta}D(t, T)\,ds - \frac{\sigma^2}{2\gamma^2}\int_t^T (1 - 2e^{-\gamma(T-s)} + e^{-2\gamma(T-s)})\,ds$$

Simplifying and solving the second integral, one has

$$-\ln C(t, T) = \int_t^T \bar{\eta} D(t, T)\, ds - \frac{\sigma^2}{2\gamma^2}\left\{ [s]_t^T + \int_t^T \left(-2e^{-\gamma(T-s)} + e^{-2\gamma(T-s)}\right) ds \right\}$$

Changing sign, one obtains

$$\ln C(t, T) = -\int_t^T \bar{\eta} D(t, T)\, ds + \frac{\sigma^2}{2\gamma^2}\left\{ [s]_t^T + \int_t^T \left(-2e^{-\gamma(T-s)} + e^{-2\gamma(T-s)}\right) ds \right\}$$

$$= -\int_t^T \bar{\eta} D(t, T)\, ds$$

$$+ \frac{\sigma^2}{2\gamma^2}\left\{ (T - t) + \int_t^T \left(-2e^{-\gamma(T-s)} + e^{-2\gamma(T-s)}\right) ds \right\}$$

Multiplying and simplifying, one has

$$\ln C(t, T)$$

$$= -\int_t^T \bar{\eta} D(t, T)\, ds + \frac{\sigma^2}{2\gamma^2}(T - t) - \frac{\sigma^2}{\gamma^2}\int_t^T e^{-\gamma(T-s)}\, ds$$

$$+ \frac{\sigma^2}{2\gamma^2}\int_t^T e^{-2\gamma(T-s)}\, ds$$

$$= -\int_t^T \bar{\eta} D(t, T)\, ds + \frac{\sigma^2}{2\gamma^2}(T - t) - \frac{\sigma^2}{\gamma^2}\left[\frac{1}{\gamma}e^{-\gamma(T-s)}\right]_t^T$$

$$+ \frac{\sigma^2}{2\gamma^2}\int_t^T e^{-2\gamma(T-s)}\, ds$$

$$= -\int_t^T \bar{\eta} D(t, T)\, ds + \frac{\sigma^2}{2\gamma^2}(T - t) - \frac{\sigma^2}{\gamma^2}\left[\frac{1}{\gamma}e^{-\gamma(T-T)} - \frac{1}{\gamma}e^{-\gamma(T-t)}\right]$$

$$+ \frac{\sigma^2}{2\gamma^2}\int_t^T e^{-2\gamma(T-s)}\, ds$$

$$= -\int_t^T \bar{\eta} D(t, T)\, ds + \frac{\sigma^2}{2\gamma^2}(T - t) - \frac{\sigma^2}{\gamma^2}\left[\frac{1}{\gamma} - \frac{1}{\gamma}e^{-\gamma(T-t)}\right]$$

$$+ \frac{\sigma^2}{2\gamma^2}\int_t^T e^{-2\gamma(T-s)}\, ds \quad \text{(by simplifying)}$$

$$= -\int_t^T \bar{\eta} D(t, T)\, ds + \frac{\sigma^2}{2\gamma^2}(T - t) - \frac{\sigma^2}{\gamma^2}\left[\frac{1}{\gamma} - \frac{1}{\gamma}e^{-\gamma(T-t)}\right]$$

$$+ \frac{\sigma^2}{2\gamma^2}\left[\frac{1}{2\gamma}e^{-2\gamma(T-s)}\right]_t^T \quad \text{(continuing in the integration)}$$

$$= -\int_t^T \bar{\eta} D(t, T)\, ds + \frac{\sigma^2}{2\gamma^2}(T - t) - \frac{\sigma^2}{\gamma^2}\left[\frac{1}{\gamma} - \frac{1}{\gamma}e^{-\gamma(T-t)}\right]$$

$$+ \frac{\sigma^2}{2\gamma^2}\left[\frac{1}{\gamma}e^{-2\gamma(T-T)} - \frac{1}{\gamma}e^{-2\gamma(T-t)}\right] \quad \text{(expanding)}$$

$$= -\int_t^T \bar{\eta} D(t, T)\, ds + \frac{\sigma^2}{2\gamma^2}(T - t) - \frac{\sigma^2}{\gamma^2}\left[\frac{1}{\gamma} - \frac{1}{\gamma}e^{-\gamma(T-t)}\right]$$

$$+ \frac{\sigma^2}{2\gamma^2}\left[\frac{1 - e^{-2\gamma(T-t)}}{2\gamma}\right] \quad \text{(simplifying)}$$

$$= -\int_t^T \bar{\eta} D(t, T)\, ds + \frac{\sigma^2}{2\gamma^2}(T - t) - \frac{\sigma^2}{\gamma^2}\left[\left[\frac{1}{\gamma} - \frac{1}{\gamma}e^{-\gamma(T-t)}\right]\right.$$

$$\left. - \frac{1}{2}\cdot\frac{(1 - e^{-2\gamma(T-t)})}{2\gamma}\right] \quad \left(\text{factorising } -\frac{\sigma^2}{\gamma^2}\right)$$

$$= -\int_t^T \bar{\eta}\frac{(1 - e^{-\gamma(T-s)})}{\gamma}\, ds + \frac{\sigma^2}{2\gamma^2}(T - t)$$

$$- \frac{\sigma^2}{\gamma^2}\left[\frac{(1 - e^{-\gamma(T-t)})}{\gamma} - \frac{1}{4}\cdot\frac{(1 - e^{-2\gamma(T-t)})}{\gamma}\right]$$

(using (16.90) and multiplying)

$$= -\int_t^T \bar{\eta}\frac{(1 - e^{-\gamma(T-s)})}{\gamma}\, ds + \frac{\sigma^2}{2\gamma^2}(T - t)$$

$$- \frac{\sigma^2}{\gamma^2}\left[\frac{(4 - 4e^{-\gamma(T-t)} - 1 + e^{-2\gamma(T-t)})}{4\gamma}\right]$$

(simplifying inside the square brackets)

$$= -\int_t^T \bar{\eta}\frac{(1 - e^{-\gamma(T-s)})}{\gamma}\, ds + \frac{\sigma^2}{2\gamma^2}(T - t) - \frac{\sigma^2}{\gamma^2}\left[\frac{(3 - 4e^{-\gamma(T-t)} + e^{-2\gamma(T-t)})}{4\gamma}\right]$$

$$= -\int_t^T \bar{\eta}\frac{(1 - e^{-\gamma(T-s)})}{\gamma}\, ds + \frac{\sigma^2}{2\gamma^2}(T - t)$$

$$- \frac{\sigma^2}{4\gamma^2}\left[\frac{(2 + 1 - 2e^{-\gamma(T-t)} - 2e^{-\gamma(T-t)} + e^{-2\gamma(T-t)})}{\gamma}\right]$$

$$= -\int_t^T \bar{\eta}\frac{(1 - e^{-\gamma(T-s)})}{\gamma}\, ds + \frac{\sigma^2}{2\gamma^2}(T - t)$$

$$- \frac{\sigma^2}{4\gamma^2}\left[\frac{2(1 - e^{-\gamma(T-t)})}{\gamma} + \frac{(1 - 2e^{-\gamma(T-t)} + e^{-2\gamma(T-t)})}{\gamma}\right]$$

$$
= -\int_t^T \bar{\eta} \frac{(1 - e^{-\gamma(T-s)})}{\gamma} \, ds + \frac{\sigma^2}{2\gamma^2}(T - t)
$$

$$
- \frac{\sigma^2}{2\gamma^2} D(t, T) - \frac{\sigma^2}{4\gamma^2} \left[\frac{(1 - 2e^{-\gamma(T-t)} + e^{-2\gamma(T-t)})}{\gamma} \right] \quad \text{(using (16.90))}
$$

$$
= -\int_t^T \bar{\eta} \frac{(1 - e^{-\gamma(T-s)})}{\gamma} \, ds + \frac{\sigma^2}{2\gamma^2}(T - t) - \frac{\sigma^2}{2\gamma^2} D(t, T)
$$

$$
- \frac{\sigma^2}{4\gamma} \left[\left(\frac{1 - e^{-\gamma(T-t)}}{\gamma} \right)^2 \right]
$$

$$
= -\int_t^T \bar{\eta} \frac{(1 - e^{-\gamma(T-s)})}{\gamma} \, ds + \frac{\sigma^2}{2\gamma^2}(T - t) - \frac{\sigma^2}{2\gamma^2} D(t, T) - \frac{\sigma^2}{4\gamma} D(t, T)^2
$$

(using (16.90) again)

$$
= -\bar{\eta} \int_t^T \frac{(1 - e^{-\gamma(T-s)})}{\gamma} \, ds + \frac{\sigma^2}{2\gamma^2}(T - t) - \frac{\sigma^2}{2\gamma^2} D(t, T) - \frac{\sigma^2}{4\gamma} D(t, T)^2
$$

$$
= -\bar{\eta} \frac{1}{\gamma} \int_t^T (1 - e^{-\gamma(T-s)}) \, ds + \frac{\sigma^2}{2\gamma^2}(T - t) - \frac{\sigma^2}{2\gamma^2} D(t, T) - \frac{\sigma^2}{4\gamma} D(t, T)^2
$$

(continuing with integration)

$$
= -\bar{\eta} \frac{1}{\gamma} \left[[s]_t^T - \left[\frac{1}{\gamma} e^{-\gamma(T-s)} \right]_t^T \right] + \frac{\sigma^2}{2\gamma^2}(T - t) - \frac{\sigma^2}{2\gamma^2} D(t, T) - \frac{\sigma^2}{4\gamma} D(t, T)^2
$$

$$
= -\bar{\eta} \frac{1}{\gamma} \left[(T - t) - \left(\frac{1}{\gamma} - \frac{1}{\gamma} e^{-\gamma(T-t)} \right) \right] + \frac{\sigma^2}{2\gamma^2}(T - t) - \frac{\sigma^2}{2\gamma^2} D(t, T)
$$

$$
- \frac{\sigma^2}{4\gamma} D(t, T)^2
$$

$$
= -\bar{\eta} \frac{1}{\gamma}(T - t) + \bar{\eta} \frac{1}{\gamma} \left(\frac{1 - e^{-\gamma(T-t)}}{\gamma} \right) + \frac{\sigma^2}{2\gamma^2}(T - t) - \frac{\sigma^2}{2\gamma^2} D(t, T)
$$

$$
- \frac{\sigma^2}{4\gamma} D(t, T)^2
$$

$$
= -\frac{1}{\gamma} D(t, T) \left(-\bar{\eta} + \frac{\sigma^2}{2\gamma} \right) + \frac{1}{\gamma}(T - t) \left(\frac{\sigma^2}{2\gamma} - \bar{\eta} \right) - \frac{\sigma^2}{4\gamma} D(t, T)^2
$$

(using (16.90) and simplifying)

$$
= \frac{1}{\gamma} \left(\frac{\sigma^2}{2\gamma} - \bar{\eta} \right) ((T - t) - D(t, T)) - \frac{\sigma^2}{4\gamma} D(t, T)^2
$$

thus

$$
\ln C(t, T) = \frac{1}{\gamma} \left(\frac{\sigma^2}{2\gamma} - \bar{\eta} \right) ((T - t) - D(t, T)) - \frac{\sigma^2}{4\gamma} D(t, T)^2 \tag{16.92}
$$

Differentiating with respect to T, one has

$$\frac{\partial}{\partial T} \ln C(t, T) = \frac{\partial}{\partial T} \left[\frac{1}{\gamma} \left(\frac{\sigma^2}{2\gamma} - \bar{\eta} \right) ((T - t) - D(t, T)) - \frac{\sigma^2}{4\gamma} D(t, T)^2 \right]$$

$$= \frac{1}{\gamma} \left(\frac{\sigma^2}{2\gamma} - \bar{\eta} \right) \frac{\partial}{\partial T} (T - t) - \frac{1}{\gamma} \left(\frac{\sigma^2}{2\gamma} - \bar{\eta} \right) \frac{\partial}{\partial T} D(t, T)$$

$$- \frac{\sigma^2}{4\gamma} \frac{\partial}{\partial T} D(t, T)^2 \quad \text{(expanding)}$$

By using the Leibniz rule of derivation (see Corollary 4.1), recalling relation (16.73), and (16.91), one has

$$\frac{\partial}{\partial T} \ln C(t, T)$$

$$= \frac{1}{\gamma} \left(\frac{\sigma^2}{2\gamma} - \bar{\eta} \right) - \frac{1}{\gamma} \left(\frac{\sigma^2}{2\gamma} - \bar{\eta} \right) e^{-\gamma(T-t)} - \frac{\sigma^2}{4\gamma} 2D(t, T) \frac{\partial}{\partial T} D(t, T)$$

$$= \frac{1}{\gamma} \left(\frac{\sigma^2}{2\gamma} - \bar{\eta} \right) - \frac{1}{\gamma} \left(\frac{\sigma^2}{2\gamma} - \bar{\eta} \right) e^{-\gamma(T-t)} - \frac{\sigma^2}{4\gamma} 2 \frac{1}{\gamma} (1 - e^{-\gamma(T-t)}) e^{-\gamma(T-t)}$$

(using (16.90) and (16.91))

$$= \frac{1}{\gamma} \left(\frac{\sigma^2}{2\gamma} - \bar{\eta} \right) - \frac{1}{\gamma} \left(\frac{\sigma^2}{2\gamma} - \bar{\eta} \right) e^{-\gamma(T-t)} - \frac{\sigma^2}{2\gamma^2} (1 - e^{-\gamma(T-t)}) e^{-\gamma(T-t)}$$

(simplifying)

$$= \frac{1}{\gamma} \left(\frac{\sigma^2}{2\gamma} - \bar{\eta} \right) - \frac{1}{\gamma} \left(\frac{\sigma^2}{2\gamma} - \bar{\eta} \right) e^{-\gamma(T-t)} - \frac{\sigma^2}{2\gamma^2} (e^{-\gamma(T-t)} - e^{-2\gamma(T-t)})$$

$$= \frac{\sigma^2}{2\gamma^2} - \frac{1}{\gamma} \bar{\eta} - \frac{\sigma^2}{2\gamma^2} e^{-\gamma(T-t)} + \frac{1}{\gamma} \bar{\eta} e^{-\gamma(T-t)} - \frac{\sigma^2}{2\gamma^2} e^{-\gamma(T-t)} + \frac{\sigma^2}{2\gamma^2} e^{-2\gamma(T-t)}$$

$$= \frac{\sigma^2}{2\gamma^2} (1 - e^{-\gamma(T-t)}) - \frac{1}{\gamma} \bar{\eta} (1 - e^{-\gamma(T-t)}) - \frac{\sigma^2}{2\gamma^2} e^{-\gamma(T-t)} (1 - e^{-\gamma(T-t)})$$

$$= \frac{\sigma^2}{2\gamma^2} (1 - e^{-\gamma(T-t)}) (1 - e^{-\gamma(T-t)}) - \frac{1}{\gamma} \bar{\eta} (1 - e^{-\gamma(T-t)})$$

$$= \frac{\sigma^2}{2} \left[\frac{(1 - e^{-\gamma(T-t)})}{\gamma} \right]^2 - \frac{1}{\gamma} \bar{\eta} (1 - e^{-\gamma(T-t)})$$

then one has

$$\frac{\partial}{\partial T} \ln C(t, T) = -\frac{1}{\gamma} \bar{\eta} (1 - e^{-\gamma(T-t)}) + \frac{\sigma^2}{2} \left[\frac{(1 - e^{-\gamma(T-t)})}{\gamma} \right]^2 \qquad (16.93)$$

hence, specifying (16.91) and (16.93) for $t = 0$, and changing the sign of this last equation, in order to specify the arbitrage-free condition (16.86), ie,

$$\frac{\partial}{\partial T} D(0, T) = e^{-\gamma T} \tag{16.94}$$

$$-\frac{\partial}{\partial T} \ln C(0, T) = \frac{1}{\gamma} \bar{\eta} (1 - e^{-\gamma T}) - \frac{\sigma^2}{2} \left[\frac{(1 - e^{-\gamma T})}{\gamma} \right]^2 \tag{16.95}$$

Recalling the arbitrage-free condition (16.86) and substituting (16.94) and (16.95) in (16.83), one obtains the arbitrage-free condition:

$$f(0, T) = \frac{\bar{\eta}}{\gamma} + e^{-\gamma T} \left[r_0 - \frac{\bar{\eta}}{\gamma} \right] - \frac{\sigma^2}{2} \left[\frac{(1 - e^{-\gamma T})}{\gamma} \right]^2 \quad \text{(arbitrage-free condition)} \tag{16.96}$$

16.3.2.1.2.1. *SDE specification*   SDE (16.75) is specified in arbitrage-free conditions. For this purpose, the value of function $\bar{\eta}$ has to be determined. Then, $\bar{\eta}$ is isolated from (16.96), ie,

$$\frac{1}{\gamma} \bar{\eta} (1 - e^{-\gamma T}) = f(0, T) - e^{-\gamma T} r_0 + \frac{\sigma^2}{2} \left[\frac{(1 - e^{-\gamma T})}{\gamma} \right]^2 \Rightarrow$$

$$\bar{\eta} = \frac{f(0, T) \gamma}{(1 - e^{-\gamma T})} - \frac{\gamma e^{-\gamma T} r_0}{(1 - e^{-\gamma T})} + \frac{\sigma^2}{2} \left[\frac{(1 - e^{-\gamma T})}{\gamma} \right] \tag{16.97}$$

which can also be expressed as

$$\bar{\eta} = \frac{f(0, T)}{D(0, T)} - \frac{e^{-\gamma T} r_0}{D(0, T)} + \frac{\sigma^2}{2} D(0, T) \tag{16.98}$$

Hence, it can be derived that the SDE of the Vasicek model in arbitrage-free conditions and under a *risk-neutral* probability measure P can be written as

$$dr_t = \left[\frac{f(0, T)}{D(0, T)} - \frac{e^{-\gamma T} r_0}{D(0, T)} + \frac{\sigma^2}{2} D(0, T) - \gamma r_t \right] dt + \sigma \, d\widetilde{W}_t \tag{16.99}$$

16.3.2.2.   *The price $P(t, T, r_t)$ in the Vasicek model*

Now Equation (16.77) is specified for the Vasicek model. For this purpose it is necessary to compute the quantity $C(t, T)$, since the value of $D(t, T)$ has already been determined and is equal to (16.90).

Considering again Equation (16.92), the arbitrage-free value of $\bar{\eta}$ in (16.98) is replaced to obtain

$$\ln C(t, T) = \frac{1}{\gamma}\left(\frac{\sigma^2}{2\gamma} - \frac{f(0, T)\gamma}{(1 - e^{-\gamma T})} + \frac{\gamma e^{-\gamma T} r_0}{(1 - e^{-\gamma T})} - \frac{\sigma^2}{2}\left[\frac{(1 - e^{-\gamma T})}{\gamma}\right]\right)$$
$$\cdot ((T - t) - D(t, T)) - \frac{\sigma^2}{4\gamma}D(t, T)^2$$

expanding, one has

$$\ln C(t, T) = \frac{\sigma^2}{2\gamma^2}(T - t) - \frac{\sigma^2}{2\gamma^2}D(t, T) - \frac{f(0, T)}{(1 - e^{-\gamma T})}(T - t)$$
$$+ \frac{f(0, T)}{(1 - e^{-\gamma T})}D(t, T) + \frac{e^{-\gamma T} r_0}{(1 - e^{-\gamma T})}(T - t) - \frac{e^{-\gamma T} r_0}{(1 - e^{-\gamma T})}D(t, T)$$
$$- \frac{\sigma^2}{2\gamma}\left[\frac{(1 - e^{-\gamma T})}{\gamma}\right](T - t) + \frac{\sigma^2}{2\gamma}\left[\frac{(1 - e^{-\gamma T})}{\gamma}\right]D(t, T) - \frac{\sigma^2}{4\gamma}D(t, T)^2$$

Using expression (16.15) one has

$$\ln C(t, T)$$
$$= \frac{\sigma^2}{2\gamma^2}(T - t) - \frac{\sigma^2}{2\gamma^2}D(t, T) - \frac{(\partial/\partial T)\ln P(0, T)}{(1 - e^{-\gamma T})}(T - t)$$
$$+ \frac{(\partial/\partial T)\ln P(0, T)}{(1 - e^{-\gamma T})}D(t, T) + \frac{e^{-\gamma T} r_0}{(1 - e^{-\gamma T})}(T - t) - \frac{e^{-\gamma T} r_0}{(1 - e^{-\gamma T})}D(t, T)$$
$$- \frac{\sigma^2}{2\gamma}\left[\frac{(1 - e^{-\gamma T})}{\gamma}\right](T - t) + \frac{\sigma^2}{2\gamma}\left[\frac{(1 - e^{-\gamma T})}{\gamma}\right]D(t, T) - \frac{\sigma^2}{4\gamma}D(t, T)^2$$

Substituting $D(t, T)$, one obtains

$$\ln C(t, T) = \frac{\sigma^2}{2\gamma^2}(T - t) - \frac{\sigma^2}{2\gamma^2}\frac{(1 - e^{-\gamma(T-t)})}{\gamma} - \frac{(\partial/\partial T)\ln P(0, T)}{(1 - e^{-\gamma T})}(T - t)$$
$$+ \frac{(\partial/\partial T)\ln P(0, T)}{(1 - e^{-\gamma T})}\frac{(1 - e^{-\gamma(T-t)})}{\gamma} + \frac{e^{-\gamma T} r_0}{(1 - e^{-\gamma T})}(T - t)$$
$$- \frac{e^{-\gamma T} r_0}{(1 - e^{-\gamma T})}\frac{(1 - e^{-\gamma(T-t)})}{\gamma} - \frac{\sigma^2}{2\gamma}\left[\frac{(1 - e^{-\gamma T})}{\gamma}\right](T - t)$$
$$+ \frac{\sigma^2}{2\gamma}\left[\frac{(1 - e^{-\gamma T})}{\gamma}\right]\frac{(1 - e^{-\gamma(T-t)})}{\gamma} - \frac{\sigma^2}{4\gamma}\left[\frac{(1 - e^{-\gamma(T-t)})}{\gamma}\right]^2$$

Expanding, one has

$$
\ln C(t, T) = \frac{\sigma^2}{2\gamma^2}(T - t) - \frac{\sigma^2(1 - e^{-\gamma(T-t)})}{2\gamma^3} - \frac{(\partial/\partial T) \ln P(0, T)(T - t)}{(1 - e^{-\gamma T})}
$$
$$
+ \frac{(\partial/\partial T) \ln P(0, T) (1 - e^{-\gamma(T-t)})}{(1 - e^{-\gamma T})} + \frac{e^{-\gamma T} r_0}{(1 - e^{-\gamma T})}(T - t)
$$
$$
- \frac{e^{-\gamma T} r_0}{(1 - e^{-\gamma T})} \frac{(1 - e^{-\gamma(T-t)})}{\gamma} - \frac{\sigma^2(1 - e^{-\gamma T})(T - t)}{2\gamma^2}
$$
$$
+ \frac{\sigma^2(1 - e^{-\gamma T})(1 - e^{-\gamma(T-t)})}{2\gamma^3} - \frac{\sigma^2(1 - e^{-\gamma(T-t)})^2}{4\gamma^3}
$$

Simplifying, one obtains

$$
\ln C(t, T)
$$
$$
= \left[\frac{\sigma^2}{2\gamma^2} - \frac{(\partial/\partial T) \ln P(0, T)}{(1 - e^{-\gamma T})} + \frac{e^{-\gamma T} r_0}{(1 - e^{-\gamma T})} - \frac{\sigma^2(1 - e^{-\gamma T})}{2\gamma^2} \right](T - t)
$$
$$
- \frac{(1 - e^{-\gamma(T-t)})}{\gamma} \left[\frac{\sigma^2}{2\gamma^2} - \frac{(\partial/\partial T) \ln P(0, T)}{(1 - e^{-\gamma T})} + \frac{e^{-\gamma T} r_0}{(1 - e^{-\gamma T})} - \frac{\sigma^2(1 - e^{-\gamma T})}{2\gamma^2} \right]
$$
$$
- \frac{\sigma^2(1 - e^{-\gamma(T-t)})^2}{4\gamma^3}
$$

Applying the exponential, one arrives at

$$
C(t, T)
$$
$$
= \exp\left\{ \left[\frac{\sigma^2}{2\gamma^2} - \frac{(\partial/\partial T) \ln P(0, T)}{(1 - e^{-\gamma T})} + \frac{e^{-\gamma T} r_0}{(1 - e^{-\gamma T})} - \frac{\sigma^2(1 - e^{-\gamma T})}{2\gamma^2} \right](T - t) \right.
$$
$$
- \frac{(1 - e^{-\gamma(T-t)})}{\gamma} \left[\frac{\sigma^2}{2\gamma^2} + \frac{e^{-\gamma T} r_0}{(1 - e^{-\gamma T})} - \frac{\sigma^2(1 - e^{-\gamma T})}{2\gamma^2} - \frac{(\partial/\partial T) \ln P(0, T)}{(1 - e^{-\gamma T})} \right]
$$
$$
\left. - \frac{\sigma^2(1 - e^{-\gamma(T-t)})^2}{4\gamma^3} \right\}
\tag{16.100}
$$

Recovering expression (16.77) and substituting in it the values of $C(t, T)$ as given in (16.100) and the value of $D(t, T)$ as given in (16.90), one obtains the risk-free pure discount bond price in arbitrage-free conditions under the risk-neutral measure of the Vasicek model:

$$P(t, T, r_t)$$

$$= \exp\left\{\left[\frac{\sigma^2}{2\gamma^2} - \frac{(\partial/\partial T)\ln P(0, T)}{(1 - e^{-\gamma T})} + \frac{e^{-\gamma T}r_0}{(1 - e^{-\gamma T})} - \frac{\sigma^2(1 - e^{-\gamma T})}{2\gamma^2}\right](T - t)\right.$$

$$- \frac{(1 - e^{-\gamma(T-t)})}{\gamma}\left[\frac{\sigma^2}{2\gamma^2} + \frac{e^{-\gamma T}r_0}{(1 - e^{-\gamma T})} - \frac{\sigma^2(1 - e^{-\gamma T})}{2\gamma^2}\right.$$

$$\left.- \frac{(\partial/\partial T)\ln P(0, T)}{(1 - e^{-\gamma T})} + r_t\right] - \left.\frac{\sigma^2(1 - e^{-\gamma(T-t)})^2}{4\gamma^3}\right\} \qquad (16.101)$$

Equation (16.101) may have a compact expression by using (16.97), ie,

$$P(t, T, r_t) = \exp\left\{\frac{1}{\gamma}\left[\frac{\sigma^2}{2\gamma} - \bar{\eta}\right](T - t) - \frac{(1 - e^{-\gamma(T-t)})}{\gamma}\frac{1}{\gamma}\left[\frac{\sigma^2}{2\gamma} - \bar{\eta} + r_t\right]\right.$$

$$\left.- \frac{\sigma^2(1 - e^{-\gamma(T-t)})^2}{4\gamma^3}\right\} \qquad (16.102)$$

16.3.2.3. Ho–Lee model

16.3.2.3.1. Introduction In the Ho–Lee model, SDE (16.19) which describes the instantaneous spot rate r_t under the empirical measure Q, is specified as follows:

$$dr_t = \phi_t \, dt + \sigma \, dW_t \qquad (16.103)$$

Consequently, SDE (16.49) which describes the instantaneous spot rate r_t under the risk-neutral probability measure $\widetilde{P}$ is specified as follows:

$$dr_t = \bar{\phi}_t \, dt + \sigma \, d\widetilde{W}_t \qquad (16.104)$$

where $\bar{\phi}_t = \phi_t - \lambda_t\sigma$.

The Cauchy problem as in PDE (16.70) is then specified as follows:

$$\left[\frac{\partial}{\partial t}A(t, T) - \frac{\partial}{\partial t}D(t, T)r_t\right]P(t, T, r_t) - \bar{\phi}_t D(t, T)P(t, T, r_t)$$

$$+ \frac{\sigma^2}{2}D^2(t, T)P(t, T, r_t) - r_t P(t, T, r_t) = 0$$

Factorising, one has

$$\left[\frac{\partial}{\partial t}A(t, T) - \bar{\phi}_t D(t, T) + \frac{\sigma^2}{2}D^2(t, T)\right]P(t, T, r_t)$$

$$- r_t P(t, T, r_t)\left[1 + \frac{\partial}{\partial t}D(t, T)\right] = 0$$

which is equivalent to the following equation system:

$$\begin{cases} \dfrac{\partial}{\partial t}A(t,T) - D(t,T)\bar{\phi}_t + \dfrac{\sigma^2(t)}{2}D^2(t,T) = 0 \\ -r_t\left[1 + \dfrac{\partial}{\partial t}D(t,T)\right] = 0 \end{cases}$$

Recalling the boundary conditions, the Cauchy problems then becomes

$$\frac{\partial}{\partial t}A(t,T) - D(t,T)\bar{\phi}_t + \frac{\sigma^2(t)}{2}D^2(t,T) = 0 \tag{16.105}$$

$$-r_t\left[1 + \frac{\partial}{\partial t}D(t,T)\right] = 0 \tag{16.106}$$

with (16.72) and (16.73).

16.3.2.3.2. Arbitrage-free condition The arbitrage-free condition is specified for this model. For this purpose, (16.66) is recovered. Quantities $(\partial/\partial T)D(0,T)$ and $(\partial/\partial T)A(0,T)$ are now computed.

Concerning $(\partial/\partial T)D(0,T)$, Equation (16.106) is solved and is immediately verified for

$$\frac{\partial}{\partial t}D(t,T) = -1 \tag{16.107}$$

Then, one recalls (16.65) in a slightly modified form:

$$D(T,T) = D(t,T) + \int_t^T \frac{\partial}{\partial s}D(s,T)\,ds \tag{16.64}$$

For the final condition of the Cauchy problem (16.73), ie, $D(T,T) = 0$, one has

$$0 = D(t,T) + \int_t^T \frac{\partial}{\partial s}D(s,T)\,ds$$

and, using (16.107), one has

$$0 = D(t,T) + \int_t^T -1\,ds$$

and, then,

$$\int_t^T 1\,ds = D(t,T)$$

Solving the integral, one obtains

$$(T - t) = D(t,T)$$

hence

$$D(t, T) = (T - t) \tag{16.108}$$

whence

$$D(0, T) = T \tag{16.109}$$

then, deriving with respect to T, one has

$$\frac{\partial}{\partial T} D(0, T) = 1 \tag{16.110}$$

For $(\partial/\partial T)A(0, T)$, Equation (16.105) is solved; by substituting (16.108) in this equation, one has

$$\frac{\partial}{\partial t} A(t, T) - \bar{\phi}_t(T - t) + \frac{\sigma^2}{2}(T - t)^2 = 0$$

Solving for $(\partial/\partial t)A(t, T)$, one has

$$\frac{\partial}{\partial t} A(t, T) = \bar{\phi}_t(T - t) - \frac{\sigma^2}{2}(T - t)^2 = 0 \tag{16.111}$$

Recalling (16.64) in a slightly modified form:

$$A(T, T) = A(t, T) + \int_t^T \frac{\partial}{\partial s} A(s, T)\, ds \tag{16.65}$$

which, for the final condition of the Cauchy problem (16.72), becomes

$$0 = A(t, T) + \int_t^T \frac{\partial}{\partial s} A(s, T)\, ds$$

and substituting (16.111), one obtains

$$0 = A(t, T) + \int_t^T \left[\bar{\phi}_s(T - s) - \frac{\sigma^2}{2}(T - s)^2 \right] ds$$

then

$$A(t, T) = \int_t^T \left[-\bar{\phi}_s(T - s) + \frac{\sigma^2}{2}(T - s)^2 \right] ds \tag{16.112}$$

and, for $t = 0$,

$$A(0, T) = \int_0^T \left[\frac{\sigma^2}{2}(T - s)^2 - \bar{\phi}_s(T - s) \right] ds$$

and then, deriving with respect to the variable T,

$$\frac{\partial}{\partial T} A(0, T) = \frac{\partial}{\partial T} \int_0^T \left[\frac{\sigma^2}{2}(T - s)^2 - \bar{\phi}_s(T - s) \right] ds$$

$$= \int_0^T \frac{\partial}{\partial T} \left[\frac{\sigma^2}{2}(T - s)^2 - \bar{\phi}_s(T - s) \right] ds$$

$$= \int_0^T \{\sigma^2(T-s) - \bar{\phi}_s\} \, ds$$

$$= \sigma^2 \int_0^T T \, ds - \sigma^2 \int_0^T s \, ds - \int_0^T \bar{\phi}_s \, ds$$

$$= \sigma^2 T(T-0) - \sigma^2 \left(\frac{T^2}{2} - 0 \right) - \int_0^T \bar{\phi}_s \, ds$$

$$= \sigma^2 T^2 - \sigma^2 \frac{T^2}{2} - \int_0^T \bar{\phi}_s \, ds$$

$$= \sigma^2 \frac{T^2}{2} - \int_0^T \bar{\phi}_s \, ds$$

one has

$$\frac{\partial}{\partial T} A(0, T) = \sigma^2 \frac{T^2}{2} - \int_0^T \bar{\phi}_s \, ds \tag{16.113}$$

Substituting (16.110) and (16.113) in (16.66) (the model arbitrage-free condition), one arrives at

$$f(0, T) = r_0 - \sigma^2 \frac{T^2}{2} + \int_0^T \bar{\phi}_s \, ds \tag{16.114}$$

16.3.2.3.2.1. SDE specification Now SDE (16.104) is specified in arbitrage-free conditions. For this purpose, (16.114) is derived with respect to T, ie,

$$\frac{\partial}{\partial T} f(0, T) = \frac{\partial}{\partial T} \left[r_0 - \sigma^2 \frac{T^2}{2} + \int_0^T \bar{\phi}_s \, ds \right]$$

$$= -\frac{\partial}{\partial T} \sigma^2 \frac{T^2}{2} + \frac{\partial}{\partial T} \int_0^T \bar{\phi}_s \, ds$$

$$= -\frac{\partial}{\partial T} \sigma^2 \frac{T^2}{2} + \frac{\partial}{\partial T} \int_0^T \bar{\phi}_s \, ds$$

$$= -\sigma^2 T + \frac{\partial}{\partial T} \int_0^T \bar{\phi}_s \, ds$$

to obtain

$$\frac{\partial}{\partial T} f(0, T) = -\sigma^2 T + \bar{\phi}_T \tag{16.115}$$

and then, solving (16.115) for $\bar{\phi}_T$), one has

$$\bar{\phi}_T = \sigma^2 T + \frac{\partial}{\partial T} f(0, T) \tag{16.116}$$

and, for any t,

$$\bar{\phi}_t = \sigma^2 t + \frac{\partial}{\partial t} f(0, t) \tag{16.117}$$

hence, the SDE of the Ho–Lee model in arbitrage-free conditions and under the risk-neutral probability measure can be written as

$$dr_t = \left[\sigma^2 t + \frac{\partial}{\partial t} f(0, t)\right] dt + \sigma \, d\widetilde{W}_t \tag{16.118}$$

16.3.2.3.3. *The price $P(t, T, r_t)$ in the Ho–Lee model* Equation (16.63) is specified for the Ho–Lee model. For this purpose, it is necessary to compute the quantity $A(t, T)$, since the value of $D(t, T)$ has already been determined in (16.108).

Equation (16.112) is considered, and expression (16.117) is substituted:

$$A(t, T) = \int_t^T \left[\frac{\sigma^2}{2}(T - s)^2 - \left[\sigma^2 s + \frac{\partial}{\partial s} f(0, s)\right](T - s)\right] ds$$

Simplifying, one has

$$A(t, T) = \int_t^T \left[\frac{\sigma^2}{2}(T^2 - 2Ts + s^2) - \left[\sigma^2 s + \frac{\partial}{\partial s} f(0, s)\right](T - s)\right] ds$$

then rewriting the integral as the summation of two different integrals, ie,

$$A(t, T) = \underbrace{\int_t^T \frac{\sigma^2}{2}(T^2 - 2Ts + s^2) - \sigma^2(sT - s^2) \, ds}_{\text{1st integral}} - \underbrace{\int_t^T \frac{\partial}{\partial s} f(0, s)(T - s) \, ds}_{\text{2nd integral}}$$

$$\tag{16.119}$$

For the first integral, one has

$$\int_t^T \frac{\sigma^2}{2}(T^2 - 2Ts + s^2) - \sigma^2(sT - s^2) \, ds$$

$$= \sigma^2 \left[\frac{T^2 s}{2} - \frac{Ts^2}{2} + \frac{s^3}{6} - \frac{Ts^2}{2} + \frac{s^3}{3}\right]_t^T$$

$$= \sigma^2 \left[T^2 \frac{(T - t)}{2} - T \frac{(T^2 - t^2)}{2} + \frac{(T^3 - t^3)}{6} - T \frac{(T^2 - t^2)}{2} + \frac{(T^3 - t^3)}{3}\right]$$

$$= \sigma^2 \left[T^2 \frac{(T - t)}{2} - T(T^2 - t^2) + \frac{(T^3 - t^3)}{2}\right]$$

$$= \sigma^2 \left[T^2 \frac{(T - t)}{2} - T(T^2 - t^2) + \frac{(T - t)^3 + 3tT^2 - 3t^2 T}{2}\right]$$

$$= \sigma^2 \left[T^2 \frac{(T - t)}{2} - T(T - t)(T + t) + \frac{(T - t)^2(T - t) + 3tT(T - t)}{2}\right]$$

$$= \sigma^2 \left[T^2 \frac{(T-t)}{2} - (T-t)(T^2 + tT) + \frac{(T^2 + t^2 - 2tT)(T-t) + 3tT(T-t)}{2} \right]$$

$$= \sigma^2 (T-t) \left[\frac{T^2}{2} - T^2 - tT + \frac{T^2}{2} - tT + \frac{t^2}{2} + \frac{3}{2}tT \right]$$

$$= \sigma^2 (T-t) \left[-\frac{tT}{2} + \frac{t^2}{2} \right]$$

$$= \frac{\sigma^2}{2} t(T-t)(t-T)$$

$$= -\frac{\sigma^2}{2} t(T-t)^2$$

Then the first integral can be written as

$$\underbrace{\int_t^T \frac{\sigma^2}{2}(T^2 - 2Ts + s^2) - \sigma^2(sT - s^2)\, ds}_{1^{\text{st}}\text{ integral}} = -\frac{\sigma^2}{2} t(T-t)^2 \qquad (16.120)$$

For the second integral, one has

$$\int_t^T \frac{\partial}{\partial s} f(0,s)(T-s)\, ds = \int_t^T \frac{\partial}{\partial s} f(0,s) \cdot T\, ds - \int_t^T \frac{\partial}{\partial s} f(0,s) \cdot s\, ds$$

$$= T \int_t^T \frac{\partial}{\partial s} f(0,s)\, ds - \int_t^T \frac{\partial}{\partial s} f(0,s) \cdot s\, ds$$

$$= T[f(0,T) - f(0,t)] - \int_t^T \frac{\partial}{\partial s} f(0,s) \cdot s\, ds$$

$$= Tf(0,T) - Tf(0,t) - \int_t^T \frac{\partial}{\partial s} f(0,s) \cdot s\, ds$$

Integrating by parts (see Criterion 5.1) for the second addend, one has

$$\int_t^T \frac{\partial}{\partial s} f(0,s)(T-s)\, ds$$

$$= Tf(0,T) - Tf(0,t) - \left[[f(0,T) \cdot T - f(0,t) \cdot t] - \int_t^T f(0,s)\, ds \right]$$

$$= Tf(0,T) - Tf(0,t) - Tf(0,T) + tf(0,t) + \int_t^T f(0,s)\, ds$$

$$= -Tf(0,t) + tf(0,t) + \int_t^T f(0,s)\, ds$$

$$= -(T-t)f(0,t) + \int_t^T f(0,s)\, ds$$

Then the second integral can be written as

$$\underbrace{\int_t^T \frac{\partial}{\partial s} f(0, s)(T - s) \, ds}_{\text{2nd integral}} = -(T - t)f(0, t) + \int_t^T f(0, s) \, ds \qquad (16.121)$$

Substituting (16.120) and (16.121) in (16.119), one obtains

$$A(t, T) = -\frac{\sigma^2}{2} t(T - t)^2 + (T - t) \cdot f(0, T) - \int_t^T f(0, s) \, ds$$

Substituting expression (16.17) in the last addend, one has

$$A(t, T) = -\frac{\sigma^2}{2} t(T - t)^2 + (T - t) \cdot f(0, T) + \ln P(0, T, r_0)$$

and, using (16.15), one has

$$A(t, T) = -\frac{\sigma^2}{2} t(T - t)^2 + (T - t) \cdot \left[-\frac{\partial \ln P(0, T, r_0)}{\partial T} \right] + \ln P(0, T, r_0)$$

then

$$A(t, T) = -\frac{\sigma^2}{2} t(T - t)^2 - (T - t) \cdot \frac{\partial \ln P(0, T, r_0)}{\partial T} + \ln P(0, T, r_0) \qquad (16.122)$$

The value of $P(t, T, r_t)$, in the form (16.63), is explicitly derived for the Ho–Lee model. Finally, substituting (16.122) and (16.108) one obtains

$$P(t, T, r_t) = \exp\left\{ -\frac{\sigma^2}{2} t(T - t)^2 - (T - t) \cdot \frac{\partial \ln P(0, T, r_0)}{\partial T} \right.$$
$$\left. + \ln P(0, T, r_0) - (T - t)r_t \right\} \qquad (16.123)$$

16.3.2.3.4. Ho–Lee model implementation The Ho–Lee model may also be implemented in a discrete form, via the construction of a recombining binomial tree. Obviously, this model describes in every instant the behaviour of the instantaneous spot rate.

Remark 16.3. If analysed at time zero, the instantaneous spot rate at a moment after time zero defines the instantaneous forward rate.

Notation 16.2. In the following, the instantaneous forward rates will be denoted as the instantaneous spot rates, since the narrative is made with reference to the node of the tree.

The concept of instant time is left aside to refer to the one-period time represented by the step of the binomial tree. We may say that this model describes the one-period behaviour of the spot rate at any node of the tree. Or, if the rate is analysed at time zero, it describes the one-period behaviour of the forward rate.

In the following, a description of the Ho–Lee model implementation process on a spreadsheet is given, considering, first, one volatility value only for the whole reference period and, then, different values of the same time horizon.

16.3.2.3.4.1. Construction of the constant volatility tree Given an initial term structure (or *initial yield*) defined as $r(0, 1), r(0, 2), r(0, 3), \ldots, r(0, n)$ (see Definition 16.3) corresponding to a sequence of prices (or *"initial price"*) computed via expression (16.2), the Ho–Lee model generates a sequence of forward rates, ie, one-period maturity rates with respect to the different time periods, given a term structure of spot interest rates observed on the market.

A graphical example of the binomial tree generated by the Ho–Lee model is shown in Figure 16.1 where every node corresponds to a forward interest rate with maturity $1dt$.

This model determines different forward rates r_t^i (forward rate at state i at time t) via computing a median rate $\hat{r}_t$ which is exactly equal to the median value of the forward rates r_t^i at each node of the binomial tree for each state.

Proposition 16.8. *The relation between $\hat{r}_t$ and the forward rates r_t^i at the nodes of the tree is given by*

$$
\begin{aligned}
r_t^i = r_u = \hat{r}_t + i \cdot u \quad \text{if the movement is upward} \\
r_t^{-i} = r_d = \hat{r}_t + i \cdot d \quad \text{if the movement is downward}
\end{aligned}
\tag{16.124}
$$

because the model assumes that the (vertical) distance between the nodes is constant and equal to u (with $u = -d$) at the same moment.

Proposition 16.9. *The probability of an upward movement on the tree is the same as a downward movement:*

$$
p = (1 - p) = 0.5
\tag{16.125}
$$

Proposition 16.10. *The rate variance generated by the binomial tree at each state is as*

$$
\text{VAR}(r_t^i) = p(1 - p)(r_u - r_d)^2
\tag{16.126}
$$

Figure 16.1 Graphical example of the binomial tree generated by the Ho–Lee model.

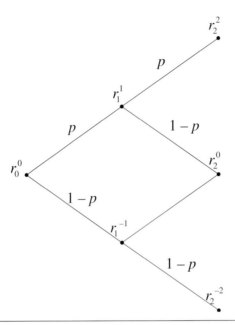

Proof. One has

$$
\begin{aligned}
\mathrm{VAR}(r_t^i) &= E\big((r_t^i)^2\big) - \big(E(r_t^i)\big)^2 \\
&= [p(r_u)^2 + (1-p)(r_d)^2] - [p(r_u) + (1-p)(r_d)]^2 \\
&= p(r_u)^2 + (1-p)(r_d)^2 - p^2(r_u)^2 - (1-p)^2(r_d)^2 - 2p(1-p)r_u r_d \\
&= p(r_u)^2 + (r_d)^2 - p(r_d)^2 - p^2(r_u)^2 - (r_d)^2 - p^2(r_d)^2 + 2p(r_d)^2 \\
&\quad - 2pr_u r_d + 2p^2 r_u r_d \\
&= p(r_u)^2 + p(r_d)^2 - p^2(r_u)^2 - p^2(r_d)^2 - 2pr_u r_d + 2p^2 r_u r_d \\
&= p[(r_u)^2 + (r_d)^2 - p(r_u)^2 - p(r_d)^2 - 2r_u r_d + 2pr_u r_d] \quad \text{(factorising } p) \\
&= p[((r_u)^2 + (r_d)^2 - 2r_u r_d) - p((r_u)^2 + (r_d)^2 - 2r_u r_d)]
\end{aligned}
$$

one recalls a perfect square and one obtains (16.126). □

Proposition 16.11. *The value of u to build the binomial tree is*

$$
u = \sigma\sqrt{dt} = -d \tag{16.127}
$$

Proof. Under (16.126), the variance of the forward rate generated by the binomial tree is

$$\text{VAR}(r_t^i) = p(1 - p)(r_u - r_d)^2$$

considering that the variance of (16.103), by construction, is equal to

$$\text{VAR}(r_t^i) = \sigma^2\, dt$$

by equating these quantities, one has

$$p(1 - p)(r_u - r_d)^2 = \sigma^2\, dt$$

Then, under Proposition 16.9, one has

$$p(1 - p)(r_u - r_d)^2 = \left(\tfrac{1}{2}\right)^2 (r_t^i - r_t^{-i})^2 = \sigma^2\, dt$$

and, under Proposition 16.8, one has

$$\tfrac{1}{2}(\hat{r}_t + u - \hat{r}_t - d) = \sigma\sqrt{dt}$$
$$\tfrac{1}{2}(u - d) = \sigma\sqrt{dt}$$
$$\tfrac{1}{2}(u + u) = \sigma\sqrt{dt}$$

hence, the value of u is derived:

$$u = \sigma\sqrt{dt} \qquad\qquad \square$$

The binomial tree is built by using the forward induction method based on five recursive steps, plus a final step merely necessary to verify whether the number of the tree fits the initial term structure.

(1) Determination of the discount factors corresponding to the interest rates generated by the tree.
(2) Determination of Arrow–Debreu prices for each discount factor.
(3) Determination of the bond value implied in the term structure of the tree.
(4) Computation of the median rates.
(5) Computation of the median rates corresponding to each tree node.
(6) Verification of the model fit to the term structure.

(1) *Determination of the discount factors corresponding to the interest rates generated by the tree*

Any rate found on any node of the tree corresponds to a discount factor relative to the same period; the relation which binds any rate to its discount

Figure 16.2 Graphical example of the binomial tree generated by the Ho–Lee model – the discount factors.

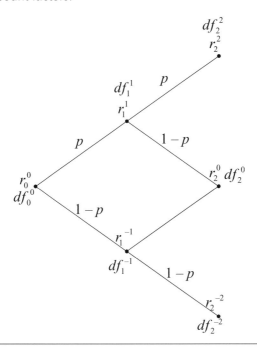

factor is (see Figure 16.2)

$$df_t^i = e^{-r_t^i \times dt} \tag{16.128}$$

where:

- df_t^i denotes the discount factor at time t at node i;
- r_t^i is the rate of the binomial tree for to the same node.

(2) *Determination of Arrow–Debreu prices for each discount factor*
Arrow–Debreu prices at each node represent, in a 2^Ω dimension space, the risk-neutral probability of reaching that node via all of the possible paths drawn by the binomial tree. This happens because:

- these prices are computed as the current value of an asset which pays off one if a certain state i occurs at time t, or zero in every other state;
- the current value of the asset is broken down into as many components of the same quantitative amount.

Figure 16.3 Graphical example of the binomial tree generated by the Ho–Lee model – the Arrow–Debreu prices.

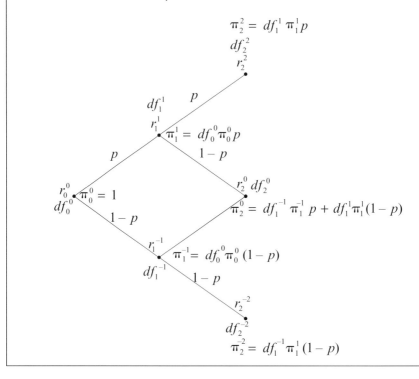

The first observation allows one to shift from a measure space to a probability space, while the second provides that such probability measure is risk-neutral.

Hence, in each state (i, t), the Arrow–Debreu price is equal to π_t^i:

$$\pi_t^i = p\pi_{t-1}^{i-1} df_{t-1}^{i-1} + (1 - p)\pi_{t-1}^{i+1} df_{t-1}^{i+1} \qquad (16.129)$$

where $p = (1 - p) = 0.5$.

In (16.129) the current value of the asset with payoff one is the result of the Arrow–Debreu price multiplied by the discount factor, while the decomposition into two equal components is the product of p by $(1 - p)$ (see Figure 16.3).

(3) *Determination of the bond value implied in the term structure of the tree*
By construction, given a reference time period $(t = 1, 2, 3, \ldots, t)$, the summation of the Arrow–Debreu prices computed on each node of the tree structure at time t, represents the price (at time zero) of a zero-coupon bond with maturity t.

Generalising, once the Arrow–Debreu prices are known, the zero-coupon bond values corresponding to the same maturity (t) are obtained by using the following relation:

$$P_0(t) = \sum_{i=-t}^{t} \pi_t^i \tag{16.130}$$

In Figure 16.3:

- at time $t = 0 \Rightarrow P_0(0) = \pi_0^0$;
- at time $t = 1 \Rightarrow P_0(1) = \pi_1^1 + \pi_1^{-1}$;
- at time $t = 2 \Rightarrow P_0(2) = \pi_2^2 + \pi_2^0 + \pi_2^{-2}$.

(4) *Computation of the median rates*

The median rates represent the output of this model. They represent the median forward rates of the tree, with duration $1dt$. They correspond to each sub-period which composes the reference time horizon.

Proposition 16.12. *The median rate in the Ho–Lee model is equal to:*

$$\hat{r}_t = \frac{\ln\left[\sum_{i=-t}^{t} \pi_t^i e^{-i \times u \times dt}\right] - \ln[P_0(t+1)]}{dt} \tag{16.131}$$

Proof. The demonstration is made by induction. It is demonstrated that this formula is valid for $t = 1$, then for $t = 2$, for $t = n - 1$ and, hence, for $t = n$.

The first median rate $(\hat{r}_0)$, or the median rate for time period $[0,1]$ coincides with the first rate of the yield curve just because, since it is located at the root of the binomial tree, it is unique.

The second median rate $(\hat{r}_1)$, for time $[1, 2]$, just like all of the successive median rates, is computed on the basis of the zero-coupon bond price obtained by the summation of the Arrow–Debreu prices (see formula (16.130)) corresponding to the successive time instant $(t = 2)$. This because, under (16.130), one knows that

$$P_0(2) = \sum_{i=-2}^{2} \pi_2^i = \pi_2^{-2} + \pi_2^0 + \pi_2^2 \tag{16.132}$$

under (16.129), one has

$$\pi_2^{-2} = (1 - p)\pi_1^{-1} df_1^{-1}$$
$$\pi_2^0 = p\pi_1^{-1} df_1^{-1} + (1 - p)\pi_1^1 df_1^1$$
$$\pi_2^2 = p\pi_1^1 df_1^1$$

and, then, under (16.128), one has

$$\pi_2^{-2} = (1 - p)\pi_1^{-1} e^{-r_1^{-1} dt} \tag{16.133}$$

$$\pi_2^0 = p\pi_1^{-1} e^{-r_1^{-1} dt} + (1 - p)\pi_1^1 e^{-r_1^1 dt} \tag{16.134}$$

$$\pi_2^2 = p\pi_1^1 e^{-r_1^1 dt} \tag{16.135}$$

Substituting (16.133), (16.134) and (16.135) in (16.132), one obtains

$$P_0(2) = (1-p)\pi_1^{-1}e^{-r_1^{-1}dt} + p\pi_1^{-1}e^{-r_1^{-1}dt} + (1-p)\pi_1^1 e^{-r_1^1 dt} + p\pi_1^1 e^{-r_1^1 dt}$$
$$= \pi_1^{-1}e^{-r_1^{-1}dt} + \pi_1^1 e^{-r_1^1 dt}$$

and, under Proposition 16.8, one has

$$P_0(2) = \pi_1^{-1}e^{-\hat{r}_1 dt}e^{-d\,dt} + \pi_1^1 e^{-\hat{r}_1 dt}e^{-u\,dt}$$

Factorising and multiplying both members by the same quantity $e^{\hat{r}_1}$, one obtains

$$e^{\hat{r}_1 dt}P_0(2) = \pi_1^{-1}e^{-d\,dt} + \pi_1^1 e^{-u\,dt}$$

applying the logarithm, one has

$$\hat{r}_1\,dt + \ln[P_0(2)] = \ln[\pi_1^{-1}e^{-d\,dt} + \pi_1^1 e^{-u\,dt}]$$

hence

$$\hat{r}_1 = \frac{\ln[\pi_1^{-1}e^{-d\,dt} + \pi_1^1 e^{-u\,dt}] - \ln[P_0(2)]}{dt}$$

or, since $d = -u$,

$$\hat{r}_1 = \frac{\ln[\pi_1^{-1}e^{u\,dt} + \pi_1^1 e^{-u\,dt}] - \ln[P_0(2)]}{dt} \tag{16.136}$$

The median rate of the successive time instant $(t = 2)$ computed by using the same procedure, will be equal to

$$P_0(3) = \sum_{i=-3}^{3} \pi_3^i = \pi_3^{-3} + \pi_3^{-1} + \pi_3^1 + \pi_3^3 \tag{16.137}$$

under (16.129), one has

$$\pi_3^{-3} = (1-p)\pi_2^{-2}\,df_2^{-2}$$
$$\pi_3^{-1} = p\pi_2^{-2}\,df_2^{-2} + (1-p)\pi_2^0\,df_2^0$$
$$\pi_3^1 = p\pi_2^0\,df_2^0 + (1-p)\pi_2^2\,df_2^2$$
$$\pi_3^3 = p\pi_2^2\,df_2^2$$

and, under (16.128), one obtains

$$\pi_3^{-3} = (1-p)\pi_2^{-2}e^{-r_2^{-2}dt} \tag{16.138}$$
$$\pi_3^{-1} = p\pi_2^{-2}e^{-r_2^{-2}dt} + (1-p)\pi_2^0 e^{-r_2^0 dt} \tag{16.139}$$
$$\pi_3^1 = p\pi_2^0 e^{-r_2^0 dt} + (1-p)\pi_2^2 e^{-r_2^2 dt} \tag{16.140}$$
$$\pi_3^3 = p\pi_2^2 e^{-r_2^2 dt} \tag{16.141}$$

Substituting (16.138), (16.139), (16.140) and (16.141) in (16.137), one obtains

$$P_0(3) = (1-p)\pi_2^{-2}e^{-r_2^{-2}\,dt} + p\pi_2^{-2}e^{-r_2^{-2}\,dt} + (1-p)\pi_2^0 e^{-r_2^0\,dt} + p\pi_2^0 e^{-r_2^0\,dt}$$
$$+ (1-p)\pi_2^2 e^{-r_2^2\,dt} + p\pi_2^2 e^{-r_2^2\,dt}$$

Simplifying, one has

$$P_0(3) = \pi_2^{-2}e^{-r_2^{-2}\,dt} + \pi_2^0 e^{-r_2^0\,dt} + \pi_2^2 e^{-r_2^2\,dt}$$

and, under Proposition 16.8, one has

$$P_0(3) = \pi_2^{-2}e^{-(\hat{r}_2-2d)\,dt} + \pi_2^0 e^{-(\hat{r}_2)\,dt} + \pi_2^2 e^{-(\hat{r}_2+2u)\,dt}$$

Factorising and multiplying both members by the same quantity $e^{\hat{r}_2}$, one obtains

$$e^{\hat{r}_2\,dt}P_0(2) = \pi_2^{-2}e^{2d\cdot dt} + \pi_2^0 e^{0\,dt} + \pi_2^2 e^{-2u\cdot dt}$$

applying the logarithm, one has

$$\hat{r}_2\,dt + \ln[P_0(2)] = \ln[\pi_2^{-2}e^{2d\cdot dt} + \pi_2^0 e^{0\,dt} + \pi_2^2 e^{-2u\cdot dt}]$$

hence

$$\hat{r}_2 = \frac{\ln[\pi_2^{-2}e^{-2d\times dt} + \pi_2^0 e^0 + \pi_2^2 e^{-2u\times dt}] - \ln[P_0(3)]}{dt}$$

or, since $d = -u$,

$$\hat{r}_2 = \frac{\ln[\pi_2^{-2}e^{2u\times dt} + \pi_2^0 e^0 + \pi_2^2 e^{-2u\times dt}] - \ln[P_0(3)]}{dt} \qquad (16.142)$$

By the same procedure, one may compute the median rate for the last time instant, ie, for $t = n - 1$: under formula (16.130), one knows that

$$P_0(n) = \sum_{i=-(n)}^{(n)} \pi_n^i = \pi_n^{-n} + \pi_n^{-n+2} + \pi_n^{-n+4} + \cdots + \pi_n^{n-2} + \pi_n^n \qquad (16.143)$$

under (16.129), one has

$$\pi_n^{-n} = (1-p)\pi_{n-1}^{-(n-1)}\,df_{n-1}^{-(n-1)}$$
$$\pi_n^{-n+2} = p\pi_{n-1}^{-(n-1)}df_{n-1}^{-(n-1)} + (1-p)\pi_{n-1}^{-(n-3)}\,df_{n-1}^{-(n-3)}$$
$$\vdots$$
$$\pi_n^n = p\pi_{n-1}^{n-1}\,df_{n-1}^{n-1}$$

and under (16.128), one has

$$\pi_n^{-n} = (1-p)\pi_{n-1}^{-(n-1)}e^{-r_{n-1}^{-(n-1)}}\,dt \tag{16.144}$$

$$\pi_n^{-n+2} = p\pi_{n-1}^{-(n-1)}e^{-r_{n-1}^{-(n-1)}}\,dt + (1-p)\pi_{n-1}^{-(n-3)}e^{-r_{n-1}^{-(n-3)}}\,dt \tag{16.145}$$

$$\vdots$$

$$\pi_n^n = p\pi_{n-1}^{n-1}e^{-r_{n-1}^{n-1}}\,dt \tag{16.146}$$

Substituting (16.144)–(16.146) in (16.143), one obtains

$$P_0(n) = (1-p)\pi_{n-1}^{-(n-1)}e^{-r_{n-1}^{-(n-1)}}\,dt + p\pi_{n-1}^{-(n-1)}e^{-r_{n-1}^{-(n-1)}}\,dt$$
$$+ (1-p)\pi_{n-1}^{-(n-3)}e^{-r_{n-1}^{-(n-3)}}\,dt + p\pi_{n-1}^{-(n-3)}e^{-r_{n-1}^{-(n-3)}}\,dt + \cdots$$
$$+ (1-p)\pi_{n-1}^{n-1}e^{-r_{n-1}^{n-1}}\,dt + p\pi_{n-1}^{n-1}e^{-r_{n-1}^{n-1}}\,dt$$

simplifying, one has

$$P_0(n) = \pi_{n-1}^{-(n-1)}e^{-r_{n-1}^{-(n-1)}}\,dt + \pi_{n-1}^{-(n-3)}e^{-r_{n-1}^{-(n-3)}}\,dt + \cdots + \pi_{n-1}^{n-1}e^{-r_{n-1}^{n-1}}\,dt \tag{16.147}$$

Under Proposition 16.8, factorising and simplifying, one obtains (see (16.147))

$$P_0(n) = \pi_{n-1}^{-(n-1)}e^{-\hat{r}_{n-1}\,dt}e^{-(n-1)d\,dt} + \pi_{n-1}^{-(n-3)}e^{-\hat{r}_{n-1}\,dt}e^{-(n-3)d\,dt} + \cdots$$
$$+ \pi_{n-1}^{n-1}e^{-\hat{r}_{n-1}\,dt}e^{-(n-1)u\,dt}$$

Factorising again and multiplying both members by the same quantity $e^{\hat{r}_{n-1}}$, one obtains

$$e^{\hat{r}_{n-1}\,dt}P_0(n) = \pi_{n-1}^{-(n-1)}e^{-(n-1)d\,dt} + \pi_{n-1}^{-(n-3)}e^{-(n-3)d\,dt} + \cdots + \pi_{n-1}^{n-1}e^{-(n-1)u\,dt}$$

Applying the logarithm, one has

$$\hat{r}_{n-1}\,dt + \ln[P_0(n)] = \ln[\pi_{n-1}^{-(n-1)}e^{-(n-1)d\,dt} + \pi_{n-1}^{-(n-3)}e^{-(n-3)d\,dt} + \cdots$$
$$+ \pi_{n-1}^{n-1}e^{-(n-1)u\,dt}]$$

hence

$$\hat{r}_{n-1} = \frac{1}{dt}\{\ln[\pi_{n-1}^{-(n-1)}e^{-(n-1)d\,dt} + \pi_{n-1}^{-(n-3)}e^{-(n-3)d\,dt} + \cdots + \pi_{n-1}^{n-1}e^{-(n-1)u\,dt}]$$
$$- \ln[P_0(n)]\}$$

Figure 16.4 Graphical example of the binomial tree generated by the Ho–Lee model – the median rates.

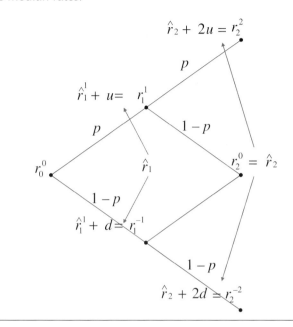

ie, since $d = -u$,

$$\hat{r}_{n-1} = \frac{\ln\left[\sum_{i=-(n-1)}^{(n-1)} \pi_{n-1}^i e^{-i \times u \times dt}\right] - \ln[P_0(n)]}{dt}$$

After demonstrating the validity of the median rate expression for $t = 1$, $t = 2$ and $t = n - 1$, by induction, one may generalise the median rate formula for $t = n$ as

$$\hat{r}_t = \frac{\ln\left[\sum_{i=-t}^{t} \pi_t^i e^{-i \times u \times dt}\right] - \ln[P_0(t + 1)]}{dt} \qquad \square$$

(5) *Determination of the forward rates corresponding to each tree node*
Once the median rate is known, it may be decomposed by using the relation in Proposition 16.8 to obtain the short-rate values corresponding to the different nodes of the binomial tree (see Figure 16.4).

(6) *Verification of the model fit to the term structure*
After the forward rate tree has been entirely built, it is possible to verify the computation made to build up the term structure generated by the model.

Figure 16.5 Graphical example of the binomial tree generated by the Ho–Lee model – the shifted Arrow–Debreu trees.

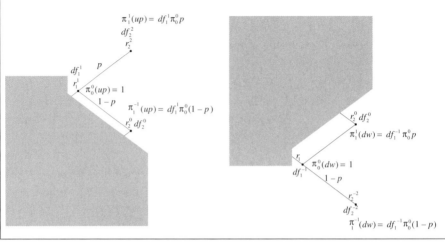

In order to do so, it must be verified that rate volatility derived from the model is perfectly matching to market rate volatility observed at any time t.

In order to verify that rate volatility generated by the model is constant and equal to market volatility, the following steps have to be followed.

(a) Determination of two Arrow–Debreu price binomial trees generated by an upward *shift* (known as *A.D.treeUp*) and by a downward *shift* (known as *A.D.treeDown*) with respect to the original Arrow–Debreu tree.
(b) Computation of the zero-coupon bond price implied in the trees *A.D.treeUp/Down*, referred to as $P_t^{up/down}$.
(c) Computation of the yields implied in the price $P_t^{up/down}$, referred to as $r_t^{up/down}$.
(d) Computation, at each node, of the volatility between r_t^{up} and r_t^{down}.
(e) Verification of matching to market volatility.

The construction of the *A.D.treeUp/Down* trees does not require the computation of a new sequence of median rates. The median rates and discount factors derived previously will be used (see Figure 16.5.

To determine $P_t^{up/down}$, formula (16.130) is applied.

To determine $r_t^{up/down}$, formula (16.3) is applied, which, here, becomes

$$r_t^{up/down} = -\frac{\ln P_t^{up/down}}{t} \tag{16.148}$$

Figure 16.6 Numerical example of the binomial tree generated by the Ho–Lee model – initial yield.

Time	0	1	2	3	4	5
Initial yield		3,89%	4,10%	4,30%	4,47%	4,62%

Figure 16.7 Numerical example of the binomial tree generated by the Ho–Lee model – initial ZCB prices.

Time	0	1	2	3	4	5
Initial yield		3,89%	4,10%	4,30%	4,47%	4,62%
Initial price		0,9618	0,9213	0,8790	0,836 2	0,7936

To determine the volatility between r_t^{up} and r_t^{down} at each node, (16.128) is used and, here, this becomes

$$\sigma = \frac{\sqrt{p(1-p)(r_t^{up} - r_t^{down})^2}}{\sqrt{dt}} \qquad (16.149)$$

Now, for any t, one may compute volatility and verify whether this is equivalent to input data.

In the following, an example is given on a spreadsheet of the recursive procedure used to construct the tree and of the steps described so far.

Example 16.1. Let an initial term structure be defined as the "initial yield" given on a five-year time horizon (see Figure 16.6) with its corresponding zero-coupon bond prices defined as the "initial price" (see Figure 16.7).

For example, for $t = 0$ and $T = 3$, the three-year maturity zero-coupon bond current value is computed as $P_0(3) = e^{-4.30\% \times 3} = 0.8790$.

First, the variables to support the construction of the tree are defined:

- T (five here) identifies the end of time horizon for the term structure;
- steps (five here) identifies the node number on the tree used to represent the term structure;
- dt (one here) identifies the time interval which characterises each step and is computed as $T/$steps;
- σ (0.58% here) is the term structure volatility;
- $u = -d$ (0.58% here) is computed as $\sigma\sqrt{dt}$ and is the quantity which links the median rates $\hat{r}_t$ to the forward rates r_t^i.

Figure 16.8 Numerical example of the binomial tree generated by the Ho–Lee model – computation of the first median rate.

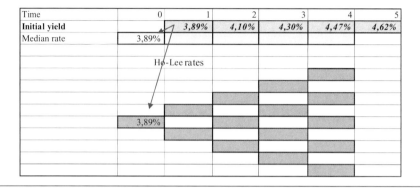

Figure 16.9 Numerical example of the binomial tree generated by the Ho–Lee model – computation of the first discount factor.

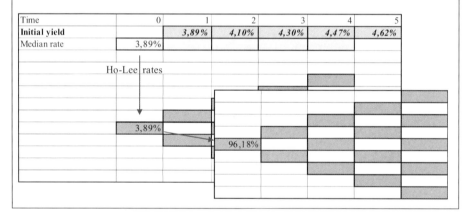

The first *median rate* $\hat{r}_0$ for time interval $[0, 1]$ coincides with the first rate of the *yield curve* r_0^0 because, since this is located at the base of the binomial tree, it is unique (see Figure 16.8).

Rate r_0^0, ie, the rate occurring at the first period (from time zero to time one) allows one to determine the discount factor for time interval $[0,1]$, ie, df_0^0, via the relation $df_0^0 = e^{-\hat{r}_0 \times dt} = e^{-3.89\% \times 1} = 96.18\%$ (see Figure 16.9).

Knowing the discount factor, it becomes possible to derive the Arrow–Debreu prices. In the first period, the Arrow–Debreu prices corresponding to

Figure 16.10 Numerical example of the binomial tree generated by the Ho–Lee model – computation of the Arrow–Debreu prices.

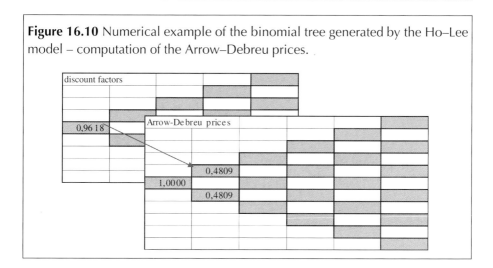

the two first nodes of the binomial tree result in (see Figure 16.10)

$$\pi_1^{-1} = (1-p)\pi_0^0\, df_0^0 = 0.5 \times 1 \times 0.9618 = 0.4809$$
$$\pi_1^1 = p\pi_0^0\, df_0^0 = 0.5 \times 1 \times 0.9618 = 0.4809$$

It then becomes possible to determine the bond value implied in the term structure of the tree. The two Arrow–Debreu prices give the one-period zero-coupon bond current value in correspondence with the two equiprobable scenarios, with probabilities p and $(1-p)$:

$$P_0(1) = \pi_1^1 + \pi_1^{-1} = 0.4809 + 0.4809 = 0.9618$$

which matches exactly with the zero-coupon bond implied in the input term structure (see Figure 16.11).

Given the Arrow–Debreu prices and the zero-coupon bond value relative to the next maturity $P_0(2)$ (computed on the market term structure), via the relation (16.136) one may obtain the second median rate value, $\hat{r}_1$, for period $[1, 2]$, ie,

$$\hat{r}_1 = \frac{\ln(e^{-u \times dt}\pi_1^1 + e^{-d \times dt}\pi_1^{-1}) - \ln P_0(2)}{dt} \tag{16.136}$$

Here one has

$$\hat{r}_1 = \frac{\ln(0.9942 \times 0.4809 + 1.0058 \times 0.4809) - \ln(0.9213)}{1} = 4.304$$

This computation may be performed on a spreadsheet as shown in Figure 16.12, where, for convenience, a vector which computes the values of the quantity

Figure 16.11 Numerical example of the binomial tree generated by the Ho–Lee model – computation of ZCB price implicit in the lattice.

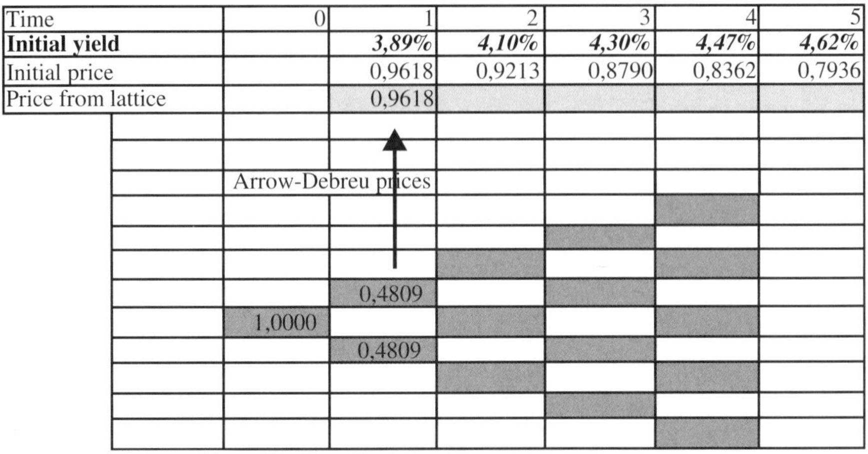

Time	0	1	2	3	4	5
Initial yield		*3,89%*	*4,10%*	*4,30%*	*4,47%*	*4,62%*
Initial price		0,9618	0,9213	0,8790	0,8362	0,7936
Price from lattice		0,9618				

Arrow-Debreu prices

0,4809

1,0000

0,4809

Figure 16.12 Numerical example of the binomial tree generated by the Ho–Lee model – computation of the second median rate.

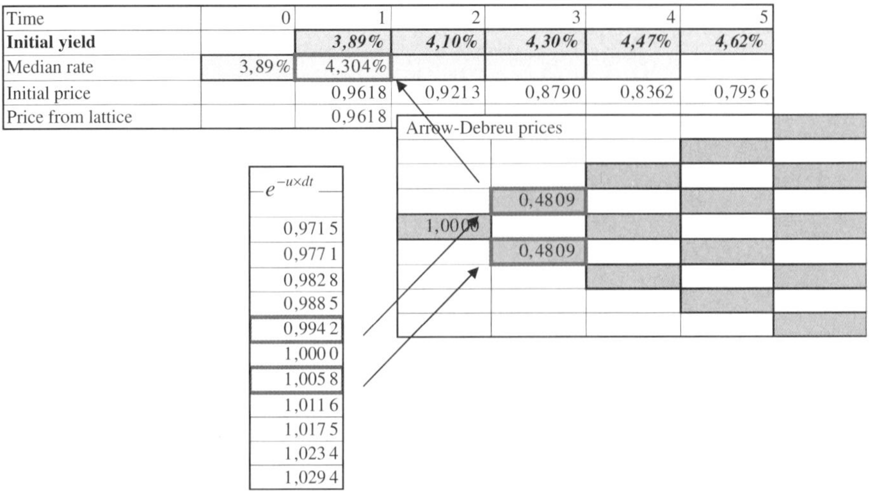

Time	0	1	2	3	4	5
Initial yield		*3,89%*	*4,10%*	*4,30%*	*4,47%*	*4,62%*
Median rate	3,89%	4,304%				
Initial price		0,9618	0,9213	0,8790	0,8362	0,7936
Price from lattice		0,9618				

Arrow-Debreu prices

$e^{-u \times dt}$

0,9715
0,9771
0,9828
0,9885
0,9942
1,0000
1,0058
1,0116
1,0175
1,0234
1,0294

1,0000

0,4809

0,4809

Figure 16.13 Numerical example of the binomial tree generated by the Ho–Lee model – computation of the Ho–Lee rates.

Time	0	1	2	3	4	5
Initial yield		*3,89%*	*4,10%*	*4,30%*	*4,47%*	*4,62%*
Median rate	3,89%	4,304 %				
Initial price		0,9618	0,9213	0,8790	0,8362	0,7936
Price from lattice		0,9618				
		Ho Lee rates				
		4,88%				
	3,89%					
		3,73%				

$e^{-u \times dt}$ for each dt has been created. Then, the forward rates are determined for each node of the tree, ie, those for period $[1, 2]$, or ($t = 1$) (see Figure 16.13):

$$r_1^1 = \hat{r}_1 + 1 \times u = 4.304 + 1 \times 0.0058 = 4.88\%$$
$$r_1^{-1} = \hat{r}_1 + 1 \times d = 4.304 + 1 \times (-0.0058) = 3.73\%$$

Steps described at points (1)–(5) are repeated to derive $\hat{r}_2$ and the corresponding forward rates. Actually, knowing r_1^1 and r_1^{-1}, one may determine the corresponding discount factors (see Figure 16.14):

$$df_1^{-1} = e^{-r_1^{-1} \times dt} = e^{-3.73\%} = 0.9634$$
$$df_1^1 = e^{-r_1^1 \times dt} = e^{-4.88\%} = 0.9523$$

and, then, the corresponding Arrow–Debreu prices (see Figure 16.15):

$$\pi_2^{-2} = (1 - p)\pi_1^{-1} df_1^{-1} = 0.5 \times 0.4809 \times 0.9634 = 0.2317$$
$$\pi_2^0 = p\pi_1^{-1} df_1^{-1} + (1 - p)\pi_1^1 df_1^1 = 0.5 \times 0.4809 \times 0.9634$$
$$+ 0.5 \times 0.4809 \times 0.9523 = 0.4607$$
$$\pi_2^2 = p\pi_1^1 df_1^1 = 0.5 \times 0.4809 \times 0.9523 = 0.2290$$

then one may determine the bond value inside the term *structure* of the tree which exactly matches the zero-coupon bond implied in the input term

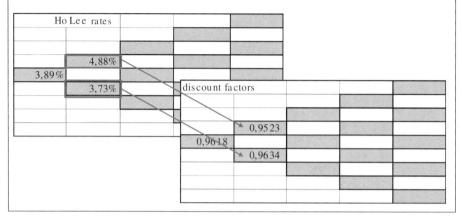

Figure 16.14 Numerical example of the binomial tree generated by the Ho–Lee model – computation of the discount factor.

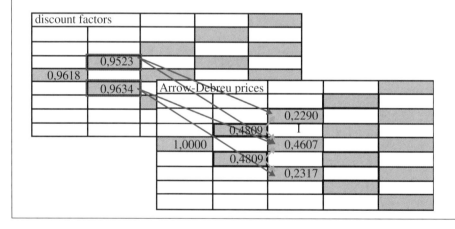

Figure 16.15 Numerical example of the binomial tree generated by the Ho–Lee model – computation of the Arrow–Debreu prices.

structure (see Figure 16.16), ie,

$$P_0(2) = \pi_2^2 + \pi_2^0 + \pi_2^{-2}$$
$$P_0(2) = 0.4607 + 0.2290 + 0.2317 = 0.9213$$

Given the Arrow–Debreu prices and the zero-coupon bond value corresponding to the next maturity $P_0(2)$ (computed on the market term structure), by using relation (16.142), one may derive the second median rate value $\hat{r}_2$

Figure 16.16 Numerical example of the binomial tree generated by the Ho–Lee model – computation of ZCB price implicit in the lattice.

Time	0	1	2	3	4	5
Initial yield		*3,89%*	*4,10%*	*4,30%*	*4,47%*	*4,62%*
Median rate	3,89%	4,30%				
Initial price		0,9618	0,9213	0,8790	0,8362	0,7936
price from lattice		0,9618	0,9213			

Arrow-Debreu prices				
		0,2290		
	0,4809			
1,0000		0,4607		
	0,4809			
		0,2317		

corresponding to period [2,3]. Here, one has

$$\hat{r}_2 = \frac{\ln(e^{-2\times0.0058}0.2290 + 0.4607 + e^{-2\times(-0.0058)}0.2317) - \ln(0.8790)}{1} = 4.70$$

This computation may be performed on a spreadsheet as shown in Figure 16.17, where, for convenience, a vector which computes the values of the quantity $e^{-u\times dt}$ for each dt has been created.

Then, the forward rates are determined for each node of the tree (see Figure 16.18), ie, those for period [2, 3], or ($t = 2$):

$$r_2^2 = \hat{r}_2 + 2 \times u = 4.7 + 2 \times 0.0058 = 5.86\%$$
$$r_2^{-2} = \hat{r}_2 + 2 \times d = 4.7 + 2 \times (-0.0058) = 3.55\%$$

Steps described at points (1)–(5) are repeated to derive the whole tree in order to generate the rates corresponding to each maturity.

After completing the tree, one may verify the model fit to the term structure, ie, test that the volatility of the rates generated by the tree matches those observed at the beginning.

Next comes the construction of the two Arrow–Debreu binomial trees, corresponding to an upward and a downward shift, respectively called *A.D.treeUp* and *A.D.treeDown* (see Figure 16.19).

Figure 16.17 Numerical example of the binomial tree generated by the Ho–Lee model – computation of the median rate.

Time	0	1	2	3	4	5
Initial yield		*3,89%*	*4,10%*	*4,30%*	*4,47%*	*4,62%*
Median rate	3,89%	4,30%	4,70%			
Initial price		0,9618	0,9213	0,8790	0,8362	0,7936
Price from lattice		0,9618	0,9213			

Arrow-Debreu prices					$-e^{-u \times dt}$
		0,2290			0,9715
	0,4809				0,9771
1,0000		0,4607			0,9828
	0,4809				0,9885
		0,2317			0,9942
					1,0000
					1,0058
					1,0116
					1,0175
					1,0234
					1,0294

Figure 16.18 Numerical example of the binomial tree generated by the Ho–Lee model – computation of the Ho–Lee rates.

Time	0	1	2	3	4	5
Initial yield		*3,89%*	*4,10%*	*4,30%*	*4,47%*	*4,62%*
Median rate	3,89%	4,30%	4,70%			
Initial price		0,9618	0,9213	0,8790	0,8362	0,7936
Price from lattice		0,9618	0,9213			

		Ho Lee rates				
			5,86%			
		4,88%				
	3,89%		4,70%			
		3,73%				
			3,55%			

Figure 16.19 Numerical example of the binomial tree generated by the Ho–Lee model – the shifted Arrow–Debreu trees.

0	1	2	3	4	5
	Shift up				0,0486
				0,1049	
			0,2245		0,1980
		0,4762		0,3185	
	1,0000		0,4517		0,3022
		0,4762		0,3222	
			0,2271		0,2050
				0,1086	
					0,0521

0	1	2	3	4	5
	Shift down				
					0,0509
				0,1086	
			0,2298		0,2074
		0,4817		0,3298	
	1,0000		0,4623		0,3165
		0,4817		0,3336	
			0,2325		0,2147
				0,1125	
					0,0546

Figure 16.20 Numerical example of the binomial tree generated by the Ho–Lee model – the shifted ZCB price implicit in the lattice.

Time	0	1	2	3	4	5
Initial yield		*3,89%*	*4,10%*	*4,30%*	*4,47%*	*4,62%*
Price_up		1,0000	0,9523	0,9034	0,8543	0,8060
Price_dn		1,0000	0,9634	0,9245	0,8845	0,8442

Figure 16.21 Numerical example of the binomial tree generated by the Ho–Lee model – the shifted term structure implicit in the lattice.

Time	0	1	2	3	4	5
Initial yield		*3,89%*	*4,10%*	*4,30%*	*4,47%*	*4,62%*
Price_up		1,0000	0,9523	0,9034	0,8543	0,8060
Price_dn		1,0000	0,9634	0,9245	0,8845	0,8442
r_up			0,0488	0,0508	0,0525	0,0539
r_dn			0,0373	0,0392	0,0409	0,0424

The zero-coupon bond prices with respect to the upward and downward shift, also called $P_t^{up/down}$, are derived from the Arrow–Debreu prices computed as above (see Figure 16.20).

Formula (16.148) allows one to compute from zero-coupon bond the rates which represent the new term structure deriving from an upward or a downward shift, ie, $r_t^{up/down}$ (see Figure 16.21).

After completing the tree, one may verify the fit of the model to the term structure, ie, test whether the volatility of the rates generated by the tree matches those observed at the beginning.

Figure 16.22 Numerical example of the binomial tree generated by the Ho–Lee model – the full iterative procedure.

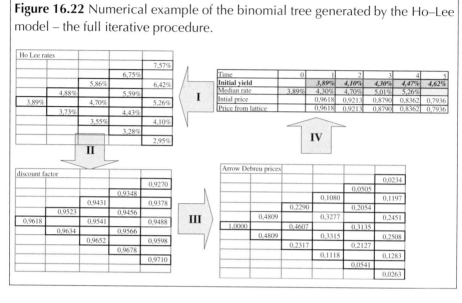

Example 16.2. Then, by formula (16.149) one may compute the volatility that will exactly match the initial term structure volatility, ie, for the second period, one will have

$$\sigma = \frac{\sqrt{p(1-p)(r_t^{\text{up}} - r_t^{\text{down}})^2}}{\sqrt{dt}} = \frac{\sqrt{0.5 \times 0.5(0.0488 - 0.0373)^2}}{\sqrt{1}} = 0.0058$$

Alternatively, the procedure described in steps (1)–(5) may be followed by using a second method on an Excel spreadsheet. There, it is assumed that the median rates are identified by matching the zero-coupon bond prices observed on the market with those computed by the Arrow–Debreu price model. This method, based on Excel solver, builds up the tree as the solution of a bounded optimisation problem.

The following is an example of this method.

Example 16.3. Figure 16.22 shows the setup of an Excel file by the recursive logic of the model.

After compiling the spreadsheet, the "solver" tool is launched. It will be set as in Figure 16.23, ie, as follows

- "Target cell": dt; this choice is not relevant to problem solution, it is important that the target cell contains a formula that makes the solver work properly;

Figure 16.23 Numerical example of the binomial tree generated by the Ho–Lee model – the full procedure as a bounded optimisation problem.

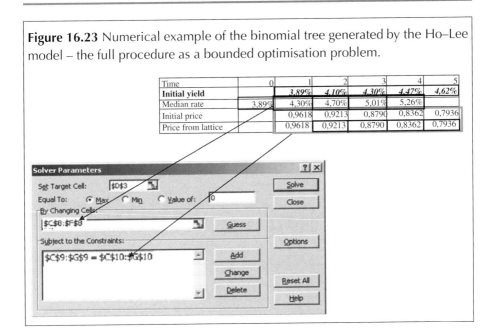

- "Changing cells": the median rate vector to be found;
- "Boundaries": matching between the zero-coupon bond price vectors observed on the market and those computed by the model via the Arrow–Debreu prices.

After launching the solver, the cells with the median rates will keep on varying until a solution has been determined, with the zero-coupon bond price vectors observed on the market matching those *computed by the model on the basis of the Arrow–Debreu prices*

At the end of this procedure, the tree is constructed. Hence, it is possible to verify the model fit to the term structure, ie, to verify that the volatility of the tree-generated rates exactly matches those observed at the beginning.

16.3.2.4. Hull–White model

16.3.2.4.1. Introduction In the Hull–White model, the parameters $\phi(r_t, t)$ and $\sigma(r_t, t)$ of SDE (16.19), which describes the instantaneous spot rate r_t under the original probability measure Q, are specified as follows:

$$dr_t = [\phi_t - ar_t] \, dt + \sigma \, dW_t \tag{16.150}$$

hence, under the risk-neutral probability measure P, one has

$$dr_t = [\bar{\phi}_t - ar_t] \, dt + \sigma \, d\widetilde{W}_t \tag{16.151}$$

where

$$\bar{\phi}_t = \phi_t - \lambda_t \sigma$$

The Cauchy problem is derived from this model. For this purpose, recall relations (16.77)–(16.80) derived for the Vasicek model.

One recalls (16.35), to be specified by using the partial derivatives in (16.78), (16.79) and (16.80) and the corresponding values of $\bar{\phi}$ and σ of the SDE (16.49) expressed in (16.151):

$$\left[\frac{\partial}{\partial t} C(t, T) - C(t, T) \frac{\partial}{\partial t} D(t, T) r_t \right] e^{-D(t,T)r_t} - [\bar{\phi}_t - a r_t] C(t, T) D(t, T)$$

$$\cdot e^{-D(t,T)r_t} + \frac{\sigma^2}{2} C(t, T) D^2(t, T) e^{-D(t,T)r_t} - r_t C(t, T) e^{-D(t,T)r_t} = 0$$

Dividing by $e^{-D(t,T)r_t}$ and factorising as necessary, one has

$$\left[\frac{\partial}{\partial t} C(t, T) - C(t, T) D(t, T) \bar{\phi}_t + \frac{\sigma^2}{2} C(t, T) D^2(t, T) \right]$$

$$- \left[\frac{\partial}{\partial t} D(t, T) - a D(t, T) + 1 \right] \cdot r_t \cdot C(t, T) = 0 \qquad (16.152)$$

Equation (16.152) is equivalent to the summation of the two addends which have to be equal to zero, ie,

$$\frac{\partial}{\partial t} C(t, T) - C(t, T) D(t, T) \bar{\phi}_t + \frac{\sigma^2}{2} C(t, T) D^2(t, T) = 0 \qquad (16.153)$$

$$1 - a D(t, T) + \frac{\partial}{\partial t} D(t, T) = 0 \qquad (16.154)$$

The final conditions analogous to (16.72) and (16.73) are given by (16.84) and (16.73) itself.

Finally, the Cauchy problem for the Hull–White model is composed by Equation (16.153) and (16.154) with contour conditions (16.73) and (16.84).

16.3.2.4.2. Arbitrage-free condition The arbitrage-free condition for the Hull–White model is, by construction and given the functional form of $P(t, T, r_t)$, analogous to that derived for the Vasicek model, ie, (16.86).

Quantities $(\partial/\partial T)D(t, T)$ and $(\partial/\partial T) \ln C(t, T)$ are now computed.

Concerning $(\partial/\partial T)D(t, T)$, the Cauchy problem given by Equation (16.154) and by the final condition inside (16.73) is solved, observing that (16.154) is identical to (16.83) for $a = \gamma$. One may then compute $D(t, T)$ and $(\partial/\partial T)D(t, T)$

specifying for $a = \gamma$ the expressions (16.90) and (16.91), ie,

$$D(t, T) = \frac{1}{a}(1 - e^{-a(T-t)}) \qquad (16.155)$$

$$\frac{\partial}{\partial T}D(t, T) = e^{-a(T-t)} \qquad (16.156)$$

Concerning $(\partial/\partial T) \ln C(t, T)$ the Cauchy problem is given by Equation (16.153) and the final condition by (16.73).

By using (16.155) in the last term, (16.153) becomes

$$\frac{\partial}{\partial t}C(t, T) - C(t, T)D(t, T)\bar{\phi}_t + \frac{\sigma^2}{2}C(t, T)\frac{(1 - e^{-a(T-t)})^2}{a^2} = 0$$

then

$$\frac{\partial}{\partial t}C(t, T) = C(t, T)D(t, T)\bar{\phi}_t - \frac{\sigma^2}{2}C(t, T)\frac{(1 - e^{-a(T-t)})^2}{a^2}$$

Dividing by $C(t, T)$, one has

$$\frac{(\partial/\partial t)C(t, T)}{C(t, T)} = D(t, T)\bar{\phi}_t - \frac{\sigma^2}{2}\frac{(1 - e^{-a(T-t)})^2}{a^2}$$

ie,

$$\frac{dC(t, T)}{C(t, T)} = \left(D(t, T)\bar{\phi}_t - \frac{\sigma^2}{2}\frac{(1 - e^{-a(T-t)})^2}{a^2}\right)dt$$

Integrating both terms, one obtains

$$\int_t^T \frac{dC(s, T)}{C(s, T)} = \int_t^T (D(t, T)\bar{\phi}_s - \frac{\sigma^2}{2}\frac{(1 - e^{-a(T-s)})^2}{a^2})ds$$

$$\ln C(T, T) - \ln C(t, T) = \int_t^T \bar{\phi}_s D(t, T)\, ds$$
$$- \frac{\sigma^2}{2}\int_t^T \frac{(1 - 2e^{-a(T-s)} + e^{-2a(T-s)})}{a^2}\, ds$$

By using (16.84), one has

$$\ln 1 - \ln C(t, T) = \int_t^T \bar{\phi}_s D(t, T)\, ds - \frac{\sigma^2}{2a^2}\int_t^T (1 - 2e^{-a(T-s)} + e^{-2a(T-s)})\, ds$$

Simplifying and solving the second integral, one has

$$- \ln C(t, T) = \int_t^T \bar{\phi}_s D(t, T)\, ds - \frac{\sigma^2}{2a^2}\left\{[s]_t^T + \int_t^T (-2e^{-a(T-s)} + e^{-2a(T-s)})\, ds\right\}$$

Changing sign, one has

$\ln C(t, T)$

$$= -\int_t^T \bar{\phi}_s D(t, T)\, ds + \frac{\sigma^2}{2a^2}\left\{[s]_t^T + \int_t^T \left(-2e^{-a(T-s)} + e^{-2a(T-s)}\right) ds\right\}$$

$$= -\int_t^T \bar{\phi}_s D(t, T)\, ds + \frac{\sigma^2}{2a^2}\left\{(T - t) + \int_t^T \left(-2e^{-a(T-s)} + e^{-2a(T-s)}\right) ds\right\}$$

$$= -\int_t^T \bar{\phi}_s D(t, T)\, ds + \frac{\sigma^2}{2a^2}(T - t) - \frac{\sigma^2}{a^2}\int_t^T e^{-a(T-s)}\, ds + \frac{\sigma^2}{2a^2}\int_t^T e^{-2a(T-s)}\, ds$$

(by multiplying and simplifying)

$$= -\int_t^T \bar{\phi}_s D(t, T)\, ds + \frac{\sigma^2}{2a^2}(T - t) - \frac{\sigma^2}{a^2}\left[\frac{1}{a}e^{-a(T-s)}\right]_t^T + \frac{\sigma^2}{2a^2}\int_t^T e^{-2a(T-s)}\, ds$$

$$= -\int_t^T \bar{\phi}_s D(t, T)\, ds + \frac{\sigma^2}{2a^2}(T - t) - \frac{\sigma^2}{a^2}\left[\frac{1}{a}e^{-a(T-T)} - \frac{1}{a}e^{-a(T-t)}\right]$$
$$+ \frac{\sigma^2}{2a^2}\int_t^T e^{-2a(T-s)}\, ds$$

$$= -\int_t^T \bar{\phi}_s D(t, T)\, ds + \frac{\sigma^2}{2a^2}(T - t) - \frac{\sigma^2}{a^2}\left[\frac{1}{a} - \frac{1}{a}e^{-a(T-t)}\right]$$
$$+ \frac{\sigma^2}{2a^2}\int_t^T e^{-2a(T-s)}\, ds \quad \text{(simplifying)}$$

$$= -\int_t^T \bar{\phi}_s D(t, T)\, ds + \frac{\sigma^2}{2a^2}(T - t) - \frac{\sigma^2}{a^2}\left[\frac{1}{a} - \frac{1}{a}e^{-a(T-t)}\right] + \frac{\sigma^2}{2a^2}\left[\frac{1}{2a}e^{-2a(T-s)}\right]_t^T$$

(integrating)

$$= -\int_t^T \bar{\phi}_s D(t, T)\, ds + \frac{\sigma^2}{2a^2}(T - t) - \frac{\sigma^2}{a^2}\left[\frac{1}{a} - \frac{1}{a}e^{-a(T-t)}\right]$$
$$+ \frac{\sigma^2}{2a^2}\left[\frac{1}{a}e^{-2a(T-T)} - \frac{1}{a}e^{-2a(T-t)}\right] \quad \text{(expanding)}$$

$$= -\int_t^T \bar{\phi}_s D(t, T)\, ds + \frac{\sigma^2}{2a^2}(T - t) - \frac{\sigma^2}{a^2}\left[\frac{1}{a} - \frac{1}{a}e^{-a(T-t)}\right]$$
$$+ \frac{\sigma^2}{2a^2}\left[\frac{1 - e^{-2a(T-t)}}{2a}\right] \quad \text{(simplifying)}$$

$$= -\int_t^T \bar{\phi}_s D(t, T)\, ds + \frac{\sigma^2}{2a^2}(T - t) - \frac{\sigma^2}{a^2}\left[\left[\frac{1}{a} - \frac{1}{a}e^{-a(T-t)}\right]\right.$$
$$\left. - \frac{1}{2} \cdot \frac{(1 - e^{-2a(T-t)})}{2a}\right] \quad \left(\text{factorising by } \frac{\sigma^2}{a^2}\right)$$

$$= -\int_t^T \bar{\phi}_s \frac{(1 - e^{-a(T-s)})}{a} \, ds + \frac{\sigma^2}{2a^2} (T - t)$$
$$- \frac{\sigma^2}{a^2} \left[\frac{(1 - e^{-a(T-t)})}{a} - \frac{1}{4} \cdot \frac{(1 - e^{-2a(T-t)})}{a} \right]$$

(using (16.155) and multiplying)

$$= -\int_t^T \bar{\phi}_s \frac{(1 - e^{-a(T-s)})}{a} \, ds + \frac{\sigma^2}{2a^2} (T - t)$$
$$- \frac{\sigma^2}{a^2} \left[\frac{(4 - 4e^{-a(T-t)} - 1 + e^{-2a(T-t)})}{4a} \right]$$

(by simplifying inside the square brackets)

$$= -\int_t^T \bar{\phi}_s \frac{(1 - e^{-a(T-s)})}{a} \, ds + \frac{\sigma^2}{2a^2} (T - t) - \frac{\sigma^2}{a^2} \left[\frac{(3 - 4e^{-a(T-t)} + e^{-2a(T-t)})}{4a} \right]$$

$$= -\int_t^T \bar{\phi}_s \frac{(1 - e^{-a(T-s)})}{a} \, ds + \frac{\sigma^2}{2a^2} (T - t)$$
$$- \frac{\sigma^2}{4a^2} \left[\frac{(2 + 1 - 2e^{-a(T-t)} - 2e^{-a(T-t)} + e^{-2a(T-t)})}{a} \right]$$

$$= -\int_t^T \bar{\phi}_s \frac{(1 - e^{-a(T-s)})}{a} \, ds + \frac{\sigma^2}{2a^2} (T - t)$$
$$- \frac{\sigma^2}{4a^2} \left[\frac{2(1 - e^{-a(T-t)})}{a} + \frac{(1 - 2e^{-a(T-t)} + e^{-2a(T-t)})}{a} \right]$$

$$= -\int_t^T \bar{\phi}_s \frac{(1 - e^{-a(T-s)})}{a} \, ds + \frac{\sigma^2}{2a^2} (T - t)$$
$$- \frac{\sigma^2}{2a^2} D(t, T) - \frac{\sigma^2}{4a^2} \left[\frac{(1 - 2e^{-a(T-t)} + e^{-2a(T-t)})}{a} \right] \quad \text{(using (16.155))}$$

$$= -\int_t^T \bar{\phi}_s \frac{(1 - e^{-a(T-s)})}{a} \, ds + \frac{\sigma^2}{2a^2} (T - t) - \frac{\sigma^2}{2a^2} D(t, T)$$
$$- \frac{\sigma^2}{4a} \left[\left(\frac{1 - e^{-a(T-t)}}{a} \right)^2 \right]$$

$$= -\int_t^T \bar{\phi}_s D(s, T) \, ds + \frac{\sigma^2}{2a^2} (T - t) - \frac{\sigma^2}{2a^2} D(t, T) - \frac{\sigma^2}{4a} D(t, T)^2$$

(using (16.155) again)

thus

$$\ln C(t, T) = -\int_t^T \bar{\phi}_s D(s, T) \, ds + \frac{\sigma^2}{2a^2} (T - t) - \frac{\sigma^2}{2a^2} D(t, T) - \frac{\sigma^2}{4a} D(t, T)^2$$
$$(16.157)$$

Differentiating with respect to T, one has

$$
\begin{aligned}
\frac{\partial}{\partial T} \ln C(t, T) &= \frac{\partial}{\partial T} \left[- \int_t^T \bar{\phi}_s D(s, T) \, ds + \frac{\sigma^2}{2a^2}(T - t) - \frac{\sigma^2}{2a^2} D(t, T) \right. \\
&\qquad \left. - \frac{\sigma^2}{4a} D(t, T)^2 \right] \\
&= -\frac{\partial}{\partial T} \int_t^T \bar{\phi}_s D(s, T) \, ds + \frac{\sigma^2}{2a^2} \frac{\partial}{\partial T}(T - t) - \frac{\sigma^2}{2a^2} \frac{\partial}{\partial T} D(t, T) \\
&\qquad - \frac{\sigma^2}{4a} \frac{\partial}{\partial T} D(t, T)^2 \quad \text{(by expanding)}
\end{aligned}
$$

By using the Leibniz derivation rule (see Corollary 4.1), recalling relations (16.73) and (16.156), one obtains

$$
\begin{aligned}
\frac{\partial}{\partial T} \ln C(t, T) &= -\left[\int_t^T \bar{\phi}_s \frac{\partial}{\partial T} D(s, T) \, ds \right] + \frac{\sigma^2}{2a^2} - \frac{\sigma^2}{2a^2} e^{-a(T-t)} \\
&\qquad - \frac{\sigma^2}{4a} 2 D(t, T) \frac{\partial}{\partial T} D(t, T) \\
&= -\left[\int_t^T \bar{\phi}_s \frac{\partial}{\partial T} D(s, T) \, ds \right] + \frac{\sigma^2}{2a^2} - \frac{\sigma^2}{2a^2} e^{-a(T-t)} \\
&\qquad - \frac{\sigma^2}{4a} 2 \frac{1}{a}(1 - e^{-a(T-t)}) e^{-a(T-t)} \quad \text{(using (16.155) and (16.156))} \\
&= -\left[\int_t^T \bar{\phi}_s \frac{\partial}{\partial T} D(s, T) \, ds \right] + \frac{\sigma^2}{2a^2} - \frac{\sigma^2}{2a^2} e^{-a(T-t)} \\
&\qquad - \frac{\sigma^2}{2a^2}(1 - e^{-a(T-t)}) e^{-a(T-t)} \quad \text{(simplifying)} \\
&= -\left[\int_t^T \bar{\phi}_s \frac{\partial}{\partial T} D(s, T) \, ds \right] + \frac{\sigma^2}{2a^2} - \frac{\sigma^2}{2a^2} e^{-a(T-t)} \\
&\qquad - \frac{\sigma^2}{2a^2}(e^{-a(T-t)} - e^{-2a(T-t)}) \\
&= -\left[\int_t^T \bar{\phi}_s \frac{\partial}{\partial T} D(s, T) \, ds \right] + \frac{\sigma^2}{2a^2}(1 - e^{-a(T-t)}) \\
&\qquad - \frac{\sigma^2}{2a^2} e^{-a(T-t)}(1 - e^{-a(T-t)}) \\
&= -\left[\int_t^T \bar{\phi}_s \frac{\partial}{\partial T} D(s, T) \, ds \right] + \frac{\sigma^2}{2} \frac{(1 - e^{-a(T-t)})}{a} \frac{(1 - e^{-a(T-t)})}{a}
\end{aligned}
$$

$$= - \left[\int_t^T \bar{\phi}_s \frac{\partial}{\partial T} D(s, T) \, ds \right] + \frac{\sigma^2}{2} \left[\frac{(1 - e^{-a(T-t)})}{a} \right]^2$$

$$= - \left[\int_t^T \bar{\phi}_s e^{-a(T-s)} \, ds \right] + \frac{\sigma^2}{2} \left[\frac{(1 - e^{-a(T-t)})}{a} \right]^2 \quad \text{(using (16.156))}$$

one obtains

$$\frac{\partial}{\partial T} \ln C(t, T) = - \int_t^T \bar{\phi}_s e^{-a(T-s)} \, ds + \frac{\sigma^2}{2} \left[\frac{(1 - e^{-a(T-t)})}{a} \right]^2 \quad (16.158)$$

Then simplifying (16.156) and (16.158) for $t = 0$, changing sign in this last equation, one can specify the arbitrage-free condition (see (16.86)), ie,

$$\frac{\partial}{\partial T} D(t, T) = e^{-aT} \quad (16.159)$$

$$-\frac{\partial}{\partial T} \ln C(0, T) = \int_0^T \bar{\phi}_s e^{-a(T-s)} \, ds - \frac{\sigma^2}{2} \left[\frac{(1 - e^{-aT})}{a} \right]^2 \quad (16.160)$$

Recalling this condition, ie, (16.86), substituting (16.159) and (16.160) in (16.83), one obtains the arbitrage-free condition:

$$f(0, T)$$

$$= e^{-aT} r_0 + \int_0^T \bar{\phi}_s e^{-a(T-s)} \, ds - \frac{\sigma^2}{2} \left[\frac{(1 - e^{-aT})}{a} \right]^2 \quad \text{(arbitrage-free condition)}$$

$$(16.161)$$

16.3.2.4.2.1. SDE specification Now, SDE (16.151) is specified in arbitrage-free conditions. For this purpose the value of function $\bar{\phi}$ is determined. Equation (16.161) is derived with respect to T, ie,

$$\frac{\partial}{\partial T} f(0, T) = \frac{\partial}{\partial T} e^{-aT} r_0 + \frac{\partial}{\partial T} \int_0^T \bar{\phi}_s e^{-a(T-s)} \, ds - \frac{\partial}{\partial T} \frac{\sigma^2}{2a^2} (1 - e^{-aT})^2$$

By using the Leibniz derivation rule (see Corollary 4.4) and the chain rule (see Proposition 4.3) one obtains

$$\frac{\partial}{\partial T} f(0, T) = -a e^{-aT} r_0 + \left[\bar{\phi}_T + \int_0^T \bar{\phi}_s \frac{\partial}{\partial T} e^{-a(T-s)} \, ds \right] - \frac{\sigma^2}{2a^2} a e^{-aT} 2(1 - e^{-aT})$$

$$= -a e^{-aT} r_0 + \left[\bar{\phi}_T - a \int_0^T \bar{\phi}_s e^{-a(T-s)} \, ds \right] - \frac{\sigma^2}{a} e^{-aT} (1 - e^{-aT})$$

(by expanding)

$$= -a e^{-aT} r_0 + \bar{\phi}_T - a \int_0^T \bar{\phi}_s e^{-a(T-s)} \, ds - \frac{\sigma^2}{a} e^{-aT} (1 - e^{-aT})$$

The following can be derived:

$$\frac{\partial}{\partial T} f(0, T) = -ae^{-aT} r_0 + \bar{\phi}_T - a \int_0^T \bar{\phi}_s e^{-a(T-s)} \, ds - \frac{\sigma^2}{a} e^{-aT} (1 - e^{-aT})$$

$$(16.162)$$

Then the following quantity is computed:

$$\frac{\partial}{\partial T} f(0, T) + af(0, T)$$

$$= -ae^{-aT} r_0 + \bar{\phi}_T - a \int_0^T \bar{\phi}_s e^{-a(T-s)} \, ds - \frac{\sigma^2}{a} e^{-aT} (1 - e^{-aT})$$

$$+ a \left[e^{-aT} r_0 + \int_0^T \bar{\phi}_s e^{-a(T-s)} \, ds - \frac{\sigma^2}{2} \left[\frac{(1 - e^{-aT})}{a} \right]^2 \right]$$

by expanding, one has

$$\frac{\partial}{\partial T} f(0, T) + af(0, T)$$

$$= -ae^{-aT} r_0 + \bar{\phi}_T - a \int_0^T \bar{\phi}_s e^{-a(T-s)} \, ds - \frac{\sigma^2}{a} e^{-aT} (1 - e^{-aT})$$

$$+ ae^{-aT} r_0 + a \int_0^T \bar{\phi}_s e^{-a(T-s)} \, ds - \frac{a\sigma^2}{2} \left[\frac{(1 - e^{-aT})}{a} \right]^2$$

simplifying, one obtains

$$\frac{\partial}{\partial T} f(0, T) + af(0, T)$$

$$= \bar{\phi}_T - \frac{\sigma^2}{a} e^{-aT} (1 - e^{-aT}) - \frac{a\sigma^2}{2} \left[\frac{(1 - e^{-aT})}{a} \right]^2$$

$$= \bar{\phi}_T - \frac{\sigma^2}{a} e^{-aT} + \frac{\sigma^2}{a} e^{-2aT} - \frac{a\sigma^2}{2} \frac{(1 - 2e^{-aT} + e^{-2aT})}{a^2}$$

$$= \bar{\phi}_T - \frac{\sigma^2}{a} e^{-aT} + \frac{\sigma^2}{a} e^{-2aT} - \frac{\sigma^2}{2} \frac{(1 - 2e^{-aT} + e^{-2aT})}{a}$$

$$= \bar{\phi}_T - \frac{\sigma^2}{a} e^{-aT} + \frac{\sigma^2}{a} e^{-2aT} - \frac{1}{2} \frac{\sigma^2}{a} (1 - 2e^{-aT} + e^{-2aT})$$

$$= \bar{\phi}_T - \frac{\sigma^2}{a} e^{-aT} + \frac{\sigma^2}{a} e^{-2aT} - \frac{1}{2} \frac{\sigma^2}{a} + \frac{1}{2} \frac{\sigma^2}{a} 2e^{-aT} - \frac{1}{2} \frac{\sigma^2}{a} e^{-2aT}$$

$$= \bar{\phi}_T - \frac{\sigma^2}{a} e^{-aT} + \frac{\sigma^2}{a} e^{-2aT} - \frac{1}{2} \frac{\sigma^2}{a} + \frac{\sigma^2}{a} e^{-aT} - \frac{1}{2} \frac{\sigma^2}{a} e^{-2aT}$$

$$= \bar{\phi}_T - \frac{1}{2} \frac{\sigma^2}{a} + \frac{1}{2} \frac{\sigma^2}{a} e^{-2aT}$$

$$= \bar{\phi}_T - \frac{\sigma^2}{2a} [1 - e^{-2aT}]$$

Solving for $\bar{\phi}_T$, one has

$$\bar{\phi}_T = af(0, T) + \frac{\partial}{\partial T}f(0, T) + \frac{\sigma^2}{2a}(1 - e^{-2aT}) \qquad (16.163)$$

and, for any t,

$$\bar{\phi}_t = af(0, t) + \frac{\partial}{\partial t}f(0, t) + \frac{\sigma^2}{2a}(1 - e^{-2at}) \qquad (16.164)$$

hence, the SDE of the Hull–White model under arbitrage-free conditions and under the risk-neutral probability measure P can be written as:

$$dr_t = \left[af(0, t) + \frac{\partial}{\partial t}f(0, t) + \frac{\sigma^2}{2a}(1 - e^{-2at}) - ar_t\right]dt + \sigma\, d\widetilde{W}_t \qquad (16.165)$$

16.3.2.4.3.   *The price $P(t, T, r_t)$ in the Hull–White model*   Equation (16.77) is specified for the Hull–White model. For this purpose, it is necessary to compute the quantity $C(t, T)$, since the value of $D(t, T)$ has already been determined, and is equal to (16.155).

Equation (16.157) is considered, then the arbitrage-free value of $\bar{\phi}_t$ given by (16.164) is substituted to obtain

$$\ln C(t, T) = -\int_t^T \left[af(0, s) + \frac{\partial}{\partial s}f(0, s) + \frac{\sigma^2}{2a}(1 - e^{-2as})\right]D(s, T)\, ds$$
$$+ \frac{\sigma^2}{2a^2}(T - t) - \frac{\sigma^2}{2a^2}D(t, T) - \frac{\sigma^2}{4a}D(t, T)^2$$

Expanding, one has

$$\ln C(t, T) = -\int_t^T af(0, s)D(s, T)\, ds - \int_t^T \frac{\partial}{\partial s}f(0, s)D(s, T)\, ds$$
$$- \int_t^T \frac{\sigma^2}{2a}(1 - e^{-2as})D(s, T)\, ds + \frac{\sigma^2}{2a^2}(T - t) - \frac{\sigma^2}{2a^2}D(t, T)$$
$$- \frac{\sigma^2}{4a}D(t, T)^2$$

By using expression (16.15), one has

$$\ln C(t, T) = a\int_t^T \frac{\partial}{\partial s}\ln P(0, s, r_s)D(s, T)\, ds - \int_t^T D(s, T)\frac{\partial}{\partial s}f(0, s)\, ds$$
$$- \frac{\sigma^2}{2a}\int_t^T D(s, T)\, ds + \frac{\sigma^2}{2a}\int_t^T e^{-2as}D(s, T)\, ds + \frac{\sigma^2}{2a^2}(T - t)$$
$$- \frac{\sigma^2}{2a^2}D(t, T) - \frac{\sigma^2}{4a}D(t, T)^2$$

Integrating by parts, one has

$$
\ln C(t, T) = a \int_t^T \frac{\partial}{\partial s} \ln P(0, s, r_s) D(s, T)\, ds
$$
$$
- [f(0, s) D(s, T)]_t^T - \int_t^T f(0, s) \frac{\partial}{\partial s} D(s, T)\, ds
$$
$$
- \frac{\sigma^2}{2a} \int_t^T D(s, T)\, ds + \frac{\sigma^2}{2a} \int_t^T e^{-2as} D(s, T)\, ds
$$
$$
+ \frac{\sigma^2}{2a^2}(T - t) - \frac{\sigma^2}{2a^2} D(t, T) - \frac{\sigma^2}{4a} D(t, T)^2
$$

By simplifying, one obtains

$$
\ln C(t, T) = a \int_t^T \frac{\partial}{\partial s} \ln P(0, s, r_s) D(s, T)\, ds
$$
$$
- [f(0, T) D(T, T) - f(0, t) D(t, T)] - \int_t^T f(0, s) \frac{\partial}{\partial s} D(s, T)\, ds
$$
$$
- \frac{\sigma^2}{2a} \int_t^T D(s, T)\, ds + \frac{\sigma^2}{2a} \int_t^T e^{-2as} D(s, T)\, ds
$$
$$
+ \frac{\sigma^2}{2a^2}(T - t) - \frac{\sigma^2}{2a^2} D(t, T) - \frac{\sigma^2}{4a} D(t, T)^2
$$

Recalling (16.73), one obtains

$$
\ln C(t, T) = a \int_t^T \frac{\partial}{\partial s} \ln P(0, s, r_s) D(s, T)\, ds
$$
$$
+ f(0, t) D(t, T) - \int_t^T f(0, s) \frac{\partial}{\partial s} D(s, T)\, ds
$$
$$
- \frac{\sigma^2}{2a} \int_t^T D(s, T)\, ds + \frac{\sigma^2}{2a} \int_t^T e^{-2as} D(s, T)\, ds
$$
$$
+ \frac{\sigma^2}{2a^2}(T - t) - \frac{\sigma^2}{2a^2} D(t, T) - \frac{\sigma^2}{4a} D(t, T)^2
$$

Using expression (16.15), one has

$$
\ln C(t, T) = a \int_t^T \frac{\partial}{\partial s} \ln P(0, s, r_s) D(s, T)\, ds
$$
$$
+ f(0, t) D(t, T) + \int_t^T \frac{\partial}{\partial s} \ln P(0, s, r_s) \frac{\partial}{\partial s} D(s, T)\, ds
$$

$$-\frac{\sigma^2}{2a}\int_t^T D(s,T)\,ds + \frac{\sigma^2}{2a}\int_t^T e^{-2as}D(s,T)\,ds$$

$$+\frac{\sigma^2}{2a^2}(T-t) - \frac{\sigma^2}{2a^2}D(t,T) - \frac{\sigma^2}{4a}D(t,T)^2$$

Factorising the terms with expression $(\partial/\partial s)\ln P(0,s,r_s)$, one obtains

$$\ln C(t,T) = a\int_t^T \frac{\partial}{\partial s}\ln P(0,s,r_s)D(s,T)\,ds$$

$$+\int_t^T \frac{\partial}{\partial s}\ln P(0,s,r_s)\frac{\partial}{\partial s}D(s,T)\,ds + f(0,t)D(t,T)$$

$$-\frac{\sigma^2}{2a}\int_t^T D(s,T)\,ds + \frac{\sigma^2}{2a}\int_t^T e^{-2as}D(s,T)\,ds$$

$$+\frac{\sigma^2}{2a^2}(T-t) - \frac{\sigma^2}{2a^2}D(t,T) - \frac{\sigma^2}{4a}D(t,T)^2$$

Using (16.155) and (16.156), one has

$$\ln C(t,T) = a\int_t^T \frac{\partial}{\partial s}\ln P(0,s,r_s)\left(\frac{1-e^{-a(T-s)}}{a}\right)ds$$

$$+\int_t^T \frac{\partial}{\partial s}\ln P(0,s,r_s)e^{-a(T-s)}\,ds + f(0,t)D(t,T)$$

$$-\frac{\sigma^2}{2a}\int_t^T D(s,T)\,ds + \frac{\sigma^2}{2a}\int_t^T e^{-2as}D(s,T)\,ds$$

$$+\frac{\sigma^2}{2a^2}(T-t) - \frac{\sigma^2}{2a^2}D(t,T) - \frac{\sigma^2}{4a}D(t,T)^2$$

Simplifying, one has

$$\ln C(t,T) = \int_t^T \frac{\partial}{\partial s}\ln P(0,s,r_s)(1-e^{-a(T-s)})\,ds$$

$$+\int_t^T \frac{\partial}{\partial s}\ln P(0,s,r_s)e^{-a(T-s)}\,ds + f(0,t)D(t,T)$$

$$-\frac{\sigma^2}{2a}\int_t^T D(s,T)\,ds + \frac{\sigma^2}{2a}\int_t^T e^{-2as}D(s,T)\,ds$$

$$+\frac{\sigma^2}{2a^2}(T-t) - \frac{\sigma^2}{2a^2}D(t,T) - \frac{\sigma^2}{4a}D(t,T)^2$$

Simplifying again, one obtains

$$
\begin{aligned}
\ln C(t, T) = & \int_t^T \frac{\partial}{\partial s} \ln P(0, s, r_s) \, ds + f(0, t)D(t, T) \\
& - \frac{\sigma^2}{2a} \int_t^T D(s, T) \, ds + \frac{\sigma^2}{2a} \int_t^T e^{-2as} D(s, T) \, ds \\
& + \frac{\sigma^2}{2a^2}(T - t) - \frac{\sigma^2}{2a^2} D(t, T) - \frac{\sigma^2}{4a} D(t, T)^2
\end{aligned}
$$

Integrating, one has

$$
\begin{aligned}
\ln C(t, T) = & [\ln P(0, s, r_s)]_t^T + f(0, t)D(t, T) \\
& - \frac{\sigma^2}{2a} \int_t^T D(s, T) \, ds + \frac{\sigma^2}{2a} \int_t^T e^{-2as} D(s, T) \, ds \\
& + \frac{\sigma^2}{2a^2}(T - t) - \frac{\sigma^2}{2a^2} D(t, T) - \frac{\sigma^2}{4a} D(t, T)^2
\end{aligned}
$$

By expanding, one obtains

$$
\begin{aligned}
\ln C(t, T) = & \ln P(0, T, r_T) - \ln P(0, t, r_t) + f(0, t)D(t, T) \\
& - \frac{\sigma^2}{2a} \int_t^T D(s, T) \, ds + \frac{\sigma^2}{2a} \int_t^T e^{-2as} D(s, T) \, ds \\
& + \frac{\sigma^2}{2a^2}(T - t) - \frac{\sigma^2}{2a^2} D(t, T) - \frac{\sigma^2}{4a} D(t, T)^2
\end{aligned}
$$

Under a logarithm property, one has

$$
\begin{aligned}
\ln C(t, T) = & \ln \left(\frac{P(0, T, r_T)}{P(0, t, r_t)} \right) + f(0, t)D(t, T) \\
& - \frac{\sigma^2}{2a} \int_t^T D(s, T) \, ds + \frac{\sigma^2}{2a} \int_t^T e^{-2as} D(s, T) \, ds \\
& + \frac{\sigma^2}{2a^2}(T - t) - \frac{\sigma^2}{2a^2} D(t, T) - \frac{\sigma^2}{4a} D(t, T)^2
\end{aligned}
$$

Using (16.155), one has

$$
\begin{aligned}
\ln C(t, T) = & \ln \left(\frac{P(0, T, r_T)}{P(0, t, r_t)} \right) + f(0, t)D(t, T) \\
& - \frac{\sigma^2}{2a} \int_t^T \left(\frac{1 - e^{-a(T-s)}}{a} \right) ds + \frac{\sigma^2}{2a} \int_t^T e^{-2as} \left(\frac{1 - e^{-a(T-s)}}{a} \right) ds \\
& + \frac{\sigma^2}{2a^2}(T - t) - \frac{\sigma^2}{2a^2} D(t, T) - \frac{\sigma^2}{4a} D(t, T)^2
\end{aligned}
$$

Expanding, one obtains

$$\ln C(t, T) = \ln\left(\frac{P(0, T, r_T)}{P(0, t, r_t)}\right) + f(0, t)D(t, T)$$

$$- \frac{\sigma^2}{2a^2}\int_t^T \left(1 - e^{-a(T-s)} - e^{-2as} + e^{-2as-aT+as}\right) ds$$

$$+ \frac{\sigma^2}{2a^2}(T - t) - \frac{\sigma^2}{2a^2}D(t, T) - \frac{\sigma^2}{4a}D(t, T)^2$$

Simplifying, one has

$$\ln C(t, T) = \ln\left(\frac{P(0, T, r_T)}{P(0, t, r_t)}\right) + f(0, t)D(t, T)$$

$$- \frac{\sigma^2}{2a^2}\int_t^T \left(-e^{-a(T-s)} - e^{-2as} + e^{-2as-aT+as}\right) ds$$

$$- \frac{\sigma^2}{2a^2}D(t, T) - \frac{\sigma^2}{4a}D(t, T)^2$$

Expanding, one obtains

$$\ln C(t, T) = \ln\left(\frac{P(0, T, r_T)}{P(0, t, r_t)}\right) + f(0, t)D(t, T)$$

$$+ \frac{\sigma^2}{2a^2}\left[\int_t^T e^{-2as} ds + \int_t^T e^{-a(T-s)} ds - \int_t^T e^{-as-aT} ds\right]$$

$$- \frac{\sigma^2}{2a^2}D(t, T) - \frac{\sigma^2}{4a}D(t, T)^2$$

Computing the integrals, one has

$$\ln C(t, T) = \ln\left(\frac{P(0, T, r_T)}{P(0, t, r_t)}\right) + f(0, t)D(t, T)$$

$$+ \frac{\sigma^2}{2a^2}\left[-\frac{e^{-2as}}{2a}\right]_t^T + \frac{\sigma^2}{2a^2}\left[\frac{e^{-a(T-s)}}{a}\right]_t^T + \frac{\sigma^2}{2a^2}\left[\frac{e^{-a(T+s)}}{a}\right]_t^T$$

$$- \frac{\sigma^2}{2a^2}D(t, T) - \frac{\sigma^2}{4a}D(t, T)^2$$

Expanding, one obtains

$$\ln C(t, T) = \ln\left(\frac{P(0, T, r_T)}{P(0, t, r_t)}\right) + f(0, t)D(t, T)$$

$$+ \frac{\sigma^2}{4a^3}(e^{-2at} - e^{-2aT}) + \frac{\sigma^2}{2a^3}(1 - e^{-a(T-t)}) + \frac{\sigma^2}{2a^3}(e^{-2aT} - e^{-a(T+t)})$$

$$- \frac{\sigma^2}{2a^2}D(t, T) - \frac{\sigma^2}{4a}D(t, T)^2$$

Using (16.155), one has

$$\ln C(t, T) = \ln\left(\frac{P(0, T, r_T)}{P(0, t, r_t)}\right) + f(0, t)\left(\frac{1 - e^{-a(T-t)}}{a}\right)$$
$$+ \frac{\sigma^2}{4a^3}\left(e^{-2at} - e^{-2aT}\right) + \frac{\sigma^2}{2a^3}(1 - e^{-a(T-t)}) + \frac{\sigma^2}{2a^3}(e^{-2aT} - e^{-a(T+t)})$$
$$- \frac{\sigma^2}{2a^2}\left(\frac{1 - e^{-a(T-t)}}{a}\right) - \frac{\sigma^2}{4a}\left(\frac{1 - e^{-a(T-t)}}{a}\right)^2$$

Expanding, one obtains

$$\ln C(t, T) = \ln\left(\frac{P(0, T, r_T)}{P(0, t, r_t)}\right) + f(0, t)\left(\frac{1 - e^{-a(T-t)}}{a}\right)$$
$$+ \frac{\sigma^2}{4a^3}(e^{-2at} - e^{-2aT}) + \frac{\sigma^2}{2a^3}(1 - e^{-a(T-t)}) + \frac{\sigma^2}{2a^3}(e^{-2aT} - e^{-a(T+t)})$$
$$- \frac{\sigma^2}{2a^3}(1 - e^{-a(T-t)}) - \frac{\sigma^2}{4a^3}(1 - e^{-a(T-t)})^2$$
$$= \ln\left(\frac{P(0, T, r_T)}{P(0, t, r_t)}\right) + f(0, t)\left(\frac{1 - e^{-a(T-t)}}{a}\right)$$
$$+ \frac{\sigma^2}{4a^3}(e^{-2at} - e^{-2aT}) + \frac{\sigma^2}{2a^3}(1 - e^{-a(T-t)}) + \frac{\sigma^2}{2a^3}(e^{-2aT} - e^{-a(T+t)})$$
$$- \frac{\sigma^2}{2a^3}(1 - e^{-a(T-t)}) - \frac{\sigma^2}{4a^3}(1 - 2e^{-a(T-t)} + e^{-2a(T-t)})$$

Expanding and simplifying, one has

$$\ln C(t, T)$$
$$= \ln\left(\frac{P(0, T, r_T)}{P(0, t, r_t)}\right) + f(0, t)\left(\frac{1 - e^{-a(T-t)}}{a}\right)$$
$$+ \frac{\sigma^2}{4a^3}e^{-2at} - \frac{\sigma^2}{4a^3}e^{-2aT} + \frac{\sigma^2}{2a^3}e^{-2aT} - \frac{\sigma^2}{2a^3}e^{-a(T+t)}$$
$$- \frac{\sigma^2}{4a^3} + \frac{\sigma^2}{2a^3}e^{-a(T-t)} - \frac{\sigma^2}{4a^3}e^{-2a(T-t)}$$
$$= \ln\left(\frac{P(0, T, r_T)}{P(0, t, r_t)}\right) + f(0, t)\left(\frac{1 - e^{-a(T-t)}}{a}\right)$$
$$+ \frac{\sigma^2}{4a^3}(e^{-2at} - e^{-2aT} + 2e^{-2aT} - 2e^{-a(T+t)} - 1 + 2e^{-a(T-t)} - e^{-2a(T-t)})$$

Simplifying, one obtains

$$\ln C(t, T) = \ln\left(\frac{P(0, T, r_T)}{P(0, t, r_t)}\right) + f(0, t)\left(\frac{1 - e^{-a(T-t)}}{a}\right)$$

$$+ \frac{\sigma^2}{4a^3}(e^{-2at} + e^{-2aT} - 2e^{-a(T+t)} - 1 + 2e^{-a(T-t)} - e^{-2a(T-t)})$$

which may also can be written as

$$\ln C(t, T) = \ln\left(\frac{P(0, T, r_T)}{P(0, t, r_t)}\right) + f(0, t)\left(\frac{1 - e^{-a(T-t)}}{a}\right)$$

$$+ \frac{\sigma^2}{4a^3}(e^{-2at} + e^{-2aT} - 2e^{-a(T+t)}$$

$$- e^{2at-2at} + 2e^{2at-2at-aT+at} - e^{2at-2at-2aT+2at})$$

Simplifying, one has

$$\ln C(t, T) = \ln\left(\frac{P(0, T, r_T)}{P(0, t, r_t)}\right) + f(0, t)\left(\frac{1 - e^{-a(T-t)}}{a}\right)$$

$$+ \frac{\sigma^2}{4a^3}[(e^{-2at} + e^{-2aT} - 2e^{-a(T+t)})$$

$$- (e^{2at-2at} - 2e^{2at-at-aT} + e^{2at-2aT})]$$

Factorising, one obtains

$$\ln C(t, T) = \ln\left(\frac{P(0, T, r_T)}{P(0, t, r_t)}\right) + f(0, t)\left(\frac{1 - e^{-a(T-t)}}{a}\right)$$

$$+ \frac{\sigma^2}{4a^3}[(e^{-2at} + e^{-2aT} - 2e^{-a(T+t)})$$

$$- e^{2at}(e^{-2at} - 2e^{-aT+at} + e^{-2aT})]$$

or

$$\ln C(t, T) = \ln\left(\frac{P(0, T, r_T)}{P(0, t, r_t)}\right) + f(0, t)\left(\frac{1 - e^{-a(T-t)}}{a}\right)$$

$$+ \frac{\sigma^2}{4a^3}[(e^{-2at} + e^{-2aT} - 2e^{-a(T+t)})$$

$$- e^{2at}(e^{-2at} + e^{-2aT} - 2e^{-a(T+t)})]$$

and, then,

$$\ln C(t, T) = \ln\left(\frac{P(0, T, r_T)}{P(0, t, r_t)}\right) + f(0, t)\left(\frac{1 - e^{-a(T-t)}}{a}\right)$$

$$+ \frac{\sigma^2}{4a^3}[(e^{-2at} + e^{-2aT} - 2e^{-a(T+t)})(1 - e^{2at})]$$

ie,

$$\ln C(t, T) = \ln\left(\frac{P(0, T, r_T)}{P(0, t, r_t)}\right) + f(0, t)\left(\frac{1 - e^{-a(T-t)}}{a}\right)$$
$$+ \frac{\sigma^2}{4a^3}[(e^{-aT} - e^{-at})^2(1 - e^{2at})]$$

Using expression (16.15), one obtains

$$\ln C(t, T) = \ln\left(\frac{P(0, T, r_T)}{P(0, t, r_t)}\right) - \frac{\partial}{\partial t}\ln P(0, t, r_t)\left(\frac{1 - e^{-a(T-t)}}{a}\right)$$
$$+ \frac{\sigma^2}{4a^3}[(e^{-aT} - e^{-at})^2(1 - e^{2at})]$$

Applying the exponential, one has

$$C(t, T) = \left(\frac{P(0, T, r_T)}{P(0, t, r_t)}\right)\exp\left\{-\frac{\partial}{\partial t}\ln P(0, t, r_t)\left(\frac{1 - e^{-a(T-t)}}{a}\right)\right.$$
$$\left. + \frac{\sigma^2}{4a^3}\left[(e^{-aT} - e^{-at})^2(1 - e^{2at})\right]\right\} \tag{16.166}$$

Recalling expression (16.77) and substituting the values of $C(t, T)$ in (16.166) and the value of $D(t, T)$ in (16.155), one obtains the risk-free pure discount bond price in arbitrage-free conditions under the risk-neutral measure P in the Hull–White model:

$$P(t, T, r_t) = \frac{P(0, T, r_T)}{P(0, t, r_t)}\exp\left\{-\frac{\partial}{\partial t}\ln P(0, t, r_t)\left(\frac{1 - e^{-a(T-t)}}{a}\right)\right.$$
$$\left. + \frac{\sigma^2}{4a^3}(1 - e^{2at})(e^{-aT} - e^{-at})^2 - \left(\frac{1 - e^{-a(T-t)}}{a}\right)r_t\right\} \tag{16.167}$$

16.3.2.5. The Hull–White II model

16.3.2.5.1. *Introduction* In the Hull–White II model, the parameters $\phi(r_t, t)$ and $\sigma(r_t, t)$ of SDE (16.19) which describes the instantaneous spot rate r_t under the original probability measure Q, are specified as follows:

$$dr_t = (\phi_t - a_t r_t)\,dt + \sigma\,dW_t \tag{16.168}$$

Hence, under the *risk-free* probability measure P, one has

$$dr_t = (\bar{\phi}_t - a_t r_t)\,dt + \sigma\,d\widetilde{W}_t \tag{16.169}$$

where

$$\bar{\phi}_t = \phi_t - \lambda_t \sigma$$

Hence, the Cauchy problem is derived for this model. For this purpose, one recalls relations (16.77)–(16.80) derived for the Vasicek model (see Section 16.3.2.1),

Then, one recalls (16.35) and specifies it by using the partial derivatives in (16.78), (16.79) and (16.80) and the corresponding values of $\bar{\phi}_t$ and σ of SDE (16.49) expressed in (16.169):

$$\left[\frac{\partial}{\partial t} C(t, T) - C(t, T) \frac{\partial}{\partial t} D(t, T) r_t \right] e^{-D(t,T)r_t} - [\bar{\phi}_t - a_t r_t] C(t, T) D(t, T) \cdot e^{-D(t,T)r_t}$$

$$+ \frac{\sigma^2}{2} C(t, T) D^2(t, T) e^{-D(t,T)r_t} - r_t C(t, T) e^{-D(t,T)r_t} = 0$$

Dividing by $e^{-D(t,T)r_t}$ and factorising as necessary, one has

$$\left[\frac{\partial}{\partial t} C(t, T) - C(t, T) D(t, T) \bar{\phi}_t + \frac{\sigma^2}{2} C(t, T) D^2(t, T) \right]$$

$$- \left[\frac{\partial}{\partial t} D(t, T) - a_t D(t, T) + 1 \right] \cdot r_t \cdot C(t, T) = 0 \qquad (16.170)$$

Equation (16.170) is equivalent to the summation of the two addends which both have to be equal to zero, ie,

$$\frac{\partial}{\partial t} C(t, T) - C(t, T) D(t, T) \bar{\phi}_t + \frac{\sigma^2}{2} C(t, T) D^2(t, T) = 0 \qquad (16.171)$$

$$\left[1 - a_t D(t, T) + \frac{\partial}{\partial t} D(t, T) \right] = 0 \qquad (16.172)$$

The final conditions analogous to (16.72) and to (16.73) are given by (16.84) and (16.73) itself.

Finally, the Cauchy problem for the Hull–White II model becomes (16.171), (16.172), (16.84) and (16.73).

16.3.2.6. Arbitrage-free condition

The arbitrage-free condition for the Hull–White II model is, by construction and given the functional form of $P(t, T, r_t)$, analogous to that derived for the Vasicek model, ie, (16.86).

Quantities $(\partial / \partial T) D(t, T)$ and $(\partial / \partial T) \ln C(t, T)$ are now computed.

Concerning $(\partial / \partial T) D(t, T)$, the Cauchy problem given by Equation (16.172) and by the final condition in (16.73) is solved. If, defining a generic function $h(t, T)$, where $T > t$, it is true that

$$\frac{\partial h(t, T)}{\partial T} = - \frac{\partial h(t, T)}{\partial t}$$

then one may rewrite the Cauchy problem given by Equation (16.172) as follows:

$$\frac{\partial}{\partial T}D(t, T) + a_t D(t, T) = 1 \tag{16.173}$$

with the final condition given by (16.73).

In order to solve the Cauchy problem given by Equation (16.173) and by the final condition given in (16.73), Theorem 8.3, may be used to obtain

$$D(t, T) = e^{\int_0^t a_s\, ds} \cdot \left[\int_t^T e^{-\int_0^s a_u\, du}\, ds \right] \tag{16.174}$$

Equation (16.174) immediately verifies the final condition (16.73).

Differentiating with respect to T, one has

$$\frac{\partial}{\partial T}D(t, T) = e^{\int_0^t a_s\, ds} \left[e^{-\int_0^T a_u\, du} \right] \tag{16.175}$$

Since

$$D(0, T) = \left[\int_0^T e^{-\int_0^s a_u\, du}\, ds \right] \tag{16.176}$$

and either from (16.175) or from (16.176)

$$\frac{\partial}{\partial T}D(0, T) = e^{-\int_0^T a_u\, du} \tag{16.177}$$

then Equation (16.174) may be expressed exclusively in the terms of $D(0, T)$, by using (16.176) and (16.177), ie,

$$D(t, T) = \frac{D(0, T) - D(0, t)}{(\partial/\partial T)D(0, T)_{|T=t}} \tag{16.178}$$

and, from (16.177), one may universally determine the value of a_t for each time. Then

$$\frac{\partial}{\partial T}D(0, T) = e^{-\int_0^T a_u\, du} \tag{16.179}$$

Applying the logarithm, one has

$$\log \frac{\partial}{\partial T}D(0, T) = -\int_0^T a_u\, du$$

Changing sign, one obtains

$$-\log \frac{\partial}{\partial T}D(0, T) = \int_0^T a_u\, du$$

Differentiating with respect to T, one has

$$\frac{\partial}{\partial T}\left[-\log\frac{\partial}{\partial T}D(0,T)\right] = a_T$$

and, for $T = t$, one has

$$a_t = \frac{\partial}{\partial t}\left[-\log\frac{\partial}{\partial t}D(0,t)\right]$$

Thus

$$a_t = \frac{\partial}{\partial t}\left[-\log\frac{\partial}{\partial t}D(0,t)\right] \tag{16.180}$$

For $(\partial/\partial T)\ln C(t,T)$ one recalls the Cauchy problem given by Equation (16.171) and by the final condition in (16.73). Hence,

$$\frac{\partial}{\partial t}C(t,T) - C(t,T)D(t,T)\bar{\phi}_t + \frac{\sigma^2}{2}C(t,T)D^2(t,T) = 0$$

then

$$\frac{\partial}{\partial t}C(t,T) = C(t,T)D(t,T)\bar{\phi}_t - \frac{\sigma^2}{2}C(t,T)D^2(t,T)$$

Dividing by $C(t,T)$, one has

$$\frac{(\partial/\partial t)C(t,T)}{C(t,T)} = D(t,T)\bar{\phi}_t - \frac{\sigma^2}{2}D^2(t,T)$$

ie,

$$\frac{dC(t,T)}{C(t,T)} = \left(D(t,T)\bar{\phi}_t - \frac{\sigma^2}{2}D^2(t,T)\right)dt$$

Integrating both members, one obtains

$$\int_t^T \frac{dC(s,T)}{C(s,T)} = \int_t^T \left(D(s,T)\bar{\phi}_s - \frac{\sigma^2}{2}D^2(s,T)\right)ds$$

$$\ln C(T,T) - \ln C(t,T) = \int_t^T \left(D(s,T)\bar{\phi}_s - \frac{\sigma^2}{2}D^2(s,T)\right)ds$$

By using (16.73), one has

$$\ln 1 - \ln C(t,T) = \int_t^T \left(D(s,T)\bar{\phi}_s - \frac{\sigma^2}{2}D^2(s,T)\right)ds$$

Simplifying, one obtains

$$-\ln C(t,T) = \int_t^T \left(D(s,T)\bar{\phi}_s - \frac{\sigma^2}{2}D^2(s,T)\right)ds$$

Changing sign, one has

$$\ln C(t, T) = - \int_t^T \left(D(s, T)\bar{\phi}_s - \frac{\sigma^2}{2} D^2(s, T) \right) ds \qquad (16.181)$$

Substituting the explicit value of (16.174):

$$\ln C(t, T) = - \int_t^T \left(\bar{\phi}_s \left[e^{\int_0^s a_u \, du} \cdot \left(\int_s^T e^{-\int_0^u a_v \, dv} \, du \right) \right] \right.$$
$$\left. - \frac{\sigma^2}{2} \left[e^{\int_0^s a_u \, du} \cdot \left(\int_s^T e^{-\int_0^u a_v \, dv} \, du \right) \right]^2 \right) ds$$

hence,

$$\ln C(t, T) = - \int_t^T \bar{\phi}_s \left[e^{\int_0^s a_u \, du} \cdot \left(\int_s^T e^{-\int_0^u a_v \, dv} \, du \right) \right] ds$$
$$+ \int_t^T \frac{\sigma^2}{2} \left[e^{\int_0^s a_u \, du} \cdot \left(\int_s^T e^{-\int_0^u a_v \, dv} \, du \right) \right]^2 ds$$

Now, computing $\ln C(0, T)$, one has

$$\ln C(0, T) = - \int_0^T \bar{\phi}_s \left[e^{\int_0^s a_u \, du} \cdot \left(\int_s^T e^{-\int_0^u a_v \, dv} \, du \right) \right] ds$$
$$+ \int_0^T \frac{\sigma^2}{2} \left[e^{\int_0^s a_u \, du} \cdot \left(\int_s^T e^{-\int_0^u a_v \, dv} \, du \right) \right]^2 ds$$

Since the following equivalence below holds (see Criterion 5.3):

$$\int_0^T e^{-\int_0^u a_v \, dv} \left(\int_0^s e^{\int_0^s a_u \, du} \, ds \right) du = \int_0^T e^{\int_0^s a_u \, du} \left(\int_s^T e^{-\int_0^u a_v \, dv} \, du \right) ds$$
$$(16.182)$$

using (16.182)

$$\ln C(0, T) = - \int_0^T \bar{\phi}_s \left[e^{\int_0^u a_v \, dv} \cdot \left(\int_0^s \bar{\phi}_s e^{-\int_0^s a_u \, du} \, ds \right) \right] du$$
$$+ \int_0^T \frac{\sigma^2}{2} \left[e^{\int_0^v a_u \, du} \cdot \left(\int_0^s e^{-\int_0^s a_u \, du} \, ds \right) \right]^2 du$$

computing the derivative with respect to T

$$\frac{\partial}{\partial T}\ln C(0,T) = \frac{\partial}{\partial T}\left[-\int_0^T \left[e^{\int_0^u a_v\,dv} \cdot \left(\int_0^s \bar\phi_s e^{-\int_0^s a_u\,du}\,ds \right) \right] du \right.$$
$$\left. + \int_0^T \frac{\sigma^2}{2}\left[e^{\int_0^u a_v\,dv} \cdot \left(\int_0^s e^{-\int_0^s a_u\,du}\,ds \right) \right]^2 du \right]$$
$$= -\left[e^{\int_0^T a_v\,dv} \cdot \left(\int_0^T \bar\phi_s e^{-\int_0^s a_u\,du}\,ds \right) \right]$$
$$+ \frac{\sigma^2}{2}\left[e^{\int_0^T a_v\,dv} \cdot \left(\int_0^T e^{-\int_0^s a_u\,du}\,ds \right) \right]^2$$

then using (16.179), one obtains

$$\frac{\partial}{\partial T}\ln C(0,T) = -\frac{1}{(\partial/\partial T)D(0,T)}\left[\int_0^T \bar\phi_s \frac{\partial}{\partial s}D(0,s)\,ds \right]$$
$$+ \frac{\sigma^2}{2}\left[\frac{1}{(\partial/\partial T)D(0,T)} \cdot \left(\int_0^T \frac{\partial}{\partial s}D(0,s)\,ds \right) \right]^2 \qquad (16.183)$$

Recalling the arbitrage-free condition, ie, (16.86), substituting (16.177) and (16.183) in (16.83), one obtains the arbitrage-free condition:

$$f(0,T) = r_0 \frac{\partial}{\partial T}D(0,T) + \frac{1}{(\partial/\partial T)D(0,T)}\left[\int_0^T \bar\phi_s \frac{\partial}{\partial s}D(0,s)\,ds \right]$$
$$- \frac{\sigma^2}{2}\left[\frac{1}{(\partial/\partial T)D(0,T)} \cdot \left(\int_0^T \frac{\partial}{\partial s}D(0,s)\,ds \right) \right]^2$$

$$\text{(arbitrage-free condition)} \qquad (16.184)$$

16.3.2.6.1. SDE specification Then, SDE (16.169) is specified in arbitrage-free conditions. For this purpose, the value of function $\bar\phi$ is determined. Some manipulations on Equation (16.183) are first made:

$$\frac{\partial}{\partial T}\ln C(0,T) = -\frac{1}{(\partial/\partial T)D(0,T)}\left[\int_0^T \bar\phi_s \frac{\partial}{\partial s}D(0,s)\,ds \right]$$
$$+ \frac{\sigma^2}{2}\left[\frac{1}{(\partial/\partial T)D(0,T)} \cdot \left(\int_0^T \frac{\partial}{\partial s}D(0,s)\,ds \right) \right]^2$$

Multiplying by $(\partial/\partial T)D(0,T)$, one has

$$\left[\frac{\partial}{\partial T}D(0,T) \cdot \frac{\partial}{\partial T}\ln C(0,T) \right] = -\left[\int_0^T \bar\phi_s \frac{\partial}{\partial s}D(0,s)\,ds \right]$$
$$+ \frac{\sigma^2}{2}\frac{1}{(\partial/\partial T)D(0,T)}\left[\left(\int_0^T \frac{\partial}{\partial s}D(0,s)\,ds \right) \right]^2$$

Differentiating with respect to T, one obtains

$$\frac{\partial}{\partial T}\left[\frac{\partial}{\partial T}D(0,T)\cdot\frac{\partial}{\partial T}\ln C(0,T)\right]$$

$$=-\bar{\phi}_T\frac{\partial}{\partial T}D(0,T)+\frac{\sigma^2}{2}\left[\frac{\partial}{\partial T}\left(\frac{1}{(\partial/\partial T)D(0,T)}\right)\cdot\left(\int_0^T\frac{\partial}{\partial s}D(0,s)\,ds\right)^2\right]$$

$$+\frac{\sigma^2}{2}\left[\frac{2}{(\partial/\partial T)D(0,T)}\cdot\left(\int_0^T\frac{\partial}{\partial s}D(0,s)\,ds\right)\cdot\frac{\partial}{\partial T}\left(\int_0^T\frac{\partial}{\partial s}D(0,s)\,ds\right)\right]$$

Computing the differentials, one has

$$\frac{\partial}{\partial T}\left[\frac{\partial}{\partial T}D(0,T)\cdot\frac{\partial}{\partial T}\ln C(0,T)\right]$$

$$=-\bar{\phi}_T\frac{\partial}{\partial T}D(0,T)+\frac{\sigma^2}{2}\left[-\frac{1}{((\partial/\partial T)D(0,T))^2}\cdot\left(\int_0^T\frac{\partial}{\partial s}D(0,s)\,ds\right)^2\right]$$

$$+\frac{\sigma^2}{2}\left[\frac{2}{(\partial/\partial T)D(0,T)}\cdot\left(\int_0^T\frac{\partial}{\partial s}D(0,s)\,ds\right)\cdot\frac{\partial}{\partial T}D(0,T)\right]$$

Simplifying, one obtains

$$\frac{\partial}{\partial T}\left[\frac{\partial}{\partial T}D(0,T)\cdot\frac{\partial}{\partial T}\ln C(0,T)\right]$$

$$=-\bar{\phi}_T\frac{\partial}{\partial T}D(0,T)-\frac{\sigma^2}{2}\left[\frac{[(\int_0^T(\partial/\partial s)D(0,s)\,ds)]^2}{((\partial/\partial T)D(0,T))^2}\right]+\sigma^2\left(\int_0^T\frac{\partial}{\partial s}D(0,s)\,ds\right)$$

Changing the order of some addends, one has

$$\bar{\phi}_T\frac{\partial}{\partial T}D(0,T)=-\frac{\sigma^2}{2}\left[\frac{[(\int_0^T(\partial/\partial s)D(0,s)\,ds)]^2}{((\partial/\partial T)D(0,T))^2}\right]+\sigma^2\left(\int_0^T\frac{\partial}{\partial s}D(0,s)\,ds\right)$$

$$-\frac{\partial}{\partial T}\left[\frac{\partial}{\partial T}D(0,T)\cdot\frac{\partial}{\partial T}\ln C(0,T)\right]$$

Solving by $\bar{\phi}_T$:

$$\bar{\phi}_T=-\frac{\sigma^2}{2}\frac{1}{(\partial/\partial T)D(0,T)}\left[\frac{[(\int_0^T(\partial/\partial s)D(0,s)\,ds)]^2}{((\partial/\partial T)D(0,T))^2}\right]$$

$$+\frac{\sigma^2(\int_0^T(\partial/\partial s)D(0,s)\,ds)}{(\partial/\partial T)D(0,T)}-\frac{[(\partial/\partial T)D(0,T)\cdot(\partial/\partial T)\ln C(0,T)]}{(\partial/\partial T)D(0,T)}$$

Simplifying, one obtains

$$\bar{\phi}_T=-\frac{\sigma^2}{2}\left[\frac{[(\int_0^T(\partial/\partial s)D(0,s)\,ds)]^2}{((\partial/\partial T)D(0,T))^3}\right]+\frac{\sigma^2(\int_0^T(\partial/\partial s)D(0,s)\,ds)}{(\partial/\partial T)D(0,T)}$$

$$-\frac{[(\partial/\partial T)D(0,T)\cdot(\partial/\partial T)\ln C(0,T)]}{(\partial/\partial T)D(0,T)}$$

and, for any t,

$$\bar{\phi}_t = -\frac{(\partial/\partial t)[(\partial/\partial t)D(0,t) \cdot (\partial/\partial t)\ln C(0,t)]}{(\partial/\partial t)D(0,t)} - \frac{\sigma^2}{2}\left[\frac{(\int_0^t(\partial/\partial s)D(0,s)\,ds)^2}{((\partial/\partial t)D(0,t))^3}\right]$$
$$+ \frac{\sigma^2(\int_0^t(\partial/\partial s)D(0,s)\,ds)}{(\partial/\partial t)D(0,t)} \tag{16.185}$$

hence, the SDE of the Hull–White II model in arbitrage-free conditions and under the risk-neutral probability measure P, can be written as

$$dr_t = \left\{ -\frac{(\partial/\partial t)[(\partial/\partial t)D(0,t) \cdot (\partial/\partial t)\ln C(0,t)]}{(\partial/\partial t)D(0,t)} - \frac{\sigma^2}{2}\left[\frac{(\int_0^t(\partial/\partial s)D(0,s)\,ds)^2}{((\partial/\partial t)D(0,t))^3}\right] \right.$$
$$\left. + \frac{\sigma^2(\int_0^t(\partial/\partial s)D(0,s)\,ds)}{(\partial/\partial t)D(0,t)} - \frac{\partial}{\partial t}\left[\log\frac{\partial}{\partial t}D(0,t)\right]r_t \right\} dt + \sigma\,d\widetilde{W}_t \tag{16.186}$$

16.3.2.7. The price $P(t, T, r_t)$ in the Hull–White II model

Equation (16.77) is specified for the Hull–White II model. For this purpose it is necessary to compute the quantity $C(t, T)$, since the value of $D(t, T)$ has already been determined, which is equal to (16.178).

The explicit expression for $\ln C(t, T)$ is considered:

$$\ln C(t, T) = -\int_t^T \left(D(s, T)\bar{\phi}_s - \frac{\sigma^2}{2}D^2(s, T) \right) ds \tag{16.187}$$

The value $D(t, T)$ is substituted and the arbitrage-free value of $\bar{\phi}_t$ is given by (16.185) to obtain

$\ln C(t, T)$
$$= -\int_0^T \left\{ \frac{D(0, T) - D(0, s)}{(\partial/\partial T)D(0, T)_{|T=s}} \cdot \left\{ -\frac{(\partial/\partial s)[(\partial/\partial s)D(0, s) \cdot (\partial/\partial t)\ln C(0, s)]}{(\partial/\partial s)D(0, s)} \right.\right.$$
$$\left. -\frac{\sigma^2}{2}\left[\frac{(\int_0^s(\partial/\partial v)D(0, v)\,dv)^2}{((\partial/\partial s)D(0, s))^3}\right] + \frac{\sigma^2(\int_0^s(\partial/\partial v)D(0, v)\,dv)}{(\partial/\partial s)D(0, s)} \right\}$$
$$\left. -\frac{\sigma^2}{2}\left(\frac{D(0, T) - D(0, s)}{(\partial/\partial T)D(0, T)_{|T=s}} \right)^2 \right\} ds$$

hence

$$
\begin{aligned}
C(t, T) = \exp\Bigg(- \int_0^T \Bigg\{ & \frac{D(0, T) - D(0, s)}{(\partial/\partial T)D(0, T)_{|T=s}} \\
\cdot \Bigg\{ & -\frac{(\partial/\partial s)[(\partial/\partial s)D(0, s) \cdot (\partial/\partial t) \ln C(0, s)]}{(\partial/\partial s)D(0, s)} \\
& -\frac{\sigma^2}{2}\Bigg[\frac{(\int_0^s (\partial/\partial v)D(0, v)\, dv)^2}{((\partial/\partial s)D(0, s))^3}\Bigg] + \frac{\sigma^2(\int_0^s (\partial/\partial v)D(0, v)\, dv)}{(\partial/\partial s)D(0, s)}\Bigg\} \\
& -\frac{\sigma^2}{2}\Bigg(\frac{D(0, T) - D(0, s)}{(\partial/\partial T)D(0, T)_{|T=s}}\Bigg)^2 \Bigg\}\, ds
\end{aligned}
\tag{16.188}
$$

Recovering expression (16.77) and substituting values of $C(t, T)$ given by (16.188) and the values of $D(t, T)$ given by (16.178) in the equivalences above, one obtains the risk-free pure discount bond price in arbitrage-free conditions under the risk-neutral probability measure P for the Hull–White II model.

16.3.2.8.   The Cox–Ingersoll–Ross model

16.3.2.8.1.   *Introduction*   In the Cox–Ingersoll–Ross model, parameters $\phi(r_t, t)$ and $\sigma(r_t, t)$ from SDE (16.19), which describe the instantaneous spot rate r_t under the original probability measure Q are specified as follows

$$
dr_t = [\theta - \kappa r_t]\, dt + \sigma \sqrt{r_t}\, dW_t
\tag{16.189}
$$

Consequently, SDE (16.49) which describes the instantaneous spot rate r_t under the risk-neutral probability measure $\widetilde{P}$ is specified as follows:

$$
dr_t = [\bar{\theta} - \kappa r_t]\, dt + \sigma \sqrt{r_t}\, d\widetilde{W}_t
\tag{16.190}
$$

where $\bar{\theta} = \theta - \lambda\sigma$.

The Cauchy problem as inside PDE (16.70) is then specified as follows:

$$
\left[\frac{\partial}{\partial t}A(t, T) - \frac{\partial}{\partial t}D(t, T)r_t\right]P(t, T, r_t) - (\bar{\theta} - \kappa r_t)D(t, T)P(t, T, r_t)
$$
$$
+ \frac{\sigma^2}{2}r_t D^2(t, T)P(t, T, r_t) - r_t P(t, T, r_t) = 0
$$
$$
\left[\frac{\partial}{\partial t}A(t, T) - \frac{\partial}{\partial t}D(t, T)r_t\right]P(t, T, r_t) + \kappa r_t D(t, T)P(t, T, r_t)
$$
$$
- \bar{\theta}D(t, T)P(t, T, r_t) + \frac{\sigma^2}{2}r_t D^2(t, T)P(t, T, r_t) - r_t P(t, T, r_t) = 0
$$

Factorising, one has

$$
\left[\frac{\partial}{\partial t} A(t, T) - \bar{\theta} D(t, T) \right] P(t, T, r_t)
$$

$$
+ P(t, T, r_t) r_t \left[-1 - \frac{\partial}{\partial t} D(t, T) + \kappa D(t, T) + \frac{\sigma^2}{2} D^2(t, T) \right] = 0
$$

which is equivalent to the following equation system:

$$
\begin{cases}
\dfrac{\partial}{\partial t} A(t, T) - \bar{\theta} D(t, T) = 0 \\[2mm]
-1 - \dfrac{\partial}{\partial t} D(t, T) + \kappa D(t, T) + \dfrac{\sigma^2}{2} D^2(t, T) = 0
\end{cases}
$$

Recalling the boundary conditions, the Cauchy problem then becomes

$$
\frac{\partial}{\partial t} A(t, T) - \bar{\theta} D(t, T) = 0 \tag{16.191}
$$

$$
-1 - \frac{\partial}{\partial t} D(t, T) + \kappa D(t, T) + \frac{\sigma^2}{2} D^2(t, T) = 0 \tag{16.192}
$$

with (16.72) and (16.73).

16.3.2.8.2. Arbitrage-free condition The arbitrage-free condition is specified for this model. For this purpose, (16.66) is recovered.

Quantities $(\partial/\partial T) D(t, T)$ and $(\partial/\partial T) A(0, T)$ are now computed.

If, defining a generic function $h(t, T)$, where $T > t$, it is true that

$$
\frac{\partial h(t, T)}{\partial T} = -\frac{\partial h(t, T)}{\partial t}
$$

one may rewrite the Cauchy problem given by Equation (16.192) as follows:

$$
\frac{\partial}{\partial T} D(t, T) = 1 - \kappa D(t, T) - \frac{\sigma^2}{2} D^2(t, T) \tag{16.193}
$$

with the final condition given by (16.73).

If function $D(t, T)$ is of the type $D(T - t)$, defining $(T - t) = \tau$, then it is true that

$$
\frac{\partial h(T - t)}{\partial T} = \frac{\partial h_\tau}{\partial \tau}
$$

and it can be derived that the Cauchy problem given by (16.193) and by the final condition in (16.73) may also be written as

$$
\frac{\partial}{\partial \tau} D_\tau = 1 - \kappa D_\tau - \frac{\sigma^2}{2} D_\tau^2 \tag{16.194}
$$

$$
D_0 = 0 \tag{16.73}
$$

ODE (16.194) is solved by recalling the à-la Riccati structure (see Section 8.1.1.2). In fact, posing:

- $y(x) = D_\tau$;
- $\hat{a}(x) = -\frac{1}{2}\sigma^2$;
- $\hat{b}(x) = -\kappa$; and
- $\hat{c}(x) = 1$;

Equation (16.194) takes the form of (8.6) ie,

$$y'(x) = \hat{a}(x)y^2(x) + \hat{b}(x)y(x) + \hat{c}(x)$$

Then substitution (8.7) is made in order to obtain the second-order ODE (8.8):

$$D_\tau = \frac{E_\tau'}{(\sigma^2/2)E_\tau} \tag{16.195}$$

The first-order derivative of (16.195) is determined (useful below), ie,

$$\frac{\partial}{\partial\tau}D_\tau = D_\tau' = -\frac{(E_\tau''(\sigma^2/2)E_\tau) - ((\sigma^2/2)(E_\tau')^2)}{((\sigma^2/2)E_\tau)^2}$$

thus

$$D_\tau' = \frac{E_\tau''E_\tau - (E_\tau')^2}{(\sigma^2/2)E_\tau^2} \tag{16.196}$$

Substituting (16.195) and (16.196) in (16.194), one obtains

$$\frac{E_\tau''E_\tau - (E_\tau')^2}{(\sigma^2/2)E_\tau^2} = 1 - \kappa\left(\frac{E_\tau'}{(\sigma^2/2)E_\tau}\right) - \frac{\sigma^2}{2}\left(\frac{E_\tau'}{(\sigma^2/2)E_\tau}\right)^2$$

Multiplying by $(\sigma^2/2)E_\tau$, one has

$$\frac{E_\tau''E_\tau}{E_\tau} - \frac{(E_\tau')^2}{E_\tau} = \frac{\sigma^2}{2}E_\tau - \kappa E_\tau' - \frac{(E_\tau')^2}{E_\tau}$$

Simplifying, one obtains

$$E_\tau'' = \frac{\sigma^2}{2}E_\tau - \kappa E_\tau'$$

thus

$$E_\tau'' + \kappa E_\tau' - \frac{\sigma^2}{2}E_\tau = 0 \tag{16.197}$$

Equation (16.197) which results from à-la Riccati substitution (8.7) is a constant coefficient homogeneous second-order linear ODE. The general solution to Equation (16.197), is (see Theorem 8.5)

$$E_\tau = A e^{\alpha_1 \tau} + B e^{\alpha_2 \tau} \qquad (16.198)$$

Solutions of the kind $E(\tau) = e^{\alpha \tau}$ are necessary to identify this general solution. Then $E'(\tau) = \alpha e^{\alpha \tau}$ and $E''(\tau) = \alpha^2 e^{\alpha \tau}$ are computed. The terms E_τ, E'_τ and E''_τ are substituted in Equation (16.197), ie,

$$\alpha^2 e^{\alpha \tau} + \kappa \alpha e^{\alpha \tau} - \frac{\sigma^2}{2} e^{\alpha \tau} = 0$$

Factorising by the term $e^{\alpha \tau}$, one has

$$e^{\alpha \tau} \left[\alpha^2 + \kappa \alpha - \frac{\sigma^2}{2} \right] = 0 \qquad (16.199)$$

Equation (16.199) is only satisfied if the second-order equation in α in the brackets has a trivial solution. Then the roots of this equation in α are computed by writing

$$\alpha = \frac{-\kappa \pm \sqrt{\kappa^2 + 2\sigma^2}}{2}$$

By posing

$$d = \sqrt{\kappa^2 + 2\sigma^2} \qquad (16.200)$$

one obtains the roots

$$\alpha_1 = \frac{-\kappa + d}{2}, \quad \alpha_2 = \frac{-\kappa - d}{2} \qquad (16.201)$$

and, then,

$$d = \alpha_1 - \alpha_2 \qquad (16.202)$$

Knowing the roots α_1 and α_2, the general solution to (16.197), based on (16.198), can be written as

$$E_\tau = A e^{(-\kappa + d)/2\tau} + B e^{(-\kappa - d)/2\tau} \qquad (16.203)$$

Equation (16.203) is then specified for the initial reference condition. This must be rearranged in light of substitution (16.195), ie,

$$D_0 = \frac{E'_0}{((\sigma^2/2)E_0)} = 0 \qquad (16.204)$$

To verify (16.204), the first-order derivative of the general solution (16.198) is computed:

$$E'_\tau = A e^{\alpha_1 \tau} \alpha_1 + B e^{\alpha_2 \tau} \alpha_2 \qquad (16.205)$$

Then (16.198) and (16.205) are specified for $\tau = 0$, ie,

$$E_0 = A + B \tag{16.206}$$

$$E_0' = A\alpha_1 + B\alpha_2 \tag{16.207}$$

Equations (16.206) and (16.207) are substituted in (16.204), ie,

$$D_0 = \frac{A\alpha_1 + B\alpha_2}{(\sigma^2/2)(A + B)} = 0 \tag{16.208}$$

Equation (16.208) implies following the system which works out the quantities A and B that allow the solution (16.203) to be specified, ie,

$$\begin{cases} A\alpha_1 + B\alpha_2 = 0 \\ E_0 = A + B \end{cases} \Rightarrow$$

$$\begin{cases} A\alpha_1 = -B\alpha_2 \\ / \end{cases} \Rightarrow$$

$$\begin{cases} B = -A\dfrac{\alpha_1}{\alpha_2} \\ / \end{cases} \Rightarrow$$

$$\begin{cases} / \\ E_0 = A - A\dfrac{\alpha_1}{\alpha_2} \end{cases} \Rightarrow$$

$$\begin{cases} / \\ A = \dfrac{E_0}{1 - \alpha_1/\alpha_2} \end{cases} \Rightarrow$$

$$\begin{cases} / \\ A = \dfrac{E_0}{(\alpha_2 - \alpha_1)/\alpha_2} \end{cases} \Rightarrow$$

$$\begin{cases} / \\ A = \dfrac{\alpha_2 E_0}{\alpha_2 - \alpha_1} \end{cases} \Rightarrow$$

using the expression $E_0 = A + B$,

$$\begin{cases} / \\ B = E_0 - A \end{cases} \Rightarrow$$

$$\begin{cases} / \\ B = E_0 - \dfrac{\alpha_2 E_0}{\alpha_2 - \alpha_1} \end{cases} \Rightarrow$$

$$\begin{cases} & / \\ B = \dfrac{(\alpha_2 - \alpha_1)E_0 - \alpha_2 E_0}{\alpha_2 - \alpha_1} & \Rightarrow \end{cases}$$

$$\begin{cases} & / \\ B = -\dfrac{\alpha_1 E_0}{\alpha_2 - \alpha_1} & \Rightarrow \end{cases}$$

$$\begin{cases} A = \dfrac{\alpha_2 E_0}{\alpha_2 - \alpha_1} \\ B = -\dfrac{\alpha_1 E_0}{\alpha_2 - \alpha_1} \end{cases} \tag{16.209}$$

The expressions in (16.209) are substituted in the general solution (16.198)

$$\begin{aligned} E_\tau &= \frac{\alpha_2 E_0}{\alpha_2 - \alpha_1} e^{\alpha_1 \tau} - \frac{\alpha_1 E_0}{\alpha_2 - \alpha_1} e^{\alpha_2 \tau} \\ &= \frac{E_0}{\alpha_2 - \alpha_1} \left(\alpha_2 e^{\alpha_1 \tau} - \alpha_1 e^{\alpha_2 \tau} \right) \end{aligned} \tag{16.210}$$

and in the first-order derivative (16.205)

$$\begin{aligned} E'_\tau &= \frac{\alpha_2 E_0}{\alpha_2 - \alpha_1} e^{\alpha_1 \tau} \alpha_1 - \frac{\alpha_1 E_0}{\alpha_2 - \alpha_1} e^{\alpha_2 \tau} \alpha_2 \\ &= \frac{E_0}{\alpha_2 - \alpha_1} \left(\alpha_2 \alpha_1 e^{\alpha_1 \tau} - \alpha_1 \alpha_2 e^{\alpha_2 \tau} \right) \end{aligned} \tag{16.211}$$

Knowing (16.210) and (16.211), recalling relation (16.195) and deriving the solution of (16.194), one has

$$\begin{aligned} D_\tau &= \frac{E'_\tau}{(\sigma^2/2)E_\tau} \\ &= \frac{2(E_0/(\alpha_2 - \alpha_1))(\alpha_2 \alpha_1 e^{\alpha_1 \tau} - \alpha_1 \alpha_2 e^{\alpha_2 \tau})}{\sigma^2(E_0/(\alpha_2 - \alpha_1))(\alpha_2 e^{\alpha_1 \tau} - \alpha_1 e^{\alpha_2 \tau})} \\ &= \frac{2(\alpha_2 \alpha_1 e^{\alpha_1 \tau} - \alpha_1 \alpha_2 e^{\alpha_2 \tau})}{\sigma^2(\alpha_2 e^{\alpha_1 \tau} - \alpha_1 e^{\alpha_2 \tau})} \quad \text{(simplifying)} \\ &= \frac{2\alpha_2 \alpha_1 e^{\alpha_2 \tau}(e^{(\alpha_1 - \alpha_2)\tau} - 1)}{\sigma^2 e^{\alpha_2 \tau}(\alpha_2 e^{(\alpha_1 - \alpha_2)\tau} - \alpha_1)} \quad \text{(factorising } e^{-\alpha_2 \tau}) \\ &= \frac{2\alpha_1 \alpha_2 e^{\alpha_2 \tau}(e^{d\tau} - 1)}{\sigma^2 e^{\alpha_2 \tau}(\alpha_2 e^{d\tau} - \alpha_1)} \quad \text{(recalling relation (16.202), ie, } d = \alpha_1 - \alpha_2) \\ &= \frac{2\alpha_1 \alpha_2 (e^{d\tau} - 1)}{\sigma^2(\alpha_2 e^{d\tau} - \alpha_1)} \\ &= \frac{2\alpha_1 \alpha_2 (1 - e^{-d\tau})}{\sigma^2(\alpha_2 - \alpha_1 e^{-d\tau})} \end{aligned}$$

$$= \frac{2}{\sigma^2} \frac{(1/4)(\kappa^2 - d^2)(1 - e^{-d\tau})}{(1/2)(-\kappa - d - (-\kappa + d)e^{-d\tau})}$$

(substituting the explicit values for α_1, α_2)

$$= \frac{2}{\sigma^2} \frac{(1/4)(\kappa^2 - \kappa^2 - 2\sigma^2)(1 - e^{-d\tau})}{(1/2)(-\kappa - d - (-\kappa + d)e^{-d\tau})} \quad \text{(substituting the explicit value of } d^2\text{)}$$

$$= \frac{2}{\sigma^2} \frac{(1/2)(-\sigma^2)(1 - e^{-d\tau})}{(1/2)(-\kappa - d - (-\kappa + d)e^{-d\tau})} \quad \text{(simplifying)}$$

$$= -2 \frac{(1 - e^{-d\tau})}{(-\kappa - d - (-\kappa + d)e^{-d\tau})}$$

$$= -2 \frac{(1 - e^{-d\tau})}{(-\kappa - (2d - d) - (-\kappa + d)e^{-d\tau})}$$

(then using the equivalence $d = 2d - d$)

$$= -2 \frac{(1 - e^{-d\tau})}{(-\kappa - 2d + d - (-\kappa + d)e^{-d\tau})}$$

$$= -2 \frac{(1 - e^{-d\tau})}{[(-\kappa + d) - 2d - (-\kappa + d)e^{-d\tau}]}$$

$$= -2 \frac{(1 - e^{-d\tau})}{[(-\kappa + d)(1 - de^{-d\tau}) - 2d]}$$

thus

$$D_\tau = \frac{2(1 - e^{-d\tau})}{2d - (d - \kappa)(1 - e^{-d\tau})} \tag{16.212}$$

Hence, substituting τ by the value $(T - t)$, one obtains

$$D(t, T) = \frac{2(1 - e^{-d(T-t)})}{2d - (d - \kappa)(1 - e^{-d(T-t)})} \tag{16.213}$$

Then, for $t = 0$, one has

$$D(0, T) = \frac{2(1 - e^{-dT})}{2d - (d - \kappa)(1 - e^{-dT})} \tag{16.214}$$

Equation (16.193) may be specified deriving (16.213) with respect to T, or substituting (16.213) in (16.193). The first solution is preferred, ie,

$$\frac{\partial}{\partial T} D(t, T)$$
$$= [2de^{-d(T-t)}(2d - (d - \kappa)(1 - e^{-d(T-t)})) - 2(1 - e^{-d(T-t)})$$
$$\cdot (-d^2 e^{-d(T-t)} + \kappa de^{-d(T-t)})] \Big/ [2d - (d - \kappa)(1 - e^{-d(T-t)})]^2$$

$$
= \frac{1}{[2d - (d - \kappa)(1 - e^{-d(T-t)})]^2} \cdot \{2de^{-d(T-t)}[2d - (d - \kappa) + ((d - \kappa)e^{-d(T-t)})]
$$
$$
- 2[-d^2 e^{-d(T-t)} + \kappa d e^{-d(T-t)} + (d^2 e^{-2d(T-t)} - \kappa d e^{-2d(T-t)})]\}
$$

$$
= \frac{1}{[2d - (d - \kappa)(1 - e^{-d(T-t)})]^2} \cdot [-2d^2 e^{-d(T-t)} + 2d\kappa e^{-d(T-t)} + 2d^2 e^{-2d(T-t)}
$$
$$
- 2d\kappa e^{-2d(T-t)} + 4d^2 e^{-d(T-t)} + 2d^2 e^{-d(T-t)} - 2\kappa d e^{-d(T-t)}
$$
$$
- 2d^2 e^{-2d(T-t)} + 2\kappa d e^{-2d(T-t)}]
$$

$$
= \frac{1}{[2d - (d - \kappa)(1 - e^{-d(T-t)})]^2} \cdot (4d^2 e^{-d(T-t)})
$$

thus

$$
\frac{\partial}{\partial T} D(t, T) = \frac{4d^2 e^{-d(T-t)}}{[2d - (d - \kappa)(1 - e^{-d(T-t)})]^2} \tag{16.215}
$$

hence

$$
\frac{\partial}{\partial T} D(0, T) = \frac{4d^2 e^{-dT}}{[2d - (d - \kappa)(1 - e^{-dT})]^2} \tag{16.216}
$$

Now $(\partial/\partial T)A(0, T)$ is expanded beginning with (16.191) and with the final condition in (16.72). If, defining a generic function $(T - t) = \tau$, it is true that

$$
\frac{\partial h(t, T)}{\partial T} = -\frac{\partial h(t, T)}{\partial t}
$$

then one may rearrange the Cauchy problem given by Equation (16.191) as follows:

$$
\frac{\partial}{\partial T} A(t, T) = -\bar{\theta} D(t, T) \tag{16.217}
$$

with the final condition given by (16.73).

If the function $A(t, T)$ is of the type $A(T - t)$, defining $(T - t) = \tau$, then it is true that

$$
\frac{\partial h(T - t)}{\partial T} = \frac{\partial h_\tau}{\partial \tau}
$$

It can be derived that the Cauchy problem given by Equation (16.217) and by the final condition in (16.72), may also be written as follows:

$$
\frac{\partial}{\partial \tau} A_\tau = -\bar{\theta} D_\tau \tag{16.218}
$$

$$
A_0 = 0 \tag{16.72}
$$

Then, it is a simple first-order integral equation:

$$\frac{\partial}{\partial \tau} A_\tau = -\bar{\theta} D_\tau$$

$$A_\tau = -\int D_\tau \bar{\theta} \, d\tau$$

$$= -\bar{\theta} \int D_\tau \, d\tau$$

By using (16.195), one has

$$A_\tau = -\int \bar{\theta} \frac{E'_\tau}{((\sigma^2/2) E_\tau)} \, d\tau$$

$$= -\int \frac{2\bar{\theta}}{\sigma^2} \frac{E'_\tau}{E_\tau} \, d\tau$$

$$= -\frac{2\bar{\theta}}{\sigma^2} \ln E_\tau - F$$

$$= -\frac{2\bar{\theta}}{\sigma^2} \ln \left[\frac{E_0}{\alpha_2 - \alpha_1} (\alpha_2 e^{\alpha_1 \tau} - \alpha_1 e^{\alpha_2 \tau}) \right] - F \quad \text{(using (16.210)}$$

thus

$$A_\tau = -\frac{2\bar{\theta}}{\sigma^2} \ln \frac{E_0}{\alpha_2 - \alpha_1} (\alpha_2 e^{\alpha_1 \tau} - \alpha_1 e^{\alpha_2 \tau}) - F \qquad (16.219)$$

Using the initial condition (16.72), the value of F is specified, ie,

$$0 = -\frac{2\bar{\theta}}{\sigma^2} \ln E_0 - F$$

$$-F = \frac{2\bar{\theta}}{\sigma^2} \ln E_0$$

The value of $-F$ is substituted in (16.219) to obtain

$$A_\tau = -\frac{2\bar{\theta}}{\sigma^2} \ln \frac{E_0}{\alpha_2 - \alpha_1} (\alpha_2 e^{\alpha_1 \tau} - \alpha_1 e^{\alpha_2 \tau}) + \frac{2\bar{\theta}}{\sigma^2} \ln E_0$$

$$= -\frac{2\bar{\theta}}{\sigma^2} \ln[E_0] - \frac{2\bar{\theta}}{\sigma^2} \ln \left[\frac{\alpha_2 e^{\alpha_1 \tau} - \alpha_1 e^{\alpha_2 \tau}}{\alpha_2 - \alpha_1} \right] + \frac{2\bar{\theta}}{\sigma^2} \ln[E_0]$$

$$= -\frac{2\bar{\theta}}{\sigma^2} \ln \left[\frac{\alpha_2 e^{\alpha_1 \tau} - \alpha_1 e^{\alpha_2 \tau}}{\alpha_2 - \alpha_1} \right]$$

$$= -\frac{2\bar{\theta}}{\sigma^2} \ln \left[e^{\alpha_1 \tau} \left(\frac{\alpha_2 - \alpha_1 e^{-d\tau}}{\alpha_2 - \alpha_1} \right) \right] \quad \text{(recalling relation (16.202), ie, } d = \alpha_1 - \alpha_2)$$

$$= -\frac{2\bar{\theta}}{\sigma^2} \ln[e^{\alpha_1 \tau}] - \frac{2\bar{\theta}}{\sigma^2} \ln \left[\frac{\alpha_2 - \alpha_1 e^{-d_1 \tau}}{\alpha_2 - \alpha_1} \right]$$

$$= -\frac{2\bar{\theta}}{\sigma^2} \alpha_1 \tau - \frac{2\bar{\theta}}{\sigma^2} \ln \left[\frac{(\alpha_1 - d) - \alpha_1 e^{-d\tau}}{\alpha_2 - \alpha_1} \right]$$

$$= -\frac{\bar{\theta}}{\sigma^2}[-\kappa + d]\tau - \frac{2\bar{\theta}}{\sigma^2}\ln\left[\frac{-d + \alpha_1(1 - e^{-d_1\tau})}{-d}\right] \quad \text{(using (16.201))}$$

$$= -\frac{\bar{\theta}}{\sigma^2}[-\kappa + d]\tau - \frac{2\bar{\theta}}{\sigma^2}\ln\left[1 - \frac{\alpha_1(1 - e^{-d\tau})}{d}\right]$$

$$= -\frac{\bar{\theta}}{\sigma^2}[-\kappa + d]\tau - \frac{2\bar{\theta}}{\sigma^2}\ln\left[1 - \frac{(-\kappa + d)(1 - e^{-d\tau})}{2d}\right]$$

$$= -\frac{\bar{\theta}}{\sigma^2}\left[(d - \kappa)\tau + 2\ln\left(1 - \frac{(1 - e^{-d\tau})(d - \kappa)}{2d}\right)\right]$$

then, substituting τ by $(T - t)$, one arrives at

$$A(t, T) = -\frac{\bar{\theta}}{\sigma^2}\left[(d - \kappa)(T - t) + 2\ln\left(1 - \frac{(1 - e^{-d(T-t)})(d - \kappa)}{2d}\right)\right] \quad (16.220)$$

It is easy to derive the following quantity from (16.220):

$$A(0, T) = -\frac{\bar{\theta}}{\sigma^2}\left[(d - \kappa)T + 2\ln\left(1 - \frac{(1 - e^{-dT})(d - \kappa)}{2d}\right)\right] \quad (16.221)$$

In addition

$$\frac{\partial}{\partial T}A(t, T) = -\frac{\bar{\theta}}{\sigma^2}\left[(d - \kappa) + 2\frac{\partial}{\partial T}\ln\left(\frac{2d - (1 - e^{-d(T-t)})(d - \kappa)}{2d}\right)\right]$$

$$= -\frac{\bar{\theta}}{\sigma^2}\left[(d - \kappa) + 2\frac{2d}{2d - (1 - e^{-d(T-t)})(d - \kappa)}\right.$$
$$\left. \cdot \frac{\partial}{\partial T}\left(\frac{2d - (1 - e^{-d(T-t)})(d - \kappa)}{2d}\right)\right]$$

$$= -\frac{\bar{\theta}}{\sigma^2}\left[(d - \kappa) + 2\frac{2d}{2d - (1 - e^{-d(T-t)})(d - \kappa)}\right.$$
$$\left. \cdot \frac{1}{2d}\frac{\partial}{\partial T}(2d - (1 - e^{-d(T-t)})(d - \kappa))\right]$$

$$= -\frac{\bar{\theta}}{\sigma^2}\left[(d - \kappa) + 2\frac{2d}{2d - (1 - e^{-d(T-t)})(d - \kappa)}\right.$$
$$\left. \cdot \left(-\frac{1}{2d}(d - \kappa)\right)\frac{\partial}{\partial T}(1 - e^{-d(T-t)})\right]$$

$$= -\frac{\bar{\theta}}{\sigma^2}\left[(d - \kappa) + 2\frac{2d}{2d - (1 - e^{-d(T-t)})(d - \kappa)}\right.$$
$$\left. \cdot \left(-\frac{1}{2d}(d - \kappa)\right)de^{-d(T-t)}\right]$$

$$= -\frac{\bar{\theta}}{\sigma^2}\left[(d-\kappa) + \frac{2d}{2d - (1 - e^{-d(T-t)})(d-\kappa)} \cdot (-(d-\kappa))e^{-d(T-t)}\right]$$

$$= -\frac{\bar{\theta}}{\sigma^2}\left[(d-\kappa) - \frac{2d(d-\kappa)e^{-d(T-t)}}{2d - (1 - e^{-d(T-t)})(d-\kappa)}\right]$$

Hence,

$$\frac{\partial}{\partial T}A(t, T) = -\frac{\bar{\theta}}{\sigma^2}\left[(d-\kappa) - \frac{2d(d-\kappa)e^{-d(T-t)}}{2d - (1 - e^{-d(T-t)})(d-\kappa)}\right] \tag{16.222}$$

The following quantity may be derived from (16.222):

$$\frac{\partial}{\partial T}A(0, T) = -\frac{\bar{\theta}}{\sigma^2}\left[(d-\kappa) - \frac{2d(d-\kappa)e^{-dT}}{2d - (1 - e^{-dT})(d-\kappa)}\right] \tag{16.223}$$

The arbitrage-free condition is recovered from (16.66) and substituting (16.216), (16.223), one obtains an explicit form for this condition:

$$f(0, T) = \frac{4d^2 e^{-dT}}{[2d - (d-\kappa)(1 - e^{-dT})]^2}r_0 + \frac{\bar{\theta}}{\sigma^2}\left[(d-\kappa) - \frac{2d(d-\kappa)e^{-dT}}{2d - (1 - e^{-dT})(d-\kappa)}\right] \tag{16.224}$$

16.3.2.8.2.1. SDE specification   Next, SDE (16.190) is specified in arbitrage-free conditions. For this purpose, the value of function $\bar{\theta}$ is determined by manipulating Equation (16.224):

$$\frac{\bar{\theta}}{\sigma^2}\left[(d-\kappa) - \frac{2d(d-\kappa)e^{-dT}}{2d - (1 - e^{-dT})(d-\kappa)}\right]$$
$$= -\frac{4d^2 e^{-dT}}{[2d - (d-\kappa)(1 - e^{-dT})]^2}r_0 + f(0, T)$$

$$\frac{\bar{\theta}}{\sigma^2}\left[\frac{(d-\kappa)\cdot(2d - (1 - e^{-dT})(d-\kappa)) - 2d(d-\kappa)e^{-dT}}{2d - (1 - e^{-dT})(d-\kappa)}\right]$$
$$= -\frac{4d^2 e^{-dT}}{[2d - (d-\kappa)(1 - e^{-dT})]^2}r_0 + f(0, T)$$

$$\frac{\bar{\theta}}{\sigma^2}\left[\frac{(2d(d-\kappa) - (1 - e^{-dT})(d-\kappa)^2) - 2d(d-\kappa)e^{-dT}}{2d - (1 - e^{-dT})(d-\kappa)}\right]$$
$$= -\frac{4d^2 e^{-dT}}{[2d - (d-\kappa)(1 - e^{-dT})]^2}r_0 + f(0, T)$$

$$\frac{\bar{\theta}}{\sigma^2}\left[\frac{(2d^2 - 2d\kappa) - (1 - e^{-dT})(d^2 + \kappa^2 - 2\kappa d) - (2d^2 - 2\kappa d)e^{-dT}}{2d - (1 - e^{-dT})(d-\kappa)}\right]$$
$$= -\frac{4d^2 e^{-dT}}{[2d - (d-\kappa)(1 - e^{-dT})]^2}r_0 + f(0, T)$$

$$\frac{\bar{\theta}}{\sigma^2}\left[\left\{(2d^2 - 2d\kappa) - (d^2 + \kappa^2 - 2\kappa d - d^2e^{-dT} - \kappa^2e^{-dT} + 2\kappa de^{-dT})\right.\right.$$

$$\left.\left. - 2d^2e^{-dT} + 2\kappa de^{-dT}\right\}\middle/\left\{2d - (1 - e^{-dT})(d - \kappa)\right\}\right]$$

$$= -\frac{4d^2e^{-dT}}{[2d - (d - \kappa)(1 - e^{-dT})]^2}r_0 + f(0, T)$$

$$\frac{\bar{\theta}}{\sigma^2}\left[\left\{2d^2 - 2d\kappa - d^2 - \kappa^2 + 2\kappa d + d^2e^{-dT} + \kappa^2e^{-dT} - 2\kappa de^{-dT}\right.\right.$$

$$\left.\left. - 2d^2e^{-dT} + 2\kappa de^{-dT}\right\}\middle/\left\{2d - (1 - e^{-dT})(d - \kappa)\right\}\right]$$

$$= -\frac{4d^2e^{-dT}}{[2d - (d - \kappa)(1 - e^{-dT})]^2}r_0 + f(0, T)$$

$$\frac{\bar{\theta}}{\sigma^2}\left[\frac{d^2 - \kappa^2 - d^2e^{-dT} + \kappa^2e^{-dT}}{2d - (1 - e^{-dT})(d - \kappa)}\right] = -\frac{4d^2e^{-dT}}{[2d - (d - \kappa)(1 - e^{-dT})]^2}r_0 + f(0, T)$$

$$\frac{\bar{\theta}}{\sigma^2}\left[\frac{(d^2 - \kappa^2)(1 - e^{-dT})}{2d - (1 - e^{-dT})(d - \kappa)}\right] = -\frac{4d^2e^{-dT}}{[2d - (d - \kappa)(1 - e^{-dT})]^2}r_0 + f(0, T)$$

$$\bar{\theta}\left[\frac{(d^2 - \kappa^2)(1 - e^{-dT})}{2d - (1 - e^{-dT})(d - \kappa)}\right] = -\frac{4d^2e^{-dT}}{[2d - (d - \kappa)(1 - e^{-dT})]^2}\sigma^2 r_0 + \sigma^2 f(0, T)$$

$$\bar{\theta} = \left[\frac{2d - (1 - e^{-dT})(d - \kappa)}{(d^2 - \kappa^2)(1 - e^{-dT})}\right] \cdot -\frac{4d^2e^{-dT}}{[2d - (d - \kappa)(1 - e^{-dT})]^2}\sigma^2 r_0$$

$$+ \left[\frac{2d - (1 - e^{-dT})(d - \kappa)}{(d^2 - \kappa^2)(1 - e^{-dT})}\right]\sigma^2 f(0, T)$$

$$= \left[\frac{1}{(d^2 - \kappa^2)(1 - e^{-dT})}\right] \cdot -\frac{4d^2e^{-dT}}{[2d - (d - \kappa)(1 - e^{-dT})]}\sigma^2 r_0$$

$$+ \left[\frac{2d - (1 - e^{-dT})(d - \kappa)}{(d^2 - \kappa^2)(1 - e^{-dT})}\right]\sigma^2 f(0, T)$$

$$= \left[\frac{1}{(d^2 - \kappa^2)(1 - e^{-dT})}\right] \cdot -\frac{4d^2e^{-dT}}{[2d - (d - \kappa)(1 - e^{-dT})]}\sigma^2 r_0$$

$$+ \left[\frac{2d - (1 - e^{-dT})(d - \kappa)}{(d^2 - \kappa^2)(1 - e^{-dT})}\right]\sigma^2 f(0, T)$$

$$= -\frac{4d^2e^{-dT}}{(d^2 - \kappa^2)(1 - e^{-dT})[2d - (d - \kappa)(1 - e^{-dT})]}\sigma^2 r_0$$

$$+ \left[\frac{2d - (1 - e^{-dT})(d - \kappa)}{(d^2 - \kappa^2)(1 - e^{-dT})}\right]\sigma^2 f(0, T)$$

Then the explicit value of $\bar{\theta}$ is equal to

$$\bar{\theta} = -\frac{4d^2 e^{-dT}}{(d^2 - \kappa^2)(1 - e^{-dT})[2d - (d - \kappa)(1 - e^{-dT})]} \sigma^2 r_0$$
$$+ \left[\frac{2d - (1 - e^{-dT})(d - \kappa)}{(d^2 - \kappa^2)(1 - e^{-dT})}\right] \sigma^2 f(0, T) \tag{16.225}$$

hence, it can be derived that the SDE of the Cox–Ingersoll–Ross model in arbitrage-free conditions and under the risk-neutral probability measure P is

$$dr_t = \left\{ -\frac{4d\kappa e^{-dT}}{(d^2 - \kappa^2)(1 - e^{-dT})[2d - (d - \kappa)(1 - e^{-dT})]} \sigma^2 r_0 \right.$$
$$\left. \cdot \left[\frac{2d - (1 - e^{-dT})(d - \kappa)}{(d^2 - \kappa^2)(1 - e^{-dT})}\right] \sigma^2 f(0, T) - \kappa r_t \right\} dt + \sigma \sqrt{r_t}\, d\widetilde{W}_t$$

16.3.2.8.3. *The price $P(t, T, r_t)$ in the Cox–Ingersoll–Ross model* Relation (16.63) is recalled. Having the expanded expressions for $D(t, T)$ (see (16.213)) and $A(t, T)$ (see (16.220)), the expanded version by $P(t, T, r_t)$ is immediate, ie,

$$P(t, T, r_t) = \exp\left\{ -\frac{\bar{\theta}}{\sigma^2}\left[(d - \kappa)(T - t) + 2\ln\left(1 - \frac{(1 - e^{-d(T-t)})(d - \kappa)}{2d}\right)\right] \right.$$
$$\left. -\frac{2(1 - e^{-d(T-t)})}{2d - (d - \kappa)(1 - e^{-d(T-t)})} r_t \right\} \tag{16.226}$$

where

$$\bar{\theta} = -\frac{4d^2 e^{-dT}}{(d^2 - \kappa^2)(1 - e^{-dT})[2d - (d - \kappa)(1 - e^{-dT})]} \sigma^2 r_0$$
$$+ \left[\frac{2d - (1 - e^{-dT})(d - \kappa)}{(d^2 - \kappa^2)(1 - e^{-dT})}\right] \sigma^2 f(0, T)$$
$$d = \sqrt{\kappa^2 + 2\sigma^2}$$

Index